THE MARINE BIOLOGY OF
THE SOUTH CHINA SEA

THE MARINE BIOLOGY OF THE SOUTH CHINA SEA

Volume 2

Proceedings of the First International Conference
on the Marine Biology of Hong Kong
and the South China Sea, Hong Kong
28 October – 3 November 1990

Edited by

Brian Morton

Hong Kong University Press
香港大學出版社

Hong Kong University Press
139 Pokfulam Road, Hong Kong
© Hong Kong University Press 1993

ISBNs 962 209 354 X (Vol. 1)
962 209 355 8 (Vol. 2)
962 209 356 6 (Set of Vol. 1 & 2)

All rights reserved. No portion of this publication may be reproduced or transmitted in any form or by any means, electronic or mechanical, including photocopy, recording or any information storage or retrieval system, without prior permission in writing from the publisher, Hong Kong University Press.

Front cover: *Parasicyonis actinostoloides,*
photograph by Cheryl Osborn

Back cover: *Dendrophyllia gracilis,*
photograph by Brian Darvell

Printed in Hong Kong by Nordica Printing Company Limited

CONTENTS

Volume 1

PLENARY SESSION 1
Plenary Paper 1
Taxonomic sufficiency and the role of systematics in marine invertebrate studies with special reference to Hong Kong — P. Graham Oliver — 3

FISHERIES 37
Plenary Paper 37
Farming of marine algae in China with special reference to the northern South China Sea — C.K. Tseng — 39

Session Papers 63
The species composition of penaeid prawns and caridean shrimps in a *gei wai* at the Mai Po Marshes Nature Reserve, Hong Kong — S.F. Leung — 65

Ecological characteristics of the fish fauna of the South China Sea — Wang Cunxin — 77

FOULING 119
Session Papers 119
Fouling organisms at Daya Bay nuclear power station, China — Z.G. Huang, C.X. Zheng, S. Lin, C.Y. Li, J.J. Wang and S.K. Yan — 121

Biofouling of ships in Daya Bay, China — S.K. Yan and Z.G. Huang — 131

A preliminary investigation of marine fungi in the South China Sea — L.L.P. Vrijmoed, C.S.W. Kueh, H.Q. Shen, C.H. Cai and Y.P. Zhou — 137

Choanoflagellates as fouling organisms — Seamus M. Jackson and E.B. Gareth Jones — 145

Biofouling of Deep Bay buoys	Z.G. Huang and S. Lin	153
An ecological study of fouling organisms in Beihai Harbour, Beibu Bay, China	J.J. Wang, Z.G. Huang, S. Lin, C.Y. Li and C.Z. Zheng	167

CONSERVATION — 181
Plenary Paper — 181

Research upon and conservation of corals and coral reefs in China	Zou Renlin and Wang Zhihao	183

Session Papers — 191

Science and the management of mangroves in Asia and the Pacific	C.D. Field	193
Invertebrate species new to science recorded from the Mai Po Marshes, Hong Kong	S.Y. Lee	199
The conservation of Deep Bay, Hong Kong	Llewellyn Young and David S. Melville	211

POLLUTION — 233
Plenary Paper — 233

Biomonitoring of marine heavy metal pollution and its application in Hong Kong waters	P.S. Rainbow	235

Session Papers — 251

The effects of pollutants on the filtration rate of *Perna viridis* (Bivalvia: Mytilidae)	Wang Chusheng, Zhou Xiulan and Cheng Rongzhong	253
Analysis and assessment of heavy metal pollution in Hong Kong's marine environment	Y.S. Fung	261
A gray model for predicting red tides	Wang Zhaoding, Peng Yunhui and Lin Yongshui	273
Ammonium uptake by *Ulva lactuca* (Chlorophyta: Ulvales)	Y.B. Ho	289
The occurrence of six species of red tide organisms and their relationship with environmental factors in the Pearl River estuary	Y.S. Lin and Z.D. Wang	301
Accumulation of an antifouling toxin, tributyltin, in *Argopecten irradians* (Bivalvia: Pectinidae)	Liu Jianjun	311

The effects of urban sewage on benthic community structure in Xiamen Bay, China	J.X. Jiang, J.S. Song and Z.G. Huang	321

Volume 2

ECOLOGY — 335
Plenary Papers — 335

Regional variation in the structure of tropical benthic communities: relation to regimes of nutrient input	John D. Taylor	337
Are there obligate marine scavengers?	J.C. Britton and Brian Morton	357
Crabs as predators of marine bivalve molluscs	R. Seed	393
Bivalve shells: chronometers of environmental change	C.A. Richardson	419

Session Papers — 435

Sacoglossa (Mollusca: Opisthobranchia) — specialist herbivores and partial predators: integrating ecological, physiological and morphological data	Kathe R. Jensen	437
The relationship between herbivorous molluscs and algae on moderately exposed Hong Kong shores	Gray A. Williams	459
Activity rhythms and 'homing' behaviour by two pairs of high and low-zoned intertidal limpets in Hong Kong	J.H. Liu	471
The orientation of cirripedes on their hosts from Hong Kong waters	Cai Ruxing and Huang Zongguo	493
Some aspects of the ecology of sediment fauna in Balingasay, Bolinao, Pangasinan (northern Philippines)	Helen T. Yap and Hildie Maria E. Nacorda	509
The chemical characteristics of soil and its association with standing litter biomass in a subtropical mangrove community in Hong Kong	N.F.Y. Tam, L.L.P. Vrijmoed and Y.S. Wong	521
Impact of euthrophication on marine plankton in Tolo Harbour, 1988–89	Alice L.C. Chan and C. Kim Wong	543
The physiological ecology of *Perna viridis* (Bivalvia: Mytilidae) from contrasting environments in Hong Kong	S.G. Cheung	559

Effects of reduced salinities on *Holothuria leucospilota* Brandt and *Polycheira rufescens* Brandt (Echinodermata: Holothuroidea) in Hong Kong	Rosita G. Ong Che	581
Leaf choice of sesarmine crabs, *Chiromanthes bidens* and *C. maipoensis,* in a Hong Kong mangal	S.Y. Lee	597
Enigmonia aenigmatica: an enigmatic molluscan chameleon	Shaun M. Moss	605
A comparative study of the effects of salinity upon growth and respiration in two species of mangrove	C.D. Field	615
The heart of *Hyotissa imbricata* (Bivalvia: Gryphaeidae)	Li Xiaoxu, Chen Tiejie, George A. Evseev and Yuri M. Yakovlev	621
The intertidal ecology of a rocky shore at Yangkou, Qingdao, China	Qi Zhongyan, Lin Guangyu, Yang Zongdai, Ren Xianqiu and Li Fenglan	627
Pelagic polychaetes from the South China Sea	B.L. Wu and Lu Hua	637
The distribution of intertidal fungi on *Rhizophora apiculata*	Kevin D. Hyde, A. Chalermpongse and T. Boonthavikoon	643
The effect of photoperiod and temperature on the release of monospores by *Porphyra suborbiculata* Kjellman	K.Y. Lee, H.C. Leung, I.J. Hodgkiss and K.W. Cheung	653
The macrobenthic infauna of Hoi Ha Wan and Tolo Channel, Hong Kong	Andrew S.Y. Mackie, P. Graham Oliver and Paul F. Kingston	657
The Calappidae (Crustacea: Brachyura) of Chinese waters	H.L. Chen	675
Marine diatoms of the Xisha Islands, South China Sea I. *Mastogloia* the Ex. Wm. Sm. species of the group *Sulcatae*	Liu Shicheng	705
Marine diatoms of the Xisha Islands, South China Sea II. Three new species of diatoms (Bacillariophyceae)	Liu Shicheng	729

ECOLOGY
PLENARY LECTURES

REGIONAL VARIATION IN THE STRUCTURE OF TROPICAL BENTHIC COMMUNITIES: RELATION TO REGIMES OF NUTRIENT INPUT

John D. Taylor

Department of Zoology, The Natural History Museum, Cromwell Road, London SW7 5BD, UK

ABSTRACT

Major regional and local differences in the composition and structure of shallow-water communities in the Indo-Pacific marine province may be related to differences in nutrient availability.

Animals in eutrophic environments tend to be fast-growing, with rapid population turnover and generalist habits. Bivalves, for instance, are much more diverse and abundant in eutrophic 'continental' environments, than on oceanic, oligotrophic atolls and reefs. Neogastropods with generalist diets include *Babylonia* which are restricted to continental shores and Nassariidae species which are much more diverse in eutrophic environments. A comparison of food webs, involving predatory gastropods from oligotrophic and eutrophic environments, shows that the oligotrophic webs are based upon benthic algae and detritus, whilst the eutrophic webs are based upon phytoplankton. There is some evidence that rates of evolutionary diversification may be related to nutrient regimes.

INTRODUCTION

The Indo-Pacific marine province covers a vast area and many of its constituent species have very wide geographical ranges. Considerable attention has been given to the biogeographical analysis of the Indo-Pacific biota and various workers have examined the distribution of organisms in relation to plate and local tectonic history, dispersal barriers, habitat diversity, temperature, and so on (Kay 1984; Rosen 1988). In these studies there has been a tendency, perhaps unconsciously, to regard the tropical Indo-Pacific as a rather uniform environment. Recently, however, some studies have demonstrated the response of coral reef communities to different regimes of nutrient availability (Birkeland 1977, 1987, 1988a, b; Hallock and Schlager 1986; Hallock 1988). It is clear from these works, that local and regional differences in nutrient availability may exert important controls both on the distribution of tropical organisms, but also upon the organization of benthic communities.

Recent results from the satellite imagery of the Coastal Zone Colour Scanner (CZCS) have vividly confirmed the large differences in primary productivity across the oceans (Lewis 1989). The open ocean waters of the tropical Indo-Pacific usually have very low levels of primary production (Ryther 1969). This is because of low levels of nutrients in the surface waters above the stable thermocline. High levels of phytoplankton production are found only in relatively restricted areas. These may be upwelling areas, such as around southern Arabia in the northern Indian Ocean (Savidge et al. 1990). Also, monsoonal rainfall brings pulses of nutrients from terrestrial run-off along the coasts of continental margins, as around most of Southeast Asia and also around high oceanic islands, such as the granitic Seychelles. Rates of nutrient supply vary both on a local scale, as for example, between an enclosed lagoon and the seaward reefs of an atoll, or on a regional scale as between Micronesia and Southeast Asia. Nutrient supply may also vary seasonally with wind direction controlling upwelling, or rainfall controlling terrestrial run-off.

Differences in the composition and diversity of marine faunas between oceanic islands and continental margins have long been known (some examples for the Indian Ocean in Taylor [1971]), but the causes of these differences were not understood. For example, the Hong Kong marine fauna contains many species which are broadly distributed in the Indo-Pacific, but in Hong Kong they often live in habitats and associations rather different from those in other parts of their ranges. Birkeland's (1987) analysis shows that many regional differences in community composition and organization may be related to the rates of nutrient supply. His studies provide a conceptual framework for the regional comparison of reefs and other shallow-water communities of the tropics.

In this review, I will summarize briefly the effects of differing rates of nutrient input upon shallow-water Indo-Pacific communities. I will then go on to show how the distribution of some groups of molluscs appears to be correlated with regimes of high nutrient input. Then some food webs involving molluscs from oligotrophic and eutrophic environments will be used to demonstrate that there are fundamental differences in the structure of webs. In conclusion, I will discuss briefly some evolutionary implications of these differences. Most of the examples used are of molluscs, for this is the group with which I am most familiar.

THE NUTRIENT CONTROL MODEL

A model of how tropical shallow water communities may be controlled by different regimes of nutrient input has been developed by Birkeland (1977, 1987, 1988a). A summary of the model is illustrated in Figure 1 and briefly outlined below. It should be stressed that the stages illustrated in Figure 1 are end-member conditions and that all transitional states exist in natural communities.

In nutrient-poor, phytoplankton-poor, oligotrophic waters, such as surround oceanic atolls, the major space-occupying organisms are largely autotrophic and phototrophic, scleractinian corals, Alcyonaria, sponges with symbiotic cyanobacteria, ascidians with *Prochloron* and *Tridacna* species. It is believed that the prevalent symbioses are an adaptation for efficient nutrient recycling (Muscatine and Porter 1977;

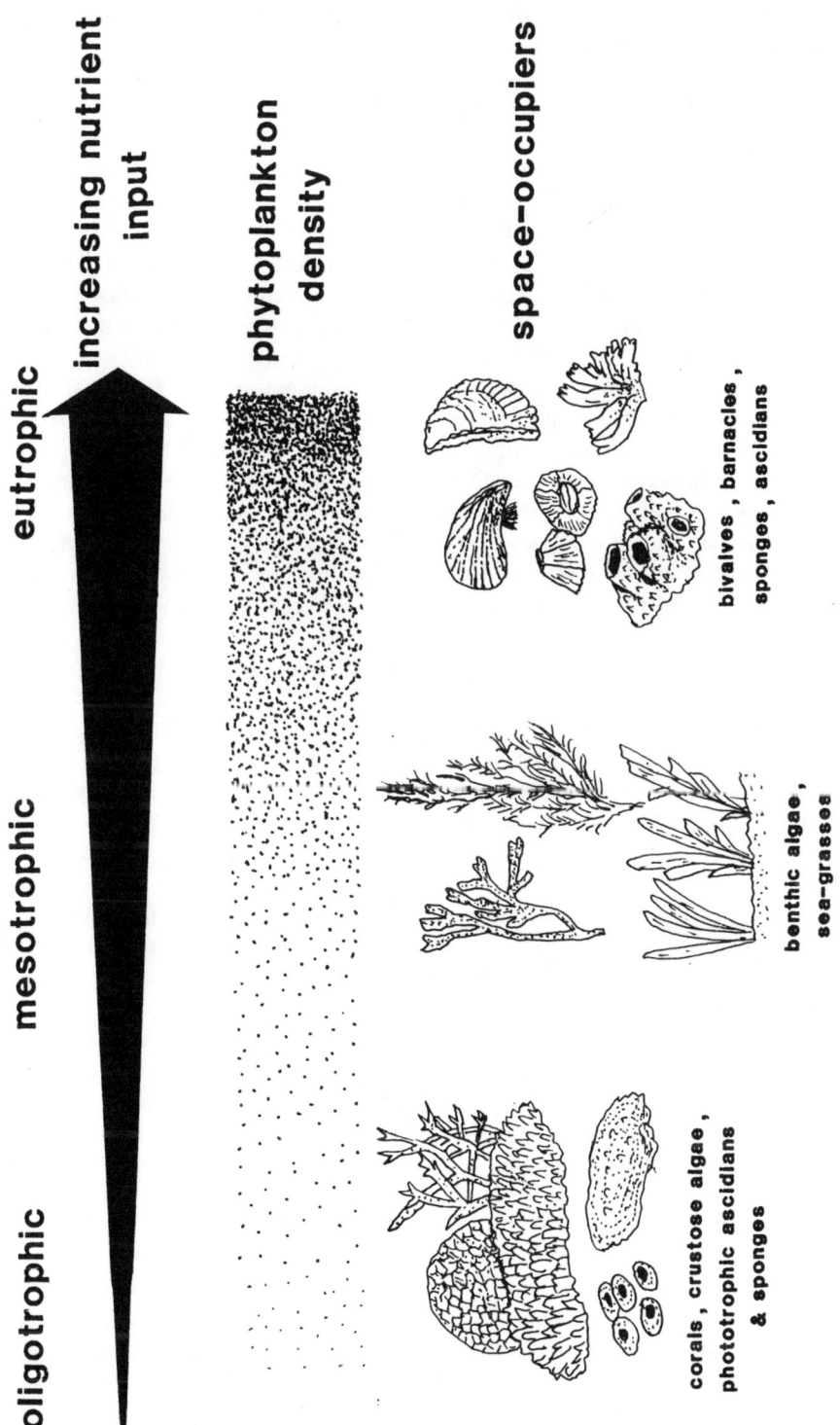

Fig.1 Diagram illustrating the effect of increasing nutrient input on tropical benthic communities. Only major groups of organisms are illustrated. All transitional states may be seen in natural communities. See text for further details.

DeAngelis et al. 1989). Crustose coralline algae are also important. Phytoplankton-feeding organisms such as barnacles and bivalves are usually uncommon in these environments.

Despite being situated in nutrient-poor oceanic waters, the reefs themselves have generally high gross productivities sustaining high biomass levels (Grigg et al. 1984; Birkeland 1988a), but net productivities are relatively low (Hallock and Schlager 1986). The high productivities are believed to be maintained because of various types of efficient nutrient recycling mechanisms within the communities (Muscatine and Porter 1977; Birkeland 1988a). For example, in a study of a Pacific reef, Grigg et al. (1984) estimate that 85% of net production is taken up amongst the heterotrophic benthos and reef fish. Only about 50% of net benthic production is passed up food chains to non-benthic consumers.

At increasing nutrient levels, benthic algae become more important and will overgrow and outcompete corals for space. Experiments have shown that rapidly-growing, filamentous algae inhibit the settlement of coral planulae (Birkeland 1977). Coralline algae may also be overgrown by other algae. Phytoplankton productivity is higher and the water may be less transparent. Where sufficient sediment is available, seagrass beds develop and are characteristic of mesotrophic environments (Wiebe 1987). Although juvenile corals are often out-competed for space by the algae, some do survive, and mixed coral-fleshy algal communities often occur.

At the extreme end of the scale, with the highest levels of nutrient input, as for example in the inshore waters of monsoonal continental margins, most primary production occurs in the water column *via* the phytoplankton. High densities of phytoplankton reduce the light levels reaching the benthos and also reduce the amount of nutrients in the water available for the growth of benthic algae. Algal growth is reduced and the bottom community becomes dominated by suspension-feeding animals such as epifaunal bivalves, barnacles, massive sponges and ascidians without symbionts, and bryozoa. Only very tolerant corals such as *Porites* and *Goniopora* can survive at low light levels in these turbid waters.

Birkeland (1987) presents much empirical and experimental evidence to support this outline model and only a few examples are cited here. An instructive example is the well-known case of Kaneohe Bay in Hawaii (Kinsey 1988) where eutrophication of a coral community was caused by sewage discharge. With increasing nutrient levels in the southern Bay, the corals were swamped by benthic algae and populations of suspension-feeding sponges, ascidians, barnacles, bivalves and polychaetes. Also the physical substrate was destroyed by boring, filter-feeding infauna. Since diversion of the sewage in 1979, the algae and filter feeding populations have declined, new corals have appeared and the biota is reverting to a more typical fringing reef community.

Some workers have used transects from oligotrophic to eutrophic environments to demonstrate changes in community structure. Wilkinson (1986) and Wilkinson and Cheshire (1989) describe the distribution of sponges in a transect across the Great Barrier Reef. In the oligotrophic conditions of the Outer Barrier, the sponges are dominantly phototrophic, deriving most of their nutrition from symbiotic cyanobacteria. In the mid- and inner parts of the reef where phytoplankton concentrations are greater, the sponges are larger, more abundant and dominantly suspension-feeding. In similar transects of the Great Barrier Reef, Williams et al. (1986) found the greatest biomass of planktivorous fish at mid-reef sites. In the Sudanese Red Sea, Taylor and Reid (1984) describe how the coastal fringing reefs have more algae and larger populations of herbivorous gastropods than the offshore patch reefs.

Typically, suspension-feeding bivalves in eutrophic regimes have high fecundity, early maturity, fast growth rates, features which enable the animals to respond to pulses of nutrient and phytoplankton growth. These are life history characters possessed by many bivalves in Hong Kong waters, for example *Mytilopsis sallei* (Récluz), a recent introduction which locally dominates polluted habitats (Morton 1989).

Various evidence suggests that the bioerosion of coral reefs is generally proportional to nutrient input and productivity (Highsmith 1980; Kinsey 1988; Hallock 1988). In discussing the eastern Pacific reef fauna, Glynn (1988) concludes that disturbance events on coral reefs have the greatest long-term consequences in waters of high productivity. The high rates of bioerosion in eutrophic waters may explain the meagre development of reefs in areas of high productivity (Hallock and Schlager 1986). In Tolo Channel, Hong Kong, Scott and Cope (1990) correlate the increased erosion of the corals lining the Channel with the progressive eutrophication of the seaway.

Increased nutrient input tends to shorten the number of trophic levels in food webs (Ryther 1969; Birkeland 1988a). Small organisms with high fecundity, rapid growth rates and short population turnover rates can respond rapidly to pulses of nutrient input. These types of organism tend to prevail in eutrophic environments and the populations, although abundant, tend to fluctuate and be short-lived. Mortalities from periodic low salinities, eutrophication and anoxia may be frequent (Wu 1982). Thus the grazers and predators which exploit these populations would be expected to have generalist feeding and diets.

Taylor and Shin (1990) have shown that in Tolo Channel, Hong Kong, those predatory gastropods with more specialized diets are being eliminated by progressive eutrophication. By contrast, in oligotrophic regimes, organisms tend to be slow growing, with slower rates of population turnover, resources are predictable and food specializations are common (Taylor 1984, 1989). In a general review of sublittoral benthos, Pearson and Rosenberg (1978) have shown how increasing eutrophication results in the dominance of short-lived, generalist, *r*-selected, species.

DISTRIBUTION OF ORGANISMS IN RELATION TO NUTRIENT INPUT

It has long been clear that in the Indo-Pacific Province, there are differences between the faunas of oceanic coral-islands and the faunas of high islands and continental margins. In many groups of molluscs there are examples of suites of species restricted to high islands or the margins of continents, as in the Strombidae (Abbott 1960), Littorinidae (Reid 1986) and *Bullia* (Taylor, 1971). The significance of these differences has not been clear and attributed to differences in habitat diversity, or turbidity (Taylor 1971). However, some groups of molluscs show distribution patterns which are strongly associated with areas of high levels of nutrient input and high productivity. A special case is the seasonal upwelling system off the south Arabian Peninsula (Savidge *et al.* 1990). Here cold, nutrient-rich, water supports a community of kelp (*Ecklonia*), coralline algae and a large abalone (*Haliotis mariae* Gray), an association more typical of temperate waters (Barratt 1985).

Most bivalve molluscs are suspension feeders on phytoplankton and they are usually neither very diverse or abundant on coral reefs in oligotrophic environments (Morton 1983; Vermeij 1990). However, they are both more diverse and abundant around high islands and at localities along continental margins where primary productivity is higher. For instance, 635 species of bivalve are recorded from Taiwan (Wu 1980), and 426 from Okinawa (Kuroda 1960). These figures may be compared with Enewetak Atoll where there are only 115 species of bivalve out of 1116 molluscs (Kay and Johnson 1987), or the Hawaiian islands where there are 141 bivalves out of 1007 molluscan species (Kay 1979), only 105 species from the entire French Polynesia (Richard 1982) and 87 bivalve species from Coco-Keeling Atoll (Maes 1967).

Overall diversity may be related to habitat variety and space. But if individual habitats are considered, for example rocky shores, then on continental shores, suspension-feeding bivalves such as *Saccostrea, Septifer, Brachidontes, Isognomon, Perna, Chama, Barbatia* are dominant space-occupying organisms (Lee and Morton 1985; Tong 1986; Tsuchiya and Lirdwitayapsit 1986). By contrast, on oceanic atolls and reefs, bivalves are much less abundant. They are for example, barely mentioned in accounts of the intertidal reef-flat fauna of Enewetak Atoll (Kohn 1987), and on the Fanning Island seaward reef-flat, 97 gastropod species were reported, but only three bivalves (Kay 1971).

Similarly, bivalves except for *Tridacna*, are relatively uncommon on the seaward shores of atolls and reefs in French Polynesia (Salvat 1967; Richard 1982). Bivalves are often much more abundant in lagoons (Kay and Switzer 1974) and strikingly so in the closed lagoons of French Polynesia, such as Takapoto, where enormously high densities and biomasses have been recorded (Salvat 1967; Richard *et al.* 1979). The main species involved are *Tridacna maxima* (Röding), *Pinctada margaritifera* (Linnaeus), *Chama iostoma* Conrad and *Arca ventricosa* Lamarck. Nutrient levels both in the oceanic and surrounding waters are low, but it is believed that the nearly enclosed nature of the atoll, increases the residence time of the water in the lagoon, allowing the recycling of nutrients into the biomass of the bivalves (Sournia and Ricard 1975; Birkeland 1985).

Species of the bivalve family Mytilidae are strongly associated with eutrophic environments; they are four to seven times more diverse on continental shores than on oceanic atolls (Table 1). There are, for instance, twice as many species recorded from Hong Kong as for the entire Hawaiian Islands. Mytilid species are frequently major space-occupying organisms on hard substrates on shores in eutrophic areas (Morton and Lee 1985; Tong 1986; Tsuchiya and Lirdwitayapsit 1986), but are generally subordinate in oceanic coral-reef environments.

An interesting example of an individual distribution is the mussel *Perna* (Siddall 1981), which often inhabits highly eutrophic waters. The distribution of the two tropical Indo-Pacific species (*P. viridis* (Linnaeus) and *P. perna* (Linnaeus)) (Fig. 2), shows the close association with continental margins and with high productivity areas, such as the southern Arabian Peninsula upwelling, and the monsoonal coasts of India and Southeast Asia. At Hong Kong, *P. viridis* has been shown to be a dominant species in the highly polluted waters of Victoria Harbour (Lee 1985). However, these populations are stressed compared with those living in other less polluted, locations around Hong Kong (Lee 1986).

The intensity of boring in coral by lithophagine bivalves was shown by Highsmith (1980) to be greater on reefs in areas of higher phytoplankton production, such as con-

Table 1

Numbers of species of the bivalve family Mytilidae recorded from some islands situated in oligotrophic environments compared with some localities situated in eutrophic environments of continental margins. Mytilidae have been divided into lithophagine and non-lithophagine taxa.

Location	Number of non-lithophagine species	Number of lithophagine species	References
Oceanic islands:			
Fanning I.	2	1	Kay and Switzer 1974
Cocos-Keeling	2	2	Maes 1967
Enewetak (1987)	6	1	Kay and Johnson 1987
Hawaii	9	2	Kay 1979
French Polynesia	3	4	Richard 1982
Continental margins:			
Hong Kong	22	7	Lee and Morton 1985
Taiwan	26	7	Wu 1980
S. Japan	21	5	Azuma 1960

tinental margins and high islands compared with oceanic reefs. He concluded that higher concentrations of phytoplankton in the water encourage more rapid growth of the bivalves.

It has been argued in the preceding section of the paper that animals tend to have more generalist diets in areas with pulses of high nutrient input. The following are two examples of benthic gastropods having generalist diets, and which are either restricted to, or having greater diversity on, continental margins.

Babylonia is a genus of the gastropod family Buccinidae with twelve living species (Altena and Gittenberger 1981). The feeding habits of two species (*B. lutosa* and *B. areolata*) have been investigated in Hong Kong and found to be generalist feeders, eating molluscs and polychaetes, but with a high proportion of carrion in their diet (Taylor and Shin 1990; Morton 1990). *Babylonia* species live in sublittoral silt and muddy habitats around the continental margins of the Indo-West Pacific, ranging from the Red Sea to Japan (Fig. 3), but they are absent from oceanic islands.

Species of Nassariidae are renowned for their generalist feeding habits, although there is little known in detail about most tropical species (Morton 1990). Most species will eat carrion when available, and many also probably feed upon organic detritus and diatoms as in the Atlantic species *Ilyanassa obsoleta* (Say) (Curtis and Hurd 1979). The few examples in Table 2 show that nassariids are at least twice as diverse on continental margins as on oceanic islands. Qualitative observations suggest that nassariids are also more abundant on continental margins, for example high abundances are recorded on mud flats at Phuket, Thailand (Frith *et al.* 1976). Moreover, reference to Cernohorsky (1984) shows that most species of Indo-Pacific Nassariidae are found either around continental margins or high islands, with those species found on coral islands usually being a small suite of very widespread species.

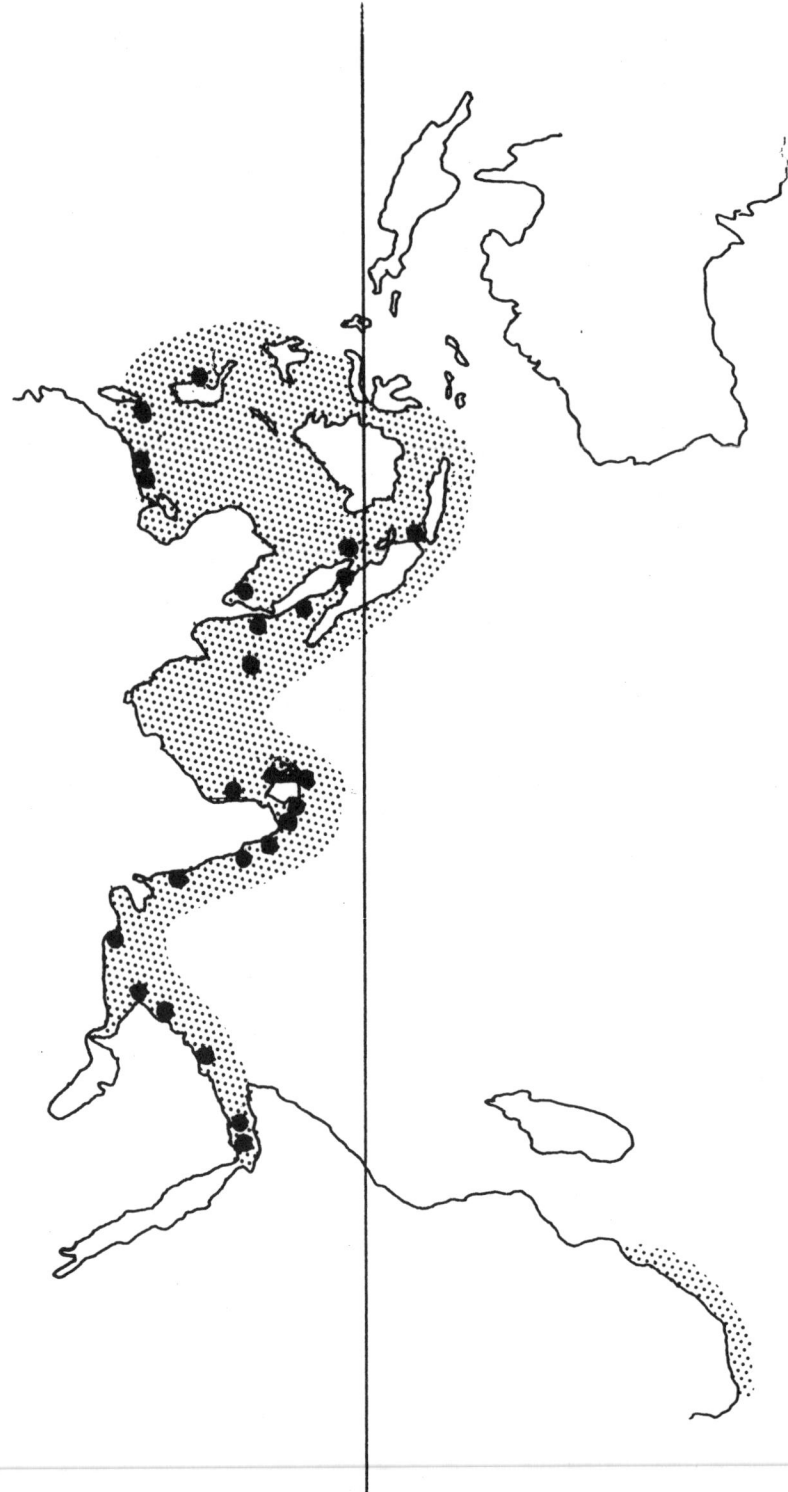

Fig. 2 Map showing distribution of *Perna* species in the Indo-W. Pacific. Points represent specimens in the Natural History Museum, London, collections.

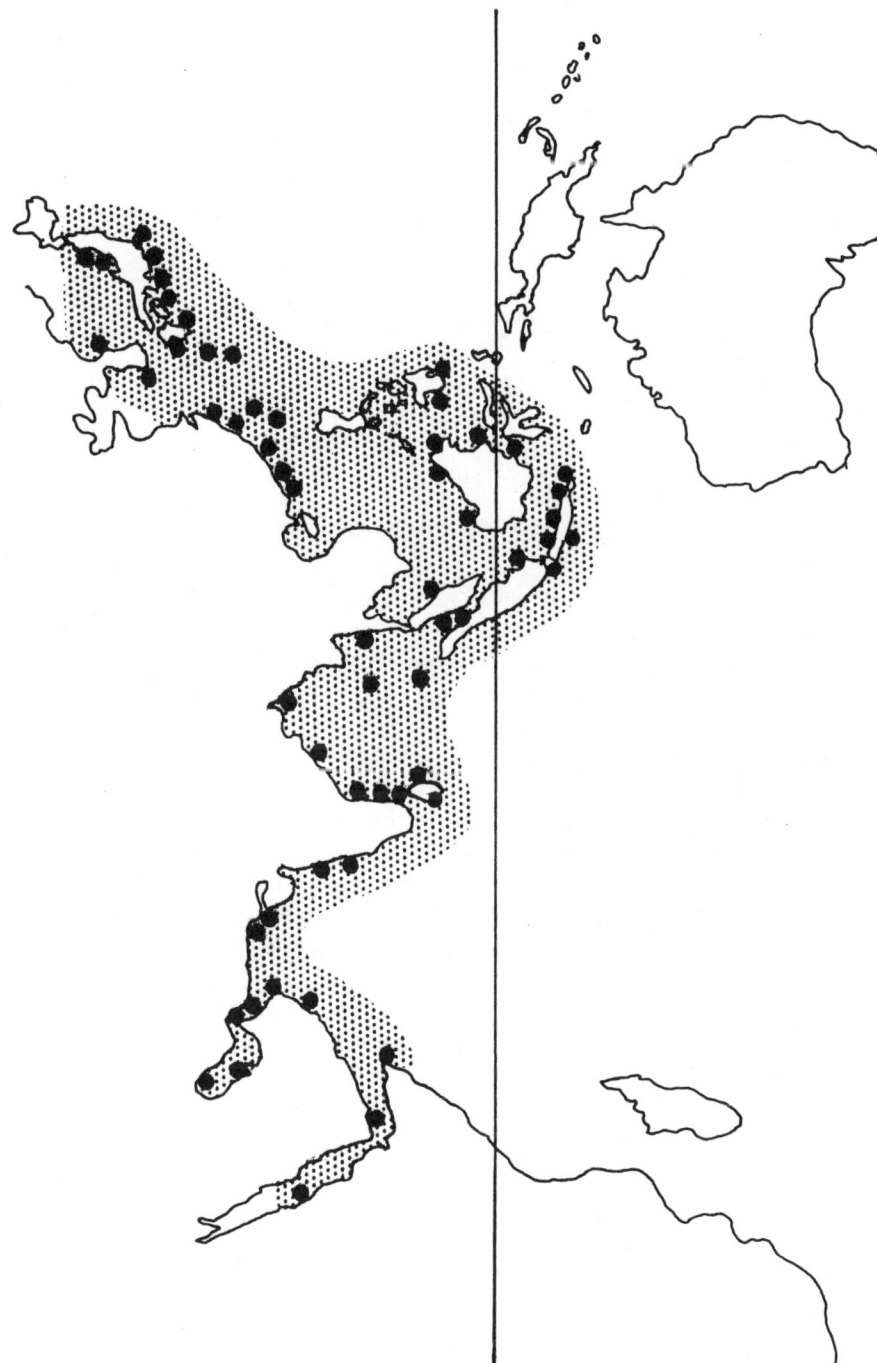

Fig. 3 Distribution of *Babylonia* species in the Indo-W.Pacific. Data from Altena and Gittenberger (1981).

Table 2
Numbers of species of Nassariidae recorded from some oceanic islands in oligotrophic situations compared with localities with monsoonal eutrophic regimes.

Location	Nassariid species	References
Oceanic islands		
Enewetak	7	Kay and Johnson 1987
Cocos-Keeling	4	Maes 1967
Fanning I.	3	Kay and Switzer 1974
Hawaii	7	Kay 1979
Continental margins		
Hong Kong	14	Cernohorsky 1984
Phuket	14	Tantanasiriwong 1978
Sagami Bay, Japan	18	Kuroda *et al.* 1971
Philippines	30	Springsteen and Leobera 1986

STRUCTURE OF FOOD WEBS

Although there are major differences in the composition of the communities between oligotrophic and eutrophic environments, do these differences affect the ways that communities are organised? Evidence from gastropods shows large differences in the structure of food webs for communities inhabiting oligotrophic and eutrophic environments.

For example, Kohn (1987) illustrated the food sub-web involving gastropods on the intertidal rock platform at Enwetak Atoll, in the Marshall Islands. This mid-Pacific atoll lies in highly oligotrophic waters of very low productivity. The food web was derived from evidence from the analysis of gut contents, faeces and field observations. Twenty-one species of predatory gastropod (Conidae, Muricidae, Mitridae, Buccinidae and Vasidae) are represented in the web, of which 17 species ate polychaetes, sipunculans and other gastropods. These prey are known to feed in turn upon benthic algae or upon deposited detritus. Only four species of predatory gastropods fed entirely upon polychaete or gastropod prey which are known to eat phytoplankton or suspended detritus. No barnacles or bivalves were recorded as prey in this web.

Similarly, Taylor (1984) described a food sub-web for predatory gastropods from another Pacific reef on Guam, Marianas Islands. Here 42 species of predatory gastropods were investigated and only two species *Morula granulata* (Duclos) and *Gutturnium muricinum* (Röding), regularly consumed bivalve prey, and barnacles were a small part of the diet of two *Cantharus* species. Most of the other species of predators ate herbivorous gastropods, polychaetes and sipunculans. A similar pattern was seen in a food web involving predatory gastropods obtained from a sandy-reef flat also on Guam (Taylor 1986). Here, 17 species of predatory gastropod ate mainly deposit-feeding polychaetes and sipunculans.

Another food web from Guam, this time from an exposed reef platform (Taylor, unpublished) is shown in Figure 4. Here, there are only nine species of predatory gastropods, the most abundant being *Morula granulata* and *M. marginatra* (Blainville)

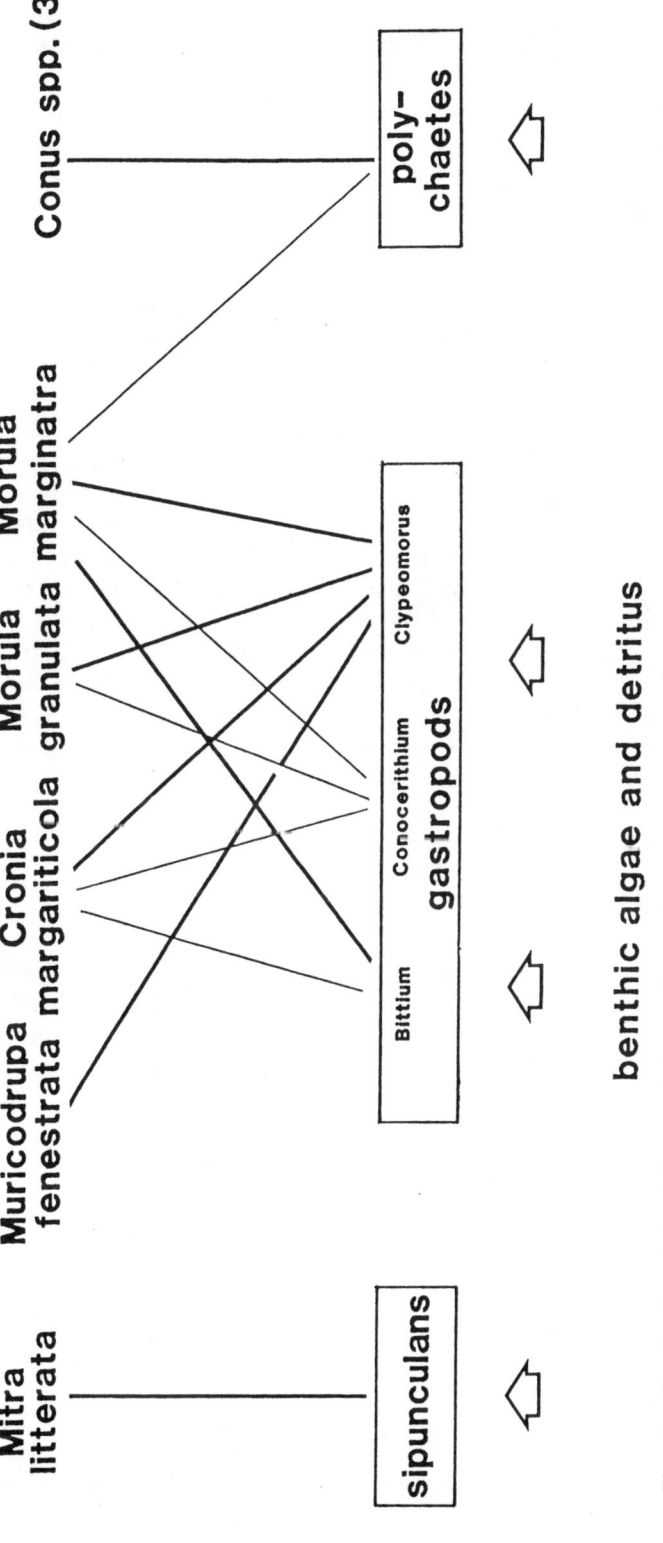

Fig. 4 Food sub-web involving predatory gastropods on an exposed intertidal rock platform at Tagachan, Guam. (Taylor, unpublished information).

(Muricidae). The former feeds almost entirely upon the small herbivorous gastropods *Bittium, Conocerithium* and *Clypeomorus nympha* (Houbrick). *Morula marginatra* also drills the same small gastropods, but gut content analysis reveals that polychaetes form a proportion of its diet. Another common gastropod is *Mitra litterata* Lamarck, which eats sipunculans and three *Conus* species (*ebraeus* Linnaeus, *miliaris* Hwass and *sponsalis* Hwass) feed upon nereid and eunicid polychaetes. Bivalves are rare in this habitat and do not figure in the food web. None of the prey species are suspension feeders.

These coral-reef food-webs have a number of common features. There are diverse assemblages of predators, with many species having specialized diets. The lowest levels in the food web consist mainly of grazers on benthic algae, or feeders on deposited detritus. Suspension-feeding animals, such as barnacles and bivalves are either very minor items in the diet of the gastropods, or are completely absent from the webs.

By contrast, food webs involving gastropods in eutrophic waters are different in structure and may be illustrated with some examples from Hong Kong.

The first example, concerns the food web involving predatory gastropods on an intertidal rocky shore at Wu Kwai Sha, in Tolo Channel. This web has been constructed from the study of Tong (1986), with some additional information from Taylor (1990).

The shore at this site supports a rich assemblage of barnacles, epifaunal bivalves and herbivorous gastropods. The dominant space-occupying organisms is the oyster *Saccostrea cucullata* (Born). There are two common predatory gastropods *Thais clavigera* (Kuster) and *Morula musiva* (Kiener), and their diets were established using a combination of gut content analysis and field observations. The results (Fig. 5) show that most of the food of the two predators consisted of the suspension-feeding bivalves *Saccostrea, Brachiodontes, Barbatia* and the barnacle *Balanus amphrite*. Algal-feeding gastropods, *Siphonaria* and *Monodonta*, formed only a minor part of the diet of *Morula musiva*. Interestingly, Tong (1986) also studied the diet of *Thais clavigera* at Cape d'Aguilar where the water is less eutrophic than in Tolo Channel and bivalves are less prominent space-dominating organisms. There, herbivorous gastropods formed a larger proportion of the gut contents.

From slightly deeper water in Tolo Channel, Taylor (1980 and unpublished data) presented dietary data on an assemblage of predatory gastropods living on the bouldered and coral sublittoral shores lining the Channel. This fauna consisted of a diverse assemblage of muricid gastropods, particularly *Chicoreus microphyllus* (Lamarck), *C. brunneus* (Link), *Mancinella echinata* (Lamarck) and *Cronia margariticola* (Blainville). In the food web derived from gut content and field observations (Fig. 6), it can be seen that suspension feeding bivalves and barnacles were the main prey items. A few herbivorous gastropods were eaten by *Cronia margariticola*. The latter species along with *Drupella rugosa* (Born) and *Coraliophila costularis* (Lamarck) also ate coral tissue.

Last, the diets of the sublittoral, soft-bottom gastropods from Tolo Channel and Mirs Bay have been investigated (Taylor and Shin 1990). Many of the gastropods have generalist diets, feeding upon a variety of prey with *Babylonia* and *Nassarius* species commonly feeding upon carrion. Overwhelming numbers of the probably annual, semelparous, opisthobranch *Philine orientalis* A. Adams, were found in the area in 1989. Although this species is a specialist feeder on bivalves when on intertidal beaches (Morton and Chiu 1990), the smaller individuals of the sublittoral population had a much broader diet. There were a few food specialists in the fauna, notably *Bursa rana* Linnaeus

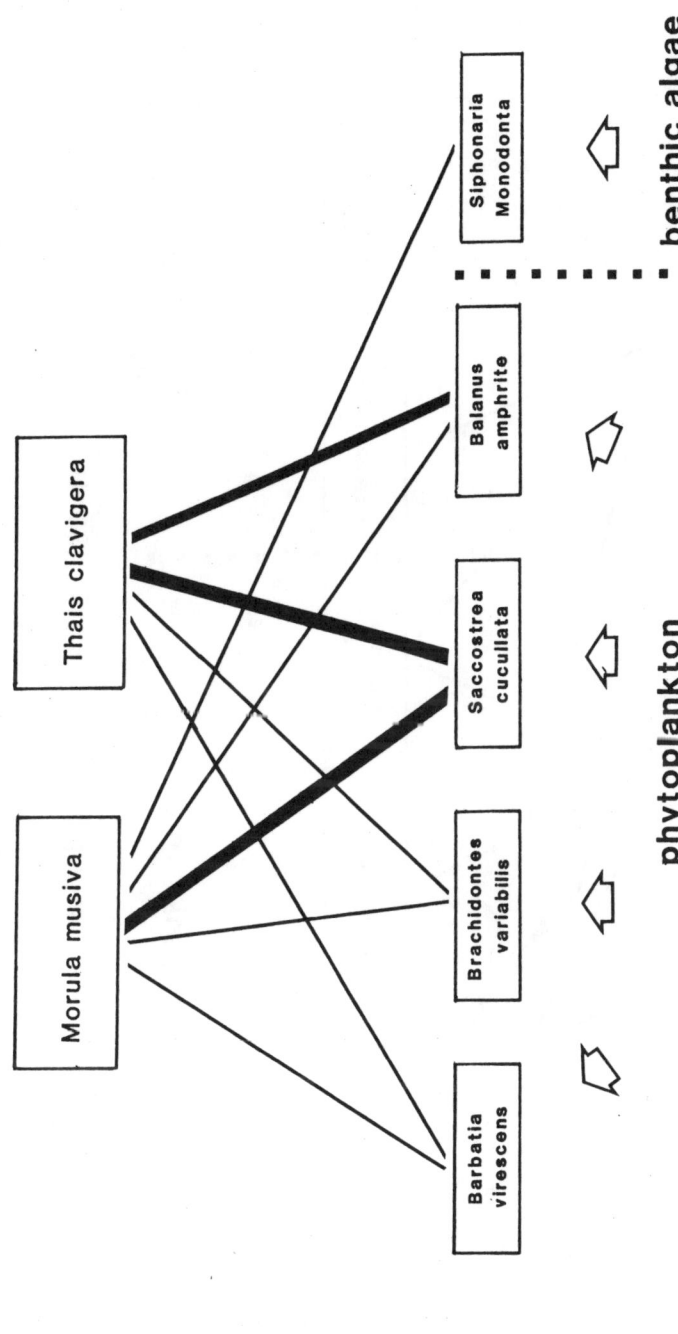

Fig. 5 Food sub-web involving predatory gastropods from an intertidal rocky shore at Hoi Sing Wan, Tolo Channel, Hong Kong. Data from Tong (1986) and Taylor (1990).

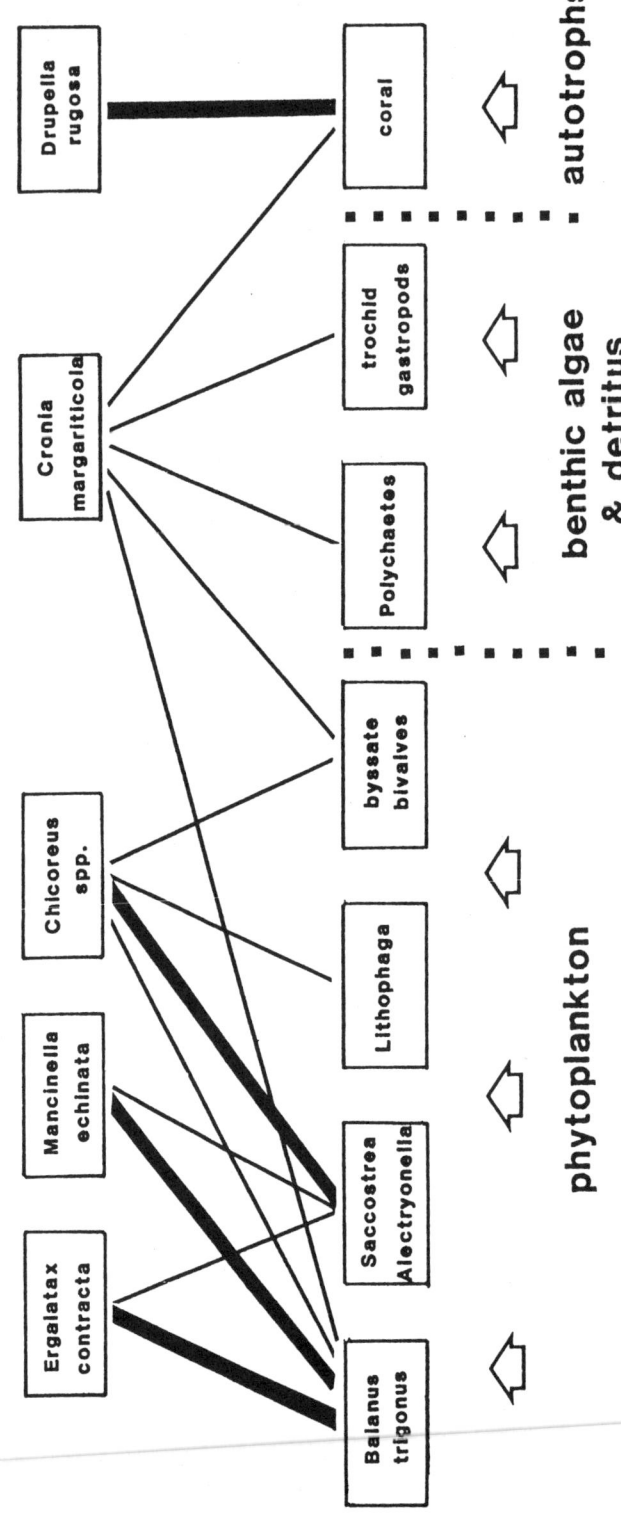

Fig. 6 Food sub-web involving predatory gastropods from the sublittoral rock and coral shores of Tolo Channel, Hong Kong. Data from Taylor (1980).

which preyed upon ophiuroids and *Distorsio reticulata* Röding which ate chaetopterid polychaetes. Most of the prey species in the web were deposit feeding polychaetes.

The two food webs for Hong Kong rocky shores show that the primary consumers at the base of the webs are mainly phytoplankton-feeding bivalves and barnacles, and prey which graze on the benthic flora are not commonly eaten. A similar pattern was described by Abe (1989) for a guild of muricid predators on a Japanese shore. These results confirm a prediction of Birkeland (1988a) that higher levels of nutrient input cause a switch from benthic algae-based food webs to phytoplankton based webs. The sublittoral, soft-substrate, web for Hong Kong, with many generalist and carrion-feeding species, may be contrasted with the sandy bottom web for Guam (Taylor 1986), where there was only one generalist-feeding species.

EVOLUTIONARY SIGNIFICANCE

Vermeij (1978, 1987) has explored and documented many examples of possible co-evolutionary adaptations and interactions between predators and their prey.

In this review, I have highlighted some differences in the composition and structure of benthic communities subjected to different regimes of nutrient input. In the food webs described in this paper, the primary consumers which are the main prey of the predatory gastropods are quite different in oligotrophic and eutrophic environments. Thus, bivalves and barnacles are the main prey in eutrophic environments and herbivorous gastropods, polychaetes and detritus feeders are the main prey at oligotrophic sites. Thus, it would appear that selection for predator-avoidance adaptations of armament, behaviour or life history traits, will involve completely different groups of animals in the different nutrient regimes. This suggests that differences in nutrient availability may lead to differences in the intensity and rates of evolutionary processes.

Vrba (1987) has recently discussed the evolutionary patterns of 'specialist' and 'generalist' clades. Various lines of argument predict that generalist clades will tend to be species-poor, having low speciation rates coupled with low extinction rates. On the other hand, specialist clades will be species-rich, with both high speciation and extinction rates.

I have noted that specialist-feeding species of gastropods are strongly associated with oligotrophic, coral-reef, environments whilst regimes characterised by pulses of nutrient input support larger numbers of generalist-feeding species. Unfortunately, no phylogenetic analyses of Indo-Pacific predatory gastropods have been made in sufficient detail to make an adequate test of any hypothesis about evolutionary rates in different nutrient regimes. However, there are some small pieces of evidence which suggest that such differences may exist. Altena and Gittenberger (1981) have documented Recent and fossil species of the genus *Babylonia*. This a generalist-feeding genus which inhabits nutrient-rich, continental margins of the northern Indo-West Pacific. Figure 7 shows that the genus has never been very diverse, with a more or less, steady-state of species from the Miocene to Recent. By contrast, the speciose, specialist-feeding, gastropod genus *Conus*, which is strongly associated with coral-reef habitats, shows a high species turn-over (Fig. 8), with a massive diversification in the Miocene and during the Pleistocene to Recent with around 500 living species (Kohn 1990). A similar pattern is seen in the specialist, sipunculan-feeding, gastropod subfamily Mitrinae (Fig. 9), which are also diverse in coral-reef habitats (Taylor 1989).

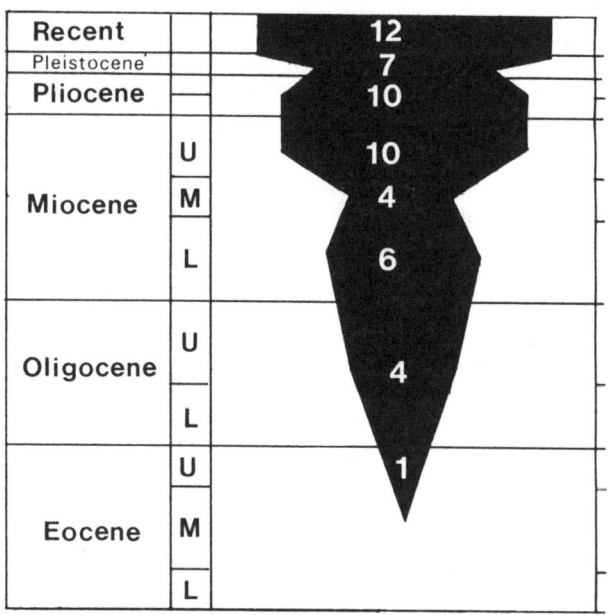

Fig. 7 Kite diagram showing species diversity through geological time for *Babylonia* species. Numbers of species given for each geological period. Data from Altena and Gittenberger (1981).

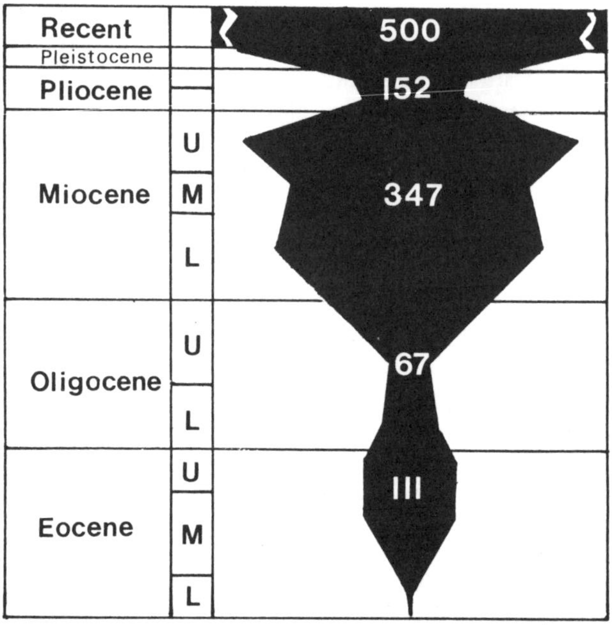

Fig. 8 Kite diagram showing diversity of species of *Conus* through geological time. Redrawn from Kohn (1990).

Vrba (1987) has suggested that the factors controlling the speciation and extinction rates of clades are environmentally controlled. If this is generally true, then the different nutrient regimes found in the Indo-Pacific may be generating important differential rates of speciation and evolutionary change.

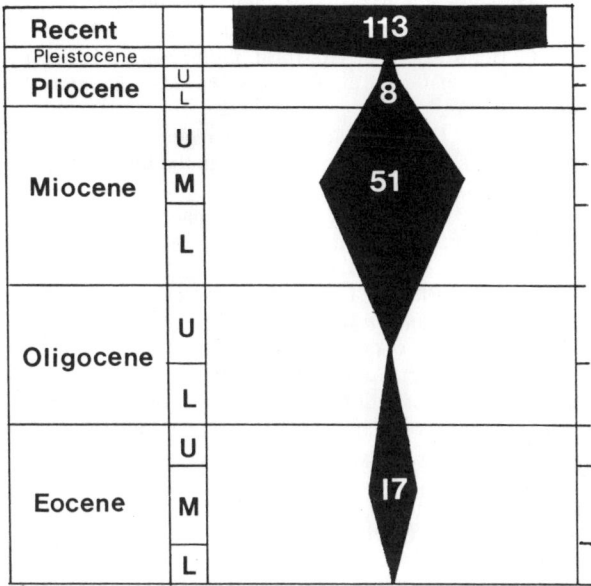

Fig. 9 Kite diagram showing diversity of species of the gastropod subfamily Mitrinae through geological time. Data from Cernohorsky (1976).

ACKNOWLEDGEMENTS

I thank my friends at The University of Hong Kong and University of Guam Marine Laboratory for facilities and hospitality whilst some of this work was carried out. I am especially grateful to Chuck Birkeland who stimulated my interest in nutrient regimes.

REFERENCES

Abbott, R.T. 1960. The genus *Strombus* in the Indo-Pacific. *Indo-Pacific Mollusca* 1:831–999.

Abe, N. 1989. Interactions between carnivorous gastropods and their sessile animal prey at a rocky intertidal shore. *Physiological Ecology, Japan* 26:1–38.

Altena, C.O. van Regteren and Gittenberger, E. 1981. The genus *Babylonia* (Prosobranchia: Buccinidae). *Zoologische Verhandelingen* 188:1–57.

Azuma, M. 1960. *A catalogue of the shell-bearing Mollusca of Okinoshima, Kasiwajima and the adjacent area (Tosa Province), Shikoku,* Barratt, Japan. L. 1985. An ecological study of the rocky shores of the southern coast of Oman. *UNEP Regional Seas Reports and Studies* 73:1–104.

Birkeland, C. 1977. The importance of rate of biomass accumulation in early successional stages of benthic communities to the survival of coral recruits. *Proceedings of the Third International Coral Reef Symposium, Miami* 1:15–21.

Birkeland, C. 1987. Nutrient availability as a major determinant of differences among coastal hard-substratum communities in different regions of the tropics. *UNESCO Reports in Marine Science* 46:45–97.

Birkeland, C. 1988a. Second-order ecological effects of nutrient input into coral communities. *Galaxea* 7:91–100.

Birkeland, C. 1988b. Geographic comparisons of coral-reef community processes. *Proccedings of the Sixth International Coral Reef Symposium, Townsville* 1:211–20.

Cernohorsky, W.O. 1976. The Mitridae of the world. *Indo-Pacific Mollusca* 3:273–528.

Cernohorsky, W.O. 1984. Systematics of the family Nassariidae. *Bulletin of the Auckland Institute and Museum* 14:1–356.

Curtis, L.A. and Hurd, L.E. 1979. On the broad nutritional requirements of the mud snail, *Ilyanassa (Nassarius) obsoleta* (Say), and its polytrophic role in the food web. *Journal of Experimental Marine Biology and Ecology* 41:289–97.

DeAngelis, D.L., Mulholland, P.J., Palumbo, A.V., Steinman, A.D., Huston, M.A. and Elwood, J.W. 1989. Nutrient dynamics and food-web stability. *Annual Review of Ecology and Systematics* 20:71–95.

Frith, D., Tantansiriwong, R. and Bhatia, O. 1976. Zonation of macrofauna on a mangrove shore, Phuket island. *Research Bulletin Phuket Marine Biological Center* 10:1–37.

Glynn, P.W. 1988. El Nino warming, coral mortality and reef framework distribution by echinoid bioerosion in the eastern Pacific. *Galaxea* 7:129–60.

Grigg, R.W., Polovina, J.J. and Atkinson, M.J. 1984. Model of a coral reef ecosystem. III. Resource limitation, community regulation, fisheries yield and resource management. *Coral Reefs* 3:23–7.

Hallock, P. 1988. The role of nutrient availability in bioreosion: consequences to carbonate buildups. *Palaeogeography, Palaeoclimatology, Palaeoecology* 63:275–91.

Hallock, P. and Schlager, W. 1986. Nutrient excess and the demise of coral reefs and carbonate platforms. *Palaios* 1:389–98.

Highsmith, R.C. 1980. Geographic patterns of coral bioerosion: a productivity hypothesis. *Journal of Experimental Marine Biology and Ecology* 46:177–96.

Kay, E.A. 1971. The littoral marine mollusks of Fanning Island. *Pacific Science* 25:260–81.

Kay, E.A. 1979. *Hawaiian Marine Shells*. Honolulu: Bishop Museum Press.

Kay, E.A. 1984. Patterns of speciation in the Indo-West Pacific. In *Biogeography of the Tropical Pacific* (ed. F.J. Radovsky, P.H. Raven and S.H. Sohmer), 15–31. Honolulu: Bernice Museum Special Publication No. 72.

Kay, E.A. and Johnson, S. 1987. Mollusca of Enewetak Atoll. In *The Natural History of Enewetak Atoll* (ed. D. Devaney, E.S. Reese, B.L. Burch and P. Helfrich), 105–46, Vol. 2. Oak Ridge: U.S. Department of Energy.

Kay, E.A. and Switzer, M.F. 1974. Molluscan distribution patterns in Fanning Island lagoon and a comparison of the mollusks of the lagoon and seaward reefs. *Pacific Science* 28:275–95.

Kinsey, D.W. 1988. Coral reef system response to some natural and anthropogenic stresses. *Galaxea* 113–28.

Kohn, A.J. 1987. Intertidal ecology at Enewetak Atoll. In *The Natural History of Enewetak Atoll* (ed. E. Devaney, E.S. Reese, B.L. Burch and P. Helfrich), 138–57, Vol. 1. Oak Ridge: U.S. Department of Energy.

Kohn, A.J. 1990. Tempo and mode of evolution in Conidae. *Malacologia* 32:55–66.

Kuroda, T. 1960. *A Catalogue of Molluscan Fauna of Okinawa Islands (exclusive of Cephalopoda)*. Tokyo.

Kuroda, T., Habe, T. and Oyama, K. 1971. *The Sea Shells of Sagami Bay*. Tokyo: Maruzen Co. Ltd.

Lee, S.Y. 1985. The population dynamics of the green mussel, *Perna viridis* (L.) in Victoria Harbour, Hong Kong- dominance in a polluted environment. *Asian Marine Biology* 2:107–18

Lee, S.Y. 1986. Growth and reproduction of the green mussel *Perna viridis* (L.) (Bivalvia: Mytilacea) in contrasting environments in Hong Kong. *Asian Marine Biology* 3:111–28.

Lee, S.Y. and Morton, B. 1985. The Hong Kong Mytilidae. In *Proceedings of the Second International Workshop on the Malacofauna of Hong Kong and Southern China, Hong Kong, 1983* (ed. B. Morton and D. Dudgeon), 49–76. Hong Kong: Hong Kong University Press.

Lewis, M.R. 1989. The variegated ocean: a view from space. *New Scientist* 124(1685):37–40.

Maes, V. 1967. The littoral marine mollusks of Cocos-Keeling Islands (Indian Ocean). *Proceedings of the Academy of Natural Sciences, Philadelphia* 119:93–217.

Morton, B. 1983. Coral-associated bivalves of the Indo-Pacific. In *The Mollusca, 6.* (Ecology) (ed. W.D. Russell-Hunter), 139 274 New York and London: Academic Press.

Morton, B. 1989. Life History characteristics and sexual strategy of *Mytilopsis sallei* (Bivalvia; Dreissenacea), introduced into Hong Kong. *Journal of Zoology, London* 219:469–85.

Morton, B. 1990. The physiology and feeding behaviour of two marine scavenging gastropods in Hong Kong: the subtidal *Babylonia lutosa* (Lamarck) and the intertidal *Nassarius festivus* (Powys). *Journal of Molluscan Studies* 56:275–88.

Morton, B. and Chiu, S.T. 1990. The diet, prey size and consumption of *Philine orientalis* (Opisthobranchia: Philinidae) in Hong Kong. *Journal of Molluscan Studies* 56:289–99.

Muscatine, L. and Porter, J.W. 1977. Reef corals: mutualistic symbiosis adapted to nutrient-poor environments. *Bioscience* 27:454–60.

Pearson, T.H. and Rosenberg, R. 1978. Macrobenthic succession in relation to organic enrichment and pollution of the marine environment. *Oceanography and Marine Biology Annual Review* 16:229–311.

Reid, D.G. 1986. *The Littorinid Molluscs of Mangrove Forests in the Indo-Pacific Region.* London: British Museum (Natural History).

Richard, G. 1982. *Mollusques Lagunaires et Récifaux de Polynesie Française.* D.Sc. Thesis, Université Pierre et Marie Curie, Paris.

Richard, G., Salvat, B. and Millous, O. 1979. Mollusques et faune benthique du lagon de Takapoto. *Journal de la Societe des Oceanistes* 62:59–68.

Rosen, B.R. 1988. Progress, problems and patterns in the biogeography of reef corals and other tropical reef organisms. *Helgolander Meeresuntersuchungen* 42:269–301.

Ryther, J.H. 1969. Photosynthesis and fish production in the sea. *Science* 166:72–6.

Salvat, B. 1967. Importance de la faune malacologique dans les atolls polynesiens. *Cahiers du Pacifique* 11:1–49.

Savidge, G., Lennon, J. and Matthews, A.J. 1990. A shore based survey of upwelling along the coast of Dhofar region, southern Oman. *Continental Shelf Research* 10:259–75.

Scott, P.J.B. and Cope, M. 1990. Tolo revisited: a resurvey of the corals in Tolo Harbour and Chennel six years and half a million people later. In *Proceedings of the Second International Marine Biological Workshop: the Marine Fauna and Flora of Hong Kong and Southern China, Hong Kong, 1986* (ed. B. Morton), 1203–20. Hong Kong: Hong Kong University Press.

Sidall, S.E. 1980. A clarification of the genus *Perna* (Mytilidae). *Bulletin of Marine Science* 30:858–70.

Sournia, A. and Ricard, M. 1975. Phytoplankton production and primary production in Takapoto Atoll, Tuamotu Islands. *Micronesia* 11:159–66.

Springsteen, F.J. and Leobera, F.M. 1986. *Shells of the Philippines.* Manila: Carfel Shell Museum.

Tantanasiriwong, R. 1978. An illustrated checklist of marine shelled gastropods from Phuket Island, adjacent mainland and offshore islands, western peninsular Thailand. *Research Bulletin Phuket Marine Biological Center* 21:1–22.

Taylor, J.D. 1971. Reef associated molluscan assemblages in the western Indian Ocean *Symposium of the Zoological Society of London* 28:501–34.

Taylor, J.D. 1980. Diets and habitats of shallow water predatory gastropods around Tolo Channel, Hong Kong. In *Proceedings of the First International Workshop on the Malacofauna of Hong Kong and Southern China, Hong Kong, 1977* (ed. B. Morton), 163–80. Hong Kong: Hong Kong University Press.

Taylor, J.D. 1984. A partial food web involving predatory gastropods on a Pacific fringing reef. *Journal of Experimental Marine Biology and Ecology* 74:273–90.

Taylor, J.D. 1986. Diets of sand-living predatory gastropods at Piti Bay, Guam. *Asian Marine Biology* 3:47–58.

Taylor, J.D. 1989. The diet of coral-reef Mitridae (Gastropoda) from Guam; with a review of other species of the family. *Journal of Natural History* 23:261–78.

Taylor, J.D. 1990. Field observations of prey selection by the muricid gastropods *Thais clavigera* and *Morula musiva* feeding upon the intertidal oyster *Saccostrea cucullata*. In *Proceedings of the Second International Marine Biological Workshop: The Marine Flora and Fauna of Hong Kong and Southern China (II), Hong Kong, 1986* (ed. B. Morton), 837–55. Hong Kong: Hong Kong University Press.

Taylor, J.D. 1992. Long-term changes in the gastropod fauna of Tolo Channel and Mirs Bay, Hong Kong: the 1989 survey. In *Proceedings of the Third International Marine Biological Workshop: The Marine Flora and Fauna of Hong Kong and Southern China, Hong Kong, 1989* (ed. B. Morton), 557–73. Hong Kong: Hong Kong University Press

Taylor, J.D. and Reid, D.G. 1984. The abundance and trophic classification of molluscs upon coral reefs in the Sudanese Red Sea. *Journal of Natural History* 18:175–209.

Taylor, J.D. and Shin, P.K.S. 1990. Trawl surveys of sublittoral gastropods in Tolo Channel and Mirs Bay; a record of change from 1976–1986. In *Proceedings of the Second International Marine Biological Workshop: The Marine Flora and Fauna of Hong Kong and Southern China (II) Hong Kong, 1986* (ed. B. Morton), 857–81. Hong Kong: Hong Kong University Press.

Tong, L.K.Y. 1986. The feeding ecology of *Thais clavigera* and *Morula musiva* (Gastropoda: Muricidae) in Hong Kong. *Asian Marine Biology* 3:163–78.

Tsuchiya, M. and Lirdwitayaprasit, T. 1986. Distribution of intertidal animals on rocky shores of the Sichang Islands, the Gulf of Thailand. *Galaxea* 15–25.

Vermeij, G.J. 1978. *Biogeography and Adaptation*. Cambidge: Harvard University Press.

Vermeij, G.J. 1987. *Evolution and Escalation. An ecological History of Life*. Princeton: Princeton University Press.

Vermeij, G.J. 1990. Tropical Pacific pelecypods and productivity: a hypothesis. *Bulletin of Marine Science* 47:62–7

Vrba, E.S. 1987. Ecology in relation to speciation rates: some case histories of Miocene-Recent mammal clades. *Evolutionary Ecology* 1:283–300.

Wiebe, W.J. 1987. Nutrient pools and dynamics in tropical, marine, coastal environments, with special reference to the Caribbean and Indo-West Pacific regions. *UNESCO Reports in Marine Science* 46:19–42.

Wilkinson, C.R. 1986. The nutritional spectrum of coral reef benthos. *Oceanus* 29:68–75.

Wilkinson, C.R. and Cheshire, A.C. 1989. Patterns in the distribution of sponge populations across the central Great Barrier Reef. *Coral Reefs* 8:127–34

Williams, D. McB., Russ, G. and Doherty, P.J. 1986. Reef fish. *Oceanus* 29:76–82.

Wu, W.L. 1980. The list of Taiwan bivalve fauna. *Quarterly Journal of the Taiwan Museum* 33:1–208.

Wu, R.S.S. 1982. Periodic defaunation and recovery in a sub-tropical epibenthic community in relation to organic pollution. *Journal of Experimental Marine Biology and Ecology* 64:253–69.

The Marine Biology of the South China Sea
(ed. B. Morton). Proceedings of the First
International Conference on the Marine
Biology of Hong Kong and the South China Sea,
Hong Kong, 28 October – 3 November 1990.
Hong Kong: Hong Kong University Press, 1993.

ARE THERE OBLIGATE MARINE SCAVENGERS?

Joseph C. Britton

Department of Biology, Texas Christian University, Fort Worth, Texas 76129, USA

and

Brian Morton

Department of Zoology and The Swire Marine Laboratory,
The University of Hong Kong, Hong Kong

ABSTRACT

A variety of animals derive nutrition by macrophagous scavenging of marine carrion. The greatest number of scavenging species are representatives of the Arthropoda, including numerous marine Amphipoda, Isopoda, Decapoda and terrestrial Insecta, the latter only periodically entering the intertidal zone. Other groups with significant numbers of marine scavengers include the Turbellaria, Nemertea, Polychaeta, Gastropoda, Asteroidea, Ophiuroidea, and Vertebrata. Scavenging behaviour is especially intense in intertidal and subtidal habitats composed of unconsolidated and/or unstabilized sediments. The significance of carrion in intertidal and subtidal environments probably varies in relation to its spatial and temporal inveteracy.

Macrophagous scavenging is not widespread among the Gastropoda, being restricted mostly to the neogastropod Buccinoidea and sporadically among other Neogastropoda and Opisthobranchia. One family, the Nassariidae, has, however, been especially successful in exploiting this feeding niche. Nassariids and other neogastropod scavengers are derived from a fundamentally predatory molluscan stock, but several species are obligatory omnivores, relying upon herbivory and, in some cases, predation to supplement a diet of carrion. The Nassariidae is rich in species, several of which are often present at a locality. Accordingly, the family offers many examples of intraspecific and interspecific resource partitioning, including habitat utilization, e.g., intertidal vs. subtidal species, food preference, and event timing, e.g., diurnal activity, feeding, seasonal migration, reproductive effort. Some species also demonstrate clear examples of intraspecific competition.

Scavenging behaviour provides nutritional resources generally unavailable to strict predators or herbivores, but often in quantities insufficient to sustain the total energy requirements of the scavenger. It also fosters contact between a diverse assemblage of species which must either compete directly for the limited carrion resources or adopt behaviours which reduce competitive conflicts. Neogastropod scavengers, especially members of the Nassariidae, effectively demonstrate both of these attributes of the scavenging lifestyle. We conclude that there is probably no obligate scavenger because ephemeral food is inconducive to the evolution of such a life style. Only the Nassariidae, possibly, represent an evolutionary excursion in this direction.

INTRODUCTION

In the recent general ecological literature, the concept of 'scavenger' is frequently relegated to a sub-discipline of predation. Yet, a 'scavenger' may display one or several different feeding behaviours, each of which overlaps, by differing degrees, feeding methodologies other than active predation. Several crustacean and asteroid 'scavengers', for example, derive nutrition from microscopic detritus located in the water column, on or near the surface of unconsolidated sediments, or adhering to rock or gravel surfaces. Depending upon habitat, these microphagous scavengers extract nutrient-rich detritus from such markedly different sources that their feeding behaviours can be more appropriately associated with those of either suspension feeding, deposit feeding, or grazing, respectively, than to predators which seek an active prey. In contrast, scavengers of macrophagous carrion (defined herein as a mass of moribund tissue with sufficient structural integrity and size that it can clearly be differentiated from the medium or substratum in or upon which it is located) more closely resemble active predators in that they usually detect a specific food object from afar and conduct a dedicated search for it with little regard for other sources of nutrition in the immediate vicinity.

Despite the diversity of behaviours attributed to 'scavenging', it was at first difficult for us to comprehend why this concept is often misused, avoided or ignored in the literature. Necrophagous scavengers are frequently lumped with either carnivores or omnivores with little distinction between live-prey capture, necrophagy, detritivory or consumption of disarticulated animal remains, i.e., carrion. Nicol (1969), for example, grouped scavengers with carnivores as animals which have 'methods for seizing prey'. The many reviews of general feeding ecology which have appeared during the last two decades have either ignored the process of macrophagous scavenging (necrophagy) or treated it as a form of predation (Schoener 1971; Krebs 1978; Hainsworth and Wolf 1979; Kohn 1983). The *degree* to which the concept of 'scavenging' has been avoided or relegated to unimportance, however, was surprising to us. A computer-based search of *Biological Abstracts* from January 1975 to August 1990 using the keywords 'marine' and 'scavenger' generated only 52 references, most of which were concerned with chemical scavenging, e.g., 'The hydrolytic scavenging of metal ions by particulate matter' (Clegg and Sarmiento 1989). Only 13 papers pertaining to scavenging of animal carrion were abstracted and, for most of these, macrophagous scavenging was not the primary focus of the paper! Equally surprising was the paucity of information on scavenging behaviour in many well respected texts and reviews. The recent text by Barnes *et al.* (1988), for example, devotes one chapter to invertebrate feeding (pp. 273–313), but virtually ignores scavenging behaviour. Microphagous scavenging, though never explicitly defined, was relegated to a section on deposit feeding and macrophagous carrion scavenging was excepted from deposit feeding (p. 295), but otherwise never discussed.

Many animals derive nutrition by necrophagy, but we found little effort to either enumerate systematically those species or groups which employ it or to evaluate this behaviour in comparison with other forms of feeding available to the scavengers or their close relatives. This paper shall attempt to fill this void, but in so doing it raises an important question related to the reticence of authors to define or elucidate 'scavenging', which is: are there obligate scavengers?

A GENERAL SURVEY OF MARINE SCAVENGERS

In this survey we focus attention on necrophagous animals, i.e., those that feed by macrophagous scavenging. Some groups whose members are noted primarily for other feeding habits, e.g., filter-feeding copepods or grazing herbivorous gastropods, will receive little or no attention. Conversely, non-scavenging habits are sometimes noted among groups containing necrophagous scavengers, primarily to serve as either counterpoints to or permit comparisons with scavenging members. The distinction between microphagous scavenging and detritivory is particularly difficult, especially with respect to those animals that combine these feeding methods with necrophagy. Microphagous scavenging and detritivory will thus appear frequently in our survey in comparison with macrophagous scavenging, despite the fact that neither one is a primary focus of the paper nor are they exhaustively treated.

Turbellaria

Turbellarian flatworms are mainly carnivorous, but many are attracted to fresh carrion. Some marine species are collected by baiting with dead fish. They may be attracted from several metres, indicating the presence of distance chemosensory receptors (Hyman 1951; Jennings 1957).

Nemertea

Dietary preferences are known for only a few nemerteans. Most are selective carnivores which favour specific prey (McDermott and Roe 1985) but some, especially members of the Lineidae, may also be macrophagous scavengers. *Cerebratulus lacteus*, *Gorgonohyynchus bermudensis*, *Lineus ruber*, *Lineus vegetus* and *Lineus viridis* will feed on one or more of the following items of dead flesh in aquaria: polychaetes, bivalves, small crustaceans, liver (McDermott and Roe 1985). Lineids employ the proboscis for capture of live prey, but forego its use when scavenging. None of these species has been observed naturally feeding on carrion, but large numbers of *Parborlasia corrugatus* from shallow Antarctic waters were observed converging and feeding upon recently killed asteroids, *Acodontaster conspicuous* (Dayton *et al.* 1974). Non-lineid nemertean scavengers include *Ototyphlonemertes brevis*, an interstitial species reported to congregate and feed upon recently killed fish (Corrêa 1948).

Nematoda

The vast sea is likely rich in uncounted numbers of undescribed nematodes, but dietary preferences are poorly known even for the majority of described, common, species. Many nematodes derive sustenance from 'the decomposing bodies of plants and animals' (Barnes 1980), but the scavenging relationship is likely more saprophagous than macrophagous (Hyman 1951).

Mollusca

The Cephalopoda are mostly predators of living fish, prawns, crabs and even other cephalopods (Boucaud-Camou and Boucher-Rodoni 1983), but some deep sea octopods are attracted to fish bait (Issacs and Schwartzlose 1975). Among the bivalves, only representatives of the deep water genera *Poromya* and *Cuspidaria* were considered scavengers of plankton-derived carcasses (Yonge 1928). These, and other members of the 'septibranch' Anomalodesmata, are now known, however, to be active predators (Reid and Reid 1974; Morton 1981).

Macrophagous scavenging appears sporadically among several, diverse, groups of the Gastropoda such as the muricids *Chicoreus pomum*, which feeds commonly upon fish carcasses (personal observations) and *Thais orbita* (= *Dicathais aegrota*), which is reported to consume carrion on shallow intertidal rock platforms in Western Australia (Phillips 1969); the olive snail, *Oliva sayana*, which also feeds upon fish carrion (Kohn 1961); and species of the opisthobranch *Pleurobranchus*, which feed upon various items of carrion (Nicol 1969). Weaver and duPont (1970) reported that the volutes *Adelomelon beckii* and *Cymbiola aulica* are sometimes taken by fishermen on baited fish hooks; a review of the diets of members of this family, however, has shown them to be specialised predators of bivalves and, especially, other gastropods (Morton 1986c). Macrophagous scavenging is, however, a principal feeding habit of three closely related neogastropod families: the Buccinidae, Melongenidae and, especially, the Nassariidae which, together with several smaller neogastropod families, constitute the Buccinoidea.

Malacologists usually trace the roots of neogastropod scavenging behaviour to a remote predatory ancestor (Fretter and Graham 1962; Ponder 1973). This is supported, to some extent, by an examination of the diets of various Buccinidae and Melongenidae. Large whelks often exhibit catholic diets. *Buccinum undatum*, which is collected commercially in carrion-baited pots, was once considered to be predominantly necrophagous (Dakin 1912). It does scavenge (Himmelman 1988), often moving rapidly toward baited pots (Gros and Santarelli 1986), but is also a generalized predator. Taylor (1978) identified 35 species of presumed prey belonging to eight animal phyla from *B. undatum* gut contents. Nielsen (1975) describes how *B. undatum* feeds upon living bivalves by wedging the tip of its shell between parted valves, inserting its proboscis in the gap and using the radula to tear out flesh. Another buccinid, *Cominella eburnea*, scavenges upon Western Australian shores, but it is principally a bivalve predator (Morton and Britton 1991). In New Zealand, *Cominella glandiformis* is reported to commonly scavenge moribund bivalves, especially *Austrovenus stuchburyi* (Walsby 1990) although Morton and Miller (1968) note that, like *C. eburnea* in Australia, *C. glandiformis* is principally a predator of bivalves. In Puget Sound, Washington, U.S.A., the rocky intertidal buccinid, *Searlsia dira*, feeds on barnacles, limpets and chitons, although other prey and carrion are also taken (Louda 1979). Four species of *Neptunea* feed primarily upon bivalves and polychaetes, secondarily upon carrion, with other prey taxa also represented in their diets (Shimek 1984).

The Melongenidae also contain opportunistic scavenging species, especially species of *Melongena* and *Busycon* from the western Atlantic. Most of these, however, are now known to be primarily bivalve predators (Magalhaes 1948; Paine 1962). Similarly, western Pacific melongenid whelks of the genus *Hemifusus* consume some carrion, but are also principally bivalve predators (Morton 1985, 1986a, b, 1987).

The Nassariidae contain some of the best known necrophagous molluscs, but the feeding preferences of several members of this family are decidedly capricious (Taylor 1981; Taylor and Shin 1990). In fact, of the approximately 317 living species of Nassariidae (Cernohorsky 1984), the diets of < 10% are known (Table 1), and these are intertidal or shallow subtidal species. The subtidal South African *Bullia laevissima* feeds on carrion in relatively non-turbulent shallow waters (Brown 1961). Intertidal *Bullia digitalis* and *Bullia rhodostoma* of South African sandy beaches also feed on carrion, especially cnidarians stranded within or slightly above the wash zone (Brown 1982). *Bullia digitalis* may consume live prey (Brown 1971, 1982; Brown et al. 1989) but also feeds on green algae attached to its shell (da Silva and Brown 1984; Harris et al. 1986). *Nassarius kraussianus*, also from South Africa, can survive for at least two months by grazing upon algae in the absence of a preferred diet of carrion (Brown 1982). *Ilyanassa obsoleta* of the temperate western Atlantic feeds upon carrion when available, but is primarily a deposit-feeding omnivorous detritivore (Scheltema 1964; Curtis and Hurd 1979). The latter authors have experimentally demonstrated *Ilyanassa obsoleta* to be an obligate omnivore, requiring a mixed diet of both plants and animals. Food preferences of *Nassarius reticulatus* from Gullmar Fjord on the western coast of Sweden (Tallmark 1980) vary with size and age. Younger, smaller, individuals feed mostly upon detritus from fine, unconsolidated, sediments but larger, older, animals prefer carrion, especially moribund cockles. *Nassarius festivus* from Hong Kong and *Nassarius pyrrhus* from Western Australia feed upon recently moribund bivalves, fish, or decapod crustaceans (Morton and Britton 1991; Britton and Morton 1992). It is unknown if either of the latter species have additional dietary preferences. The omnivorous *Nassarius pauperatus* from South Australia feeds on algae and carrion (McKillup and Butler 1979), especially moribund *Katelysia scalarina*, a sandflat bivalve, which is also scavenged by *N. pyrrhus* (Morton and Britton 1991). The intertidal *Nassarius trivittatus* feeds upon the egg capsules of the naticid *Euspira heros* (Clarke 1956). The few shallow subtidal nassariids whose gut contents have been examined, e.g., *Nassarius albescens* and *N. arcularis* from the Red Sea (Taylor and Reid 1984) and *N. siquijorensis* and *N. crematus* from Tolo Channel and Mirs Bay, Hong Kong (Taylor and Shin 1990) usually include numerous polychaete and crustacean fragments, sediments, detritus and various other vertebrate and invertebrate skeletal remains (Table 1).

The shell shape of several Nassariidae, e.g., *Bullia digitalis*, facilitates their burial within unconsolidated substrata (Trueman and Brown 1989). *Cyclope neritea*, *Hinia reticulata*, and *Sphaeronassa variabilis* generally repose within the substratum during the day with only the tips of their siphons exposed (Bedulli 1976). More robust species such as *Ilyanassa obsoleta* may also seek shelter by burial, but the accumulation of extensive mats of filamentous algae upon their shells suggest that other sites of repose are also utilized. Most nassariids emerge from the substratum and become active when

Table 1
The diets of some species of Nassariidae.

Species	Food	Source
Bullia spp.	Carrion: Cnidaria, especially *Physalia* & scyphozoan medusae; annelids; other molluscs, esp. the bivalves *Choromytilus*, *Aulacomya*, & *Schizodesma*; crustaceans; insects; tunicates(*Pyura*); fish of all kinds; birds; mammals. Live prey: Amphipods; polychaetes; bivalves (*Donax*); crustaceans (*Callianassa*)	Brown 1961; Brown 1964; Brown 1971; McLachlan *et al.* 1981; Brown 1982.
Bullia digitalis	All of the above, plus green algae	Harris *et al.* 1986
Ilyanassa obsoleta	Primarily a deposit feeder, feeding upon microalgae; dead molluscs, crustaceans and fish when available, but not a principal food; do not take living prey	Scheltema 1964
	Plant (spinach) and animal (shrimp) tissue	Curtis and Hurd 1979
	Predation on eggs and juveniles of *Cerithidea californica*	Race 1982
Nassarius albescens	Polychaetes (*Praxilella*, *Scalibregma*, *Ceratonereis*, *Glycera*, Capitellidae, Nereiidae, Terebellidae); crustaceans	Taylor and Reid 1984
Nassarius arcularis	Polychaetes (*Ceratonereis*, Spionidae, Nereiidae); crustaceans	Taylor and Reid 1984
Nassarius crematus	Polychaetes (*Sthenolepis*, *Aglaophamus*); fish, bone and scales; sediment and detritus	Taylor and Shin 1990
Nassarius festivus	Dead and dying bivalves (*Tapes philippinarum*), gastropods (*Philine orientalis*), crustaceans (*Mictyris longicarpus*); fish carrion	Britton and Morton 1991
Nassarius kraussianus	Carrion, algae and *Zostera*	Palmer 1980 *fide* Brown, 1982
Nassarius pauperatus	Omnivorous, feeding upon both algae and animal carrion, especially bivalves (*Katelysia scalarina*)	McKillup and Butler 1979; McKillup and Butler 1983; McKillup 1983
Nassarius pyrrhus	Dead and dying bivalves (*Katelysia scalarina*); fish carrion	Morton and Britton 1991

Table 1 (Continued)

Species	Food	Source
Nassarius reticulatus	Predominantly predatory; scavenger; will browse on diatoms	Rasmussen 1973
	Scavenger; dead *Carcinus maenas*	Crisp 1978; Crisp *et al.* 1978
	Food preference varies with size; smaller individuals are detritivores; larger individuals prefer carrion, including dead and dying fish, crabs and bivalves, especially *Cardium edule*.	Tallmark 1980
Nassarius siquijorensis	Polychaetes (*Prionospio, Lepidonotus, Sthenolepis, Aglaophamus, Lagis,* Syllidae, Flabelligeridae); fish bone and scales; ophiuroid ossicles; crustaceans; bivalves; sediment and detritus	Taylor and Shin 1990

food is placed within the range of detection (Trueman and Brown 1987; Morton and Britton 1991; Britton and Morton 1992). An immediate increase in oxygen uptake accompanies this activity (Crisp *et al.* 1978). Nassariids are acutely sensitive to physical and chemical stimuli, the latter conveyed either by contact or water. Aspects of chemoreception in nassariids and other scavengers will be considered in a separate section.

Polychaeta

Fauchald and Jumars (1979) point out that the majority of polychaetes are either microphagous suspension feeders or deposit feeding detrivores. Microphagous scavenging is thus well represented among the Polychaeta. Fauchald and Jumars also recognize 19 families of carnivorous polychaetes. Unfortunately, they fail to list macrophagous scavenging among their otherwise defined polychaete feeding guilds, apparently including this feeding behaviour with carnivory. Many families of predominantly carnivorous polychaetes include members which are at least facultative detritivores. Similarly, many omnivorous polychaetes, e.g., some Nereidae and Nerillidae, ingest animal debris (but not necessarily fresh carrion). Families containing members which exhibit macrophagous scavenging behaviour include the Lumbrineridae, Nereidae, Onuphidae (*Diopatra* spp., *Hyalinoecia*), Phyllodocidae (*Eumida* sp.), Polydontidae, Polyodontidae and, possibly, the Spintheridae.

Because lumbrinerids are difficult to identify, Fauchald and Jumars (1979) were uncertain exactly which species fed on carrion based upon literature reports. They, nevertheless, indicated that macrophagous scavenging is practised by some members of this family. Nereids include species with many different feeding strategies. Omnivores or detritivores are well represented. *Nereis virens* is 'an errant carnivore which also feeds on dead animals and algae' (Nicol 1969, p. 238). *Cheilonereis cyclurus* and *Nereis fucata* live as commensals with hermit crabs, and steal food from their hosts (MacGinitie and

MacGinitie 1968; Goerke 1971a, b). Members of the onuphid genus *Hyalinocia* are attracted to carrion, and hundreds of individuals can aggregate on a single moribund fish (Dayton and Hessler 1972). Another tube-dwelling onuphid, *Diopatra cuprea*, captures live prey, scavenges detritus which attaches to the elevated chimney of its tube, or feeds opportunistically upon nearby carrion (Mangum *et al.* 1968; Myers 1972). Spintherids are apparently carnivorous or ectoparasitic on sponges, and may ingest sponge carrion (Fauchald and Jumars 1979). Other polychaete families include species with highly variable diets and may rely, at least in part, on either carrion or animal detritus.

Arthropoda

The arthropod digestive tract is designed primarily to process either finely particulate or liquid foods. Mastication, tissue shredding or particle sorting, if it occurs at all, does so externally. Accordingly, many arthropods are facultatively and/or actually microphagous gatherers, with feeding structures designed to extract nutrients either from fluids or soft sediments. Arthropods which gather organic detritus floating in water are included among suspension feeders, but those which extract it from sediments are microphagous scavengers.

Not all arthropods selectively ingest fine particles. The extreme adaptability and plasticity of their appendages have liberated arthropods from compulsory microphagous diets. Raptorial arms, chelipeds, fangs, stingers and other structures enable many arthropods to capture and hold large objects. The capturing appendages and/or additional ones near the mouth often reduce large food items to fine particles prior to it entering the digestive tract. If, however, larger food particles such as shredded vegetation or bits of flesh enter the digestive tract, they are usually well pulverized in an internal gastric mill, gizzard or similar structure of the foregut prior to digestion and assimilation. The specific form and function of food-gathering appendages varies widely throughout the phylum, permitting a diversity of microphagous and macrophagous diets and feeding behaviours (including suspension feeding, suctorial fluid ingestion, herbivory, carnivory, omnivory, detritivory and scavenging). Thus, arthropod feeding strategies are not constrained by mechanical demands of the digestive tract or feeding process (as, for example, are many gastropods and most bivalve molluscs), but are free to evolve according to the availability of nutrients in the environment and the adaptability of appendages to deal with them. Like other animals, some arthropods have highly specialized diets. But many taxa, at a variety of levels from species to order (especially among the Crustacea), have developed a repertoire of several feeding strategies which they selectively exercise depending upon the food available. These arthropods move easily from microphagous scavenger to macrophagous carnivore, herbivore, omnivore or scavenger. This makes it difficult for us to generalize with respect to arthropod macrophagous scavenging, for it frequently appears opportunistically in many groups.

Merostomes are a good case in point. The Atlantic *Limulus polyphemus*, the Indo-Pacific *Tachypleus tridentatus* and other extant merostomes are well adapted for microphagous scavenging. Small chelate appendages collect fine detritus from unconsolidated sediments and transfer it to the gnathobases where it is pulverized further before being passed anteriorly to the mouth. Yet, organic detritus is only part of the diet. Horseshoe crabs opportunistically capture and ingest bottom dwelling algae and live prey — mostly benthic worms, molluscs, and other small invertebrates — all of which are subjected to the same particle-reducing process before entering the digestive tract. It is a small step from live prey to macrophagous carrion, which is also processed and ingested when available. Carrion is likely detected by chemoreceptors located on spines of coxal gnathobases of the walking legs, on chelae, chelicerae and other prosomal appendages, and on chilaria spines (Barber and Hayes 1963).

Many small, free-living, non-malacostracans feed upon microphagous particles of necessity. Planktonic species usually do this by suspension or filter-feeding. Conversely, the primitive cephalocarid *Hutchinsoniella macracantha* is a suitable simple model of a benthic, non-selective, microphagous scavenging arthropod (Sanders 1963). The movements of similar pairs of thoracic limbs produce a current of water in which seston is drawn into the medial space between limb pairs. Such material is caught by setae and transferred into a ventral food groove, wherein it passes forward to the mouth. This basic model, though modified, embellished, perfected and frequently made selective by other crustaceans, apparently represents a fundamental feeding method for benthic aquatic arthropods (Manton 1977).

Yet, body size and food resources are not strictly correlated in the Crustacea. Some balanoid barnacles number among the largest non-malacostracans, but feed mostly upon microplankton and seston. In contrast, some benthic ostracods and copepods capture or feed upon food items half or more their size, as do some freshwater branchiopods (Marshall and Orr 1960) and ostracods (Kaestner 1970). In comparison to the total number of species of Crustacea, the number whose diet and feeding habits have been investigated is small, with many tiny non-malacostracans being especially poorly known. It is clear, however, that some groups of predominantly small-bodied non-malacostracans express the same diversity of feeding habits as are found in larger malacostracans.

Ostracods and copepods are best known as either suspension feeders or microphagous detritivores, but both groups contain members which demonstrate several other feeding behaviours. Predatory myodocopid ostracods, including *Gigantocypris mulleri*, *Conchoecia* sp., *Cypridina castanea* and *Cypridina norvegica*, capture copepods, mysids, euphausiids, chaetognaths, polychaetes and fish fry (Cannon 1933; Hardy 1956; Lochhead 1968; Kaestner 1970). Species of *Cypridina* and *Vargula* are scavengers of planktonic carrion. Benthic carrion-feeding podocopid ostracods include *Paradoxostoma variabilis*, *Macrocypris* sp. (Cannon 1933) and several freshwater species (Kaestner 1970). Several predatory cyclopoid and calanoid copepods will also eat recently dead carrion; many benthic harpacticoids are microphagous detritivores, and some freshwater Cyclopidae feed upon fish carrion (Fryer 1957). The planktonic cyclopid copepod, *Onacaea mediterranea*, crawls upon and scavenges the mucous walls of abandoned larvacean houses while other crustaceans, such as the harpacticoid *Microsetella norvegica*, the calanoid *Paracalanus aculeatus*, and the ostracod *Conchoecia rotundata*, may supplement their diets with the rich field of nannoplankton that becomes trapped upon the floating mucous house of larvaceans (Alldredge 1972).

Barnacles are predominantly filter feeding crustaceans, but *Lepas anatifera*, *Pollicipes polymerus* (Howard and Scott 1959) and *Tetraclita squamosa* (Marshall and Orr 1960) capture and ingest copepods, amphipods, isopods, polychaetes, and tiny gastropods and bivalves. Contact with any of these potential food items is passively opportunistic; the characterization of feeding behaviour as either predation or scavenging thus depends upon the condition of the food item when contact is made with the barnacle cirri. Kaestner (1970) has stated that when lepadomorphs such as *Lepas* or

Scalpellum are presented with small pieces of meat, their cirri will grasp it and pass it to the mouth.

Microphagous detritivores are widespread throughout the Malacostraca, including the primitive freshwater syncarideans such as *Anaspides tasmaniae* (Cannon and Manton 1929; Williams 1965), the monophyletic *Spelaeogriphus lepidops*, known only from a single South African stream, tanaidaceans, cumaceans, isopods, amphipods and numerous decapods. Many of these species are also opportunistic macrophagous scavengers.

As with most other major groups of marine arthropods, it is difficult to formulate a generalized decapod diet, for this diverse group exhibits a wide range of feeding habits. In addition to primary feeding behaviours that differ widely among species, a high percentage of decapods are also facultative scavengers.

Many semi-terrestrial Decapoda, despite a primary dietary preference, may also engage in macrophagous scavenging. Sandy beaches throughout the world are occupied by ocypodid ghost crabs, most of which are predators (Wolcott 1988) that also take carrion. Some, such as the western Atlantic *Ocypode quadrata*, were once considered exclusively scavengers. In fact, *O. quadrata* is another example of arthropod adaptability, preying upon beach macrofauna for 90% of its diet (Wolcott 1978), but feeding upon a variety of carrion and decaying vegetation, including *Sargassum*, insects, fish, cnidarians, other ghost crabs, turtles, and even cetacean and bovine carcasses (Teerling 1970). This species is equally adept at microphagous scavenging (Robertson and Pfeiffer 1982). The western Pacific species, *Ocypode ceratophthalmus*, has a similarly broad range of feeding behaviours (Jones 1972).

Ghost crabs which share sandy beaches often partition the environment with respect to both vertical shore position and feeding preferences. *Ocypode cordimana*, an east African supratidal species, feeds upon insects, ants, small reptiles and carrion (Burggren and McMahon 1988). A lower shore species, *Ocypode ryderi* (= *O. kuhli*) relies upon macrophagous algae for long-term sustenance, but also takes living or recently moribund hippids, congeners and insects. When presented with a choice, *O. ryderi* prefers animal to plant food (Evans *et al.* 1976).

The Grapsidae are a large, diverse, family with many semi-terrestrial species. Some are herbivorous, such as the rocky shore *Grapsus grapsus*, which is often observed feeding upon bits of intertidal algae; some are detritivores, such as mangrove-dwelling species of *Chiromanthes*, which process mangrove leaf litter (Malley 1978; Lee 1989); some are decidedly omnivorous, such as *Aratus pisonii*, which feeds upon mangrove leaves and preys upon insects and juvenile conspecifics (Warner 1967); and some are mainly carnivores, such as *Goniopsis cruentata*, which preys upon *A. pisonii*, species of *Uca*, and other mangrove fauna (Warner 1967). Many grapsids, despite their preferred cuisine, are also facultative scavengers. Species especially noted for their diet of carrion include *Geograpsus crinipes* from sandy beaches throughout the Indo-Pacific (Alexander 1979), *Geograpsus stormi* from rocky shores in the same region (Gilchrist 1988), and *Sesarma roberti* from coastal forests of the Caribbean basin (von Hagen 1977).

The Gecarcinidae are predominantly herbivores, feeding upon leaves, fruits, algae, mosses, and other plant products (Wolcott 1988); but all members of the family are also opportunistic scavengers. Even mangrove-dwelling species, e.g., *Cardisoma guanhumi*, which are mainly leaf-litter detritivores, readily take carrion when it is available (Herreid 1963). Higher upon the shore, various species of *Gecarcinus* not only scavenge carrion, but sometimes feed upon living insects, young reptiles, juvenile conspecifics and other prey (Fimple 1975; Bliss et al. 1978; Wolcott and Wolcott 1984). *Gecarcinus planatus* from Clipperton Island is particularly notable for its aggressive consumption of any animal protein, living or dead, which comes within its grasp (Ehrhardt and Niaussat 1970).

Most predominantly herbivorous semi-terrestrial anomurans are also opportunistic macrophagous scavengers. *Coenobita perlatus* is such an efficient scavenger on Indo-Pacific islands that the low numbers of carrion-breeding flies on many of them is attributed to its presence (Alexander 1979; Page and Willason 1982). The western Atlantic *Coenobita clypeatus* will feed upon virtually any carrion it encounters. De Wilde (1973) provides a vivid account of hundreds of *C. clypeatus* feeding on the carcass of a dead donkey. Even the predominantly herbivorous coconut crab, *Birgus latro*, scavenges for animal protein (Grubb 1971; Alexander 1979). Specimens maintained for prolonged periods in the laboratory are reported to require it (Harms 1932).

Intertidal and shallow subtidal anomurans are also known to scavenge carrion. *Hippa pacifica* feeds upon stranded *Physalia*, ingesting zooids and fishing tentacles with nematocysts (Matthews 1955). Various hermit crabs, especially intertidal Diogenidae, are macrophagous carrion scavengers in addition to being microphagous detritivores (Boltt 1961; Roberts 1968). On many beaches one or more diogenid crustaceans compete with nassariid scavengers for carrion resources (Morton and Britton 1991; Britton and Morton 1992). Intertidal hermit crabs often feed in cycles correlated with tidal flux. *Calcinus latens*, for example, actively forages for either detritus or carrion at low tide but finds shelter under rocks and coral boulders at high tide (Reese 1969). Conversely, *Clibanarius cubensis* is active during high tides, day and night (Hazlett 1966). Other hermit crabs feed on diurnal cycles. *Clibanarius tricolor*, *Calcinus tibicen* and *Pagurus miamensis* forage primarily at night. One of us (JCB) was able to attract *C. tricolor* to fresh bivalve or crab baits during morning low tides, but not afternoon high tides (total tidal range < 0.33 m)(Fig. 1).

Isopod diets are as varied as that of most other large malacostracan groups. Microphagous scavenging seems to unite the benthic isopod fabric, but several different threads contribute to the weave. Many isopods favour detritivory on either mud or sand, but especially within decaying vegetation. Others, such as the gribble *Limnoria*, are highly specialized herbivores of wood. Predators and parasites are common, as are macrophagous carrion scavengers. The Cirolanidae and Idoteidae include many well known carrion feeders. *Natatolana* (= *Cirolana*) *borealis* of north European coasts feeds primarily upon fish and crustacean carrion (Nickell 1989), and is reported to attack diseased and netted fish (Vader and Romppainen 1985). *Cirolana hartfordi* frequents rock-strewn sandy beaches of North American Pacific shores. It captures and feeds upon living polychaetes and amphipods, but is attracted to carrion, especially fish, detecting it from considerable distances by acute chemoreceptors (Johnson 1976a,b). Hundreds of individuals often gather at a dead fish and reduce it to bones within a few hours. *Chiridotea coeca*, occupying the sandy beaches of temperate eastern North America, seizes carrion with its gnathopods and bites off pieces with its mandibles (Nicol 1969). *Glyptonotus antarcticus* is a shallow subtidal scavenger of the Southern Ocean (Dearborn 1967). These and numerous other isopods rely upon carrion as a central component of the diet. Still others are opportunistic carrion scavengers. Species of *Ligia* are primarily algal herbivores, but readily feed upon carrion when it is available (personal observations). Species of *Serolis* are mostly detritivores, but will also feed upon decaying meat (Kaestner 1970). The giant (35 cm) isopod *Bathynomus giganteus* has been collected off the Yucatan Peninsula, Mexico, in benthic baited with jack mackerel and skip-jack tuna at depths from 350 to 500 m (Briones-Fourzn personal communication). Macrophagous isopod scavengers are sufficiently numerous that a review devoted exclusively to this group is warranted.

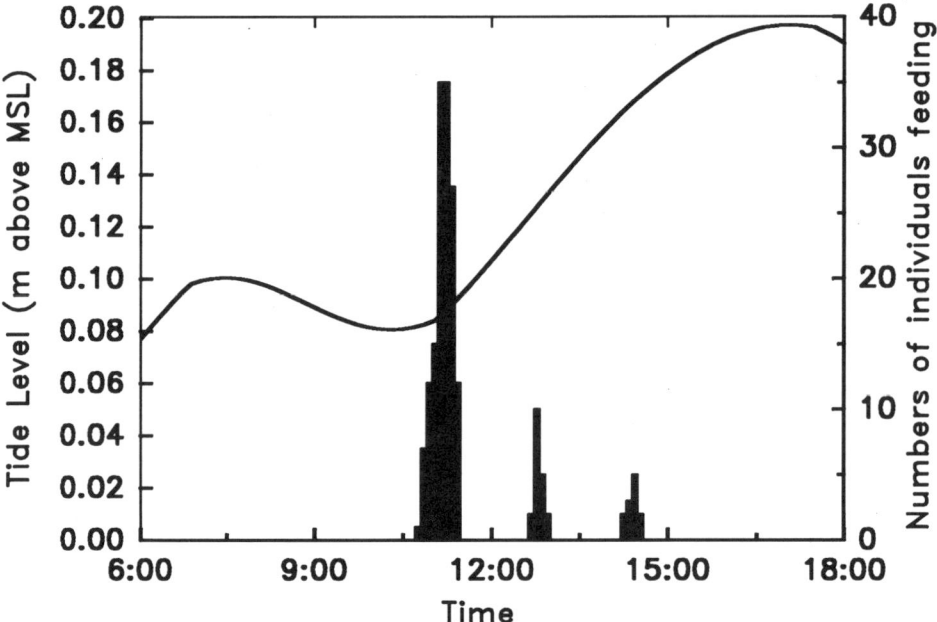

Fig. 1. Feeding behaviour of *Clibanarius tricolor* in relation to tidal position at Wee Wee Cay, Belize, C.A. Tide level is indicated by the curved line; numbers of feeding individuals are indicated by the histogram. From data collected by J.C. Britton and K. Risse, March 1990.

The amphipod Lysianassidae and Talitridae include some of the better known macrophagous amphipod scavengers. Large numbers of *Orchomenella nana*, *Tmetonyx cicada*, *Anonyx* sp. and *Scopelocheirus* sp. are attracted to fish carrion on sandy North Sea shores (Kaestner 1970; Vader and Romppainen 1985). *Orchestia gamarella* and *Talitrus saltator* are opportunistic omnivores which scavenge small fish and other carrion washed upon Mediterranean beaches. *Psammonyx nobilis*, an inhabitant of well sorted, fine, sand on temperate western Atlantic (New England) beaches, aggregates upon carrion washing ashore (Scott and Croker 1976). Even the predominantly herbivorous *Idotea emarginata* will feed upon carrion when it is available (Naylor 1955). Many of these amphipods forage on carrion, flotsam or detritus according to endogenous activity rhythms (Wildish 1970; Bregazzi and Naylor 1972).

Amphipod scavengers are not, however, limited to intertidal sands. They are also relatively common inhabitants of unconsolidated sediments on continental shelves (Nickell 1989) and deep sea floors (Hessler 1974; Shulenberger and Hessler 1974;

Shulenberger and Barnard 1976). In a survey of more than 40 species of epibenthic scavenging invertebrates from subtidal continental shelf habitats, all but two were trophic generalists (Nickell 1989). Only the lysianassid amphipod *Scopelocheirus hopei* and the cirolanid isopod *Natatolana borealis* were found feeding only upon carrion. Necrophagy seems to become an increasingly important feeding method with increasing depth (Stockton and DeLaca 1982). Less than seven hours after placing fish bait on the floor of the Philippine Trench, at a depth of 9605 m, swarms of *Hirondella gigas* had reduced the intact carcasses to little more than articulated vertebrae (Hessler *et al.* 1978). At depths of between 3800 to 1800 m in the Arctic abyss, *Eurythenes gryllus* is similarly attracted to fish bait (Bowman and Manning 1972; Paul 1973). The abundance of these amphipods and other abyssal scavengers, even in some of the least productive regions of the world's oceans (Hessler *et al.* 1972), suggests that macrophagous scavenging may be more important among the abyssal benthos than once supposed (Sokolova 1972; Dahl 1979; Stockton and DeLuca 1982).

Caine (1974) records four methods of food acquisition among caprellid amphipods: predation, scavenging detritus or carrion, scraping sessile epibenthos and filter feeding. Some species seemed to have a restricted feeding repertoire, such as the mostly predatory *Luconacia incerta*. Others have more catholic habits. *Caprella penantis* combines filter feeding and scraping behaviours; *Paracaprella tenuis* employs all four feeding methods.

Insects, especially Diptera, Coleoptera and some Hymenoptera (ants), frequently dominate carrion-consuming scavengers of the upper shore. In a study of sea bird carrion on islands in the Gulf of Maine, the impact of amphipods and decapods was decidedly secondary to that of insect scavengers in the decomposition of carcasses (Lord and Burger 1984). Coleopterans which may resort to feeding on seashore carrion include the Staphylinidae (rove beetles), the Cicindelidae (tiger beetles), the carrion-feeding members of the Nitidulidae (sap beetles), and the Scarabaeidae. Beach-dwelling members of the dipteran family Anthomyiidae (kelpflies), especially species of *Fucilia*, are known to feed upon beached carrion.

Echinodermata

Echinoderm scavengers include members of the Asteroidea, Ophiuroidea, and Holothuroidea. Many adult predatory asteroids exhibit a juvenile predilection for scavenging. Prior to adopting the adult diet, juvenile *Linckia laevigata*, *Mediaster aequalis*, *Asterina gibbosa*, *Henricia leviuscula*, *Stichaster australis* have been described as variously discriminating detritivores (Sloan 1980 and references therein), whereas juvenile *Luidia ciliaris* feed upon asteroid and molluscan carrion within a week of metamorphosis (Wilson 1978).

The focus of asteroid scavenging varies considerably. Species of *Asterina* from the Indian Ocean and Australia are microphagous scavengers, feeding upon detritus, surface films, diatoms and bacteria (Crump and Emson 1978; Emson and Crump 1979). Normally predatory *Asteropsis carinifera*, *Choriaster granulatus*, *Linckia guildingi*, *Linckia laevigata*, *Protoreaster nodosus* and *Patiria pectinifera* from the central Pacific, *Patiria miniata*, *Pisaster brevispinus*, *Pisaster giganteus* and *Pycnopodia helianthoides* from the eastern Pacific, *Oreaster reticulatus*, *Echinaster serpentarius* and *Asterias forbesi* from the western Atlantic, *Henricia oculata* from the eastern Atlantic,

Cuenotaster involutus, Porania antarctica, Diplasterias brucei, Lyasterias perrieri and *Neosmilaster georgianus* from Antarctica and *Patiriella brevispina* and *Coscinasterias calamaria* from southern Australia have been reported to feed upon carrion (Sloan 1980; Sloan and Campbell 1982; Jangoux 1982; and references therein). The normal prey of these species varies, but includes bivalves, gastropods, polychaetes, barnacles and other echinoderms. Several of these carnivorous asteroids employ chemoreception to detect both prey and carrion, however (Sloan and Campbell 1982). Meat juices (Romanes 1883), acetylcholine (Anderson 1953), coral extracts (Collins 1974; Ormond *et al.* 1976), and various proteins and amino acids (Heeb 1973; Valentindid 1975) stimulate feeding responses in various asteroids. Wobber (1975) comments upon the scavenging behaviour of *Patiria miniata* from Monterey Bay, California. This opportunistic asteroid will aggregate on any available carrion, and aggressively jousts for a suitable feeding position.

Despite having the simplest digestive system of the echinoderms, ophiuroids have a surprisingly diverse inventory of food and feeding behaviours. They include herbivores, carnivores, and omnivores obtaining food by deposit feeding, suspension feeding and microphagous and macrophagous scavenging. Many species employ several different feeding behaviours opportunistically. Microphagous scavenging occurs widely throughout the class, and macrophagous scavenging is probably more common than previously acknowledged. Warner (1982) differentiates between microphagous and macrophagous scavenging ophiuroids in that the former utilize particles small enough to be passed to the mouth by tube feet, whereas the latter manipulate food particles by either arm or whole body movements. Several ophiuroids, including *Ophiura albida, Ophiura texturata, Ophiocomina nigra* and *Ophiothrix fragilis*, have been observed feeding on dead fish in aquaria (Nagabushanan and Colman 1959). *Ophiura lutkeni* grasps carrion in its jaws and applies leverage with its arms to tear flesh from a moribund fish (Austin 1966). Several Antarctic ophiuroids, including *Astrotoma agassizii, Amphiophiura brevispina, Ophiacantha vivipara, Ophionotus victoriae, Ophionotus hexactis* and *Ophiosparte gigas* were attracted to fish-baited traps in the natural environment (Arnaud 1974). Warner (1982) lists 23 species of necrophagous ophiuroids, although none of these feeds exclusively upon carrion.

Most holothurians are either deposit or suspension feeders, but a few, mainly deep-sea Elasipodida, are known to feed upon macrophagous carrion (Massin 1982). Pawson (1976) reported upon a species of *Scotoplantes* attracted to fish remains. Hessler (1972) obtained elasipods from baited traps and Laubier and Sibuet (1977) captured *Peniagone* sp. in a similar way.

CHEMORECEPTION AND FEEDING BY MACROPHAGOUS SCAVENGERS

Chemoreception is used by marine organisms in a variety of ways, including predator recognition and the possible consequential adoption of either behavioural avoidance reactions or production of defensive secretions, establishment of symbiotic associations, reproductive activities and detection of and/or orientation towards food (Mackie and Grant 1974; Kohn 1983). Decomposing carrion gives off a variety of chemical cues, and it is presumably these substances that attract macrophagous scavengers to their moribund prey, although some may also utilize visual cues. Chemoreception is not, however, the exclusive domain of scavengers, for predators and herbivores alike can be attracted to food by chemical stimuli. Species of *Conus*, for example, become active when a live fish is introduced into an aquarium (Kohn 1956). Many predatory opisthobranchs employ chemosensory receptors to detect and stalk their prey (Cook 1962; Waters 1973; Willows 1978). Similarly, when the green alga, *Ulva lactuca*, (or when water in which *U. lactuca* has been held) is introduced into an aquarium containing the Hawaiian sea hare, *Aplysia juliana*, the latter orients towards the introduction site (Frings and Frings 1965). The basis for food detection by chemoreception is, thus, well founded among animals, and requires only some degree of focus according to specific food preferences (Lindstedt 1971; Lenhoff and Lindstedt 1974). Macrophagous scavengers apparently focus upon chemical cues normally not released by living prey.

The feeding behaviours of scavengers are usually complex, involving several sequential steps. Kohn (1983) described a feeding sequence for many gastropods which is also appropriate for many macrophagous invertebrate scavengers. Chemical cues alert scavengers to the presence of a potential food and elicit arousal behaviour. This is usually followed by orientation and eventual locomotion toward the perceived food source. Consumption or ingestion may either commence immediately upon arrival at the food, or may be preceded by exploratory behaviour. As we will demonstrate, the duration of feeding may also follow a predictable behavioural sequence, related either to the degree of hunger or satiation or to other intrinsic factors.

Chemical cues which elicit arousal behaviour may be the result of physical contact with the potential food or delivered from a distance by the intervening seawater medium. Contact chemoreceptors on several appendages of the horseshoe crab, *Limulus*, elicit strong electrophysiological responses when stimulated by aqueous extracts of marine bivalves, yeast and beef (Barber and Hayes 1963). The hermit crab, *Clibanarius vittatus*, initiates feeding behaviour when antennule receptors detect certain chemical stimuli carried in fluids extracted from recently killed fish (Hazlett 1968). Chemoreceptor cells are abundant on the anterior margin of the foot, the tips of the cephalic tentacles and the ventral external surface of the siphon of *Nassarius reticulatus* (Crisp 1971, 1976). Direct application of crab extract to either the anterior border of the foot or tentacles elicited a feeding response more often than when the siphon tip or posterior foot of *N. reticulatus* was stimulated (Crisp 1971). Similarly, the application of various food extracts and amino acids to the leading propodial edge of *Bullia digitalis* stimulated proboscis eversion, but amines applied to the same location did not (Hodgson and Brown 1985, 1987). Contact chemoreception may trigger an immediate feeding response by the detecting organism, which is already in close proximity to the food. This is a desirable situation for herbivores and detritivores which forage in intimate proximity to a variety of potential foods, some of which are likely to be either more palatable or nutritious than others (Lubchenco 1978). Contact chemoreception would be clearly ineffective, however, in alerting scavengers to remote but accessible food. In this instance, distance chemoreception is important.

Distance chemoreception has been best studied in echinoderms and gastropod molluscs. As Sloan and Campbell (1982) provide an extensive review of chemoreception in the Echinodermata, we will restrict most of our remarks to the Gastropoda. Kohn (1961) reviewed much of the earlier literature on gastropod chemoreception and concluded that distance chemoreception was the most important means of food detection among carrion-eating species. The osphradium is usually implicated as the primary site of distance chemoreception associated with food recognition and location (Brown and Noble 1960, Kohn 1961). Active macrophagous gastropod scavengers and predators generally have larger, more elaborate, osphradia than either herbivores or predators seeking sessile prey (Taylor and Miller 1989).

Many substances are now known to be important stimuli of distance and contact chemoreceptors in gastropod scavengers. A variety of proteins, including those from human blood plasma, fluids and extracts from oysters, scallops, other bivalves, the blue crab *Callinectes sapidus*, and fishes induce a strong feeding response in *Ilyanassa obsoleta* (Gurin and Carr 1971; Carr et al. 1974). Trimethylamine, emanating from carrion, stimulates chemoreceptors on the osphradium of *Bullia* sp. (Brown and Noble 1960). When trimethylamine and other volatile amines are brought into contact with the osphradium, *Bullia digitalis* commences food searching behaviour (Brown 1971). When crushed conspecifics are presented to *I. obsoleta*, however, an escape reaction ensues (Atema and Burd 1975). We have exposed starving *Nassarius festivus* to crushed conspecifics, but feeding continued with no detectable apparent reaction to the presence of the fatally damaged specimen. Conversely, well-fed individuals departed the bait.

Reports of gastropods sensing carrion from distances of between one to several metres are common, especially with respect to intertidal nassariids (Copeland 1918; Morton 1960; Bedulli 1976; Morton 1990; Morton and Britton 1991; Britton and Morton 1992). Large subtidal buccinids can detect bait from many metres (Gros and Santarelli 1986). The record for distance chemoreception by a gastropod, however, must be the observation by MacGinitie and MacGinitie (1968) who reported witnessing *Nassarius fossatus* moving upstream toward a dead fish from a distance of more than 30 m. Deep-sea scavengers, particularly lysianassid amphipods and fishes, are attracted from significantly greater distances than those reported for shallow-water and intertidal scavengers (Sainte-Marie and Hargrave 1987).

Upon sensing potential food, most gastropod scavengers commence moving towards it. Sand-dwelling species, especially nassariids, emerge from the substratum, sweep the siphon across the direction of water flow, and generally move toward the food, e.g., *Ilyanassa obsoleta* (Carr 1967), *Bullia rhodostoma* and *Bullia digitalis* (Brown 1982), *Nassarius festivus* (Britton and Morton 1992), and *Nassarius pyrrus* and the buccinid *Cominella eburnea* (Morton and Britton 1991). The effectiveness of their movement toward the food is dependent on the current patterns sweeping around it and the strength of the stimulus emanating from it (Britton and Morton 1992).

The speed by which gastropod scavengers move towards food in the presence of an uninterrupted chemical stimulus varies according to the species, but is usually rapid. Gros and Santarelli (1986) recorded a mean speed of 20 cm·min^{-1} for *Buccinum undatum* moving upstream toward a baited trap, while Morton (1990) has shown that the subtidal *Babylonia lutosa* (Buccinidae) was relatively slower at reaching food than the intertidal *Nassarius festivus*. Morton and Britton (1991) have shown that the intertidal *Nassarius pyrrhus* took a mean time of 8.45 minutes to find food placed 20 cm away, whereas the predominantly subtidal *Cominella eburnea* took 18.9 minutes. All individuals of *Nassarius pauperatus* that responded to bivalve bait (*Katelysia scalarina*) made available to field populations usually arrived at the bait within ten minutes of it being set out (McKillup and Butler 1983). The rate of locomotion in *Ilyanassa obsoleta* is negatively correlated with size (Dimock 1985).

Bullia digitalis is perhaps the fastest moving nassariid, utilizing a unique means of locomotion apparently evolved as an adaptation to its wave-swept sandy beach habitat. This snail relocates up or down a shore by extending and spreading its broad foot and allowing waves to transport it (Brown 1971). Surfing activity is employed for both diurnal tidal migrations and in response to chemical cues revealing the presence of carrion (Trueman and Brown 1976; Brown et al. 1989).

Upon reaching food, nassariid scavengers often initiate a proboscis search reaction, consisting of repeated thrusts and withdrawals of the proboscis (Carr 1967; Brown 1982). The duration of feeding varies considerably for most scavenging gastropods, but some trends have become apparent. Most nassariids feed quickly on carrion, with the duration of feeding sometimes mediated by the time since the last meal (Crisp 1978) (Table 2). Buccinids feed longer, and seem less likely to alter the duration of feeding based upon the last meal. *Bullia digitalis* has been reported to ingest up to one-third of its own tissue weight in food during ten minutes of feeding (Brown 1961). Morton (1990) found the mean time spent on fish carrion by *Nassarius festivus* to be 7.97 minutes after 10 days of starvation, but about half that time when fed one day after a previous feeding. In contrast, the mean time spent on fish carrion by *Babylonia lutosa* was about 15 minutes whether 1 or 10 days had elapsed following a meal, although the variance

Table 2
The time spent feeding on carrion by various neogastropod scavengers.

Species/Condition	Time on Food (min ± S.D.)	Site	Source
Babylonia lutosa			
Well fed	15.0 ± 2.35	L	Morton 1990
Starved for 10 days	14.9 ± 8.71	L	Morton 1990
Cominella eburnea			
Fish carrion	26.5 ± 17.9	L	Morton and Britton 1991
Crushed bivalve	29.9 ± 15.0	L	Morton and Britton 1991
Nassarius festivus			
Well fed	3.64 ± 1.18	L	Morton 1990
Starved 10 days	7.97 ± 4.95	L	Morton 1990
Crushed bivalve	-15.0	F	Britton and Morton 1992
Crushed bivalve	14.2 ± 8.00	L	Britton and Morton 1992
Nassarius pyrrhus			
Fish carrion	6.75 ± 2.65	L	Morton and Britton 1991
Crushed bivalve	5.74 ± 3.86	L	Morton and Britton 1991
Bullia digitalis			
Scyphozoan carrion	10.0	?	Brown 1982
Bivalve gill	7.0	L	Brown et al. 1989
Ilyanassa obsoleta			
Crushed bivalve	14.1 ± 8.22	L	Britton and Risse unpubl. data

abbreviations: L, laboratory; F, field

was considerably greater after 10 days starvation. Morton and Britton (1991) described a similar relationship for *Nassarius pyrrhus* and *Cominella eburnea* from southwestern Australia. The former arrived at food first and departed after feeding for ~ 6 to 7 minutes; the latter arrived about the time most nassariids were departing and fed for considerably longer (Table 2). Oxygen uptake increases immediately when *Nassarius reticulatus* feeds or is exposed to food odours (Crisp et al. 1978).

Ilyanassa obsoleta also feeds on carrion, but is described by Curtis and Hurd (1979) as an obligate omnivore, even predating the eggs and juveniles of *Cerithidea californica* (Race, 1982). When 50 adult *Ilyanassa obsoleta* were provided mussel tissue (*Geukensia demissa*) and allowed to feed to satiation without competition, the mean time spent on the food was 14.1 minutes (Fig. 2). Size and the time spent feeding was poorly correlated over the range of sizes investigated. In contrast, when Curtis and Hurd (1979) maintained laboratory populations on three separate dietary regimes (shrimp, spinach and a mixture of both), they found that only individuals maintained on the mixed diet exhibited growth during the 13 month experiment. *Ilyanassa obsoleta* is apparently unique among the Neogastropoda in that it possesses a crystalline style (Noguchi 1921; Jenner 1956; Brown 1969). Other nassariids are, however, known to harbour carbohydrase enzymes. *Nassarius reticulatus* produces high levels of laminarinase, although there is no record of this whelk feeding upon brown algae (Kristensen 1972). *Bullia*

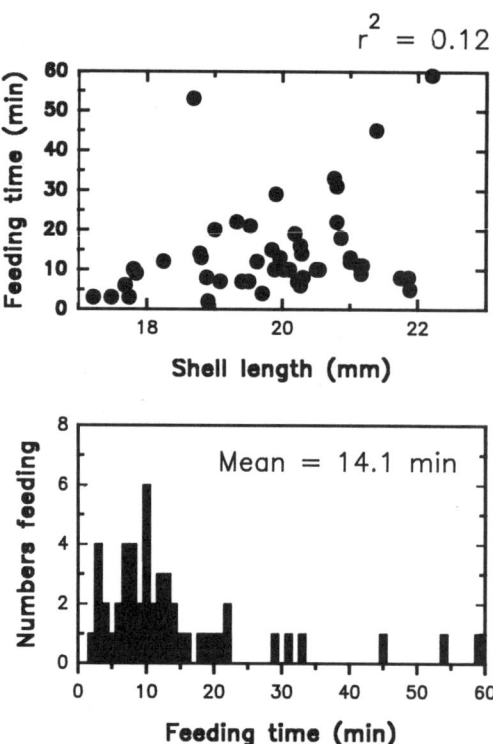

Fig. 2. Duration on bivalve carrion (*Geukensia demissa*) when *Ilyanassa obsoleta* (n = 50) feeds to satiation without competition. Data from J.C. Britton and K. Risse, Woods Hole, Massachusetts, U.S.A., July 1990.

digitalis contains α-amylase, cellulase, laminarinase and cellulolytic symbiotic bacteria in the gut and ingests green algae growing on its shell (Harris et al. 1986).

There is little information on energetic relationships for most necrophagous animals. Exceptions are the energetics estimates presented by Stenton-Dozey and Brown (1988) and Brown et al. (1989) for *Bullia digitalis* and those of Edwards and Welsh (1982) for *Ilyanassa obsoleta*. Absorption efficiencies were found to be high (88%) for *B. digitalis* feeding upon mussel gill tissue. High absorption efficiencies are advantageous for animals which rely upon unpredictable food supplies such as carrion. Food consumption in proportion to body weight was found to be much greater in smaller individuals of *B. digitalis* than in larger (Stenton-Dozey and Brown 1988). The annual production of *I. obsoleta* tissue on a Connecticut mudflat was estimated to be 20.0 g·m^{-2}, of which less than 1% was contributed by juveniles (Edwards and Welsh 1982). From adult weight loss after spawning, it was estimated that 66% of annual production was allocated to reproduction. Gross trophic efficiency calculations indicated that most consumption by *I. obsoleta* was not assimilated, but was defaecated. This is in striking contrast to the high assimilation efficiencies reported for *B. digitalis* (Stenton-Dozey and Brown 1988), but which is to be expected of an indiscriminate detritivore. Mucus production by *I. obsoleta* was estimated to be 80% of total assimilation (Edwards and Welsh 1982).

COMPETITION AND RESOURCE PARTITIONING

Several field experiments have demonstrated interspecific competition among marine scavengers (Schoener 1983). Active competition for a limited quantity of good quality shells, for example, significantly influences the spatial distributions of three species of tropical hermit crabs (Bertness 1981). Similarly, the introduction of *Ilyanassa obsoleta* into San Francisco Bay has resulted in the displacement of the native mud snail, *Cerithidea californica* (Race 1982).

Sympatric scavengers may also partition either the environment or resources within it, either as a result of competition, as in the case with the hermit crabs above (Bertness 1981), or to reduce or avoid it. We have already mentioned that sympatric species of east African *Ocypode* partition the environment with respect to both vertical position on the shore and feeding preferences. Similarly, three intertidal hermit crabs from the broken coral rubble of Hawaiian reef flats and shores partition the environment spatially and behaviourally with respect to the tide (Reese 1969). *Clibanarius zebra* commonly occupies the supralittoral fringe, taking shelter under rocks and coral rubble during low tide when the zone lies most exposed to thermal stress, desiccation and insolation. *Calcinus laevimanus* is a mid-shore species that generally remains active at the water's edge, moving as the tide rises and falls. *Calcinus latens* occupies the lower shore and shallow sublittoral where it is active at low tide, but seeks shelter when the tide is high. Each of these species has a similar diet, but avoids competition for the same food by differences in shore position and activity periods mediated by the tides.

Some subtidal nassariids partition the environment according to environmental gradients. Two sympatric subtidal nassariids occupy sandy substrata off the Lebanese coast in the eastern Mediterranean. *Nassarius gibbosulus* prevails 3:1 on sandy subtidal substrata markedly influenced by waves, whereas *Nassarius granum* dominates in localities with finer sand in more protected localities (Khairallah and Mattar 1987).

One of the more interesting examples of resource partitioning and competition avoidance involves two sympatric species of neogastropods from southwestern Australia, the buccinid *Cominella eburnea* and the nassariid *Nassarius pyrrhus* (Morton and Britton 1991). These species occupy broad, unvegetated, intertidal sand flats, where the former is a predator and scavenger upon sand-dwelling bivalves, especially *Katelysia scalarina*. *C. eburnea* is a small whelk (maximum shell length, 31 mm) which occurred in Princess Royal Harbour, Western Australia at densities of 7.4 individuals·m^{-2}. *N. pyrrhus* is smaller (maximum shell length, 22 mm) and more abundant (30.5 individuals·m^{-2}). It is a scavenger which feeds upon a variety of animal carrion, including *K. scalarina* recently killed by *C. eburnea*. When a crushed bivalve is placed upon the sand flat during a falling tide, many individuals representing several species of scavengers are attracted to it, including *Nassarius burchardi*, *Nassarius pauperatus*, *Nassarius jonasii*, *Cominella tasmanica*, and the two previously mentioned species. *N. pyrrhus* and *C. eburnea* comprised 42.8% and 54.5%, or 97.3%, of all individuals attracted to bivalve baits, indicating alternate feeding strategies, different diets, different primary habitats, or some other situation with respect to the commingling buccinid and nassariid species. Nevertheless, since *N. pyrrhus* and *C. eburneus* are attracted to the same foods in roughly equal numbers, it appears, superficially, that they are in direct competition for the same resource. This is not the case. Nearby *N. pyrrhus* are attracted quickly to a bait (crushed bivalve or fish carrion) from a maximum distance of ~ 1 m, feed for six to seven minutes and depart. The departure time of most *N. pyrrhus* corresponds approximately with the arrival time of most *C. eburnea*, which are attracted from a maximum distance of ~ 4 m. *C. eburnea* feeds much longer than *N. pyrrhus*, upwards of 30 minutes, and usually of sufficient time and in sufficient numbers to consume a bivalve entirely. As *C. eburnea* also preys upon living *K. scalarina*, it is not unusual to find a buccinid predator attacking a bivalve, releasing chemical stimuli and thus attracting *N. pyrrhus* to the freshly killed prey. The nassariids arrive in such large numbers as to displace the original predator from its prey. *N. pyrrhus* feeds quickly and, as they depart, additional *C. eburnea* are attracted to the recently killed bivalve. Bivalve carrion similarly attracts numerous specimens of *Cominella glandiformis* on New Zealand shores, but apparently without an intervening nassariid (Walsby 1990).

SCAVENGER HABITATS

Natural water movements assure that chemical cues from potential food sources will be dispersed. Food detection by chemoreception is enhanced considerably when currents impose directional gradients (Carthy 1958). Subtidal and intertidal habitats may be fundamentally different with respect to the nature of the water currents which influence them and the way chemical messages are delivered.

Shallow subtidal currents may be either weak and ineffective, especially within large embayments experiencing only minimal tidal flux, or they may be fast and strong, dispersing not only olfactory cues, but also setting the food in motion. Fast subtidal longshore currents occur off exposed beaches and fast, tidally-generated, flows may penetrate and depart restricted tidal channels and entrances to embayments. In shallow subtidal habitats, therefore, either the lack of water motion or too-rapid current flow hamper the distribution of chemical cues to scavengers. Sluggish currents, on the other hand, may be the primary means by which information on the presence of carrion on the deep-sea floor is disseminated to scavengers (Thurston 1979; Smith 1985; Sainte-Marie 1986; Sainte-Marie and Hargrave 1987).

An incursing tide (aided by waves) both assists and hampers an intertidal scavenger's search for food. Potential food is brought onto the beach as allochthonous flotsam by the incursing tide, waves and longshore drift, thereby enhancing the natural productivity of the shore. With time, it may be lifted up, moved upshore and stranded, where it is unavailable to most marine scavengers. As the stranded flesh decomposes, a subsequent tide or wave backwash may return it to the sea to begin the cycle again. Beached carrion may, thus, be a highly ephemeral resource, requiring many tidal incursions and exchanges before it is finally consumed. In contrast, subtidal habitats carry potential food material at more constant speeds until a final resting place focuses attention upon it.

Useful olfactory cues are disrupted by turbulent flow on wave-swept rocky shores (Dayton 1971; Lubchenco and Menge 1978; Louda 1979; Sloan 1980). Under these conditions, successful scavenging seems primarily dependent upon fortuitous encounters (Menge 1972; Dayton et al. 1977). In contrast, water flow on a low-relief, sheltered, beach is less likely to disperse olfactory signals (Britton and Morton 1992) and becomes an important asset enabling scavengers to find food. In this situation, flow may result from (1) the broad, regular, predictable tidal flux; (2) the directional discharge of a stream onto the beach or (3) lapping waves which serve to extend the time over which a chemical cue is kept water-borne. Because of the gentle slope, usually characteristic of sandy beaches experiencing minimal wave energy, chemical cues emanating from stranded carrion are thus (a) concentrated in the receding water and (b) directional; both facilitate the food-finding process.

On shores with considerable tidal range, chemical cues, while subjected to potentially greater dilution, are also transported greater distances during a falling tide than on shores where the tidal range is narrow. Scavengers on these beaches often repose either on or in the more protected substratum of the mid- and lower intertidal, being assured of receiving chemical messages when food arrives up-shore, but avoiding desiccation, temperature extremes, predation pressures and other hardships which characterize the higher shore. The gentle flow of each falling tide transports chemical cues down tidal flats, alerting reposing scavengers to two kinds of potential food: (1) carrion washed in by the last high tide and stranded during the current falling tide and (2) dying or recently moribund denizens of the upper shore which have succumbed to the natural stresses which characterize such an environment. These two kinds of food are frequently cited as the focus of feeding intertidal scavengers, e.g., *Ilyanassa obsoleta* in the western Atlantic from New Brunswick, Canada to northern Florida (Scheltema 1964), *Nassarius reticulatus* from the eastern Atlantic (Tallmark 1980), *Nassarius pauperatus* from southern Australia (McKillup and Butler 1979, 1983), *Nassarius pyrrhus* from southwestern Australia (Morton and Britton 1991), *Nassarius festivus* from Hong Kong (Morton 1990; Britton and Morton 1992), *Nassarius luteotsoma* from the western coast of Coasta Rica and *Nassarius tiarula* from the Gulf of California (Houston 1978). Each cited species scavenges upon intertidal flats under the conditions just described.

When food is present, gastropod and hermit crab scavengers frequently move to higher parts of the shore to feed. This may occur either on rising or, more commonly, on falling tides. This is in contrast to most marine predators, which occupy the upper shore during high tides, and retreat to deeper water during low tides (Paine 1966; Louda 1979). Scavengers are usually among the common invertebrates observed on broad intertidal flats which otherwise afford little protection against terrestrial predators such as birds (Reese 1969). Scavengers of intertidal flats often, therefore, encase their bodies within thick, predator-resistant, shells and which also provide some degree of protection to environmental extremes encountered during feeding excursions. Species occupying temperate climates may move off intertidal flats in winter and return in spring, often in mass migrations, e.g., *Nassarius reticulatus* (Tallmark 1980) and *Ilyanassa obsoleta* (Crisp 1969; Borowsky 1979; Brenchley 1980).

A few intertidal gastropod scavengers have different adaptations which enable them to succeed upon sand beaches with a broad tidal amplitude and moderate to high wave energy. *Bullia rhodostoma*, *Bullia vittata*, *Bullia melanoides*, *Bullia natalensis* and *Bullia pura* are intertidal nassariids of the Southern Ocean (South Africa) which, like *B. digitalis*, employ a broad, thin foot like a sail, surfing either up or down the beach (Ansell and Trevallion 1969; Brown 1971; McLachlan *et al.* 1979). The behaviour is similar to that reported for *Hastula salleana*, a terebrid carnivore from Gulf of Mexico sandy beaches which feeds upon intertidal polychaetes (Kornicker 1961). *Bullia* spp. employ such behaviour for diurnal migrations up and down the beach, in part, at least, to access carrion (Brown 1982).

Intertidal scavengers on shores of narrow tidal range are almost entirely limited to arthropods, especially hermit crabs, amphipods and isopods (Reese 1969; Britton and Morton 1989). Gastropod scavengers are notably absent from these shores. Despite, for example, a suitable substratum and being relatively well-protected from strong, turbulent wave energy, shores of the western Gulf of Mexico lack significant populations of intertidal gastropod scavengers, and hermit crabs, although represented by *Clibanarius vittatus*, do not occur in dense aggregations (Britton and Morton 1989). The tidal range is narrow throughout the western Gulf region, generally < 0.5 m. As a result, intertidal scavengers would be limited to an extremely narrow zone of repose. Chemical cues, rather than flowing gently down a broad tidal flat, are captured quickly by currents and swept away. The importance of shore geomorphology to intertidal scavenging behaviour is difficult to evaluate empirically, but these data seem to suggest that, with the exception of the surfing nassariids of the Southern Ocean, a broad tidal range on a sheltered beach of unconsolidated sediments facilitates intertidal scavenging.

The sea bed, overlain by a column of water of more or less constant height and in which significant currents flow, is markedly unlike an intertidal habitat. Most common sources of carrion are engendered in the water column, and pass through it before reaching the bottom (Stockton and DeLaca 1982). In this fall, it is attacked by pelagic scavengers, especially fishes and isopods, and may never reach the bottom. Conversely, it may float and be carried as flotsam to a shore. Pelagic carrion is rare on the sea bed, except where it is of altogether larger dimensions. Once deposited, however, it may become the focus of scavenging benthic fish, amphipods, and other macrobenthos. Fish scavengers may be less important on the floor of deeper oceanic basins, but pelagic and demersal necrophagous species are rarely absent (Hessler 1974; Isaacs and Schwartzlose 1975; Hessler *et al.* 1978). Smaller invertebrate scavengers, especially amphipods (Hessler *et al.* 1978; Hargrave 1985; Sainte-Marie and LaMarche 1985) and ophiuroids

(Smith 1985), are important components of the abyssal scavenging benthos, despite infrequent episodic encounters. Under such conditions, abyssal benthic invertebrates are likely best perceived as facultative scavengers capable of opportunistically exploiting a rare, albeit potentially essential, resource (Smith 1985).

The subtidal sea floor has not engendered a community of reposing scavengers typical of soft shores. The more successful subtidal scavengers, especially fishes and, in deeper waters, pelagic amphipods, are fast and agile (Sainte-Marie and Hargrave 1987). Experiments to detect subtidal scavenging have been of two types: (1) those in which fish have been included and (2) those in which fish were either deliberately or mistakenly excluded. In the former case, fish are important primary consumers of carrion (Dayton and Hessler 1972; Hessler and Jumars 1974; Wilson and Smith 1984; Smith 1985). When baited pots placed upon shallow subtidal bottoms exclude fish, a suite of what would normally be secondary arrivals are recorded. Thus, Eriksson et al. (1975) indicate that 'important' subtidal scavengers from Gullmar Fjord, Sweden, were *Carcinus maenas*, *Pagurus bernhardus*, *Crangon vulgaris*, *Asterias rubens* and *Nassarius reticulatus*. It seems possible that the accidental exclusion of fish may misrepresent the scavenging community. *Buccinum undatum* has long been regarded as a scavenger because it is regularly taken in baited traps (Dakin 1912). Nielsen (1975) and Taylor (1978) have, however, demonstrated that *B. undatum* is primarily a predator of bivalves and polychaetes, scavenging only opportunistically. Similarly, *Carcinus maenas* is now regarded as a significant predator of cockles (*Cerastoderma edule*) in European waters (Sanchez-Salazar et al. 1987a, b), and its reported significance as a scavenger is, in reality, a consequence of both opportunistic behaviour and faulty experimental design. The same is true of *Asterias rubens*, naturally a predator of bivalves, polychaetes, barnacles and other living invertebrates (Jangoux 1982). Most deep-sea experiments designed to attract scavengers to bait (usually fish set on hooks or lines) will attract, in addition to various invertebrate scavengers, one to several species of fishes (Issacs and Schwartzlose 1975).

OBLIGATE VS. FACULATIVE MACROPHAGOUS SCAVENGERS

We now have almost come full circle in considering the status of scavengers. We began this paper questioning why macrophagous scavenging by marine invertebrates has received such little attention in the general biological literature. After surveying the groups that contain scavenging members, examining scavenging processes, especially by gastropods, and considering the environments where such feeding occurs, we finally come to question whether the dietary preferences of species once regarded as scavengers are actually understood. The unlikely scenario described for *Cominella eburnea* and *Nassarius pyrrhus* (Morton and Britton 1991) is indicative of the complexity of feeding strategies in the sea, and the dangers inherent with any attempt to strictly categorize dietary preferences. We conclude, therefore, that scavenging behaviour is, more often than not, coupled with one or more additional feeding strategies. There remains, however, a final question that must be considered.

Are there species of marine invertebrates that feed exclusively upon carrion, or are marine scavengers only opportunists, supplementing their diets with carrion when it is available? An increasing body of literature supports the latter view. Obligate scavengers are unlikely to be found among the arthropods, given the range of foods taken by most species. Necrophagous arthropods are primarily carnivores, omnivores, detritivores or any combination of these. Arthropods may have specialized in many ways, but most shallow-water species remain adaptable with regard to diet. Too little is known with respect to the deep-sea arthropod scavengers to justify proclaiming any as definitive obligate scavengers. Macrophagous scavenging also seems to supplement the diets of other animals, including turbellarians, nemerteans, nematodes, polychaetes and echinoderms. Moribund tissue is not their primary source of food. If there are obligate scavengers among marine invertebrates, they will most likely be found among the Gastropoda, and especially within the Nassariidae. We will thus consider some general attributes of this family, the food of some well-studied species, the availability of carrion to nassariids and other marine scavengers in intertidal and subtidal habitats, and finally assess the prospect of obligate scavengers in the sea.

Cernohorsky (1984) enumerated substratum preferences and depth ranges from collection records for many species of Indo-Pacific Nassariidae. We have compiled these data for all species represented by more than five museum records, producing a data base of about 114 Nassariidae, or about 36% of species within the family. Not surprisingly, the majority of species were collected from soft substrata, with fewer than 5% indicated from rocks or reefs. The distinctions made in Figure 3 with respect to soft

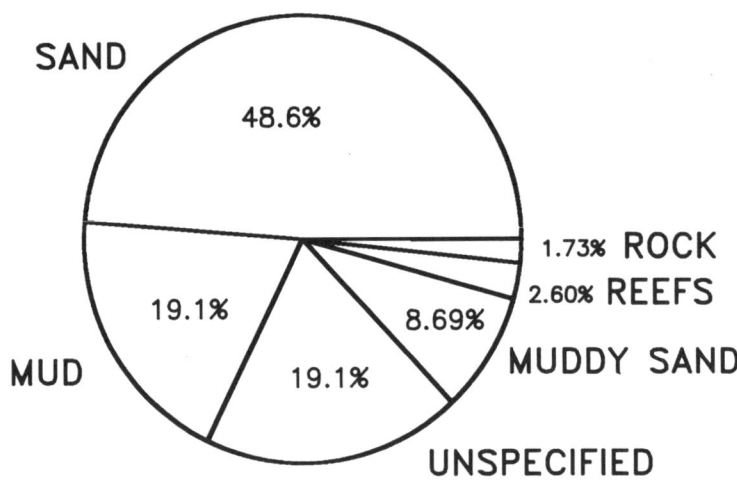

Fig. 3. Substratum preferences for Indo-Pacific Nassariidae (after Cernohorsky 1984).

substrata are somewhat arbitrary, and numerous other sub-categories were included among species descriptions. Nevertheless, it is clear from this survey that nassariids are predominantly adapted for life on soft substrata.

The depth distributions were also illuminating. Approximately one-fifth of the Indo-Pacific Nassariidae are exclusively intertidal species, and more than half range from the intertidal to shallow subtidal depths (Fig. 4). Most of the species which occur intertidally and subtidally range to a depth of only a few metres below sea level. The species ranges which extend from shore to a depth of ~ 200 m (Fig. 4) are exceptional, and these may be based upon erroneous information. Exclusively subtidal Nassariidae comprise 43% of the species surveyed and, extrapolating, must constitute an important component of the entire family. Stated another way, the Nassariidae seems to comprise two primary ecological groups: intertidal/shallow subtidal species on soft substrata and subtidal species on soft substrata. Several members of the former assemblage have been subjected to intense biological scrutiny, whereas we have been unable to locate any studies apart from taxonomic treatments for members of the latter.

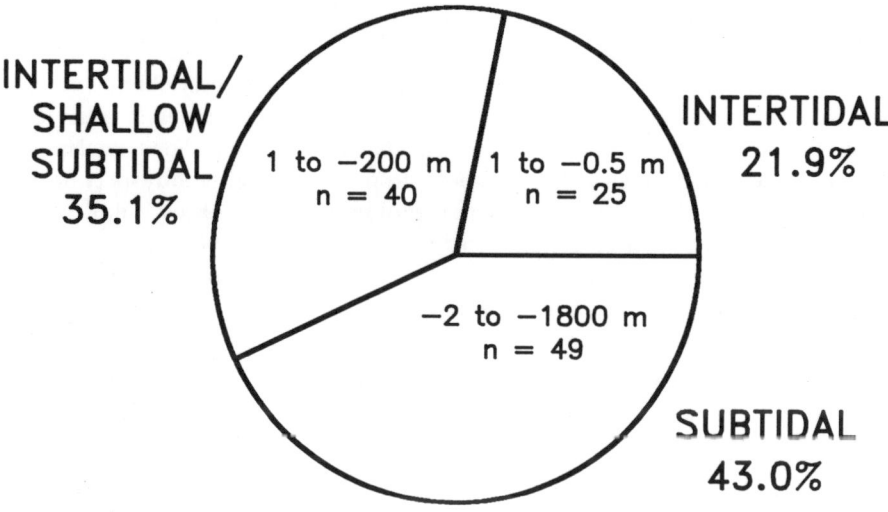

Fig. 4. Depth distributions of Indo-Pacific Nassariidae (after Cernohorsky 1984).

Dietary preferences of nassariids are poorly focused, and several species rely upon detritus or primary producers for sustenance in addition to carrion (Table 1). The supply of carrion to beaches throughout the world is unpredictable. It is sometimes possible that more washes ashore than intertidal scavengers can process. At other times, the beach may remain free of carrion for extended periods of time. To counter this, nassariids and buccinids are able to survive prolonged periods of starvation. Laboratory-held individuals of *Nassarius festivus* and *Babylonia lutosa* both survived > 100 days without food (Morton 1990). *Nassarius obsoletus* similarly can survive up to 120 days without food (Curtis and Hurd 1979). With such an unreliable food source, intertidal scavengers may also seek alternative foods that can sustain them through carrion-deficient times. Some species, such as *Ilyanassa obsoleta* opportunistically consume what carrion washes in, but seem capable of living many months on detritus and algae. Others, such as *Bullia digitalis*, represent the opposite extreme. This species seemed to be the best candidate for an obligate scavenger, but this is not so. A.C. Brown had studied *B. digitalis* intensely for 25 years before it was discovered that this nassariid, like several other members of the family, could feed and possibly sustain itself upon algae which grow on its shell (Harris et al. 1986). *Bullia digitalis* and *I. obsoleta* are also now known to take live prey (Race 1982; Brown et al. 1989). *Nassarius trivittatus* feeds upon the egg capsules of *Euspira heros* but is, in turn, the prey of the adult naticid. Upon closer examination, it is likely that most Nassariidae rely upon a variety of alternate food sources in the absence of carrion. Although the diets of subtidal nassariids are virtually unknown (the diets of over 80% of the family are unknown), it is equally unlikely, given the constraints imposed by their environment, that obligate scavengers will be found amongst them. Thus, marine scavengers are most likely exactly what they seem — opportunistic omnivores capable of deriving nutrition from a variety of sources. Intertidal scavengers may be able to locate carrion more efficiently than their subtidal counterparts, but this seems more a function of environmental fostering than organismal specialization. The surf-entrained *B. digitalis* is possibly a notable exception, and the Nassariidae, as a group, may represent the closest attempt at an obligate scavenging life style. Both the species and the family occasionally (or frequently) must compromise obligate scavenging for survival. It remains to be determined how the Nassariidae, seemingly within the mainstream of neogastropod evolution with respect to most attributes, have deviated so markedly with regard to the variety of foods utilized, and the surprising opportunism of at least some species which have possibly reverted to herbivory. In this respect, adult Nassariidae are not unlike juveniles of other Neogastropoda, e.g., the melongenid *Hemifusus tuba* (Morton 1986), and juveniles and adults of some Mesogastropoda, e.g., *Strombus maculatus* (Berg 1972). Juveniles of the former species, for example, are carnivorous in the egg capsule, feeding on nurse eggs and siblings, but emerge to pursue a microphagous scavenging life-style, only eventually taking up an adult predatory existence feeding on bivalves (Morton 1986a; 1987).

The Nassariidae alone may represent an evolutionary excursion toward necrophagy by retention of a juvenile feeding strategy into adulthood. Even they resort to a miscellany of other non-necrophagous foods, attesting to the ephemeral nature of carrion in the marine environment. The general lack of obligate scavenging in the sea emphasizes the importance of a sustainable source of food in the evolution of specialist feeding strategies, and the importance of carrion to a wide variety of dietary generalists which exploit it opportunistically.

REFERENCES

Alexander, H.G.L. 1979. A preliminary assessment of the role of the terrestrial decapod crustaceans in the Aldabran ecosystem. *Philosophical Transactions of the Royal Society of London, Series B* 286:241–6.

Alldredge, A.L. 1972. Abandoned larvacean houses: a unique source of food in the pelagic environment. *Science* 177:885–7.

Anderson, J.M. 1953. Structure and function in the pyloric caeca of *Asterias forbesi*. *Biological Bulletin* 105:47–61.

Ansell, A.D. and Trevallion, A. 1969. Behavioural adaptations of intertidal molluscs from a tropical sandy beach. *Journal of Experimental Marine Biology and Ecology* 4:9–35.

Arnaud, P.M. 1974. Contribution a la bionomie marine benthique des regions antarctiques et subantarctiques. *Tethys* 6:467–653.

Atema, J. and Burd, G.D. 1975. A field study of chemotactic responses of the marine mud snail *Nassarius obsoletus*. *Journal of Chemical Ecology* 1:243–51.

Austin, W.C. 1966. *Feeding mechanisms, digestive tracts and circulatory systems in the ophiuroids Ophiothrix spiculata Le Conte, 1851 and Ophiura luetkeni (Lyman, 1860).* Ph.D. Dissertation, Stanford University, pp. 278.
Barber, S.B. and Hayes, W.F. 1963. Properties of *Limulus* chemoreceptors. *Proceedings of the International Congress of Zoology* 16:76–8.
Barnes, R.D. 1980. *Invertebrate Zoology, Fourth Edition*. Philadelphia: Saunders.
Barnes, R.S.K., Calow, P. and Olive, P.J.W. 1988. *The Invertebrates: A New Synthesis*. Oxford: Blackwell Scientific Publications.
Bedulli, D. 1976. A preliminary study of the reaction of emersion of *Cyclope neritea* (L.), *Hinia reticulata* (Rehieri), and *Sphaeronassa variabilis* (L.). *Anteneo Parmense Acta Naturale* 12:239–50.
Berg, C.J. 1972. Ontogeny of the behavior of *Strombus maculatus* (Gastropoda: Strombidae). *American Zoologist* 12:427–43.
Bertness, M.D. 1981. Competitive dynamics of a tropical hermit crab assemblage. *Ecology* 62:751–61.
Bliss, D.E., Van Montfrans, J., Van Montfrans, M. and Boyer, J.R. 1978. Behavior and growth of the land crab *Gecarcinus lateralis* (Freminville) in southern Florida. *Bulletin of the American Museum of Natural History* 160:113–51.
Boltt, R.E. 1961. Antennary feeding of the crab, *Diogenes brevirostris* Stimpson. *Nature* 192:1099–1100.
Borowsky, B. 1979. The nature of aggregations in *Nassarius obsoletus* in the intertidal zone before the fall offshore migration. *Malacological Review* 12:89–90.
Boucaud-Camou, E. and Boucher-Rodoni, R. 1983. Feeding and digestion in cephalopods. In *The Mollusca. Volume 5, Physiology, Part 2* (ed. A.S.M. Saleuddin and K.M. Wilbur), 149–87. New York: Academic Press.
Bowman, T.E. and Manning, R.B. 1972. Two Arctic bathyl crustaceans: the shrimp *Bythocaris cryonesus* new species and the amphipod *Eurythenes gryllus*, with *in situ* photographs from Ice Island T-3. *Crustaceana* 23:187–201.
Bregazzi, P.K. and Naylor, E. 1972. The locomotor activity rhythm of *Talitrus saltator* (Montagu) (Crustacea: Amphipoda). *Journal of Experimental Biology* 57:393–99.
Brenchley, G.A. 1980. Distribution and migratory behavior of *Ilyanassa obsoleta* in Barnstable Harbor. *Biological Bulletin* 159:456–7.
Britton, J.C. and Morton, B. 1989. *Shore Ecology of the Gulf of Mexico*. Austin: University of Texas Press.
Britton, J.C. and Morton, B. 1992. The ecology and feeding behaviour of *Nassarius festivus* (Prosobranchia: Nassariidae) from two Hong Kong bays. In *Proceedings of the Fourth International Marine Biological Workshop: the Marine Flora and Fauna of Hong Kong and southern China, Hong Kong, 1989* (ed. B. Morton), 395–416. Hong Kong: Hong Kong University Press.
Brown, A.C. 1961. Physiological-ecological studies on two sandy-beach Gastropoda from South Africa: *Bullia digitalis* Meuschen and *Bullia laevissima* (Gmelin). *Zeitschrift für Morphologie und Ekologie der Tiere* 49:629–57.
Brown, A.C. 1964. Food relationships on the intertidal sandy beaches of the Cape Peninsula. *South African Journal of Science* 60:35–41.
Brown, A.C. 1971. The ecology of the sandy beaches of the Cape Peninsula, South Africa. Part 2: the mode of life of *Bullia* (Gastropoda). *Transactions of the Royal Society of South Africa* 39:281–333.
Brown, A.C. 1982. The biology of sandy-beach whelks of the genus *Bullia* (Nassariidae). *Oceanography and Marine Biology Annual Review* 20:309–61.
Brown, A.C. and Noble, R.G. 1960. Function of the osphradium in *Bullia* (Gastropoda). *Nature* 188:1045.
Brown, A.C., Stenton-Dozey, J.M.E. and Trueman, E.R. 1989. Sandy-beach bivalves and gastropods: a comparison between *Donax serra* and *Bullia digitalis*. *Advances in Marine Biology* 25:179–247.
Brown, S.C. 1969. The structure and function of the digestive system of the mud snail *Nassarius obsoletus* (Say). *Malacologia* 9:477–98.

Burggren, W.W. and McMahon, B.R. (eds.) 1988. *Biology of Land Crabs.* Cambridge: Cambridge University Press.

Caine, E.A. 1974. Comparative functional morphology of feeding in three species of caprellids (Crustacea: Amphipoda) from the northwestern Florida Gulf coast. *Journal of Experimental Marine Biology and Ecology* 15:81–96.

Cannon, H.G. 1933. On the feeding mechanism of certain marine ostracods. *Transactions of the Royal Society of Edinburgh* 57:739–64.

Cannon, H.G. and Manton, S.M. 1929. On the feeding mechanism of the syncarid Crustacea. *Transactions of the Royal Society of Edinburgh* 56:175–89.

Carr, W.E.S. 1967. Chemoreception in the mud snail, *Nassarius obsoletus.* I. Properties of stimulatory substances extracted from shrimp. *Biological Bulletin* 133:90–105.

Carr, W.E.S., Hall, E.R. and Gurin, S. 1974. Chemoreception and the role of proteins: a comparative study. *Comparative Biochemistry and Physiology* 47A:559–66.

Carthy, J.D. 1958. *An Introduction to the Behaviour of Invertebrates.* London: Allen & Unwin.

Cernohorsky, W.O. 1984. Systematics of the family Nassariidae (Mollusca: Gastropoda). *Bulletin of the Auckland Institute and Museum* 14:i-iv, 1–356.

Clegg, S.L. and Sarmiento, J.L. 1989. The hydrolytic scavenging of metal ions by marine particulate matter. *Progress in Oceanography* 23:1–22.

Collins, A.R.S. 1974. Biochemical investigation of two responses involved in the feeding behaviour of *Acanthaster planci* (L.). 1. Assay methods and preliminary results. *Journal of Experimental Marine Biology and Ecology* 15:173–84.

Cook, E.F. 1962. A study of food choices of two opisthobranchs, *Rostanga pulchra* MacFarland and *Archidoris montereyensis* (Cooper). *The Veliger* 4:194–6.

Copeland, M. 1918. The olfactory reactions and the organs of the marine snails *Alectrion obsoleta* (Say) and *Busycon canaliculatum* (Linn.). *Journal of Experimental Zoology* 25:177–227.

Correa, D.D. 1948. *Ototyphlonemertes* from the Brazilian coast. *Comunicaciones Zoologicas del Museo de Historia Natural de Montevideo* 2:1–12.

Crisp, M. 1969. Studies on the behavior of *Nassarius obsoletus* (Say). *Biological Bulletin* 136:355–73.

Crisp, M. 1971. Structure and abundance of receptors of the unspecialized external epithelium of *Nassarius reticulatus* (Gastropoda, Prosobranchia). *Journal of the Marine Biological Association of the United Kingdom* 51:865–90.

Crisp, M. 1976. Structure and abundance of receptors of the unspecialized epithelium of *Nassarius reticulatus* (Gastropoda, Prosobranchia). *Journal of the Marine Biological Association of the United Kingdom* 51:865–90.

Crisp, M. 1978. Effects of feeding on the behaviour of *Nassarius* species (Gastropoda: Prosobranchia). *Journal of the Marine Biological Association of the United Kingdom* 58:659–69.

Crisp, M., Davenport, J. and Shumway, S.E. 1978. Effects of feeding and of chemical stimulation on the oxygen uptake of *Nassarius reticulatus* (Gastropoda: Prosobranchia). *Journal of the Marine Biological Association of the United Kingdom* 58:387–99.

Crump, R.G. and Emson, R.H. 1978. Some aspects of the population dynamics of *Asterina gibbosa* (Asteroidea). *Journal of the Marine Biological Association of the United Kingdom* 58:451–66.

Curtis, L.A. and Hurd, L.E. 1979. On the broad nutritional requirements of the mud snail, *Ilyanassa (Nassarius) obsoleta* (Say), and its polytrophic role in the food web. *Journal of Experimental Marine Biology and Ecology* 41:289–97.

Dahl, E. 1979. Deep-sea carrion feeding amphipods: evolutionary patterns in niche adaptation. *Oikos* 33:67–175.

Dakin, W.J. 1912. *Buccinum* (the whelk). *Liverpool Marine Biological Committee,* Memoir. 20. London: Williams and Norgate.

da Silva, F.M. and Brown, A.C. 1984. The gardens of the sandy beach whelk *Bullia digitalis* (Dillwyn). *Journal of Molluscan Studies* 50:64–5.

Dayton, P.K. 1971. Competition, disturbance and community organization: the provision and subsequent utilization of space in a rocky intertidal community. *Ecological Monographs* 41:351–89.

Dayton, P.K. and Hessler, R.R. 1972. The role of disturbance in the maintenance of deep sea diversity. *Deep-Sea Research* 19:199–208.
Dayton, P.K., Robilliard, G.A., Paine, R.T. and Dayton, L.B. 1974. Biological accommodation in the benthic community of McMurdo Sound, Antarctica. *Ecological Monographs* 44:105–28.
Dayton, P.K., Rosenthal, R.J., Mahen, L.C. and Antezana, T. 1977. Population structure and foraging biology of the predaceous Chilean asteroid *Meyenaster gelatinosus* and the escape biology of its prey. *Marine Biology (Berlin)* 39:361–70.
De Wilde, P.A.W.J. 1973. On the ecology of *Coenobita clypeatus* in Curacao with reference to reproduction, water economy and osmoregulation in terrestrial hermit crabs. *Studies on the Fauna of Curacao and other Caribbean Islands* 44:1–138.
Dimock, R.V. 1985. Quantitative aspects of locomotion by the mud snail, *Ilyanassa obsoleta*. *Malacologia* 26:165–72.
Dearborn, J.H. 1967. Food and reproduction of *Glyptonotus antarcticus*. *Transactions of the Royal Society of New Zealand* 8:163–8.
Edwards, S.F. and Welsh, B.L. 1982. Trophic dynamics of a mud snail [*Ilyanassa obsoleta* (Say)] population on an intertidal mudflat. *Estuarine, Coastal and Shelf Science* 14:663–86.
Ehrhardt, J.P. and Niaussat, P. 1970. Ecologie et physiologie du brachyoure terrestre *Gecarcinus planatus* Stimpson (d'apres les individus de l'atoll de Clipperton). *Bulletin Societe Zoologique de France* 95:41–54.
Emson, R.H. and Crump, R.G. 1979. Description of a new species of *Asterina* (Asteroidea), with an account of its ecology. *Journal of the Marine Biological Association of the United Kingdom* 59:77–94.
Eriksson, S., Evans, E. and Tallmark, B. 1975. On the coexistence of scavengers on shallow, sandy bottoms in Gullmar Fjord (Sweden): activity patterns and feeding ability. *Zoon* 3:121–4.
Evans, S.M., Cram, A., Eaton, K., Torrance, R. and Wood, V. 1976. Foraging and agonistic behavior in the ghost crab *Ocypode kuhli* de Haan. *Marine Behavior and Physiology* 4:121–35.
Fauchald, K. and Jumars, P.A. 1979. The diet of worms: A study of polychaete feeding guilds. *Oceanography and Marine Biology Annual Review* 17:193–284.
Fimple, E. 1975. Phaenomene der Landadaptation bei terrestrischen und semiterrestrischen Brachyura der Brasilianischen Kueste (Malacostraca, Decapoda). *Zoologische Jahrbücher Abteilung für Systematik Oekologie und Geographie der Tiere* 102:173–214.
Fretter, V. and Graham, A. 1962. *British Prosobranch Molluscs*. London: Ray Society.
Frings, H. and Frings, C. 1965. Chemosensory bases of food-finding in *Aplysia juliana* (Mollusca, Opisthobranchia). *Biological Bulletin* 128:211–7.
Fryer, G. 1957. The food of some freshwater cyclopoid copepods. *Journal of Animal Ecology* 26:263–8.
Gilchrist, S.L. 1988. Natural histories of selected terrestrial crabs. In *Biology of the Land Crabs* (ed. W.W. Burggren and B.R. McMahon), 382–90. Cambridge: Cambridge University Press.
Goerke, H. 1971a. Die Ernaehrungsweise der Nereis-Arten (Polychaeta, Nereidae) der deutschen Kuesten. *Veroeffentichungen des Instituts für Meeresforschung in Bremerhaven* 13:1–50.
Goerke, H. 1971b. *Nereis fucata* (Polychaeta, Nereidae) als Kommensale von *Eupagurus bernhardus* (Crustacea, Paguridae): Entwicklung einer Population und Verhalten der Art. *Veroeffentichungen des Instituts für Meeresforschung in Bremerhaven* 13:79–118.
Gros, P. and Santarelli, L. 1986. Methode d'estimation de la surface de peche d'un casier a l'aide filiere experimentale. *Oceanologia Acta* 9:81–7.
Grubb, P. 1971. Ecology of terrestrial decapod crustaceans on Aldabra. *Philosophical Transactions of the Royal Society of London, Series B* 260:411–6.
Gurin, S. and Carr, W.E. 1971. Chemoreception in *Nassarius obsoletus*: the role of specific stimulatory proteins. *Science* 174:293–5.
Hainsworth, F. R. and Wolf, L.L. 1979. Feeding: an ecological approach. In *Advances in the Study of Behavior* (ed. J.S. Rosenblatt, R.A. Hinde, C. Beer, and M.C. Busnel), 53–96. New York: Academic Press.
Hardy, A.C. 1956. *The Open Sea. Its Natural History: The World of Plankton*. London: Collins.
Hargrave, B.T. 1985. Feeding rates of abyssal scavenging amphipods (*Eurythenes gryllus*) determined *in situ* by time-lapse photography. *Deep Sea Research* 32:443–50.

Harms, J.W. 1932. Die realisation von Genen und die consekutive adaptation. II. *Birgus latro* L. als landkrebs und seine Beziekungen zu den Coenobiten. *Zeitschrift für Wissenschaftliche Zoologie* 140:167–290.

Harris, S.A., da Silva, F.M., Bolton, J.J. and Brown, A.C. 1986. Algal gardens and herbivory in a scavenging sandy-beach nassariid whelk. *Malacologia* 27:299–305.

Hazlett, B.A. 1966. Social behavior of the Paguridae and Diogenidae of Curacao. *Studies on the Fauna of Curacao and other Caribbean Islands* 23:1–143.

Hazlett, B.A. 1968. Stimuli involved in the feeding behaviour of the hermit crab *Clibanarius vittatus* (Decapoda, Paguridea). *Crustaceana* 15:305–11.

Heeb, M.A. 1973. Large molecules and chemical control of feeding behavior in the starfish *Asterias forbesi*. *Helgolander wissenschaftliche Meeresuntersuchungen* 24:425–35.

Herreid, C.F. 1963. Observations on the feeding behavior of *Cardisoma guanhumi* (Latreille) in southern Florida. *Crustaceana* 5:176–80.

Hessler, R.R. 1972. Deep water organisms for high pressure aquarium studies. In *Barobiology and the Experimental Biology of the Deep Sea* (ed. R. Brauer), 151–61. Chapel Hill: North Carolina Sea Grant Program.

Hessler, R.R. 1974. The structure of deep benthic communities from central oceanic waters. In *The Biology of the Oceanic Pacific* (ed. C.B. Miller), 79–93. Corvallis: Oregon State University Press.

Hessler, R.R., Ingram, C.L., Yayanos, A.A. and Burnett, B.R. 1978. Scavenging amphipods from the floor of the Philippine Trench. *Deep Sea Research* 25:1029–147.

Hessler, R.R., Isaacs, J.D. and Mills, E.L. 1972. Giant amphipod from the abyssal Pacific Ocean. *Science* 175:636–7.

Hessler, R.R. and Jumars, P.A. 1974. Abyssal community analysis from replicate box cores in the central North Pacific. *Deep Sea Research* 21:185–209.

Himmelman, J.H. 1988. Movement of whelks towards a baited trap. *Marine Biology (Berlin)* 97:521–31.

Hodgson, A.N. and Brown, A.C. 1985. Contact chemoreception by the podium of the sandy-beach whelk *Bullia digitalis* (Gastropoda: Nassariidae). *Comparative Biochemistry and Physiology* 82A:425–7.

Hodgson, A.N. and Brown, A.C. 1987. Responses of *Bullia digitalis* (Prosobranchia, Nassariidae) to amino acids. *Journal of Molluscan Studies* 53:291–2.

Houston, R.S. 1978. Notes on the spawning and egg capsules of two prosobranch gastropods: *Nassarius tiarula* (Kiener, 1841) and *Solenosteira macrospira* (Berry, 1957). *Veliger* 20:367–8.

Howard, G.K. and Scott, H.C. 1959. Predaceous feeding in two common gooseneck barnacles. *Science* 129:717–8.

Hyman, L.H. 1951. *The Invertebrates. II. Platyhelminthes and Rhynchocoela, The Acoelomate Bilateria*. New York: McGraw Hill.

Isaacs, J.D. and Schwartzlose, R.A. 1975. Active animals of the deep-sea floor. *Scientific American* 233:84–91.

Jangoux, M. 1982. Food and feeding mechanisms: Asteroidea. In *Echinoderm Nutrition* (ed. M. Jangoux and J.M. Lawrence), 117–59. Rotterdam: A.A. Balkema.

Jenner, C.E. 1956. Occurrence of a crystalline style in the marine snail, *Nassarius obsoletus*. *Biological Bulletin* 111:304.

Jennings, J.B. 1957. Studies on feeding, digestion and food storage in free-living flatworms. *Biological Bulletin* 112:63–80.

Johnson, W.S. 1976a. Biology and population dynamics of the intertidal isopod *Cirolana hartfordi*. *Marine Biology (Berlin)* 36:343–50.

Johnson, W.S. 1976b. Population energetics of the intertidal isopod *Cirolana hartfordi*. *Marine Biology (Berlin)* 36:351–7.

Jones, D.A. 1972. Aspects of the ecology and behaviour of *Ocypode ceratopthalmus* (Pallus) and *O. kuhli* de Haan (Crustacea: Ocypodidae) *Journal of Experimental Marine Biology and Ecology* 8:31–43.

Kaestner, A. 1970. *Invertebrate Zoology. Volume 3. Crustacea*. New York: Wiley-Interscience.

Khairallah, N.H. and Mattar, N. 1987. On the coexistences of two *Nassarius* species. *Bollettino Malacologico* 23:304–6.

Kohn, A.J. 1956. Piscivorous gastropods of the genus *Conus*. *Proceedings of the National Academy of Science* 42:168–71.
Kohn, A.J. 1961. Chemoreception in gastropod molluscs. *American Zoologist* 1:291–308.
Kohn, A.J. 1983. Feeding biology of gastropods. In *The Mollusca. Volume 5, Physiology, Part 2* (ed. A.S.M. Saleuddin and K.M. Wilbur), 1–63. New York: Academic Press.
Kornicker, L.S. 1961. Observations on the behavior of the littoral gastropod *Terebra salleana*. *Ecology* 42:207.
Krebs, J.R. 1978. Optimal foraging: decision rules for predators. In *Behavioural Ecology, An Evolutionary Approach* (ed. J.R. Krebs and N.B. Daves), 23–63. London: Blackwell Scientific Publications.
Kristensen, J.H. 1972. Carbohydrases of some marine invertebrates with notes on their food and on the natural occurrence of the carbohydrates studied. *Marine Biology (Berlin)* 14:130–42.
Laubier, L. and Sibuet, M. 1977. *Campagnes Biogas 3/8/72 au 4/11/74. Resultats des campagnes a la Mer No. 11* (Publications CNEXO).
Lee, S.Y. 1989. The importance of sesarmiinae crabs *Chiromanthes* spp. and inundation frequency on mangrove (*Kandelia candel* (L.) Druce) leaf litter turnover in a Hong Kong tidal shrimp pond. *Journal of Experimental Marine Biology and Ecology* 131:23–43.
Lenhoff, H.M. and Lindstedt, K.J. 1974. Chemoreception in aquatic invertebrates with special emphasis on the feeding behavior of coelenterates. In *Chemoreception in Marine Organisms* (ed. P.T. Grant and A.M. Mackie), 143–75. New York: Academic Press.
Lindstedt, K.J. 1971. Chemical control of feeding behavior. *Comparative Biochemistry and Physiology* 39A:553–81.
Lochhead, J.H. 1968. The feeding and swimming of *Conchoecia*. *Biological Bulletin* 134:456–64.
Lord, W.D. and Burger, J.F. 1984. Arthropods associated with herring gull (*Larus argentatus*) and great black-backed gull (*Larus marinus*) carrion on islands in the Gulf of Maine, U.S.A. *Environmental Entomology* 13:1261–8.
Louda, S.M. 1979. Distribution, movement and diet of the snail *Searlesia dira* in the intertidal community of San Juan Island, Puget Sound, Washington. *Marine Biology (Berlin)* 51:119–31.
Lubchenco, J. 1978. Plant species diversity in a marine intertidal community: importance of herbivore food preference and algal competitive abilities. *American Naturalist* 112:23–39.
Lubchenco, J. and Menge, B.A. 1978. Community development and persistence in a low rocky intertidal zone. *Ecological Monographs* 48:67–94.
MacGinitie, G.E. and MacGinitie, N. 1968. *Natural History of Marine Animals, Second Edition*. New York: McGraw-Hill.
Mackie, A.M. and Grant, P.T. 1974. Interspecies and intraspecies chemoreception by marine invertebrates. In *Chemoreception in Marine Organisms* (ed. P.T. Grant and A.M. Mackie), 105–41. New York: Academic Press.
Magalhaes, H. 1948. An ecological study of snails of the genus *Busycon* at Beaufort, North Carolina. *Ecological Monographs* 18:377–409.
Malley, D.F. 1978. Degradation of mangrove litter by the tropical sesarmid crab *Chiromanthes*. *Marine Biology (Berlin)* 49:377–86.
Mangum, C.P., Santos, S.L. and Rhodes, W.R. Jr. 1968. Distribution and feeding in the onuphid polychaete *Diopatra cuprea* (Bosc). *Marine Biology (Berlin)* 2:33–40.
Manton, S.M. 1977. *The Arthropoda: Habits, Functional Morphology and Evolution*. New York: Oxford University Press.
Marshall, S.M. and Orr, A.P. 1960. Feeding and nutrition. In *The Physiology of Crustacea. Vol. 1. Metabolism and Growth* (ed. T.H. Waterman), 227–258. New York: Academic Press.
Massin, C. 1982. Food and feeding mechanisms: Holothuroidea. In *Echinoderm Nutrition* (ed. M. Jangoux and J.M. Lawrence), 43–55. Rotterdam: A.A. Balkema.
Matthews, D.C. 1955. Feeding of the sand crab *Hippa pacifica* (Dana). *Pacific Science* 9:382–6.
McDermott, J.J. and Roe, P. 1985. Food, feeding behavior and feeding ecology of nemerteans. *American Zoologist* 25:113–25.
McKillup, S.C. 1983. A behavioural polymorphism in the marine snail *Nassarius pauperatus*: geographic variation correlated with food availability, and differences in competitive ability between morphs. *Oecologia* 56:58–66.

McKillup, S.C. and Butler, A.J. 1979. Modification of egg production and packaging in response to food availability by *Nassarius pauperatus*. *Oecologia* 43:221–31.

McKillup, S.C. and Butler, A.J. 1983. The measurement of hunger as a relative estimate of food available to populations of *Nassarius pauperatus*. *Oecologia* 56:16–22.

McLachlan, A., Wooldridge, T. and van der Horst, G. 1979. Tidal movements of the macrofauna on an exposed sandy beach in South Africa. *Journal of Zoology, London* 187:433–42.

Menge, B.A. 1972. Foraging strategy of a starfish in relation to actual prey availability and environmental predictability. *Ecological Monographs* 42:25–50.

Morton, B. 1981. The Anomalodesmata. *Malacologia* 21:35–60.

Morton, B. 1985. Prey preference, capture and ration in *Hemifusus tuba* (Gmelin)(Prosobranchia: Melongenidae). *Journal of Experimental Marine Biology and Ecology* 94:191–210.

Morton, B. 1986a. Reproduction, juvenile growth, consumption and the effects of starvation upon the South China Sea whelk *Hemifusus tuba* (Gmelin) (Prosobranchia: Melongenidae). *Journal of Experimental Marine Biology and Ecology* 102:257–80.

Morton, B. 1986b. Prey preference and capture by *Hemifusus ternatanus* (Gastropoda: Melongenidae). *Malacological Review* 19:107–10.

Morton, B. 1986c. The diet and prey capture mechanism of *Melo melo* (Prosobranchia: Volutidae). *Journal of Molluscan Studies* 52:156–60.

Morton, B. 1987. Juvenile growth of the South China Sea whelk *Hemifusus tuba* (Gmelin)(Prosobranchia: Melongenidae) and the importance of sibling cannibalism in estimates of consumption. *Journal of Experimental Marine Biology and Ecology* 109:1–14.

Morton, B. 1990. The physiology and feeding behaviour of two marine scavenging gastropods in Hong Kong: the subtidal *Babylonia lutosa* (Lamarck) and the intertidal *Nassarius festivus* (Powys). *Journal of Molluscan Studies* 56:275–88.

Morton, B. and Britton, J.C. 1991. Resource partitioning strategies of two sympatric scavenging snails on a sandy beach in Western Australia. In *Proceedings of the Third International Marine Biological Workshop: the Marine Flora and Fauna of Albany, Western Australia, 1988* (ed. F.E. Wells, D.I. Walker, H. Kirkman and R. Lethbridge), 579–95. Perth: Western Australian Museum.

Morton, J.E. 1960. The habits of *Cyclope neritea*, a style-bearing stenoglossan gastropod. *Proceedings of the Malacological Society of London* 34:96–105.

Myers, A.C. 1972. Tube-worm sediment relationships of *Diopatra cuprea*. *Marine Biology (Berlin)* 17:350–6.

Nagabhushanam, A.K. and Colman, J.S. 1959. Carrion-eating by ophiuroids. *Nature* 184:285.

Naylor, E. 1955. The diet and feeding-mechanism of *Idotea*. *Journal of the Marine Biological Association of the United Kingdom* 34:347–55.

Nickell, T.D. 1989. *The behavioural ecology of epibenthic scavenging invertebrates*. Ph.D. Dissertation, University of London, 257 pp.

Nielsen, C. 1975. Observations on *Buccinum undatum* L. attacking bivalves and on prey responses, with a short review of attack methods of other prosobranchs. *Ophelia* 13:87–108.

Nicol, J.A.C. 1969. *The Biology of Marine Animals*. New York: John Wiley & Sons, Inc.

Noguchi, H. 1921. *Cristispira* in North American shellfish. A note on a spirillium found in oysters. *Journal of Experimental Medicine* 34:295–315.

Ormond, R.F.G., Hanscomb, N.J. and Beach, D.A. 1976. Food selection and learning in the crown-of-thorns starfish, A*canthaster planci* (L.). *Marine Behaviour and Physiology* 4:93–105.

Page, H.M. and Willason, S.W. 1982. Distribution patterns of terrestrial hermit crabs at Enewetak Atoll, Marshall Islands. *Pacific Science* 36:107–17.

Paine, R.T. 1962. Ecological diversification in sympatric gastropods of the genus *Busycon*. *Evolution* 16:515–23.

Paine, R.T. 1966. Food web complexity and species diversity. *American Naturalist* 100:65–75.

Paul, A.Z. 1973. Trapping and recovery of living deep sea amphipods from the Arctic Ocean floor. *Deep Sea Research* 20:289–90.

Pawson, D.L. 1976. Some aspects of the biology of deep-sea echinoderms. *Thalassia Jugoslavica* 12:287–93.

Phillips, B.F. 1969. The population ecology of the whelk *Dicathais aegrota* in Western Australia. *Australian Journal of Marine and Freshwater Research* 20:225–65.

Ponder, W.F. 1973. The origin and evolution of the Neogastropoda. *Malacologia* 12:295–338.
Race, M.S. 1982. Competitive displacement and predation between introduced and native mud snails. *Oecologia* 54:337–47.
Rasmussen, E. 1973. Systematics and ecology of the Isefjord marine fauna (Denmark). *Ophelia* 11:1–507.
Reese E.S. 1969. Behavioral adaptions of intertidal hermit crabs. *American Zoologist* 9:343–55.
Reid, R.G.B. and Reid, A.M. 1974. The carnivorous habit of members of the septibranch genus *Cuspidaria* (Mollusca: Bivalvia). *Sarsia* 56:47–56.
Roberts, M.H. 1968. Functional morphology of mouth parts of the hermit crabs *Pagurus longicarpus* and *Pagurus pollicaris*. *Chesapeake Science* 9:9–20.
Robertson, J.R. and Pfeiffer, W.J. 1982. Deposit feeding by the ghost crab *Ocypode quadrata* (Fabricius). *Journal of Experimental Marine Biology and Ecology* 56:165–77.
Romanes, G.J. 1883. Observations on the physiology of Echinodermata. *Journal of the Linnean Society (Zoology)* 17:131–7.
Sainte-Marie, B. 1986. Feeding and swimming of lysianassid amphipods in a shallow cold-water bay. *Marine Biology (Berlin)* 91:219–29.
Sainte-Marie, B. and B.T. Hargrave. 1987. Estimation of scavenger abundance and distance of attraction to bait. *Marine Biology (Berlin)* 94:431–43.
Sainte-Marie, B. and LaMarche, G. 1985. The diets of six species of the carrion-feeding lysianassid genus *Anonyx* and their relation with morphology and swimming behaviour. *Sarsia* 70:119–26.
Sanchez-Salazar, M.E., Griffiths, C.L. and Seed, R. 1987a. The effect of size and temperature on the predation of cockles *Cerastoderma edule* (L.) by the shore crab *Carcinus maenas* (L.). *Journal of Experimental Marine Biology and Ecology* 111:181–93.
Sanchez-Salazar, M.E., Griffiths, C.L. and Seed, R. 1987b. The interactive roles of predation and tidal elevation in structuring populations of the edible cockle, *Cerastoderma edule*. *Estuarine, Coastal and Shelf Science* 25:245–60.
Sanders, H.L. 1963. Cephalocarida, functional morphology, larval development, comparative external anatomy. *Memoirs of the Connecticut Academy of Arts and Science* 15:1–80.
Scheltema, R.S. 1964. Feeding habits and growth in the mud-snail *Nassarius obsoletus*. *Chesapeake Science* 5:161–6.
Schoener, T.W. 1971. Theory of feeding strategies. *Annual Review of Ecology and Systematics* 2:369–404.
Schoener, T.W. 1983. Field experiments on interspecific competition. *American Naturalist* 122:240–85.
Scott, K.J. and Croker, R.A. 1976. Macroinfauna of northern New England marine sand. Part 3. The ecology of *Psammonyx nobilis* (Crustacea: Amphipoda). *Canadian Journal of Zoology* 54:1519–29.
Shimek, R.L. 1984. The diets of Alaskan *Neptunea*. *The Veliger* 26:274–81.
Shulenberger, E. and Barnard, J.L. 1976. Amphipods from an abyssal trap set in the North Pacific Gyre. *Crustaceana* 31:241–58.
Shulenberger, E. and Hessler, R.R. 1974. Scavenging abyssal benthic amphipods trapped under oligotrophic Central North Pacific Gyre waters. *Marine Biology (Berlin)* 28:185–7.
Sloan, N.A. 1980. Aspects of the feeding biology of asteroids. *Oceanography and Marine Biology Annual Review* 18:57–124.
Sloan, N.A. and Campbell, A.C. 1982. Perception of food. In *Echinoderm Nutrition* (ed. M. Jangoux and J.M. Lawrence), 3–23. Rotterdam: A.A. Balkema.
Smith, C.R. 1985. Food for the deep sea: utilization, dispersal, and the flux of nekton falls at the Santa Catalina Basin floor. *Deep Sea Research* 32:417–42.
Sokolova, M.N. 1972. Trophic structure of deep-sea macrobenthos. *Marine Biology (Berlin)* 16:1–12.
Stenton-Dozey, J.M.E. and Brown, A.C. 1988. Feeding, assimilation and scope for growth in the sandy-beach neogastropod *Bullia digitalis*. *Journal of Experimental Marine Biology and Ecology* 119:253–68.
Stockton, W.L. and DeLuca, T.E. 1982. Food falls in the deep sea: occurrence, quality and significance. *Deep Sea Research* 29:157–69.

Tallmark, B. 1980. Population dynamics of *Nassarius reticulatus* (Gastropoda, Prosobranchia) in Gullmar Fjord, Sweden. *Marine Ecology Progress Series* 3:51–62.
Taylor, J.D. 1978. The diet of *Buccinum undatum* and *Neptunea antiqua* (Gastropoda: Buccinidae). *Journal of Conchology* 29:309–18.
Taylor, J.D. 1981. The evolution of predators in the late Cretaceous and their ecological significance. In *Chance, Change and Challenge: The Evolving Biosphere* (ed. P.L. Forey), 229–40. British Museum (Natural History) and Cambridge University Press.
Taylor, J.D. and Miller, J.A. 1989. The morphology of the osphradium in relation to feeding habits in meso- and neogastropods. *Journal of Molluscan Studies* 55:227–37.
Taylor, J.D. and Reid, D.G. 1984. The abundance and trophic classification of molluscs upon coral reefs in the Sudanese Red Sea. *Journal of Natural History* 18:175–209.
Taylor, J.D. and Shin, P.K.S. 1990. Trawl surveys of sublittoral gastropods in Tolo Channel and Mirs Bay: a record of change from 1976–1986. In *Proceedings of the Second International Marine Biological Workshop: the Marine Flora and Fauna of Hong Kong and southern China, Hong Kong, 1986* (ed. B. Morton), 857–81. Hong Kong: Hong Kong University Press.
Teerling, J. 1970. *The incidence of the ghost crab Ocypode quadrata (Fabr.) on the forebeach of Padre Island, and some of its responses to man*. M.S. Thesis, Texas A & I University, pp. 71.
Thurston, M.H. 1979. Scavenging abyssal amphipods from the northeast Atlantic Ocean. *Marine Biology (Berlin)* 51:55–68.
Trueman, E.R. and Brown, A.C. 1976. Locomotion, pedal retraction and extension, and the hydraulic systems of *Bullia* (Gastropoda: Nassariidae). *Journal of Zoology, London* 178:365–84.
Trueman, E.R. and Brown, A.C. 1987. Locomotory function of the pedal musculature of the nassariid whelk *Bullia*. *Journal of Molluscan Studies* 53:287–8.
Trueman, E.R. and Brown, A.C. 1989. The effect of shell shape on the burrowing performance of species of *Bullia*. *Journal of Molluscan Studies* 55:129–31.
Vader, W. and Romppainen, K. 1985. Notes on Norwegian marine Amphipoda. 10. Scavengers and fish associates. *Fauna Norvegica. Series A* 6:3–8.
Valentindid, T. 1975. Amino-acid chemoreception and other releasing factors in the feeding response of the sea star *Marthasterias glacialis* (D.). In *Proceedings of the Ninth European Marine Biology Symposium* (ed. H. Barnes), 693–705. University of Aberdeen Press.
von Hagen, H.O. 1977. The tree-climbing crabs of Trinidad. *Studies on the Fauna of Curacao and other Caribbean Islands* 54:25–50.
Walsby, J. 1990. *Nature Watching at the Beach*. Auckland: Wilson and Horton, Ltd.
Warner, G.F. 1967. The life history of the mangrove tree crab, *Aratus pisoni*. *Journal of Zoology, London* 153:321–35.
Warner, G.F. 1982. Food and feeding mechanisms: Ophiuroidea. In *Echinoderm Nutrition* (ed. M. Jangoux and J.M. Lawrence), 161–81. Rotterdam: A.A. Balkema.
Waters, V.L. 1973. Food-preference of the nudibranch *Aeolidia papillosa*, and the effects of the defenses of the prey on predation. *The Veliger* 15:174–92.
Weaver, C.S. and duPont, J.E. 1970. The living volutes. *Delaware Museum of Natural History, Monograph Series* 1:1–375.
Wildish, D.J. 1970. Locomotory activity rhythms in some littoral *Orchestia* (Crustacea: Amphipoda). *Journal of the Marine Biological Association of the United Kingdom* 50:241–52.
Williams, A.B. 1965. Marine decapod crustaceans of the Carolinas. *Fisheries Bulletin of the United States Fish and Wildlife Service* 65:1–298.
Willows, A.O.D. 1978. Physiology of feeding in *Tritonia*. I. Behavior and mechanics. *Marine Behavior and Physiology* 5:115–35.
Wilson, D.P. 1978. Some observations on bipinnariae and juveniles of the starfish genus *Luidia*. *Journal of the Marine Biological Association of the United Kingdom* 58:467–78.
Wilson, R.R. and Smith, K.L. 1984. Effect of near-bottom currents on detection of bait by the abyssal grenadier fishes *Coryphaenoides* spp., recorded *in situ* with a video camera on a free vehicle. *Marine Biology (Berlin)* 84:83–91.
Wobber, D.R. 1975. Agonism in asteroids. *Biological Bulletin* 148:483–96.
Wolcott, T.G. 1978. Ecological role of ghost crabs, *Ocypode quadrata* (Fabricius) on an ocean

beach: scavengers or predators? *Journal of Experimental Marine Biology and Ecology* 31:67–82.

Wolcott, T.G. 1988. Ecology. In *Biology of the Land Crabs* (ed. W.W. Burggren and B.R. McMahon), 55–96. Cambridge: Cambridge University Press.

Wolcott, T.G. and Wolcott, D.L. 1984. Impact of off-road vehicles on macroinvertebrates of a mid-Atlantic beach. *Biological Conservation* 29:217–40.

Yonge, C.M. 1928. Structure and function of the organs of feeding and digestion in the septibranchs, *Cuspidaria* and *Poromya*. *Philosophical Transactions of the Royal Society of London, Series B* 216:221–63.

CRABS AS PREDATORS OF MARINE BIVALVE MOLLUSCS

R. SEED

School of Ocean Sciences, University of Wales Bangor, Menai Bridge,
Gwynedd, LL59 5EY, UK

ABSTRACT

Bivalve molluscs have been widely reported in the diets of brachyuran crabs. These predators have the potential to influence the spatial distribution and abundance of their prey, especially when they are abundant and/or the prey species is an important component of the diet. Some species are also known to alter population structure by foraging selectively on particular size classes of prey. However, several morphological and ecological characteristics exhibited by bivalves have been interpreted as having evolved in order to minimize the risk of such predation. These include shell features, temporal and spatial refuges and even life history characteristics. This paper examines the behavioural and mechanical aspects of predation in several species of brachyuran crabs particularly those belonging to the family Portunidae that are known to forage extensively on bivalve molluscs. The impact of such predation on local distribution patterns and population characteristics of the prey is considered and the contribution that such studies have made to our understanding of the optimality of prey selection briefly discussed.

INTRODUCTION

Crab-mollusc predatory prey systems have aroused considerable attention over the past decade or so and have provided valuable experimental evidence concerning the optimality of prey selection. Studies have embraced several families of brachyuran crabs with contrasting chelal morphologies and foraging behaviours. These include the Portunidae (Hughes and Seed 1981; Davidson 1986; Seed 1990a), Cancridae (Boulding and Hay 1984; Lawton and Elner 1985; Cresswell and McClay 1990), Xanthidae (Seed 1980; Hughes 1989; Lin 1990), Ocypodidae (Wolcott 1978) and the Calappidae (Hughes and Elner 1989), many of which contain genera that feed extensively on bivalve molluscs.

Studies of crab foraging behaviour and the vulnerability of their prey requires knowledge of the morphological and mechanical characteristics of the predators' chelae. Elner (1978) proposed that chelae serve as a template upon which feeding habits and prey preferences are determined, a hypothesis which has subsequently been verified by several researches such as Blundon and Kennedy (1982a), Boulding (1984), ap Rheinallt and Hughes (1985). Crab claws, however, have functions other than feeding, e.g., defense, reproduction, communication, burrowing and these can sometimes confound simple correlations between form and feeding habits; claw morphology is thus a compromise between several conflicting evolutionary pressures. Chelal characteristics and foraging behaviour also vary globally; compared with temperate water species tropical crabs are considered to be morphologically and behaviourally more specialised for attacking molluscan prey (Vermeij 1987; Hughes and Elner 1989), arguably as a result of the prolonged and intense coevolution between exploiters and their victims (Hughes 1989). Crabs would, therefore, appear to follow the general trend for tropical species to have narrower niches than those of their temperate water counterparts, particularly with regard to food.

This paper examines the behavioural and mechanical aspects of predation in several species of crabs that are known to forage extensively on bivalves, particularly those belonging to the Portunidae. The impact of these predators on bivalve populations and the morphological and ecological 'responses' of the prey which serve to minimize the risk of such predation are also briefly considered. The paper is not a comprehensive review of crab feeding and the author has intentionally drawn heavily on his own studies of three particular portunids, i.e., *Carcinus maenas* (L.)(UK), *Callinectes sapidus* Rathbun (USA) and *Thalamita danae* (Stimpson) (Hong Kong).

PREY HANDLING TECHNIQUES

Most crustaceans that feed on shelled molluscs are decapods, many of which use more than one method of attack depending upon the prey species, its overall size and relative shell thickness (Table 1). Certain techniques, especially those required to open large resistant prey, involve a substantial structural investment in the form of powerful chelae; for other techniques this investment is minimal but the size of prey that can be opened, relative to that of the predator, is substantially reduced. Chelate predators generally open bivalves by crushing the shell or, depending on the strength of the chela relative to the prey's shell, chipping the edge of the valves until the flesh is exposed. Sometimes more specialised claw morphology and shell opening behaviour is used as in the box crab, *Calappa ocellata* Holthuis, in which a hooked peg and cusp on the outer face of the right chela applies a shearing force across the shell of the mussel *Brachidontes domingensis* (Lamarck) (Hughes and Elner 1989). The massive chelae of *Scylla serrata* Förskal are also well adapted for applying powerful shearing forces to the shells of bivalve prey (Williams 1978). Non-chelate decapods have evolved alternative shell opening procedures; some use specialised flaring dactyli to wedge open the shell valves of bivalve molluscs, others crush the thin valve edges with their mandibles (Lau 1987).

When the blue crab, *Callinectes sapidus*, is fed on marsh mussels, *Geukensia demissa* (Dillwyn), in laboratory aquaria each foraging bout is usually prefaced by a period of active swimming and vigorous movements of the mouth parts. Prey can be detected at a distance of several cm. apparently by chemoreceptors on the antennae, although any mussel touched by the chelae or walking legs elicits an immediate response from a hungry crab. Vision does not seem to be important in locating mussels, although

Table 1
Decapod attack methods for opening bivalve molluscs (after Lau 1987).

	Tactic	Description	Relative Handling Time	Relative Prey Size	Structural Investment
1.	Swallowing whole:	- Prey completely engulfed	Short	Small	Low
2.	Chipping/biting:	- Mandibles chip edge of shell	Moderate	Medium	Low
3.	Wedging:	- Dactyli wedge open shell; adductors severed	Short-Mod	Medium	Low
4.	Prying:	- Dactyli pull valves apart	Moderate	Medium	Low
5.	Crushing:	- Chelae crush shell outright	Short	Med-Large	High
6.	Chipping/Peeling:	- Chelae break off edges of shell	Long	Med-Large	Mod
7.	Boring:	- Chela bores through hinge	Long	Medium	Mod
8.	Tubercular Peeling:	- Chelae specialised for peeling and chipping	Long	Med-Large	Mod
9.	Shearing:	- Chelae exert shearing force along plane where valves meet	Short	Medium	Mod

other prey types such as fish, periwinkles and fiddler crabs are evidently detected visually, e.g., Hughes and Seed (1981), West and Williams (1986). The fringes of hairs on the inner edges of the walking legs are particularly sensitive and once these contact a suitable prey item it is immediately drawn towards the mouth. Mussels are repeatedly manipulated by the powerful chelae, the anterior walking legs and the large outer pair of maxillipeds (Plate IA).

The techniques used by *Callinectes sapidus* to open mussels are quite specific and vary according to the size and strength of the prey. Small mussels are easily crushed, often by a single application of force. These are held by one chela whilst force is applied by the other chela. Once the shell has been crushed, flesh is torn out by the claws and mouthparts and ingested. Attacks on somewhat larger mussels are centred on the weaker umbonal region. Following each unsuccessful crushing attempt the prey is reorientated until a weak spot is located and the umbones smashed (Plate IB, C). Crushed mussels are discarded only after most of the shell fragments have passed through the mouthparts several times and all the flesh has been removed. For larger mussels which cannot be crushed, an alternative, slower method of attack is adopted. Here the poste-

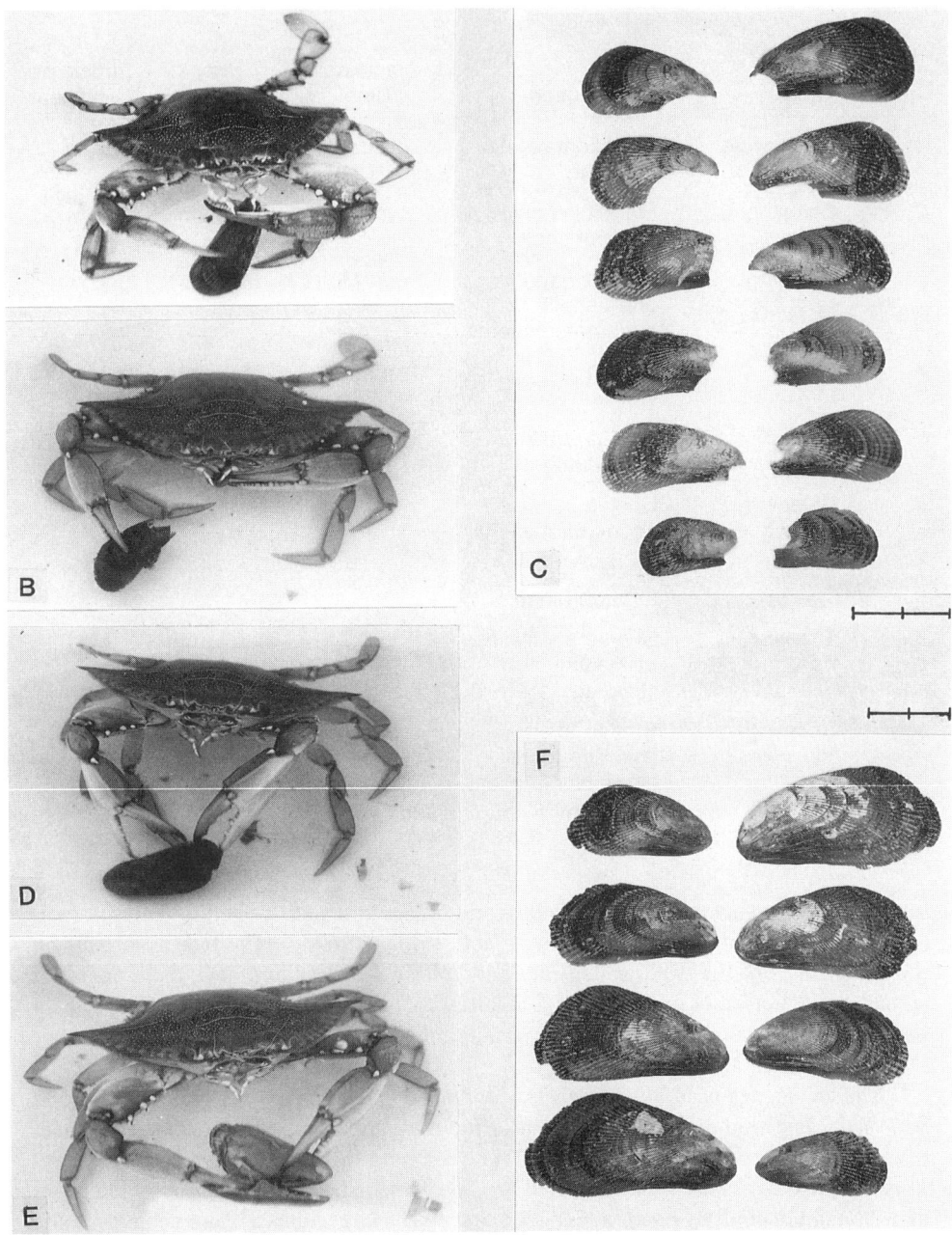

Plate I. Handling techniques used by *Callinectes sapidus* to open *Geukensia demissa*. A and B, Umbone crushing; C, shells opened by umbone crushing; D and E, edge chipping; F, shells opened by edge chipping; note ragged posterior valve margins. Scale in cm (after Seed 1982).

rior edges of the shell are gradually chipped until the chelae can be forced between the valves thus severing the posterior adductor muscle (Plate ID). The two valves are then grasped and twisted open to expose the flesh (Plate IE). When alternative prey is unavailable some crabs will spend several hours manipulating large mussels before these are eventually opened. Mussel shells attacked in this way have a rather ragged appearance but otherwise remain intact (Plate IF).

The methods used by *Callinectes sapidus* to open *Geukensia* are broadly similar to those described for other portunids, e.g., *Carcinus maenas* (Elner 1978; Akumfi and Hughes 1987), *Liocarcinus puber* (L.)(ap Rheinallt and Hughes 1985; Choy1986), *Ovalipes catharus* (White) (Davidson 1986) and *Thalamita danae* (Seed 1990) when these are allowed to feed on mussels. It is uncertain whether such techniques are innate or learned although Cunningham and Hughes (1984) have shown that the mean number of attacks required by *C. maenas* to open *Mytilus edulis* L. decreases with practice; crabs also learnt how to remove individual mussels from tightly packed clumps. The learning of predatory skills has also been demonstrated in other portunids, e.g., *Ovalipes catharus* (Davidson 1986). The effectiveness of the posterior edge chipping method, its complexity and consistency in several portunids suggests that this is a specific mussel opening technique. Certainly *C. maenas* was never observed to use this method when feeding on the cockle, *Cerastoderma edule* (L.), (Sanchez-Salazar et al. 1987a), a species with a more globular shell and interlocking valve margins.

Elner (1978) described several largely size-related mussel opening techniques in *Carcinus maenas*. Crabs sought out and exploited weak spots in the shell by a process of trial and error, eventually smashing the mussel through a cumulative process whereby minor fractures in the shell substructure were gradually extended. The ability to open relatively large bivalves by repeatedly loading the shell has also been reported in other crabs. Boulding and Labarbera (1986) showed that *Cancer productus* Randall often squeezed the clam *Protothaca staminea* (Conrad) more than 200 times over a three day period before the shell eventually failed. The persistent application of smaller forces enabled crabs to open much larger clams than could be crushed outright, thereby greatly extending the size range of prey available to them.

Although epifaunal and semi-infaunal bivalves are extensively consumed by portunids these crabs are also significant predators of infaunal bivalves such as cockles and clams, e.g., Hill (1979), Sanchez-Salazar et al. (1987b), Wear and Haddon (1987). These appear to be located by the chemosensory dactyli of the walking legs and chelae as they systematically probe beneath the sediment surface. Once a suitable prey item is encountered it is rapidly brought to the surface and drawn forwards under the body towards the mouth.

CHELAL MORPHOLOGY AND BIOMECHANICS

Most portunids are heterochelous having one large, more powerful, crusher claw and one narrower, less robust, cutter claw. These function differently during feeding, the cutter usually holding or manipulating the prey whilst force is applied by the crusher. Male crabs typically have more powerful chelae than females of comparable body size and these sexual differences tend to become more exaggerated amongst larger crabs (Seed 1990c).

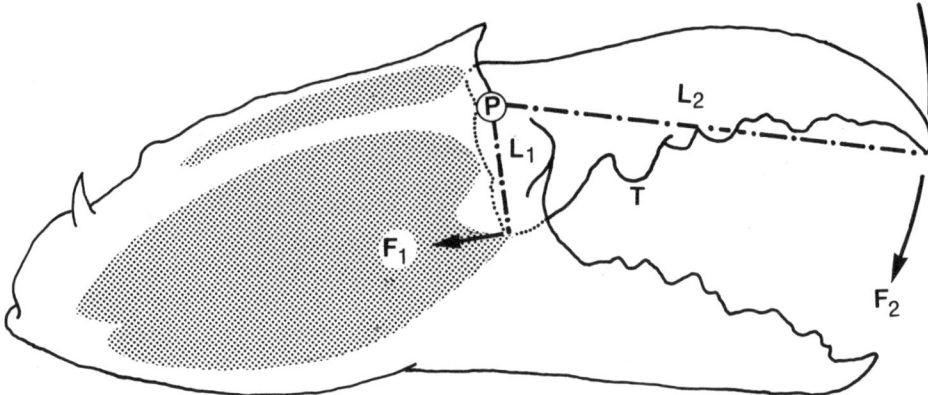

Fig. 1. Dimensions used to calculate mechanical advantage at the claw tip ($L_1 : L_2$). Stippled areas represent the opener (small) and closer (large) apodeme plates housed in the propus; arrows denote directions through which forces F_1 and F_2 act; P. pivot; T. dactylar tooth.

The crushing power of a crab's claw depends on the magnitude of the force that can be produced by the closer muscle located within the propus and on the way that force is altered by the crab's lever system. The magnitude of the force (F1) applied to the dactylus by the closer muscle depends on the length and arrangement of the sarcomere fibres comprising that muscle, as well as on its cross-sectional area, which in turn is directly correlated with the size of the closer apodeme plate onto which this muscle is inserted (Warner and Jones 1976; Vermeij 1977). Assuming that the chelal lever system operates on a frictionless pivot, mechanical advantage or grip strength at the claw tip can be calculated as the ratio between the lever lengths L1, the distance between the pivotal point of the dactylus and the point of insertion of the closer apodeme, and L2, the distance between the pivot and the distal tip of the dactylus (Fig. 1). This ratio remains relatively constant with crab size. The force applied by the claw at the chelal tip (F2) increases with mechanical advantage though the speed and distance of any resulting movement decreases proportionately; there is thus an irreconcilable conflict between the speed of closure and sustained crushing power. The magnitude of the force exerted also varies according to the position along the dactylus where the prey is held. Prey nearer the chelal pivot will be at greater mechanical advantage and subjected to greater forces for a given input than prey nearer the claw tips. The ratio L1:L2 (Table 2) thus represents the minimum value for mechanical advantage at the claw tip.

Crusher claws pinch more strongly than cutters because of their greater mechanical advantage, larger closer apodemes and the greater stress within the closer muscle (Warner et al. 1982). These claws are, therefore, able to apply a powerful force in slow but prolonged pulses; cutter claws, by contrast, have a faster but less powerful closure. The higher mechanical advantage of the crusher chelae is generally achieved by an increase in L1 rather than L2. Whilst mechanical advantage provides a useful measure of relative chelal strength it can, like other single descriptors of claw form, seriously underestimate the potential capability of the chelae to which it is applied (Brown et al. 1979).

Table 2
Mean mechanical advantage ($L_1:L_2$) at the chelal tips of several portunid crabs; male and female data presented separately.

Chelal type	Thalamita danae[1]		Callinectes sapidus[3]		Carcinus maenas[5]	
	M	F	M	F	M	F
Crusher	0.295	0.276 (0.321)[2]	0.230	0.232 (0.293)[4]	0.327	0.282
Cutter	0.216	0.220 (0.220)[2]	0.178	0.185 (0.232)[4]	0.264	0.251
	Liocarcinus puber[6]		L. depurator[6]		L. holsatus[5]	
	M	F	M	F	M	F
Crusher	0.322	0.285	0.216	0.218 (0.248)[6]	0.247	0.222
Cutter	0.264	0.241	0.210	0.203 (0.177)[6]	0.224	0.215

1,2, *T. danae* and *T. crenata*, respectively (Seed 1990b); 3, Blundon and Kennedy (1982a); 4, Brown et al. (1979); 5, Lee (Pers. comm.); 6, Warner and Jones (1976).

The chelae of a typical portunid crab, *Thalamita danae*, are illustrated in Plate II. The two claws differ markedly in their morphology and occlusive geometry. The biting surfaces of the crusher claw (Plate IIB) consist of several large molariform cusps. At the base of the dactylus a large peg-like tooth bites into a shallow notch created by the three basal cusps on the propus and significantly enhances the mechanical advantage at this point. Crabs possessing such a structure are considered to be specialised for feeding on hard shelled molluscan prey (Vermeij 1977). Distal to this peg is a disjointed region where the two fingers of the claw do not meet. The blunt molar-like teeth in the proximal region of this claw provide an extensive crushing surface whilst the smaller more laterally compressed teeth towards the claw tip can be used for shearing or tearing. The occlusive surfaces of the slimmer more serrated cutter claw (Plate IIA) consist of a linear array of triangular teeth which meet over much of the claw's length. These interlocking sharp-edged teeth are slightly offset laterally to form an effective cutting or shearing surface. The sharp curving tips of both chelae overlap distally.

Differences in the mechanical and morphological features of crab chelae clearly reflect their particular function and probably account for the differences in handling behaviour reported between different species. Those which feed principally on rapidly moving prey will usually have faster chelae operating at a lower mechanical advantage; those feeding on more heavily armoured prey will tend to have slower but more powerful chelae operating at a higher mechanical advantage. Ap Rheinallt (1986) showed that small *Mytilus edulis* were more easily picked up and manipulated by *Liocarcinus puber* than by *Carcinus maenas*. The crusher claw of *C. maenas* is particularly unsuited to handling small prey items, which are frequently dropped due to the extensive gape between the proximal surfaces of the propus and dactylus. This claw is clearly better adapted to handling larger prey since the chelal teeth are broader and the propus and dactylus more nearly parallel when force is applied to the prey. Moreover, the wider chelal gape effectively enables prey to be pushed further back into the claw where it can be crushed by more proximal teeth operating at higher mechanical advantage. *C. maenas* is thus able to crush larger prey than *L. puber* (ap Rheinallt and Hughes 1985). The crusher claw of *Liocarcinus* does not possess such a large gape in which prey can

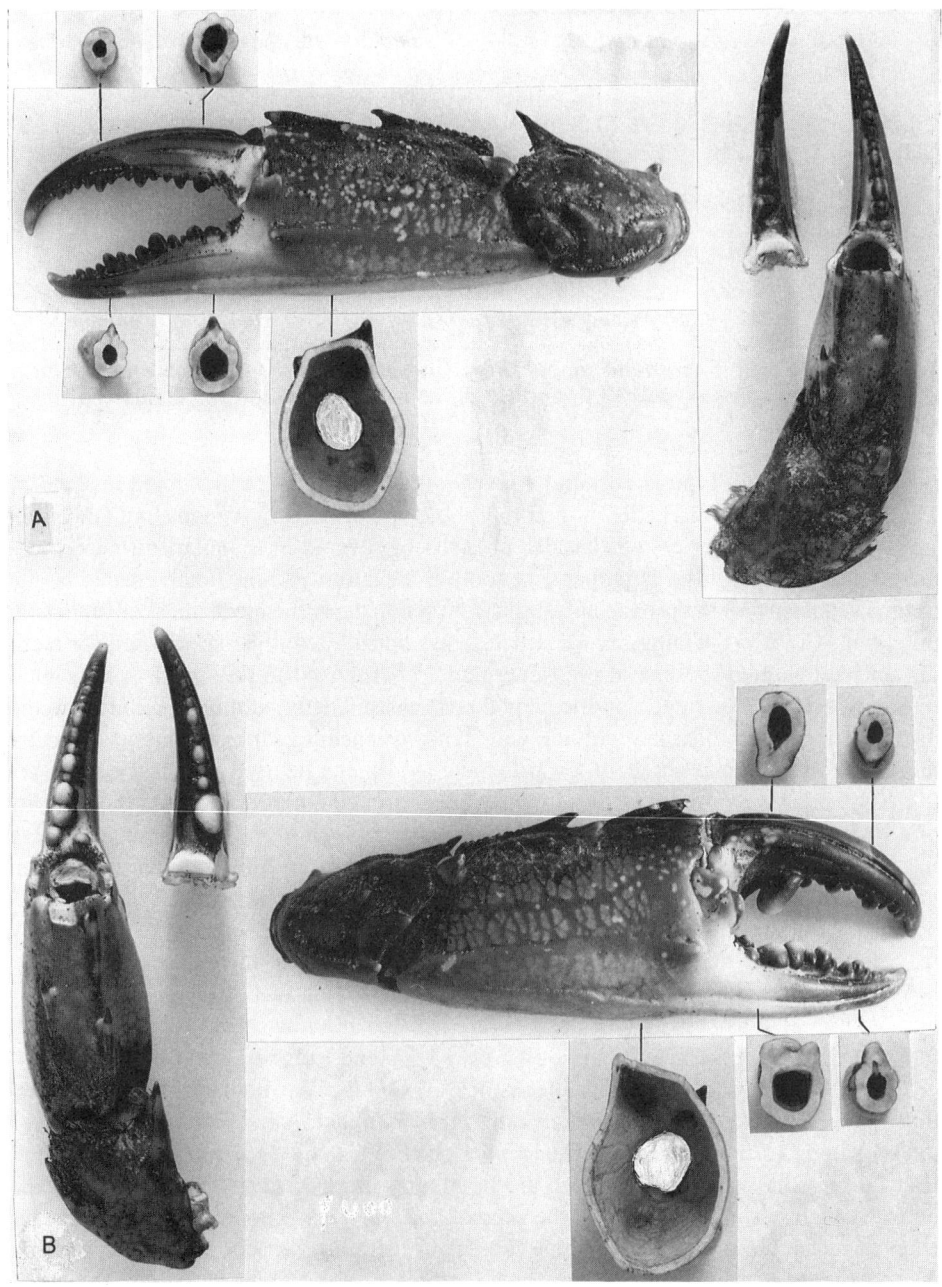

Plate II. Morphology and occlusive geometry of the claws of a large (61 cm C.W.) *Thalamita*. A, cutter claw; B, crusher claw (from Seed 1990a).

be accommodated without slipping; this claw is therefore better suited by the nature of its complementary occluding surfaces for holding small, irregularly shaped or even fast moving, soft-bodied prey. Nonetheless, the presence of a large proximal peg at the base of the crusher claw (surprisingly absent in both *Carcinus* and *Callinectes*) suggests that hard-shelled molluscan prey are in fact an important and integral part of the natural diet of *L. puber*.

Adult *Carcinus maenas* vary in colour from green to red depending at least partially on the length of intermoult. These colour varieties are now known to have distinct physiological, ecological and behavioural characteristics. Whilst there are no differences between the two forms in terms of their external morphology or mechanical advantage, red crabs have more robust crusher claws which are capable of generating maximum forces some 28% greater than those of green crabs. Consequently in laboratory experiments red crabs exhibited a significant preference for larger *Mytilus edulis* and tended to dominate green crabs in aggressive disputes over prey (Kaiser et al. 1990).

PREY VALUE

Figure 2A shows the time taken by individual *Callinectes sapidus* to open and consume *Geukensia demissa* when presented in random sequence with mussels of increasing shell length. For each crab, handling time, i.e., the time taken to break open and eat each prey item, increases quasi-exponentially with prey length as the slower edge-chipping method increasingly becomes the predominant form of attack. Larger crabs have shorter handling times for any given size of mussel, thus reflecting their greater chelal strength. Variations in handling times of similarly sized mussels exist both within and between crabs. Within crab variation is probably due to differences in shell strength and/or crab hunger levels. All experimental crabs were starved for a period of 24 hours in an attempt to standardise hunger levels, although the effectiveness of this widely used procedure has recently been questioned (Haddon and Wear 1987). Between crab variation is largely attributable to crab size though some crabs are evidently more proficient at opening mussels than others, perhaps reflecting greater experience with this type of prey prior to their capture. Breaking time curves for *Thalamita danae* when fed on either *Perna viridis* (L.) or *Brachidontes variabilis* (Krauss) are also steeply increasing functions of prey length (Fig. 2B).

Once handling times and the relationship between mussel length and flesh (or energy) content have been established, it is possible to calculate prey value or profitability, i.e., the yield of flesh per unit of handling time. Figure 3 shows that for *C. sapidus* the value of marsh mussels decreases monotonically with prey length amongst all sizes of crabs examined. This contrasts with the peaked profitability curves obtained for *Carcinus maenas* when feeding either on mussels, *Mytilus edulis* (Elner and Hughes 1978) or on cockles, *Cerastoderma edule* (Sanchez-Salazar et al. 1987a). Such differences would appear to reflect specific differences in chelal morphology. Small mussels are optimal for *C. sapidus*, as indeed they are for *Ovalipes catharus* (Davidson 1986), because the chelae of these crabs, like those of *Liocarcinus* and *Thalamita*, are finer and more dextrous than those of *C. maenas*, thus enabling even the smallest mussels to be gleaned efficiently. It is difficult, therefore, to predict the precise form of prey value curves since these can vary according to the size of the predator and the type of prey (see Cresswell

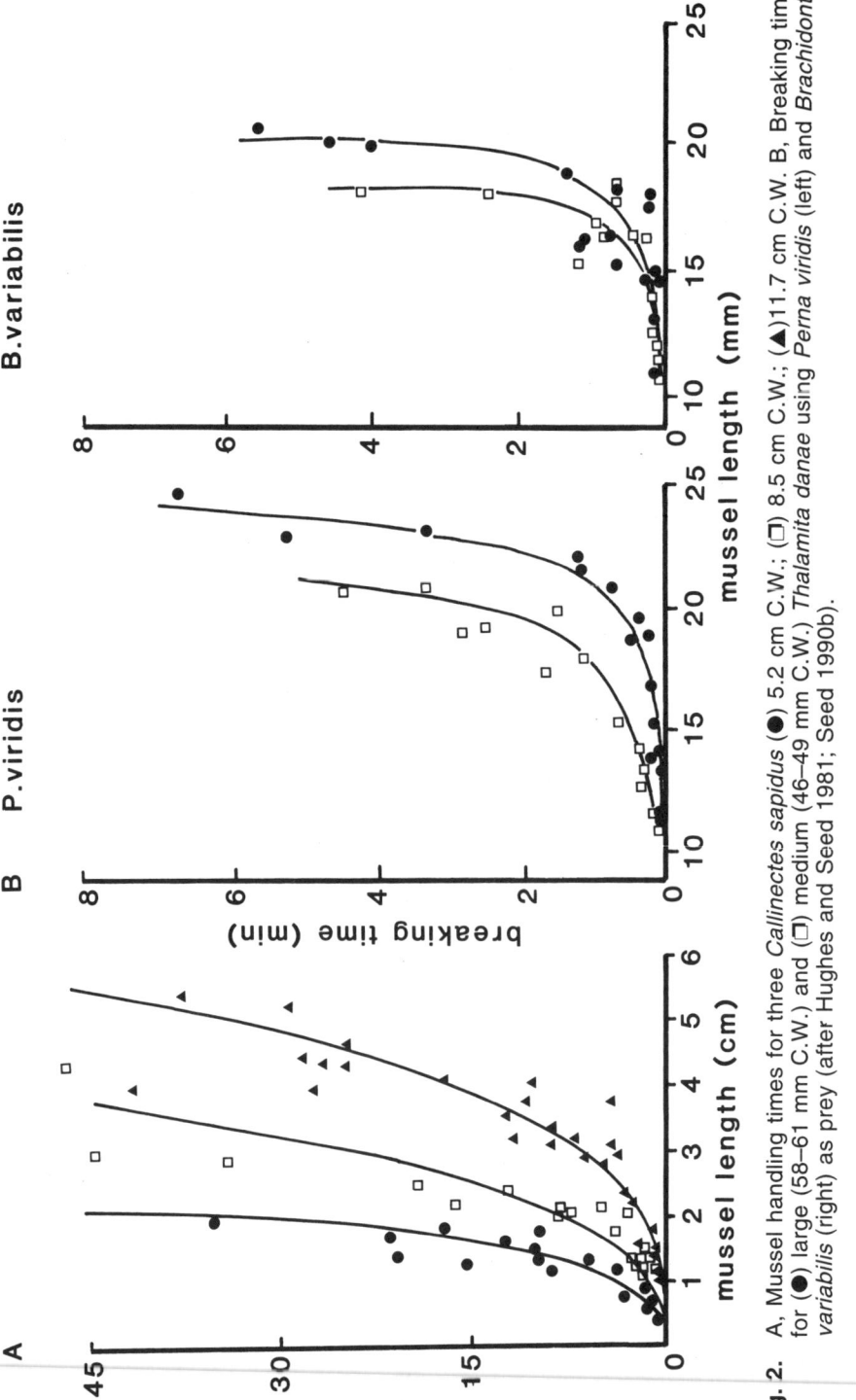

Fig. 2. A, Mussel handling times for three *Callinectes sapidus* (●) 5.2 cm C.W.; (□) 8.5 cm C.W.; (▲)11.7 cm C.W. B, Breaking times for (●) large (58–61 mm C.W.) and (□) medium (46–49 mm C.W.) *Thalamita danae* using *Perna viridis* (left) and *Brachidontes variabilis* (right) as prey (after Hughes and Seed 1981; Seed 1990b).

and McClay 1990). Profitability was independent of prey size in *Calappa ocellata* when feeding on *Brachidontes domingensis* (Hughes and Elner 1989). Consequently these crabs foraged indiscriminately on all mussels below the critical size (26–27 mm) that could be opened. Such opportunistic foraging has been observed in other tropical crabs e.g., *Ozius verreauxii* Saussure (Hughes 1989) and may be the most appropriate strategy if prey is usually scarce.

Few studies have compared the profitability of different types of prey. Sanchez-Salazar et al. (1987a) concluded that cockles ought to provide a substantially more valuable food source for *C. maenas* than mussels, but conceded that simple compari-

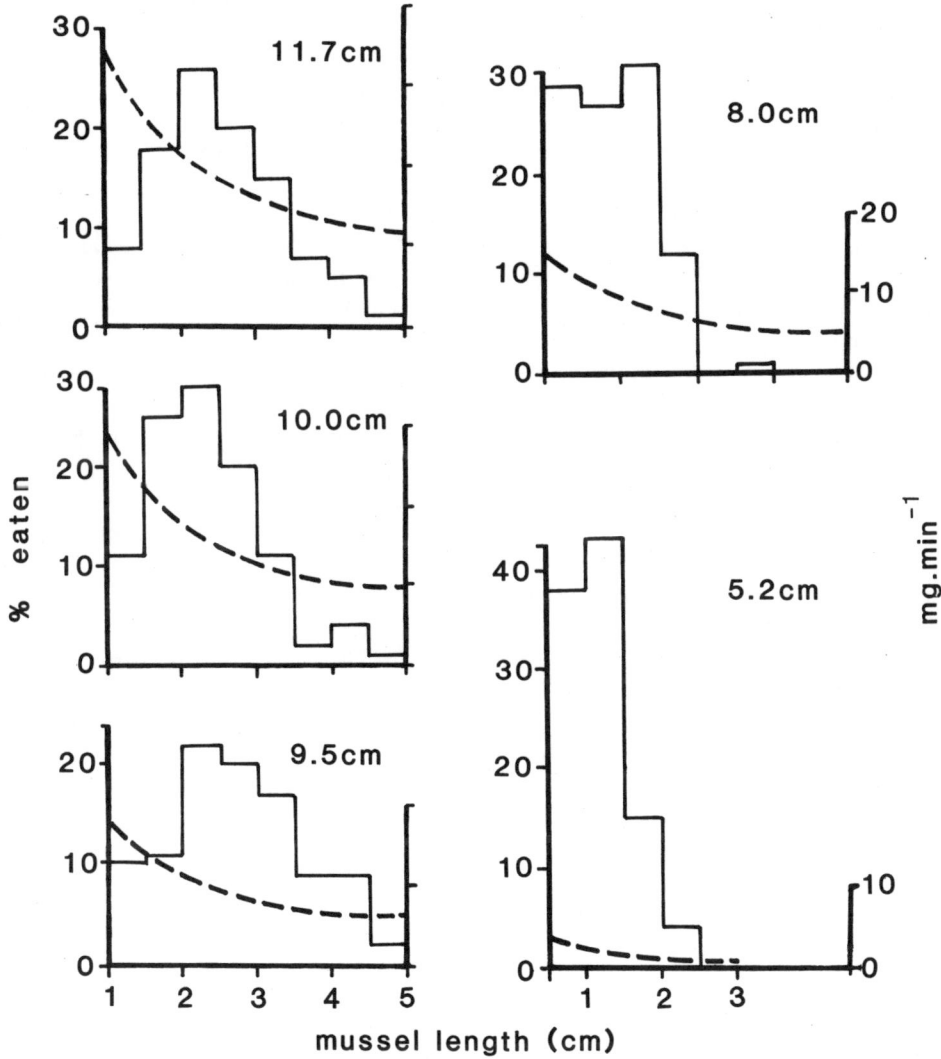

Fig, 3. Consumption of mussels of different sizes by *Callinectes sapidus* under conditions of constant prey availability. Dashed curves denote profitability of mussels of different size (after Hughes and Seed 1981).

sons may be misleading when these do not take into account the abundance and accessibility of prey in the field. West and Williams (1986) showed that *Callinectes sapidus* generally preferred fish and periwinkles to semi-infaunal marsh mussels which apparently required a greater investment of energy to excavate from the sediment. When presented with different molluscan prey *Cancer novaezelandiae* (Jacquinot) maximised its energy intake by selecting the most profitable species, although the species preferred varied according to the size range of prey offered (Cresswell and McClay 1990). Learning can significantly reduce handling time (Cunningham and Hughes 1984; Davidson 1986) which in turn will influence profitability. Under certain circumstances this can lead to certain prey items becoming transposed in rank, causing crabs to switch from one prey type to another.

FORAGING STRATEGY

Foraging behaviour has been studied with both unlimited and restricted diets, the latter by presenting crabs with equal numbers of prey in each of several size classes. The number of prey consumed is then monitored for several days without replacing any of the eaten prey. Daily feeding rates of three size classes of *C. sapidus* fed on an unrestricted diet of *Geukensia* are illustrated in Figure 4. Initially, smaller mussels were selected and only when these had been depleted did crabs proceed to attack progressively larger prey.

In experiments with unlimited diets crabs are allowed to feed for several hours; the number of prey eaten are then counted and replaced by ones of similar size to maintain constant prey availability. Experiments are continued until a consistent feeding pattern emerges. Diet curves for *C. sapidus* under conditions of constant prey availability (Fig. 3) show that larger, less profitable, mussels are seldom taken, even though these can eventually be opened by all but the smallest crabs. A surprising, yet recurring feature of these results is the apparent reluctance of crabs to feed on the smallest, most profitable mussels. Since this could simply reflect low encounter rates with small mussels, which are often obscured amongst larger individuals and broken shell debris, two size classes, 2–2.5 cm and 3.5–4 cm, representing more and less profitable prey respectively, were fed in different proportions (5:5;5:10;5:20). Each crab was then observed continuously for about 1 hour noting the acceptance-rejection sequences. Mussels were replaced as eaten to maintain constant prey availability. Whilst large mussels were indeed encountered more frequently they were rarely eaten. Smaller mussels, by contrast, were almost always eaten when encountered even when grossly outnumbered by larger mussels (Fig. 5A). Similar experiments were run using mixtures of 1–1.5 cm and 2–2.5 cm mussels. Mussels in both these size categories could easily be crushed and were rarely rejected (Fig. 5B). Such results confirm that the apparent reluctance of *C. sapidus* to feed on small mussels is due to low encounter rates. A similar reluctance to accept larger (> 20 mm) more resistant mussels, which may require a protracted period of manipulation before they can be opened, has also been demonstrated in *Thalamita danae* (Fig. 6).

The preference for smaller size classes of bivalves well below the maximum size that can be opened is characteristic of many portunids, e.g., ap Rheinallt (1986), Davidson (1986), Akumfi and Hughes (1979), Sanchez-Salazar *et al.* (1987a), although the degree of selectivity usually varies according to hunger level and food availability. The reasons for such size selection are still not entirely clear although maximizing energy intake and minimizing handling time have both been suggested as causal factors. Both *Carcinus maenas* and *Liocarcinus puber* select mussels, *Mytilus edulis* according to their profitability (Elner and Hughes 1978; ap Rheinallt 1986) thus apparently conforming to predictions of Optimal Diet Theory based upon the energy maximization premise (reviewed by Hughes 1980, but see also Pierce and Ollason 1987). The behavioural basis of size selection in *C. maenas* is discussed by Jubb et al. (1983) and Akumfi and Hughes (1987). Like many crabs *C. maenas* seems to exhibit a flexible foraging behaviour which enables it to maximize its feeding efficiency.

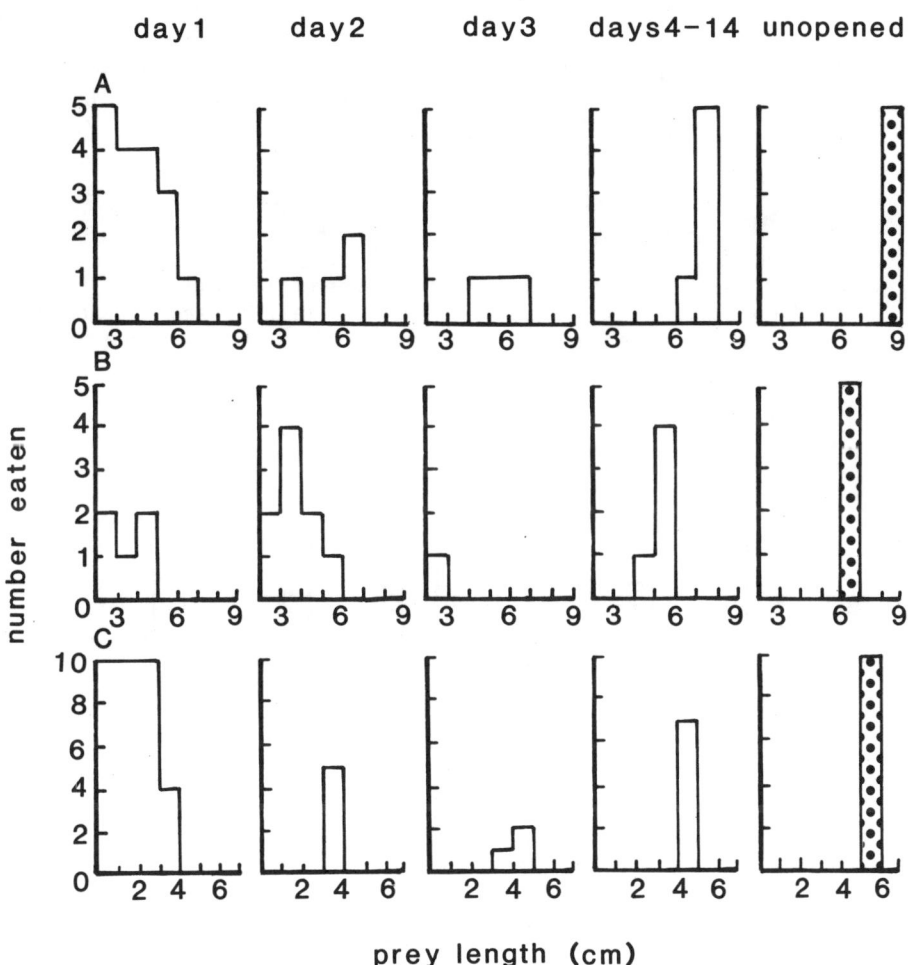

Fig. 4. Daily feeding rates of three size classes of *Callinectes sapidus* with restricted diets. A, 15–16 cm C.W.; B, 10–11 cm C.W.; C, 6–7 cm C.W. Two crabs used in A and B where five mussels in each class were offered; three crabs used in C where ten mussels in each class were offered. Stippled columns denote mussels unopened after 14 days. (after Seed 1980).

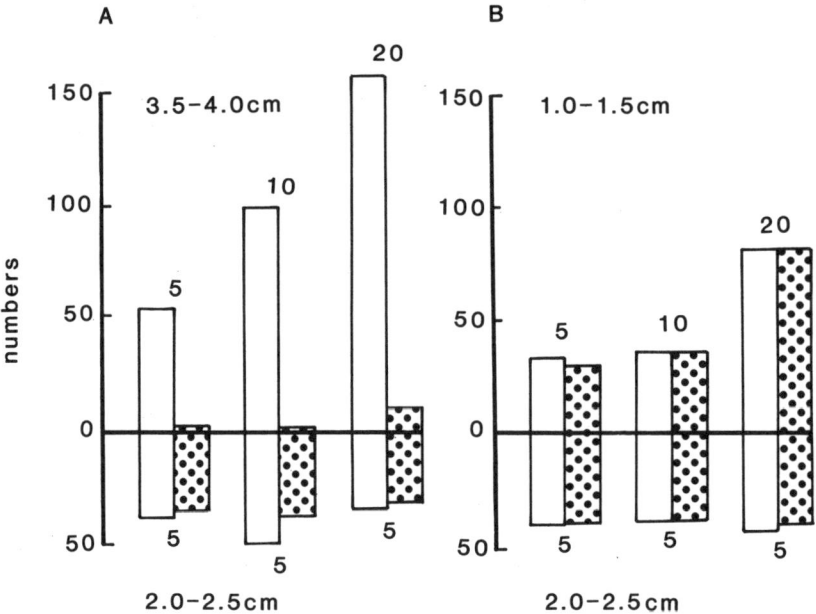

Fig. 5. Diets of *Callinectes sapidus* presented with different ratios (5:5; 5:10; 5:20) of smaller and larger mussels. Four crabs (8.5–11.7 cm C.W.) used with each ratio; open columns denote numbers encountered, stippled columns denote numbers eaten (after Seed 1982).

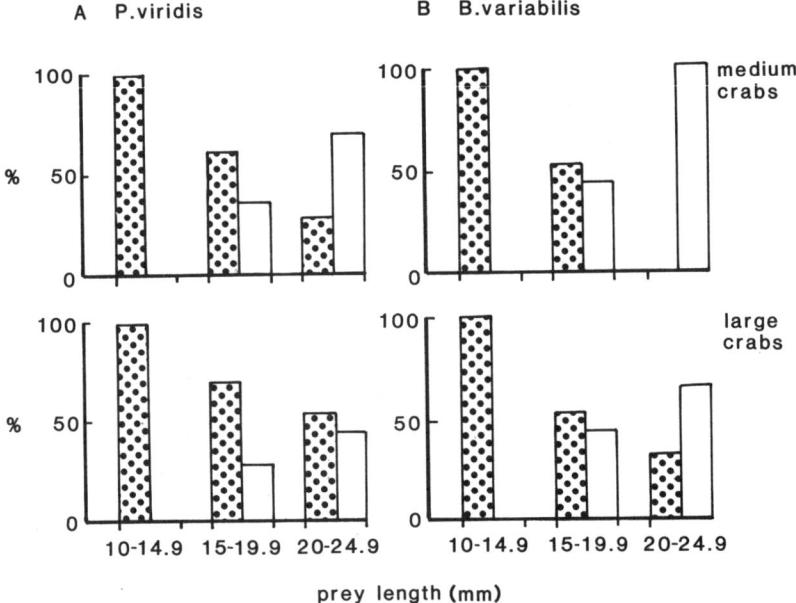

Fig. 6. Percentage of mussels offered that were either accepted (stippled) or rejected (open) by medium (46–49 mm C.W.) and large (58–61 mm C.W.) *Thalamita danae* (after Seed 1990b).

In *Callinectes* handling time increases and prey value decreases with increasing prey size. Consequently preference for smaller mussels simultaneously maximizes net energy intake and minimizes handling time. However, the equal preference for all mussels which can be easily crushed, strongly suggests that time minimization, rather than energy maximization, may be the basis for size selection in this crab (see also Boulding 1984 and Cresswell and McClay 1990 for other crab species). Time minimization may be especially important for tidally migrating crabs, since the time available for feeding will be restricted and during that time crabs themselves may be particularly vulnerable to predators. After a few minutes experience the recognition of large suboptimal prey by *C. sapidus*, whether based on profitability or expected handling time, is almost instantaneous. Such a learning capability indicates that the behavioural sophistication of *Callinectes* is sufficient for active selection according to prey value to be feasible.

Whilst smaller size categories of prey are generally preferred, many predatory crabs can in fact open larger prey items given sufficient time. These can therefore be carried to safer habitats and repeatedly loaded until the shell eventually fails. This strategy could prove to be extremely valuable when the cost of continuing an attack is low, the risk of leaving a refuge is high and alternative prey items are scarce (Boulding and Labarbera 1986).

Most experimental studies on crab predation have utilised epifaunal prey presented as isolated items dispersed over the aquarium floor. However, several researchers such as Blundon and Kennedy (1982b), West and Williams (1986), and Lin (1991), have found little or no evidence of size selective predation amongst crabs foraging on infaunal or semi-infaunal bivalves where a significant investment of time and energy may be required before such prey can be effectively evaluated and excavated from the sediment. Even epifaunal taxa such as *Mytilus* or *Perna* are usually firmly bound together by byssal threads in dense clumps with many of the smaller, more vulnerable, size classes protected between larger mussels. Elner and Hughes (1978) found that predation of small mussels by *Carcinus maenas* was lower when these were presented in clumps. Group living in *Geukensia demissa* also appears to offer some protection against predators (Bertness and Grosholz 1985). It is uncertain, therefore, to what extent laboratory experiments can be considered representative of field situations where alternative food patches and prey types will generally be available, interactions with other organisms will occur, and where energy may be expended in tidal migrations.

CRAB DIET

Most portunids are opportunistic, generalist predators feeding mainly on slow moving or sessile macro-invertebrates, particularly molluscs and crustaceans. However, some will also function as detritivores or even scavengers. Natural diets are determined by examining the foregut contents of freshly caught crabs. Results are then usually expressed either as the percentage of foreguts containing each prey item (= frequency of occurrence) or volumetrically where prey items are awarded point scores (= points method) according to their estimated volumes, e.g., Williams (1981), Choy (1986), Wear and Haddon (1987). Gravimetric analyses have also been used, e.g., Paul (1981).

In a study of *Portunus pelagicus* L. and three species of *Thalamita*, in which 22 food categories ranging from protozoans to fish were found in the gastric mill, Williams

(1981) concluded that the points method was most useful when food is ingested whole or in large recognisable pieces but was generally unsuitable for food with a high proportion of soft tissue which was rapidly reduced to unrecognisable fragments. The frequency of occurrence method was appropriate for most types of prey, but was less accurate for those with no recognisable hard parts; it also tended to overestimate the relative importance of items which occur regularly but at low volume. Errors due to the accumulation of material that is digested and cleared slowly were introduced by both methods. Williams (1981) also found that a sample of about 30 foreguts containing food included 75% of the possible taxa represented in the diet and was, therefore, adequate for describing the quality and quantity of food eaten.

For most types of food there is generally a good degree of correlation between the frequency with which each prey item appears in the diet and the actual volume of that item in the foregut. This congruence occurs because food items that are ingested are usually those eaten in greatest quantity. This correlation, however, often breaks down in the case of molluscan prey where the shells are frequently smashed. Here only small pieces of shell may actually be ingested with the flesh making it more difficult to judge the importance of these food items in the diet. Choy (1986), for example, found that although molluscs occurred in 67% of the foreguts of *Liocarcinus puber*, they accounted for only 11% of the total volume of the diet. *Mytilus edulis*, the third most important item in the diet of *L. puber* after algae and crustaceans, was present in 40% of the stomachs examined, but constituted just over 8% of the volume of the foregut contents.

To obtain reliable estimates of natural diets crabs must be examined soon after collection since, depending on temperature, the residence times of certain food items can be extremely short, e.g., Choy (1986), Haddon and Wear (1987). In the tropical portunid, *Scylla serrata*, gut clearance is virtually complete within 12 hours although shell material can be retained for several days (Fig. 7). Most portunids feed only when they are submerged, mainly at night time. Some, however, feed on the incoming or outgoing tides, irrespective of the time of day, when crustaceans and juvenile fish are most abundant and when infaunal bivalves extend their siphons and are thus most vulnerable (Choy 1986).

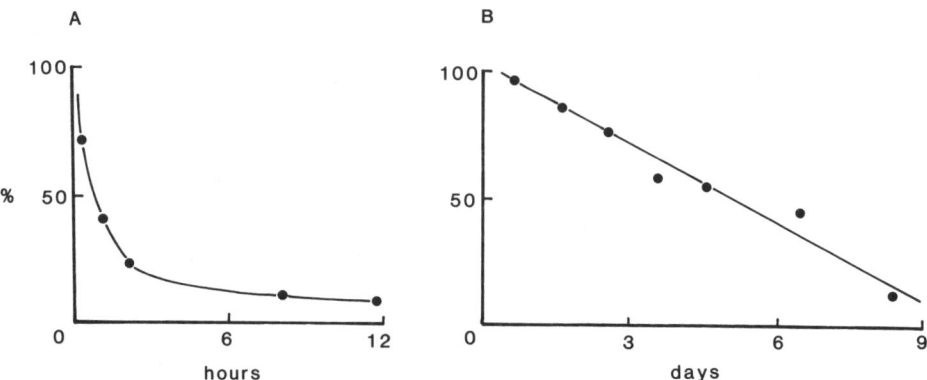

Fig. 7. A, Amount of food remaining in the gut of *Scylla serrata* as a percentage of the weight of food eaten. B, Rate of clearance of bivalve shell fragments (after Hill 1976).

Many portunids, e.g., *Callinectes* spp. (Paul 1981; Arnold 1984), *Ovalipes* spp. (du Preez 1984; Haefner 1986; Wear and Haddon 1987), *Scylla serrata* (Hill 1976), *Liocarcinus puber* (Choy 1986), *Carcinus maenas* (Elner 1981; Sanchez-Salazar et al. 1987; Raffaelli et al. 1990), *Portunus pelagicus* (Williams 1982) and *Thalamita danae* (Seed 1990a) feed extensively on bivalve molluscs. Of the 14 taxa that could be positively identified in the foregut of tidally migrating *T. danae*, the mussels *Perna viridis* and *Brachidontes variabilis* were easily the most important occurring respectively in 54% and 42% of crabs (n = 52) examined. These mussels were readily identified from indigestible fragments of shell and periostracum, byssal threads and occasionally whole byssal stems. Even these relatively high values, however, may underestimate the importance of mussels in the diet of *T. danae* since flesh is thoroughly gleaned from the shell before ingestion occurs. Of the crabs caught on the falling tide only 18% had empty stomachs compared with over 75% of those caught on a rising tide (Fig. 8). More significantly, *P. viridis* was present in only 20% and *B. variabilis* in only 4% of crabs caught on the flood tide whereas both occurred in quantity in over half of all crabs caught on the ebb tide. These data demonstrate that *T. danae* undergoes foraging excursions into the intertidal zone to feed on the small mytilids which are abundant in the middle and upper shore but which, as a result of rapid growth and heavy mortality, are relatively scarce at lower levels (Seed 1990a).

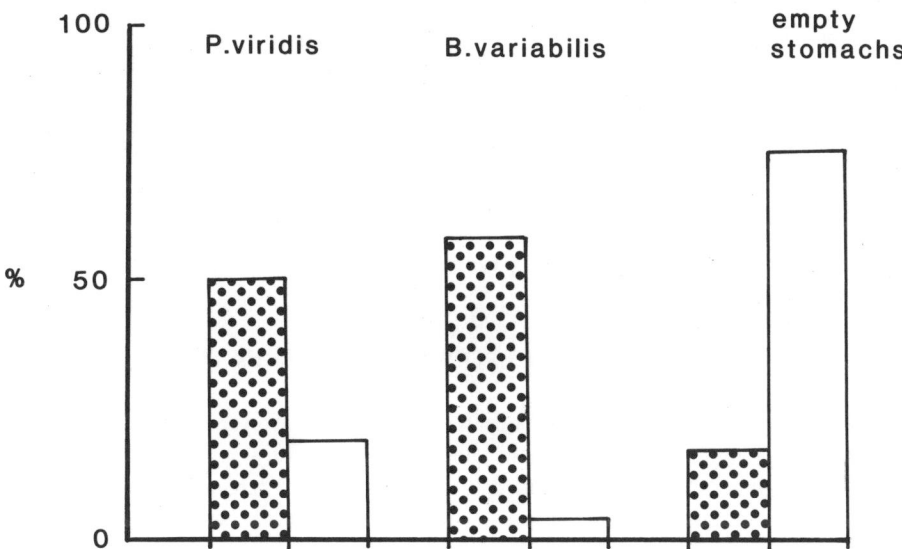

Fig. 8. Percentage occurrence of mussels in the stomachs of *Thalamita danae* collected on an ebbing (stippled) and on a flooding (open) tide (after Seed 1990b).

The spatial and temporal diversity of portunid diets probably reflects the seasonal and local availability of prey types rather than any active selection thus emphasising the opportunistic and versatile feeding behaviour of these crabs. However, du Preez (1984) found that *Ovalipes punctatus* (DeHaan) preferred prey species that were not the most abundant, suggesting that some selection may in fact occur. Compared with temperate water crabs the diets of tropical and subtropical portunids are relatively uniform (Choy 1986). This is thought to reflect the higher diversity and regular availability of prey species at lower latitudes; in temperate species diets change markedly due to the lower diversity and seasonal variation in prey availability. Diet also varies with crab size as a result of changing chelal strength and foraging behaviour. In *C. sapidus* Paul (1981) found that molluscs occurred mainly in larger (> 60 mm CW) crabs whereas smaller individuals fed predominantly on small crustaceans and plant material.

Macrophytic material occurs regularly in the foregut of many portunids. This is generally assumed to be ingested accidentally but in some species, such as *L. puber* (Choy 1986) and *Scylla serrata* (Hill 1976), it appears to be an integral part of the diet and is readily digested by strong enzymes present in foregut fluids (Norman and Jones 1990). Although *L. puber* consumes copious amounts of algae, experiments have demonstrated that animal material is generally preferred; algal material was most readily accepted by starved crabs and those in early intermoult (Choy 1986). Algal fronds encrusted with sessile invertebrates were also preferred to those lacking such 'epiphytes'.

Ingestion rates of bivalves by portunids can be quite spectacular. Haddon and Wear (1987) showed that *Ovalipes catharus* could consume over 90 cockles·d^{-1} (*Austrovenus*) and at 20°C devoured prey so quickly that the foregut was full in under 15 seconds. Foregut clearance appears to be the rate limiting step although foregut volume varies markedly between species, e.g., Haddon and Wear 1987. *Ovalipes punctatus* (du Preez 1984) and *Callinectes sapidus* (Seed 1982) respectively consumed large numbers of *Donax* (15–20·d^{-1}) and *Geukensia* (> 50·d^{-1}), whilst individual *Thalamita danae* ingested up to 20 *Perna viridis* daily (Seed 1990a). Temperature has a marked influence on feeding rates. At 15.5°C medium (50-55 mm CW) and large (65–70 mm CW) *Carcinus maenas* consumed 37 and 29 cockles, *Cerastoderma edule*, respectively, whilst at 6°C predation rates were low and some crabs even stopped feeding for prolonged periods (Sanchez-Salazar *et al.* 1987a). Feeding in portunids is also affected by light regime (Hill 1976), moulting and reproductive cycles (Dare *et al.* 1983) and stress induced by capture and environmental conditions (Haddon and Wear 1987).

PREY REFUGES AND POPULATION STRUCTURE

Predators such as crabs can influence both the spatial distribution and abundance of their prey, especially when they are abundant and/or the prey is an important component of the diet (Paul 1981; Blundon and Kennedy 1982b; Jensen and Jensen 1985; Reise 1985; Sanchez-Salazar *et al.* 1987b). Some can also alter population structure by foraging selectively on particular size classes (Seed and Brown 1975; Seed 1982, 1990; Moller and Rosenberg 1983; du Preez 1984; Dare and Edwards 1981; Sanchez-Salazar *et al.* 1987b). However, several structural and ecological characteristics exhibited by bivalves can effectively reduce the risk of predation (Table 3). These include shell features, e.g., Vermeij 1980; Boulding 1984, temporal (= size) and spatial refuges (Seed 1969; Seed and Brown 1975; Blundon and Kennedy 1982; Revelas 1982), and even life history characteristics (Seed and Brown 1978).

Predation was identified as a key factor in structuring populations of *Cerastoderma edule* in a small bay (about 330 hectares) in the Menai Strait, North Wales (Sanchez-Salazar *et al.* 1987b). Figure 9 shows the marked differences in size frequency

Table 3
Characteristics evolved by bivalve molluscs which minimize the risk of predation.

	Type	Example
1.	Structural features	- thickened shells - change in shape (e.g., increased inflation) - ornamentation (e.g., spines, lamellae) - plicate valve margins — prevents shearing - strong ligaments and adductor muscles - complex hinge dentition - stronger attachment strength (e.g., mussels) - absence of permanent gape
2.	Size refuges	- large body size
3.	Spatial refuges	- high intertidal zone - nestling amongst larger prey - increased burial depth - macrophyte beds
4.	Life history tactics	- continuous/opportunistic recruitment - rapid early growth/delayed onset of reproduction - increased reproductive output - population density (increase or decrease)

distributions that exist within this cockle population relative to tidal level. Most of the population is represented by small (< 10 mm) first year cockles, whilst larger individuals are concentrated in the middle and lower shore. Shore crabs, *Carcinus maenas*, move into the intertidal zone to feed with each flood tide and remove large numbers of small cockles from the lower tidal levels particularly during the warmer months when feeding rates are elevated. The impact of crab predation, however, rapidly declines with tidal elevation. Laboratory experiments show that virtually all (97%) cockles consumed are < 15 mm (86% are < 10 mm) suggesting that the predatory impact of these crabs on natural populations will be restricted to the smaller size classes. Consequently few cockles survive their first summer in the low shore, but many more do so at mid, and particularly upper tidal levels where crab predation is negligible.

Once beyond their first summer cockles attain a size at which they are seldom taken by *Carcinus maenas*, and this occurs more rapidly amongst the faster growing individuals in the low shore which attain a mean length of about 20 mm by their second winter. With increasing size, however, cockles enter a size range where they become progressively attractive to oystercatchers, *Haematopus ostralegus* L. The subsequent intensity of oystercatcher predation is a function of cockle size, density and duration of tidal exposure. Accordingly, mortality is highest amongst upper shore cockles with larger (> 20 mm) individuals being selectively removed. The mortality of larger cockles lower on the shore, conversely, is minimal because they are sparsely distributed as a result of crab predation early in life and they are exposed for only short periods. In the mid shore, oystercatcher predation is high but the probability of individual cockles surviving is good because cockle density at this level is maximal. Nevertheless, as these cockles grow they face an ever increasing risk of predation. Sanchez-Salazar *et al.* (1987b) estimated that *C. maenas* removed the equivalent of about 950×10^6 cockles from this small bay

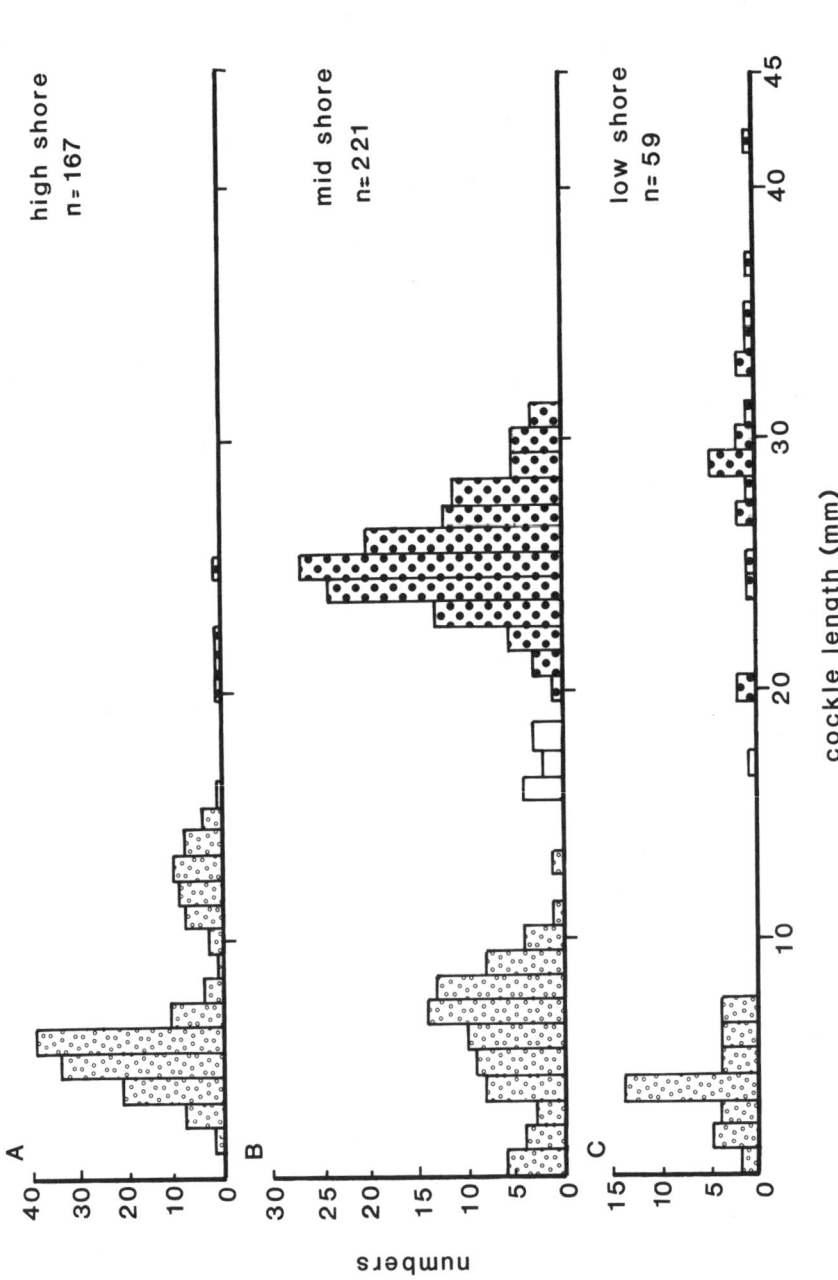

Fig. 9. Size–frequency distributions of *Cerastoderma edule* at three tidal levels in the Menai Strait, N.Wales (April 1987) before the late summer settlement. Size ranges most vulnerable to crab and oystercatcher predation shown by light and heavy stippling respectively; numbers denote actual cockle densities· m^{-2}.

each year, or 472 x 10^3·linear m^{-1}, i.e., a 1–m wide strip from HWST-LWST. In the Danish Wadden Sea juvenile shore crabs and cockle spat arrive on the tidal flats simultaneously, and in July-August consumption by these small crabs (< 9 mm CW) accounted for 26% of the elimination of cockles (Jensen and Jensen 1985). Such observations emphasise still further the importance of crabs in controlling the abundance and population structure of cockles.

Tidally migrating *Thalamita danae* feed rapaciously on small mussels (< 15 mm) and appear to be largely responsible for the scarcity of small *Perna viridis* in the low intertidal zone and subtidal waters of Hong Kong (Seed 1990a). Growth in *P. viridis* at these tidal levels, however, is extremely rapid (Lee 1985; Cheung 1990) and those mussels which do escape predation quickly enter a size refuge where they become increasingly less vulnerable to crab predation. Such size-limited predation is probably a key factor permitting *P. viridis* to become successfully established throughout much of southern and eastern Asia. At higher tidal levels both mussel growth rate and crab foraging time are substantially reduced and the *Perna* population consequently contains proportionally more small size classes (Seed 1990a). Virtually all size ranges of *Brachidontes variabilis* are vulnerable to *T. danae* but this small mytilid, like *Xenostrobus atrata* Lischke, effectively reduces the impact of crab predation by densely occupying higher tidal levels. Such spatial and temporal refuges are probably important in permitting the close coexistence of predator and prey.

Prey species may have an effective refuge in size well below the critical (maximum) size that a predator can open given sufficient time if alternative, more vulnerable prey is available at the same time. Figure 10 shows the interactive roles of wave exposure, mussel growth and crab predation in determining the distribution of *Mytilus edulis* in south-west Ireland. The absence of mussels from areas of moderate exposure is due largely to intense crab predation (Ebling et al. 1964). In more protected locations mussels grow rapidly into a size refuge whilst more wave swept shores provide a spatial refuge where crabs are largely absent.

The vulnerability of burrowing bivalves to predatory crabs is influenced strongly by shell characteristics, other than size. These include shell thickness, the degree of inflation and the presence or absence of a permanent gape (Blundon and Kennedy 1982a; Boulding 1984). Shell ornamentation such as spines and lamellae may also represent anti-predator adaptations. Indeed, any feature that increases handling time must substantially reduce the probability of a predator persisting long enough to open the prey. Shallow burrowing bivalves, which are more vulnerable to predators, typically have thicker shells and are less likely to have a permanent gape than deeper burrowers; tropical species exhibit similar trends which presumably reflect a global pattern in the intensity of predation (Vermeij and Veil 1978). Thick shells, however, have an energetic cost and some species appear to trade off increased vulnerability against the ability to grow at a faster rate. This life history tactic enables such species to persist despite high mortality to predators, because their faster growth and rapid attainment of adult size result in a higher reproductive effort (Seed and Brown 1975, 1978). Some bivalves escape predation by outdispersing their enemies; continuous recruitment can therefore result in the opportunistic invasion of predator-free habitats or persistence in the face of predation (Blundon and Kennedy 1982b). Inflated shells seem to be less easily opened by crabs. Whilst inflation may therefore provide some protection from predation, it may also lead to reduced burrowing efficiency, thus indicating how the bivalve shell probably represents an evolutionary compromise between conflicting ecological needs.

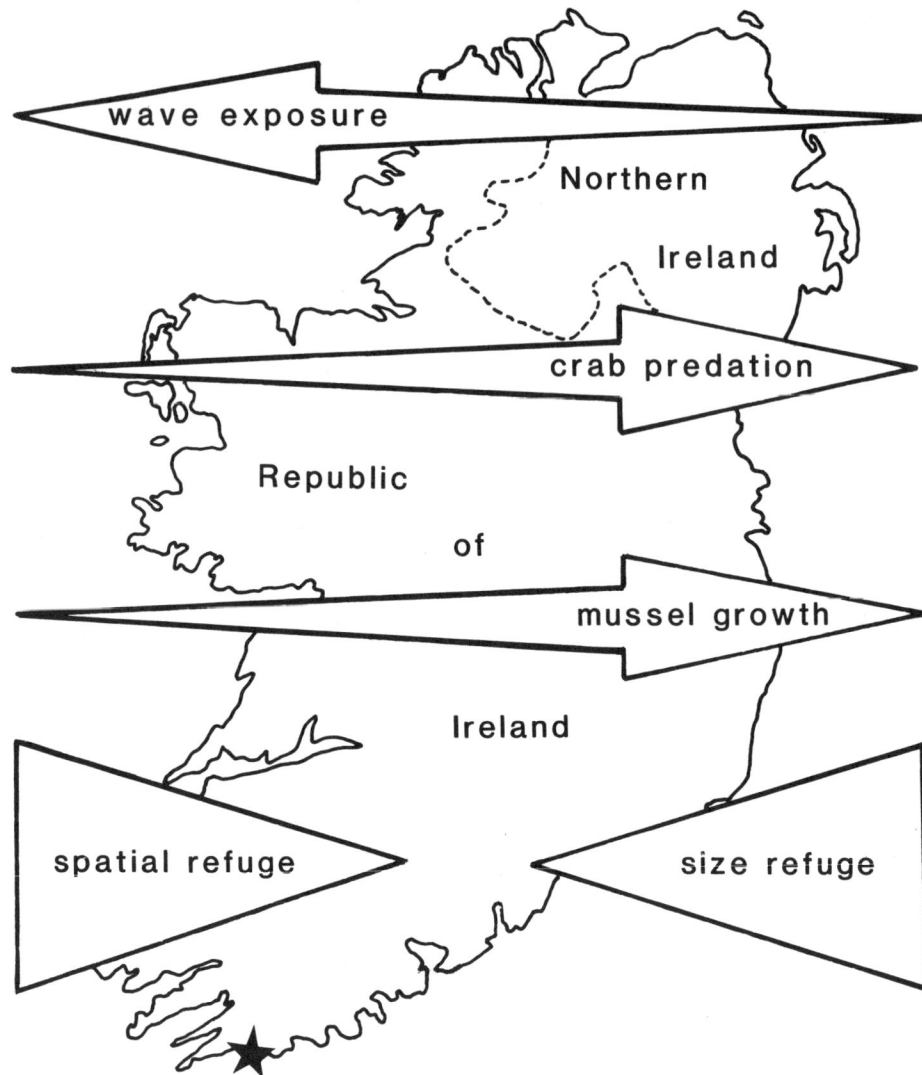

Fig. 10. Spatial and temporal (=size) refuges in *Mytilus edulis* in relation to mussel growth, crab predation and wave exposure. Star denotes study site in S.W.Ireland.

In *Protothaca staminea*, Boulding and Hay (1984) showed that predation by *Cancer productus* increased with clam density (max. 280·m^{-2}) suggesting that foraging occurs selectively in areas of high prey density. *C. productus*, like *Scylla serrata* (Hill 1979), searches large areas when foraging, returning to, or remaining longer within, patches of high prey density. Mortality of *Paphies ventricosa* (Gray) from *Ovalipes catharus* predation, by contrast, was negatively density dependent (Haddon *et al.* 1987). Here, however, clams were so closely packed (> 2000·m^{-2}), often in multilayers, that the digging ability of crabs was greatly impaired. Increased burial depth greatly reduces the risk of crab predation (Blundon and Kennedy 1982b; Boulding 1984; Haddon et al. 1987; Lin 1991), although this can also restrict feeding ability.

The erect stems of macrophytes such as *Spartina* can provide an effective barrier to foraging crabs (Blundon and Kennedy 1982b; West and Williams 1986). Consequently blue crabs from seagrass meadows had much fuller stomachs than those collected from adjacent saltmarsh (*Spartina*) creeks (Ryer 1987). In simulated 'saltmarshes' Revelas (1982) found that predation of *Mytilus edulis* by *Carcinus maenas* was 70% lower than in simulated mudflats with no vegetation, as a result of reduced predator-prey encounters. The size frequency structure of natural mussel populations could also be explained on the basis of these laboratory experiments. Mussels within the size range (< 3 cm) most frequently consumed by *C. maenas* were significantly more abundant in the saltmarsh than in the mudflat population. This broad agreement between laboratory and field observations suggest that these experimental manipulations reflect natural interactions and that habitat heterogeneity can drastically reduce the predator-prey interactions between crabs and their prey.

REFERENCES

Akumfi, C.A. and Hughes, R.N. 1987. Behaviour of *Carcinus maenas* (L.) feeding on large *Mytilus edulis* L. How do they assess the optimal diet? *Marine Ecology Progress Series* 38:213–6.

ap Rheinallt, T. 1986. Size selection by the crab *Liocarcinus puber* feeding on mussels *Mytilus edulis* and on shore crabs *Carcinus maenas*: the importance of mechanical factors. *Marine Ecology Progress Series* 29:45–53.

ap Rheinallt, T. and Hughes, R.N. 1985. Handling methods used by the velvet swimming crab *Liocarcinus puber* when feeding on molluscs and shore crabs. *Marine Ecology Progress Series* 25:63–70.

Arnold, W.S. 1984. The effects of prey size, predator size, and sediment composition on the rate of predation of the blue crab, *Callinectes sapidus* Rathbun on the hard clam *Mercenaria mercenaria* (Linne). *Journal of Experimental Marine Biology and Ecology* 80:207–19.

Bertness, M.D. and Grosholz, E. 1985. Population dynamics of the ribbed mussel, *Geukensia demissa*: the costs and benefits of an aggregated distribution. *Oecologia* 67:192–204.

Blundon, J.A. and Kennedy, V.S. 1982a. Mechanical and behavioural aspects of blue crab, *Callinectes sapidus* (Rathbun) predation on Chesapeake bivalves. *Journal of Experimental Marine Biology and Ecology* 65:47–65.

Blundon, J.A. and Kennedy, V.S. 1982b. Refuges for infaunal bivalves from blue crab, *Callinectes sapidus* (Rathbun) predation in Chesapeake Bay. *Journal of Experimental Marine Biology and Ecology* 65:67–81.

Boulding, E.G. 1984. Crab-resistant features of shells of burrowing bivalves: decreasing vulnerability by increasing handling time. *Journal of Experimental Marine Biology and Ecology* 76:201–23.

Boulding, E.G. and Hay, T.K. 1984. Crab response to prey density can result in density-dependent mortality of clams. *Canadian Journal of Fisheries and Aquatic Science* 41:521–3.

Boulding, E.G. and Labarbera, M. 1986. Fatigue damage: repeated loading enables crabs to open larger bivalves. *Biological Bulletin* 171:538–47.

Brown, S.C., Cassuto, S.R. and Loos, R.W. 1979. Biomechanics of chelipeds in some decapod crustaceans. *Journal of Zoology, London* 188:143–59.

Cheung, S.G. 1990. An energy budget for *Perna viridis* (Linnaeus) (Bivalvia: Mytilidae) in Hong Kong. Unpublished Ph.D. thesis, University of Hong Kong, 236pp.

Choy, S.C. 1986. Natural diet and feeding habits of the crabs *Liocarcinus puber* and *Liocarcinus holsatus*. *Marine Ecology Progress Series* 31:87–99.

Cresswell, P.D. and McClay, C.L. 1990. Handling times, prey size and species selection by *Can-*

cer novaezelandiae (Jacquinot, 1853) feeding on molluscan prey. *Journal of Experimental Marine Biology and Ecology* 140:13–29.

Cunningham, P.N. and Hughes, R.N. 1984. Learning of predatory skills by shorecrabs, *Carcinus maenas* feeding on mussels and dogwhelks. *Marine Ecology Progress Series* 16:21–6.

Dare, P.J. and Edwards, D.B. 1981. Underwater television observations on the intertidal movements of shore crabs, *Carcinus maenas* across a mudflat. *Journal of the Marine Biological Association of the United Kingdom* 61:107–16.

Dare, P.J., Davies, G, and Edwards, D.B. 1983. Predation on juvenile Pacific oysters (*Crassostrea gigas* Thunberg) and mussels (*Mytilus edulis* L.) by shore crabs *Carcinus maenas* (L.). *Ministry of Agriculture Fisheries and Food, Fisheries Research Technical Report* 73:15pp.

Davidson, R.J. 1986. Mussel selection by the paddle crab, *Ovalipes catharus* (White): evidence of flexible foraging behaviour. *Journal of Experimental Marine Biology and Ecology* 102:281–99.

du Preez, H.H. 1984. Molluscan predation by *Ovalipes punctatus* (de Haan) (Crustacea:Brachyura:Portunidae). *Journal of Experimental Marine Biology and Ecology* 84:55–71.

Ebling, F.J., Kitching, J.A., Muntz, L. and Taylor, C.M. 1964. Experimental observations of the destruction of *Mytilus edulis* and *Nucella lapilus* by crabs. *Journal of Animal Ecology* 33:73–82.

Elner, R.W. 1978. The mechanics of predation by the shore crab *Carcinus maenas* (L.) on the edible mussel, *Mytilus edulis* L. *Oecologia* 36:333–44.

Elner, R.W. 1981. Diet of green crab *Carcinus maenas* (L.) from Port Herbert, Southwestern Nova Scotia. *Journal of Shellfish Research* 1:89–94.

Elner, R.W. and Hughes, R.N. 1978. Energy maximisation in the diet of the shore crab, *Carcinus maenas*. *Journal of Animal Ecology* 47:103–16.

Haddon, M., and Wear, R.G. 1987. Biology of feeding in the New Zealand paddle crab *Ovalipes catharus* (Crustacea, Portunidae). *New Zealand Journal of Marine and Freshwater Research* 21:55–64.

Haddon, M., Wear, R.G. and Packer, H.A. 1987. Depth and density of burial by the bivalve *Paphies ventricosa* as refuges from predation by the crab *Ovalipes catharus*. *Marine Biology*. 94, 25–30.

Haefner, P.A. 1985. Morphometry, reproduction, diet and epizoites of *Ovalipes stephensoni* Williams, 1976 (Decapoda, Brachyura). *Journal of Crustacean Biology* 5:658–72.

Hill, B.J. 1976. Natural food, foregut clearance rate and activity of the crab *Scylla serrata*. *Marine Biology* 34:109–16.

Hill, B.J. 1979. Aspects of the feeding strategy of the predatory crab *Scylla serrata*. *Marine Biology* 55:209–14.

Hughes, R.N. 1980. Optimal foraging theory in the marine context. *Oceanography and Marine Biology Annual Review* 18:423–81.

Hughes, R.N. 1989. Foraging behaviour of a tropical crab, *Ozius verreauxii*. *Proceedings of the Royal Society of London* 237B:201–12.

Hughes, R.N. and Elner, R.W. 1989. Foraging behaviour of a tropical crab: *Calappa ocellata* Holthuis feeding upon the mussel *Brachidontes domingensis* (Lamarck). *Journal of Experimental Marine Biology and Ecology* 133:93–101.

Hughes, R.N. and Seed, R. 1981. Size selection of mussels by the blue crab *Callinectes sapidus*: energy maximizer or time minimizer? *Marine Ecology Progress Series* 6:83–9.

Jensen, K.T. and Jensen, J.N. 1985. The importance of some epibenthic predators on the density of juvenile benthic macrofauna in the Danish Wadden Sea. *Journal of Experimental Marine Biology and Ecology* 89:157–74.

Jubb, C.A., Hughes, R.N. and ap Rheinallt, T. 1983. Behavioural mechanisms of size selection by crabs, *Carcinus maenas* (L.) feeding on mussels, *Mytilus edulis* L. *Journal of Experimental Marine Biology and Ecology* 66:81–7.

Kaiser, M.J., Hughes, R.N. and Reid, D.G. 1990. Chelal morphometry, prey-size selection and aggressive competition in green and red forms of *Carcinus maenas* (L.). *Journal of Experimental Marine Biology and Ecology* 140:121–34.

Lau, C.J. 1987. Feeding behaviour of the Hawaiian slipper lobster, *Scyllarides squammosus*, with a review of decapod crustacean feeding tactics on molluscan prey. *Bulletin of Marine Science* 41:378–91.

Lawton, P. and Elner, R.W. 1985. Feeding in relation to morphometrics within the genus *Cancer*: Evolutionary and ecological considerations. In *Proceedings of the Symposium on Dungeness Crab Biology and Management. Alaskan Sea Grant Report* 85-3: 357-79.

Lee, S.Y. 1985. The population dynamics of the green mussel, *Perna viridis* (L.) in Victoria Harbour, Hong Kong-dominance in a polluted environment. *Asian Marine Biology* 2:107-18.

Lin, J. 1990. Mudcrab predation on ribbed mussels in salt marshes. *Marine Biology* 107:103-9.

Lin, J. 1991. Predator-prey interactions between blue crabs and ribbed mussels living in clumps. *Estuarine, Coastal and Shelf Science* 32:61-71.

Moller, P. and Rosenberg, R. 1983. Recruitment, abundance and production of *Mya arenaria* and *Cardium edule* in marine shallow waters, western Sweden. *Ophelia* 22:33-55.

Norman, C.P. and Jones, M.B. 1990. Utilisation of brown algae in the diet of the velvet swimming crab *Liocarcinus puber* (Brachyura: Portunidae). In *Trophic Relationships in the Marine Environment* (ed. M. Barnes and R.N. Gibson), 491-502. Aberdeen University Press.

Paul, R.K.G. 1981. Natural diet, feeding and predatory activity of the crab *Callinectes arcuatus* and *C. toxotes* (Decapoda, Brachyura, Portunidae). *Marine Ecology Progress Series* 6:91-9.

Pierce, G.J. and Ollason, J.G. 1987. Eight reasons why optimal foraging theory is a complete waste of time. *Oikos* 49:111-25.

Raffaelli, D., Conacher, A., McLachlan, H. and Emes, C. 1989. The role of epibenthic crustacean predators in an estuarine food web. *Estuarine, Coastal and Shelf Science* 28:149-61.

Reise,K. 1985. *Tidal Flat Ecology: An Experimental Approach to Species Interactions*. Ecological Studies 54. Berlin: Springer Verlag.

Revelas, E.C. 1982. The effect of habitat structure on the predator-prey relationship between the green crab *Carcinus maenas* and the blue mussel *Mytilus edulis*. *Biological Bulletin* 163:367-8.

Ryer, C.H. 1987. Temporal patterns of feeding by blue crabs (*Callinectes sapidus*) in a tidal-marsh creek and adjacent seagrass meadow in the lower Chesapeake Bay. *Estuaries* 10:136-40.

Sanchez-Salazar, M.E., Griffiths, C.L. and Seed, R. 1987a. The effects of size and temperature on the predation of cockles *Cerastoderma edule* (L.) by the shore crab *Carcinus maenas* (L.). *Journal of Experimental Marine Biology and Ecology* 111:181-93.

Sanchez-Salazar, M.E., Griffiths, C.L. and Seed, R. 1987b. The interactive roles of predation and tidal elevation in structuring populations of the edible cockle, *Cerastoderma edule*. *Estuarine, Coastal and Shelf Science* 25:245-60

Seed, R. 1969. The ecology of *Mytilus edulis* L. (Lamellibranchiata) on exposed rocky shores; 2. Growth and mortality. *Oecologia* 3:317-50.

Seed, R. 1980. Predator-prey relationships between the mudcrab, *Panopeus herbstii*, the blue crab, *Callinectes sapidus* and the Atlantic ribbed mussel, *Geukensia* (= *Modiolus*) *demissa*. *Estuarine and Coastal Marine Science* 11:445-58.

Seed, R. 1982. Predation of the ribbed mussel *Geukensia demissa* by the blue crab *Callinectes sapidus*. *Netherlands Journal of Sea Research* 16:163-72

Seed, R. 1990a. Behavioural and mechanical aspects of predation by the swimming crab *Thalamita danae* on the green-lipped mussel *Perna viridis*. In *Trophic Relationships in the Marine Environment* (ed. M. Barnes and R.N. Gibson), 528-40. Aberdeen University Press.

Seed, R. 1990b. Predator-prey relationships between the swimming crab *Thalamita danae* Stimpson (Decapoda: Portunidae) and the mussels *Perna viridis* (L.) and *Brachidontes variabilis* (Krauss). In *Proceedings of the Second International Marine Biology Workshop: The Marine Flora and Fauna of Hong Kong and Southern China, Hong Kong, 1986* (ed. B. Morton), 993-1013. Hong Kong: Hong Kong University Press.

Seed, R. 1990c. Morphology, occlusive geometry and mechanical advantage in the chelae of *Thalamita danae* (Stimpson) and *T. crenata* (Latreille) (Decapoda:Portunidae) from Hong Kong. In *Proceedings of the Second International Marine Biology Workshop: The Marine Flora and Fauna of Hong Kong and Southern China, Hong Kong, 1986* (ed. B. Morton), 1095-1111. Hong Kong: Hong Kong University Press.

Seed, R. and Brown, R.A. 1975. The influence of reproductive cycle, growth and mortality on population structure in *Modiolus modiolus* (L.), *Cerastoderma edule* (L.) and *Mytilus edulis* L. (Mollusca:Bivalvia). In *Proceedings of the Ninth European Marine Biology Symposium* (ed. H. Barnes), 257-74. Aberdeen University Press.

Seed, R. and Brown, R.A. 1978. Growth as a strategy for survival in two marine bivalves, *Cerastoderma edule* and *Modiolus modiolus*. *Journal of Animal Ecology* 47:283–92.

Vermeij, G.J. 1977. Patterns in crab claw size: the geography of crushing. *Systematic Zoology* 26:138–51.

Vermeij, G.J. 1980. *Biogeography and Adaptation: Patterns of Marine Life*. Cambridge: Harvard University Press.

Vermeij, G.J. 1987. *Evolution and Escalation: An Ecological History of Life*. Cambridge: Harvard University Press.

Vermeij, G.J. and Veil, J.A. 1978. A latitudinal pattern in bivalve shell gaping. *Malacologia* 17:57–61.

Warner, G.F. and Jones A.R. 1976. Leverage and muscle type in crab chelae (Crustacea: Brachyura). *Journal of Zoology, London* 180:57–68.

Warner, G.F., Chapman, D., Hawkey, N. and Waring, D.G. 1982. Structure and function of the chelae and chela closer muscle of the shore crab, *Carcinus maenas* (Crustacea: Brachyura). *Journal of Zoology, London* 196:431–8.

Wear, R.G. and Haddon, M. 1987. Natural diet of the crab *Ovalipes catharus* around central and northern New Zealand. *Marine Ecology Progress Series* 35:39–49.

West, D.L. and Williams, A.H. 1986. Predation by *Callinectes sapidus* (Rathbun) within *Spartina alterniflora* (Loisel) marshes. *Journal of Experimental Marine Biology and Ecology* 100:75–95.

Williams, M.J. 1978. Opening of bivalve shells by the mud crab *Scylla serrata* (Förskal). *Australian Journal of Marine and Freshwater Research* 29:699–702.

Williams, M.J. 1981. Methods for analysis of natural diet in portunid crabs (Crustacea: Decapoda: Portunidae) *Journal of Experimental Marine Biology and Ecology* 52:103–13.

Williams, M.J. 1982. Natural food and feeding in the commercial sand crab *Portunus pelagicus* Linnaeus, 1766 (Crustacea: Decapoda: Portunidae) in Moreton Bay, Queensland. *Journal of Experimental Marine Biology and Ecology* 59:165–76.

Wolcott, T.G. 1978. Ecological role of ghost crabs *Ocypode quadrata* (Fabricius) on an ocean beach: scavengers or predators? *Journal of Experimental Marine Biology and Ecology* 31:67–82.

The Marine Biology of the South China Sea
(ed. B. Morton). Proceedings of the First
International Conference on the Marine
Biology of Hong Kong and the South China Sea,
Hong Kong, 28 October – 3 November 1990.
Hong Kong: Hong Kong University Press, 1993.

BIVALVE SHELLS: CHRONOMETERS OF ENVIRONMENTAL CHANGE

C.A. Richardson

School of Ocean Sciences, University of Wales, Bangor, Marine Science Laboratories, Menai Bridge, Gwynedd, LL59 5EY, UK

ABSTRACT

The age and growth rates of several species of bivalves have been studied from the clear annual growth lines present in the outer and inner shell layers in acetate peel replicas of polished and etched shell sections. Detailed examination of the outer shell layers of intertidal bivalves including cockles, clams and mussels reveals a series of alternating light and dark microgrowth bands. The lighter wide bands represent periods of tidal immersion, whilst the dark bands are formed during emersion. The width of the light bands allows a detailed comparison to be made between tidal growth rates and the environmental conditions to which the animals have been exposed.

Sea temperatures, available food and position in the intertidal are the most important environmental factors in controlling shell growth rates. Bivalves from temperate waters show a reduced growth rate in winter. In tropical waters, where seasonal sea temperature variations are less pronounced, monsoon conditions have been shown to influence the microgrowth patterns. At mid and high tide levels cockles and mussels grow faster at spring tides during increased water flow and slower during neap tides. However, at low water the pattern of growth is reversed with the faster growth rate being achieved during neap tides when the animals are continuously immersed and slower growth at spring tides during reduced periods of immersion.

Other factors such as sudden changes in temperature, disturbance, predator attacks and detrimental algal blooms are recorded in the growth patterns in bivalve shells. Microgrowth patterns can therefore be regarded as recorders of environmental conditions.

INTRODUCTION

Records of environmental change contained within the permanent calcareous parts of individual organisms clearly have important potential implications for routine environmental monitoring studies. The discovery more than two decades ago that many widely occurring bivalve molluscs, such as the clam, *Mercenaria mercenaria* Linnaeus and the cockle, *Cerastoderma* (= *Cardium*) *edule* Linnaeus, have within their shells a complete record of their growth history from the first day of settlement to their death allows the potential for gauging the effect of environmental change on growth rate. Barker (1964) was the first to describe a hierarchy of five cyclic groupings of growth layers in the shells of several marine bivalves. He assumed these layers reflected the annual changes of temperature and salinity (first order), equinoctial storms and tides (second order), the fortnightly lunar cycle (third order), diurnal cycles (fourth order) and daily tidal rhythms (fifth order). This work was followed by studies which surveyed the range of patterns found in molluscan shells and identified the possible environmental factors involved in their formation, e.g., House and Farrow (1968), Pannella and MacClintock (1968), Rhoads and Pannella (1970), Farrow (1971, 1972) Pannella (1975), Kennish and Olsson (1975), Lutz and Rhoads (1980). However, much of the work was speculative rather than based on direct experimental evidence. In the last decade the periodicity of growth patterns in bivalve shells and the factors involved in their formation have been investigated experimentally (see Richardson 1990).

This paper discusses the relationship between environmental factors and the formation of growth patterns in bivalve shells and critically examines whether these patterns can be used as chronometers, or data loggers, of environmental change.

MATERIALS AND METHODS

A selection of bivalves (cockles, *Cerastoderma edule*), mussels, *Mytilus edulis* Linnaeus, razor clams, *Ensis siliqua* Linnaeus, oysters, *Ostrea edulis* Linnaeus, and clams *Mya truncata* Linnaeus), were collected intertidally from the shore of the Menai Strait, North Wales whilst the horse mussel, *Modiolus modiolus* Linnaeus, the clams, *Artica islandica* Linnaeus and *Mercenaria mercenaria* were dredged at various subtidal locations around the coast of the United Kingdom. Clams, *Tapes philippinarum* Adams & Reeve were obtained from stocks held at the Ministry of Agriculture, Fisheries and Food (MAFF), Conwy Laboratories.

Molluscan microgrowth patterns can be observed in acetate peel replicas of cut, polished and etched radial shell sections. Single, small shell valves (< 40 mm) are embedded in resin, e.g., Metaset, type SW, Buehler Ltd. UK, before sectioning along the umbo-rim axis using a hand-held saw (Richardson *et al.* 1979). Larger shells (> 40 mm) can be sectioned along the umbo-rim axis using a mechanical saw, e.g., a diamond circular saw or band saw prior to being embedded (Richardson and Walker 1990). Cut shell surfaces are then ground on fine grades of carborundum powder (grit size 50) or wet and dry paper (grit size 200–400), polished on a cloth soaked in Brasso (household metallic polish) and etched in a suitable dilute acid, e.g., 0.01M HCl, for between 20 and 30 minutes. The strength of the etching reagent and the duration of exposure are critical since differential etching of the crystals and organic matrix, which together make up the shell structure, result in differences in surface relief. Therefore initial trials were undertaken to ascertain the required acid strength and etching period. Acetate peel replicas of the polished and etched shell surfaces are produced by allowing a small piece of replication material (Agar Scientific Ltd.) to become almost molten in ethyl acetate (ca. 15–30 secs.) and applying the sheet to the shell surface. The 'peel' is removed when dry (10–15 mins.) mounted between a glass slide and coverslip and viewed in the light microscope. Details of a range of methods available are included in an appendix in Rhoads and Lutz (1980).

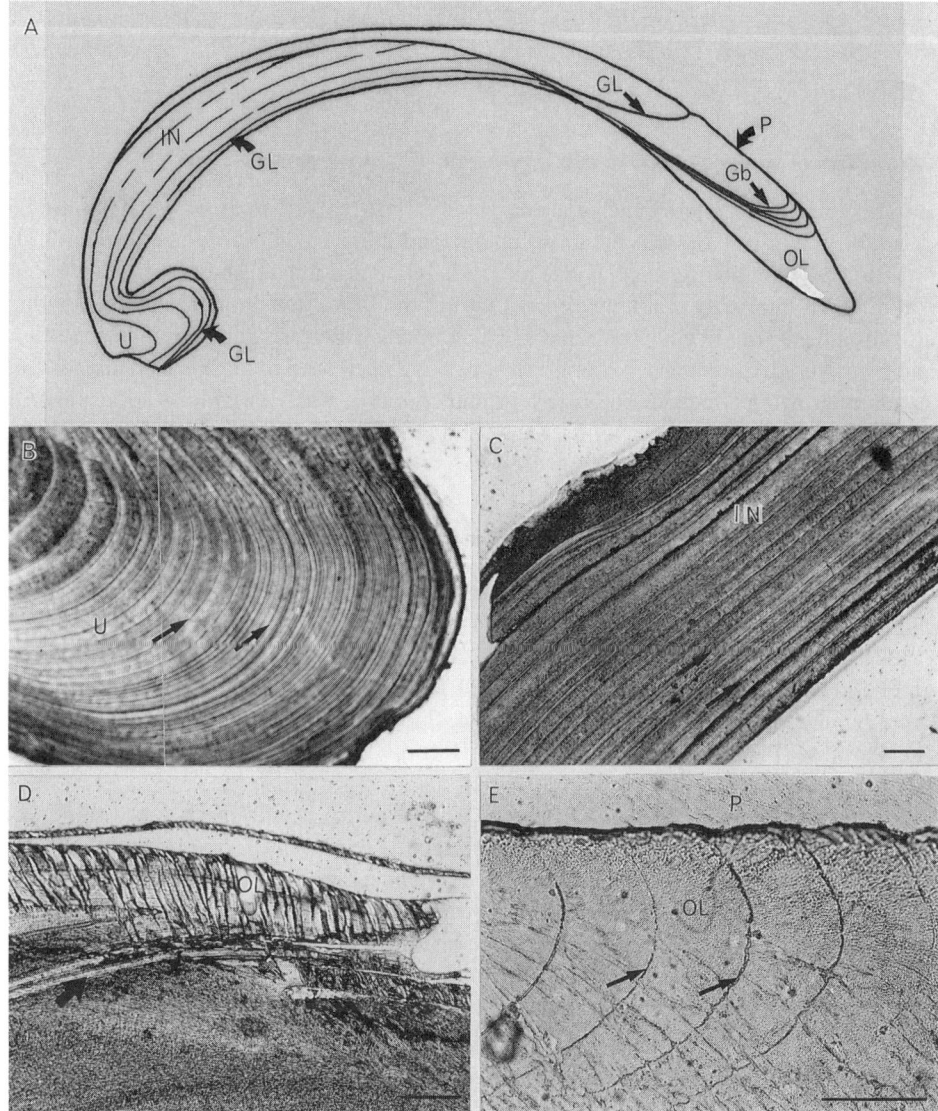

Plate 1. A, Diagrammatic section through the shell valve of a typical bivalve shell. IN, inner nacreous layer; Gb, growth band; GL, growth lines; OL, outer shell layer; P, periostracum; U, umbo. B-E, photomicrographs of acetate peels of bivalve shells. B, Growth lines (arrows) in the umbo region of *Arctica islandica*. C, Growth lines in the inner nacreous layer of *Mya truncata*. D, An annual growth line in the outer shell layer of *Ostrea edulis*. E, Growth bands (Gb) in the outer crossed lamellar layer of *Cerastoderma edule*. Scale bar on B = 500 μm, C & D= 200 μm and E = 50 μm.

When acetate peels are viewed under the microscope clearly defined patterns of growth lines are observed in various regions of the shell. Plate 1A shows a diagrammatic section through a generalised bivalve shell valve. The shell is composed of a horny periostracum (P), an outer prismatic or crossed lamellar shell layer of aragonite or calcite (OL), an inner nacreous layer (IN) and an umbo (U). Prominent growth lines appear as an alternating pattern of light and dark lines (GL) in the umbo, nacreous and outer shell layers (Plate1B–D). The lighter regions in the outer layer are in turn composed of a series of fine microgrowth bands (Gb) (Plate 1E).

Periodicity of the growth patterns

Before the growth patterns can be used to study the effects of environmental conditions on shell growth it is first necessary to understand the periodicity of their formation. In order to study the microgrowth bands in cockle, clam and mussel shells individuals were date-marked internally at a known point during the life of the animal, a point to which all subsequent growth could be related. The animals were then allowed to grow in field and laboratory experiments. Several methods have been used to mark the shells: (l) cold shock marking in which animals are maintained out of water in a moist atmosphere in a refrigerator at 4°C for periods from 24–72 hours (Richardson et al. 1979; Richardson 1987a, b, 1988b); (2) emersion for 24 hours at ambient air temperatures (Richardson 1989) and (3) file marking, in which the growing margin of the shell is gently abraded with a file (Pannella and MacClintock 1968; Richardson 1987b, 1989) or notched with a small drill (Fritz and Lutz 1986). Each of the methods has its advantages and disadvantages. Notching of the shell and cold shock marking result in the disturbance of the microgrowth bands for 2–3 days in the immediate post-shock period of growth (Richardson 1990), so that both produce a clear mark in the form of a distinct internal band and a cleft or notch in the outer shell layer. Twenty-four hour emersion on the other hand consistently produces a clearly defined band in the shell which can be easily identified (Plate IIB) with no observed effect on deposition of the growth increments in the post-shock period.

After marking, infaunal species were transferred to plastic mesh cages buried on the shore or to boxes containing sediment attached to vertical supports at the end of a small jetty on the island Ynys Faelog, in the Menai Strait. Epifaunal species such as mussels were held in plastic mesh cages. After various time intervals animals were recovered and peels of the sectioned shells prepared for examination under the microscope.

Earlier research had suggested that the microgrowth patterns have a daily periodicity of deposition, e.g., Pannella and MacClintock (1968), House and Farrow (1968), Kennish (1980), Lutz and Rhoads (1980). However, in recent years, it has been shown experimentally that the formation of microgrowth bands in the shells of intertidal bivalves are the result of periodic tidal emersion and immersion, e.g., Richardson et al. (1979), Richardson (1987). The dark narrow growth bands (Plate 2A & B) are deposited during emersion, whilst the wider light bands are formed during immersion when the bivalves are actively feeding (Richardson et al. 1981). The pattern of bands so readily observed in many species of bivalves contain a record of the tidal growth of the shells.

The annual periodicity of the prominent growth lines in the outer shell layer and umbo has been established from an analysis of the shells of marked bivalves which have been set out and then recovered after several years in the natural environment, e.g., A.

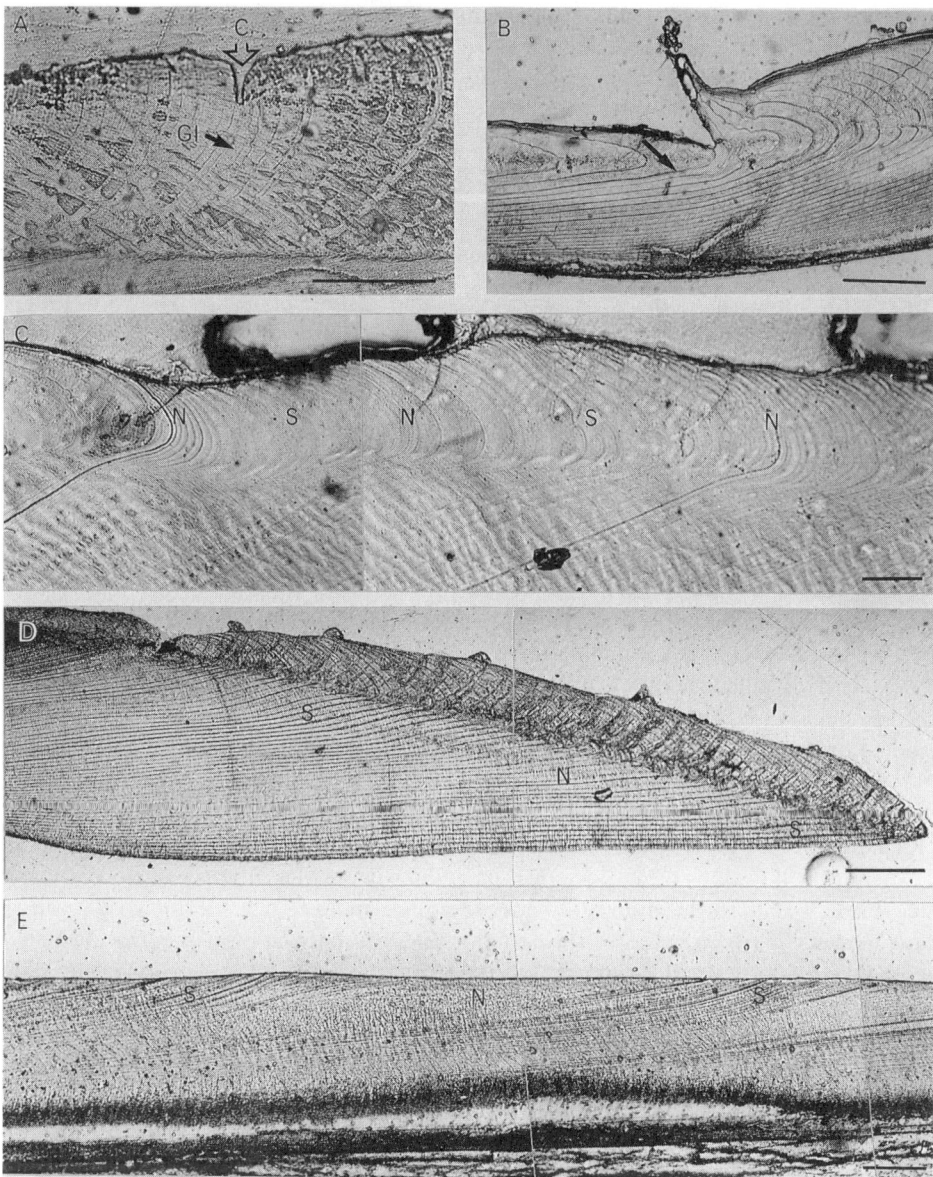

Plate 2 Photomicrographs of acetate peels of bivalve shells. A, cold shock mark (12 hours at 5°C) in the shell of *Tapes philippinarum* showing cleft (C) and narrow growth increments (GI) in the immediate post-shock period. B, 24 hour emersion mark (arrow) in the shell of *Cerastoderma edule*. C, Growth bands in the shell of *C. edule* grown at high water of neap tides (HWN) showing clustering of growth bands during neap tides (N) and wide growth increments during spring tides (S). D, Growth bands in the shell of a cockle grown at low water of neap tides (LWNT) to show wider growth increments during neap tides. E, Neap (N) - spring (S) lunar cycle in the shell of *Ensis siliqua*. All scale bars = 100 μm except D where scale bar 500 = μm.

islandica (Murawski *et al.* 1983), *Mytilus edulis* (Lutz 1976) and *Modiolus demissa* (Lutz and Castagna 1980), and from an analysis of the shells of animals whose life histories have been clearly documented e.g. *M. modiolus* (Anwar *et al.* 1990) and *M. mercenaria* (Richardson and Walker 1990).

This capacity of the bivalve shell to record environmental conditions is now discussed.

Tidal level and the influence of the neap-spring lunar cycle

Microgrowth patterns in the shells of cockles, mussels and clams are known to reflect the conditions of growth experienced by the animal at a particular tidal level. Richardson *et al.* (1980c) studied the effect of tidal level on marked cockles. Animals grown for several months at mean high water of neap tides (HWN) grew significantly more during spring tides when they were immersed for longer periods for feeding than during neap tides when they were emersed for all but a few minutes of each tidal cycle. The observed pattern of increments reflects the lunar cycle of emersion and immersion (Plate 2C). The reverse was found to hold for cockles living near low water where they grew faster during the neap periods when the shells were continuously immersed. During spring tide immersion cockles have a shorter period of time for feeding than during neap tides because of interruptions caused by periodic emersion and this results in a pattern of wide increments at neaps and narrower ones at spring tides (Plate 2D). Ohno (1983, 1985) similarly noted the importance of tidal level in determining the width of the growth increments in *C. edule* and Lønne and Gray (1988) confirmed these findings when they studied the banding patterns in cockles collected from two tidal levels on the shore in Norway. This pattern of increased growth at neap tides has also been observed in other species such as clams *T. philippinarum* (Richardson 1987b) and mussels, *M. edulis* (Richardson *et al.* 1990). Richardson *et al.* (1980c) showed that there was a 5% increase in shell growth during spring tides over neap tides in cockles growing at or near mean tide level (MTL). These animals did not experience any difference in the proportion of time emersed between neaps or spring tides, the difference in growth being attributed to an increase in water flow across the cockle beds and resuspension of particles during spring tides.

In bivalves growing at low water of neap tides the growth of the shell significantly increases at neap tides relative to spring tides but in addition the pattern of bands laid down in the shell reflects the fortnightly lunar cycle. During spring tides the animals are emersed at each low water giving rise to a clear pattern of tidal bands alternating with groups of weak bands laid down during neap tides. This pattern of bands has been observed in a range of species including cockles, *C. edule* (Richardson *et al.* 1979; Ohno 1983), *Anadara granosa* (Richardson 1987a), clams *T. philippinarum* (Richardson 1987b), mussels *M. edulis* (Richardson *et al.* 1990) and razor clams *E. siliqua* (Plate IIE; Richardson and Brown, unpublished).

The form of the neap-spring lunar cycle has been shown to influence the appearance of the microgrowth patterns. Evans (1972, 1975) for example, demonstrated that *Clinocardium nuttalli* growing in a mixed diurnal — semidiurnal tidal regime on the coast of Oregon, USA experienced bidaily emersion at neap tides resulting in a pattern of semidiurnal bands, but that during spring tides when the animals were emersed only once a day a diurnal pattern of bands was produced. Nevertheless, weaker bands were laid down between the emersion bands even though the animals remained immersed. Ohno (1985) similarly demonstrated the importance of the form of the lunar cycle in his study of the microgrowth patterns in *Fragum unedo* growing along the coast of Ishigaki Island, Japan. Animals growing on the lower part of the shore were emersed only once during spring tides but remained immersed during neap tides. The pattern of bands observed in these shells reflected the cycle of emersion and immersion. Clear diurnal emersion bands were laid down during spring tides whilst at neaps when the animals remained immersed a pattern of weaker daily bands continued to be produced. By contrast, Richardson (1987b) could find no influence of the mixed semidiurnal tidal regime at Penang, Malaysia on the appearance of the banding patterns in the Malaysian cockle *A. granosa*. Like Ishigaki Island the tidal pattern in Penang has two high and two low tides of unequal amplitude each day with the greatest difference at spring tides. Cockles from the lower part of the shore would be emersed only once a day during spring tides and remain emersed at neap tides. The banding patterns in marked cockles showed a pattern of clear bands separated by narrow increments during spring tides alternating with a few wider increments during neap tides. The wider increments were only produced for 1-3 days and occasionally had weaker bands between (Richardson 1987b, fig. 8).

It is clear from these studies that tidal level and the neap-spring lunar cycle influence the pattern of bands laid down in the shells. An understanding of the possible variations in the patterns is necessary before they can be used to study the effects of environmental change on shell growth rates.

The shallow subtidal

Microgrowth patterns in the shells of subtidal bivalves are weaker in definition than those growing in the intertidal (Richardson 1990). Rhoads and Pannella (1970) explained the presence of bands in the shells of subtidal *M. mercenaria* as the result of changes in shell deposition between the day and night, a view shared by Thompson (1975) and Kennish (1978, 1980). Apparently most shell growth was believed to occur during the night when the animals were actively feeding. However in a study of the effects of continuous immersion on marked cockles *C. edule* transplanted into the shallow subtidal, (Richardson *et al.* 1979, 1980b) demonstrated that an innate circatidal rhythm of deposition which could be entrained by periods of tidal emersion was involved in growth band formation. Richardson later showed that the pattern of endogenous bands observed in clams *T. philippinarum* (Richardson 1988a) and mussels *M. edulis* (Richardson 1989) growing continuously immersed in the laboratory and natural environment had no apparent environmental periodicity, the formation of the bands being related to shell growth. These weak growth bands observed in many species of subtidal bivalves would be of little value in measuring short term variations in shell growth.

Temperature

Of the environmental factors studied seasonal fluctuations in seawater temperatures have the most important influence on the formation of growth patterns in bivalve shells. The correlation between water temperature and growth rate, however, although obvious, may not be causal. Water temperature, for instance, may vary directly with seasonal phytoplankton abundance, thus making it difficult to generalise about the importance of temperature in regulating growth rate without the appropriate measurements of food availability (Seed and Richardson 1990). The examination of the patterns in temperate water bivalve shells reveals a characteristic narrowing of the growth increments during the autumn and winter and an increase in width the following spring and summer, e.g., *C. edule* (Plate 3A). Similar patterns have been described for *M. mercenaria*, e.g., Pannella and MacClintock (1968), Kennish (1980) and *Phacosoma japonicum* (Tanabe and Oba 1988). Richardson *et al.* (1980a) were the first to quantify changes in the width of the growth increments from monthly samples of *C. edule* collected from North Wales. They measured the width of groups of the most recently deposited twenty eight increments, equivalent to the neap-spring lunar cycle and compared them with the water temperature during shell deposition. Shell growth increased rapidly during the spring (April to June) and slowed during the autumn and winter (October to March) (Richardson *et al.* 1980a, fig. 7). Similar patterns have been observed in other species although the effect of winter temperatures on growth can be highly variable. Mussels, for example, show a narrowing of growth increments during the winter (Richardson *et al.* 1990) but shell growth does not slow down to the same extent as in cockles of similar age. Similarly razor clams, *E. siliqua* show almost no interruptions to the summer pattern of growth bands making it difficult to determine the position of winter growth (Plate 3B). Conversely other species of similar age collected from the same localities such as oysters, *O. edulis* (Plate 1D), clams, *M. mercenaria* (Richardson and Walker 1990), horse mussels, *M. modiolus* (Plate 3D), (Anwar *et al.* 1990) and *A. islandica* (Plate 3E) show a clear alternating pattern of light (summer) and dark (winter) growth lines present in the outer shell layers.

The clarity of these lines along the entire length of the shell allowed the annual rate of shell growth to be measured and the age of the shells to be determined, e.g., Tanabe and Oba (1988), Anwar *et al.* (1990), Richardson *et al.* (1990). Anwar *et al.* (1990) found that the oldest specimen of *M. modiolus* collected from the northern North Sea was 48 years old whilst *A. islandica* from North Wales have been estimated to reach more than 130 years old (Richardson and Austin, unpublished). In the USA, *A. islandica* has similarly been recorded to reach a great age living to more than 220 years old (Ropes 1987). Annual lines similar to those observed in the outer shell layer can be seen in the bivalve umbo. These lines can also be used to estimate the age of the bivalves. Plate 1B shows the appearance of the umbo from a specimen of *A. islandica* collected in the English Channel. Measurement of the variations in thickness of the increments would be especially useful for studying long term trends in shell growth rates. Such information could be important in monitoring long term climatic change in the marine environment with records of unusually warm and productive summers or unusually severe cold winter temperatures being identified from the patterns.

The extent of seasonal temperature change can be deduced from the patterns recorded in the shell. For example, Richardson *et al.* (1980a) found in cockles from Norway that shell growth became curtailed during the winter months and resulted in the formation of prominent growth lines within the shell structure (Plate 3F). These cockles were only able to grow for some 5-6 months of the year when temperatures and food supply were favourable for shell deposition. During the remaining months, little or no growth took place at temperatures close to freezing point at a time when food availability was similarly low. By contrast, in tropical waters there may only be

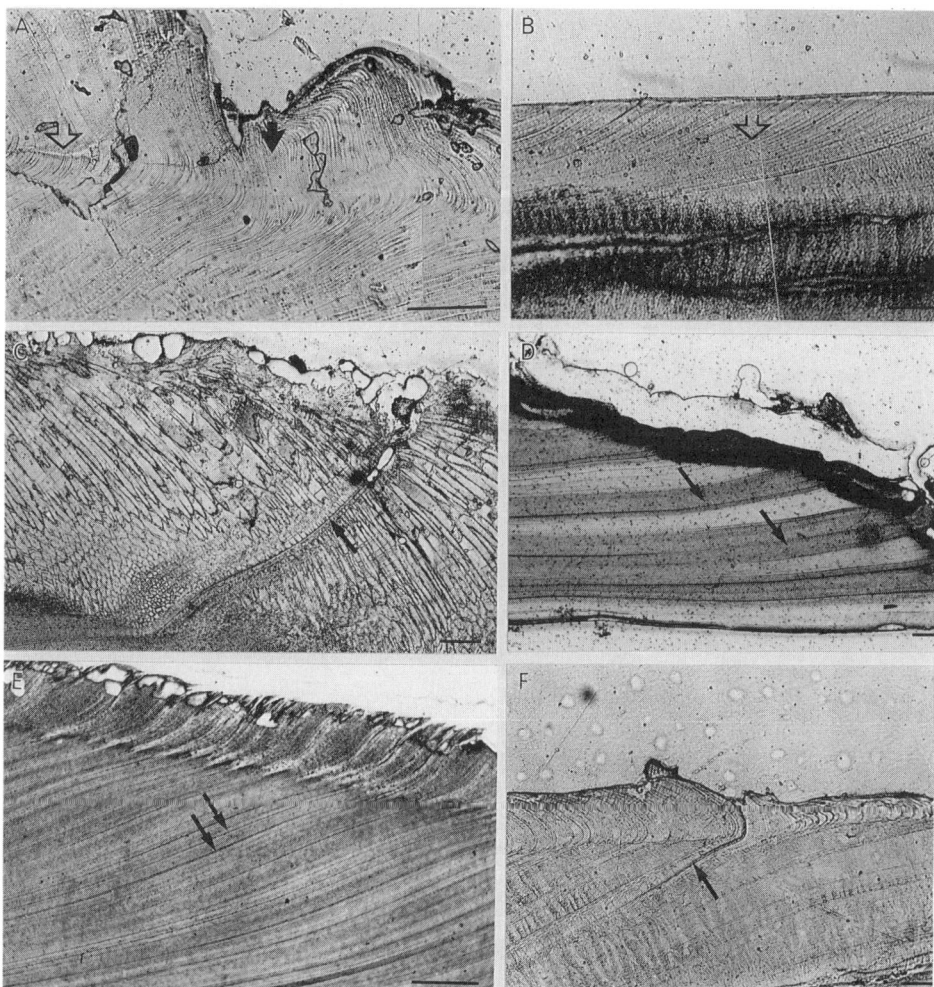

Plate 3. Photomicrographs of acetate peels of bivalve shells. A, Narrowing of growth increments in the crossed lamellar layer during the autumn (open arrow) and narrow increments in the winter (filled arrow) in a shell of *Cerastoderma edule*. B, Narrowing of growth increments in *Ensis siliqua* (open arrow). C, An annual growth line (arrow) in the outer prismatic layer of *Mercenaria mercenaria*. D, Annual growth lines (arrow) in the shell of *Modiolus modiolus*. E, Annual growth lines (arrows) in the shell of *Arctica islandica*. F, A narrow growth line (arrow) deposited during the winter in a cockle from Norway. Scale bars on B = 50 um, A & F= 100 μm, C = 200 μm, D & E = 500 μm.

small seasonal changes in water temperature. Richardson (1987b) reported the absence of a temperature related growth pattern in the shells of the Malaysian cockle *A. granosa* from Penang. However, in shells collected from an estuarine environment where they would have experienced seawater of low salinity during the intermonsoonal rains, the shells exhibited characteristically marked growth lines (Plate 4A). These lines were

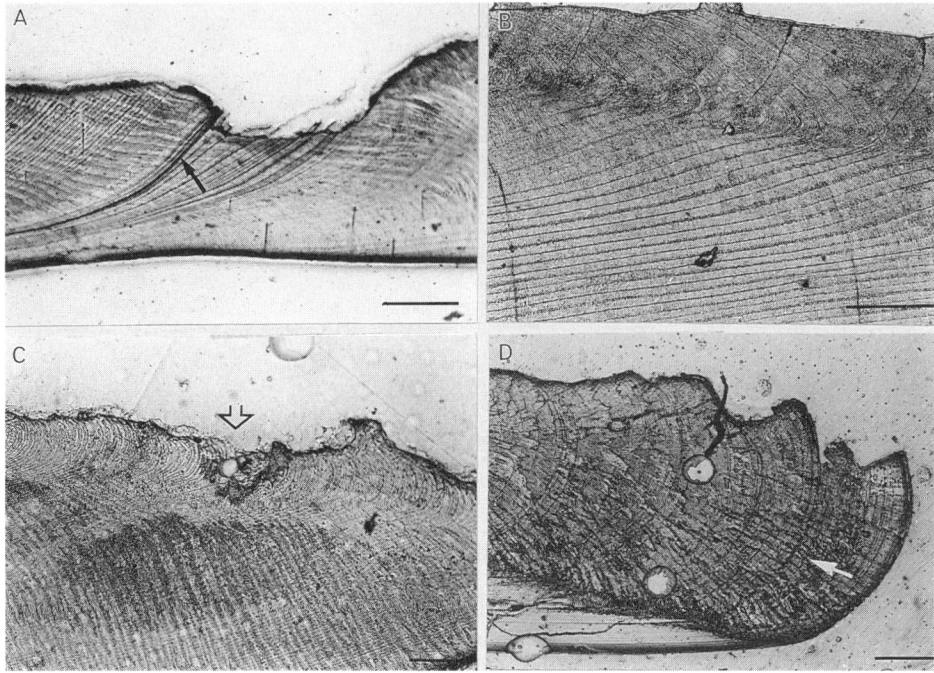

Plate 4. Photomicrographs of acetate peels of bivalve shells. A, Salinity stress lines (arrow) in the outer layer of the shell of *Anadara granosa* from Penang, Malaysia. B, Alternations in the distinctness of the growth bands formed during spring tides in *Cerastoderma edule*. C, Peel of a cockle *C. edule* which survived an attack by the crab *Liocarcinus* (= *Portunus*) *depurator*. The well-marked cleft (arrow) together with the disturbance of the normal pattern of the growth lines is thought to have resulted from an unsuccessful attack by the crab. D, Disturbance to the normal pattern of semi-diurnal bands (arrow) in *Tapes philippinarum* during a bloom of *Phaeocystis pouchetti*. All scale bars = 100 µm, except D = 200 µm.

formed during periods of lowered salinity and were presumably the result of long periods of shell valve closure during these unfavourable conditions (Davenport and Wong 1986).

Not only are seasonal seawater temperature fluctuations recorded in the shells of many bivalves but differences in the daily air temperature have been shown to be recorded in the tidal pattern of growth. Dolman (1975) and Richardson *et al*. (1979,1981) noticed that periodically groups of strong and weak bands separated by regions in which the bands were more or less uniform in definition were deposited in the shell of the cockle, *C. edule* (Plate 4B). Dolman (1975) believed that the alternation in banding could be related to tidal emersion in light and dark conditions. Since the low tide period advances progressively during the lunar cycle, there would be periods when both low tides would be at twilight and others a week later when low water was around midnight and midday, thus producing a lunar periodicity in alternating patterns. Richardson *et al*. (1981) were able to show on the basis of marked shells in which each band could be assigned to a particular low tide that the stronger bands were laid down during the heat of the afternoon low tide while the less distinct bands were formed during the cool of the morning. A similar conclusion was reached by Ohno (1985) working on *C. edule* and *M. mercenaria*. Alternating bands at spring low tides have been observed in the bivalve *Spisula subtruncata* growing at extreme low water of spring tides in the Menai Strait (Richardson 1988b) and in the Chilean mussel *Perumytilus purpuratus* (Richardson and Guinez, unpublished). Microgrowth patterns in these shells faithfully recorded differences in air temperatures during emersion, providing a record of the surrounding environmental conditions during shell formation.

Other factors

The formation of semidiurnal tidal bands in the shells of intertidal bivalves allows the analysis of tidal and daily shell growth rates. Many of the species studied produce disturbance lines caused by an interruption of the normal pattern of microgrowth band deposition in response to environmental disturbance. The clarity of these lines, which are frequently associated with a ring on the outer shell surface, depends largely on the severity and duration of the interruption in growth. Recovery from the disturbance is reflected in an increase in the width of the growth increments in the post-disturbance period. Thus in cold shock marked cockles there may be several days post marking shock trauma before normal shell deposition is resumed (Plate 2A), whilst 24 hour emersion in the laboratory has a negligible effect on growth pattern formation (Plate 2B).

Disturbance patterns have been observed in shells grown both in the laboratory and under natural conditions. For example rope-cultured mussels from Ballochmartin Bay in the Clyde Estuary, Scotland, which had been subjected to periods of disturbance formed a clear disturbance line each time they were emersed (Richardson *et al.* 1990). Similarly cockle, *C. edule* shells that suffered interference from the predatory crab *Liocarcinus* (= *Portunus*) *depurator* have been shown to leave evidence of the attack in the form of surface disturbance checks which show as clefts in peels of shell sections not unlike those produced by cold shock (Plate 4C), (Richardson *et al.* 1980c). A similar feature in both is the interrupted deposition of the outer shell layer which suggests the withdrawal of the mantle edge during the disturbance. Similar changes in the patterns would accompany a disturbance such as unusually low temperatures during the winter. Farrow (1971) reported that cockles from the Thames Estuary, South East England produced checks in growth which coincided with sub-zero air temperatures during the winter of 1964-65. Similarly disturbance patterns (thermal breaks) caused by the discharge of warm water from a nuclear generating station at Barnegat Bay, New Jersey were reported to be formed in the shells of clams, *M. mercenaria* growing in the vicinity of the power plant (Kennish and Olsson 1975). The temporary burial or uncovering of bivalves by storms and the release of gametes during the summer breeding period have both been suggested as possible factors responsible for producing disturbance marks in the shells of cockles, *C. edule* (House and Farrow 1968; Farrow 1971) and clams, *M. mercenaria* (Pannella and MacClintock 1968; Kennish and Olsson 1975). Rhoads and Pannella (1970) have speculated that the patterns they observed in the shells of deep sea bivalves might represent annual spawning events and replace the seasonally induced growth lines of temperate species. However the importance of these factors in affecting the microgrowth patterns still remains to be established experimentally.

These disturbances cause short-term cessations of growth. Prolonged changes in en-

FIGURE 1

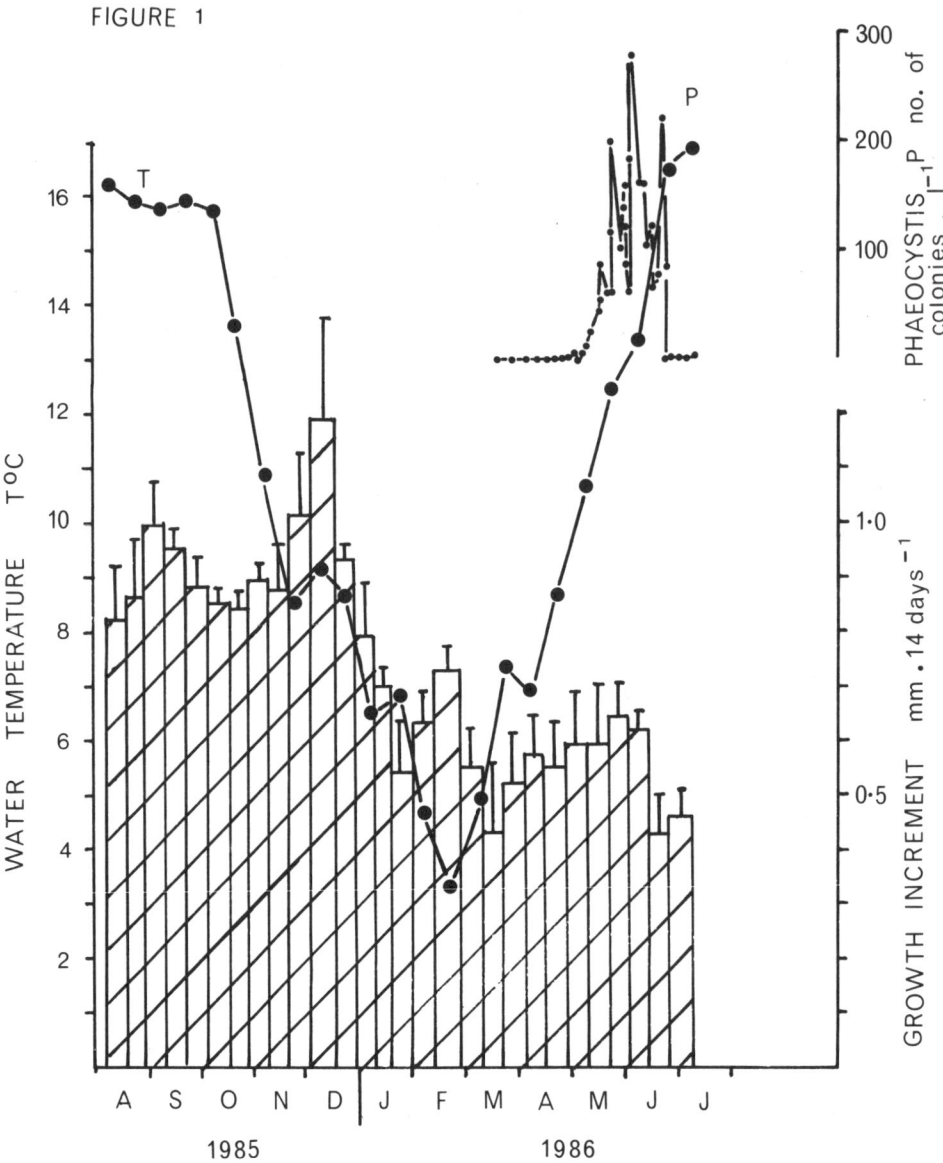

Fig. 1. A comparison of shell growth rates of *Tapes philippinarum* taken from measurements of the fortnightly neap-spring lunar pattern of microgrowth bands with the water temperature and number of *Phaeocystis pouchetti* colonies (L^{-1}) in the Menai Strait.

vironmental conditions other than the longer-term (annual) seasonal effects may also be recorded in the shell. The effect of an algal bloom, *Phaeocystis pouchetti* in the Menai Strait, North Wales has been observed to affect the growth patterns in the shell of the clam, *T. philippinarum*. Each year during May and June a bloom of *P. pouchetti* occurs which is known to cause a deterioration in water quality. The exact timing and severity of the bloom varies from year to year. Richardson (1987a) reported a decrease in growth rate of clams growing in experiments carried out in 1985 in the Menai Strait during the period when the bladders of the algae were present in the water column. Detailed measurement of the pattern of semidiurnal bands in clams grown intertidally the following season, 1985-86 has allowed an analysis of the record of growth to be made prior to and during the bloom conditions.

A comparison of the rates of shell growth, taken from measurements of the distance between the neap-spring lunar pattern of bands in the shells of three animals with the water temperature and the number of *P. pouchetti* colonies present during the spring in the Menai Strait are shown in Figure 1. Shell growth follows the decline in water temperature during October and November to reach a minimum during March. The resumption of growth begins in April, following the earlier increase in water temperature. In 1986 *P. pouchetti* appeared in early May but did not apparently affect shell growth until the middle of June at the time when the bladders were observed to be breaking up and releasing their contents. It is presumably the contents of the bladders which cause the reduction in shell growth and result in a narrowing of the growth increments during June and July (Plate 4D). The only other factor which might affect the growth pattern at this time is reproductive development. Energy normally allocated for shell growth might be required for gonad development. In 1990 the *P. pouchetti* bloom was unusually poor in the Menai Strait. Growth experiments conducted this year between May and July in which the reproductive condition of the clams was assessed (S. Ekaratne, pers. comm.) showed that even though the gonads of the clams were beginning to mature there was no widespread disruption to the growth patterns previously seen with the blooms of 1985 and 1986. Similarly growth of *C. edule* in laboratory experiments conducted during 1990 was not affected by *P. pouchetti*, even though Richardson *et al.* (1980b) had previously reported a decline in growth rate for this species growing in the natural environment during the middle of June 1978.

CONCLUSIONS

This paper has illustrated the potential use of bivalve shells as data loggers of environmental change. The use of seasonal patterns in estimating growth rate and longevity in bivalves is clearly obvious. However, the occurrence of fortnightly lunar (neap-spring) cycles and the identification of semidiurnal bands in bivalve shells has for the first time allowed an analysis of short term variations in shell growth. The accuracy and detail of the patterns in the shells provides a unique daily (tidal) record of the effects of environmental fluctuations and disturbances on shell growth. Essential to the understanding of the patterns has been the use of marked bivalves in both field experiments and laboratory simulations in which each band can in retrospect be assigned to a particular tide (day). A comparison with measured environmental variables has allowed detailed analysis of the relative importance of both seasonal and lunar and other factors in controlling the formation of growth patterns in bivalve shells.

Many of the early studies, e.g., Pannella and MacClintock (1968), Farrow (1971, 1972), speculated about the possible role of environmental factors in influencing shell deposition. Kennish and Olsson (1975) and Kennish (1980) for example, characterised disturbance patterns in the shells of *M. mercenaria* caused by spawning events, storms and unusually high or low temperatures. Spawning breaks appeared as an interruption to the normal pattern of growth increments followed by a sequence of narrow distinct increments; whilst freeze shock breaks had a characteristic cleft in the outer shell layer and a dark periostracal band that extended from the outer prismatic layer into the inner shell layer. The growth increments gradually decreased in thickness as the break was approached and began to increase in thickness in the post-break period (Kennish and Olsson 1975). Whilst it is probable that different disturbance marks can be distinguished from each other in this way, without clear evidence in which experimentally marked animals are artificially exposed to the disturbance the value of the patterns in recording environmental events is considerably weakened. The only approach is to closely monitor environmental conditions and then correlate the various measured parameters with the microgrowth pattern record in the shells of experimentally marked animals. In this way a detailed picture of the response of shell growth to environmental perturbations can be constructed. Such an example is the study of the effect of an algal bloom on the growth of the clam *T. philippinarum* in which marked clams were grown during the period of the bloom and environmental conditions carefully monitored. However, whether the effect of the bloom can be recognised in the shells of naturally occurring bivalves still remains to be established. The ability of bivalves to incorporate within their shells a record of environmental change has useful applications both in the assessment of growth rates and longevity in natural and cultured populations and for studying the effect on shell growth by anthropogenic inputs from industrial outfalls situated in environmentally sensitive areas such as harbours, estuaries and coastal embayments.

ACKNOWLEDGEMENTS

This paper was written while in support of a NERC research grant (GR3/7390). I am grateful to my colleagues Drs S.U.K. Ekaratne, G. Walker and R. Seed for reading and commenting on the manuscript and for stimulating discussions during its preparation. I would like to acknowledge the assistance of Mrs Kumudini Ekaratne, Mrs Heather Austin and Miss Melinda Brown in the preparation of shell sections and acetate peels for some of the bivalves discussed in this paper. I am grateful to the School of Ocean Sciences and the University of Wales, Bangor, for providing part of the financial support required to attend this meeting.

REFERENCES

Anwar, N.A., Richardson, C.A. and Seed, R. 1990. Age determination, growth rate and population structure of the horse mussel *Modiolus modiolus*. *Journal of the Marine Biological Association of the United Kingdom* 70:441–57.
Barker, R.M. 1964. Microtextural variation in pelecypod shells. *Malacologia* 2:69–86.
Davenport, J. and Wong, T.M. 1986. Responses of the blood cockle *Anadara granosa* (L.) (Bivalvia: Arcidae) to salinity, hypoxia and aerial exposure. *Aquaculture* 56:151–62.
Dolman, J. 1975. A technique for the extraction of environmental and geophysical information from growth records in invertebrates and stromatolites. In *Growth Rhythms and the History of the Earth's Rotation* (ed. G.D. Rosenberg and S.K. Runcorn), 191-222. London: Wiley.

Evans, J.W. 1972. Tidal growth increments in the cockle *Clinocardium nuttalli*. *Science* 176:416–7.

Evans, J.W. 1975. Growth and micromorphology of two bivalves exhibiting nondaily growth lines. In *Growth Rhythms and the History of the Earth's Rotation* (ed. G.D. Rosenberg and S.K. Runcorn), 119-34. London: Wiley.

Farrow, G.E. 1971. Periodicity structures in the bivalve shell: experiments to establish growth controls in *Cerastoderma edule* from the Thames Estuary. *Palaeontology* 14: 571–88.

Farrow, G.E. 1972. Periodicity structures in the bivalve shell: analysis of stunting in *Cerastoderma edule* from the Burry Inlet (South Wales). *Palaeontology* 15: 61–72.

Fritz, L.W. and Lutz, R.A. 1986. Environmental perturbations reflected in internal shell growth patterns of *Corbicula fluminea* (Mollusca: Bivalvia). *The Veliger* 28:401–17.

House, M.R. and Farrow, G.E. 1968. Daily growth banding in the shell of the cockle, *Cardium edule*. *Nature* 219:1384–6.

Kennish, M.J. 1978. Effects of thermal discharges on mortality of *Mercenaria mercenaria* in Barnegat Bay, New Jersey. *Environmental Geology* 2:223–54

Kennish, M.J. 1980. Shell microgrowth analysis: *Mercenaria mercenaria* as a type example for research in population dynamics. In *Skeletal Growth of Aquatic Organisms* (ed. G.D. Rosenberg and S.K. Runcorn), 255-92. New York: Plenum Press.

Kennish, M.J. and Olsson, R.K. 1975. Effects of thermal discharges on the microstructural growth of *Mercenaria mercenaria*. *Environmental Geology* 1:41–64.

Lønne, O.J. and Gray, J.S. 1988. Influence of tides on microgrowth bands in *Cerastoderma edule* from Norway. *Marine Ecology Progress Series* 42:1–7.

Lutz, R.A. 1976. Annual growth layers in the shell of *Mytilus edulis*. *Journal of the Marine Biological Association of the United Kingdom* 56:723–31.

Lutz, R.A. and Castagna, M. 1980. Age composition and growth rate of a mussel *Geukensia demissa* population in a Virginia salt marsh. *Journal of Molluscan Studies* 46:106–15.

Lutz R.A. and Rhoads, D.C. 1980. Growth patterns within the molluscan shell: an overview. In *Skeletal Growth of Aquatic Organisms* (ed. D.C. Rhoads and R.A. Lutz), 203-48. New York: Plenum Press.

Murawski, S.A., Ropes, J.W. and Serchuk, F.M. 1982. Growth of the ocean quahog *Arctica islandica* in the middle Atlantic Bight. *Fishery Bulletin. National Oceanic and Atmospheric Administration of the United States* 80:21–34.

Ohno, T. 1983. A note on the variability of growth increment formation in the shell of the common cockle *Cerastoderma edule*. In *Tidal Friction and the Earth's Rotation* (ed. P. Brosche and J. Sundenmann), 222-8. Berlin: Springer.

Ohno, T. 1985. Experimentale Analysen zur Rhythmik des Schalenwachstums einiger Bivalven und ihre palaobiologische Bedeutung. *Palaeontographica Abt A.* 189:63–123.

Pannella, G. 1975. Palaeontological clocks and the history of the earth's rotation. In *Growth Rhythms and the History of the Earth's Rotation* (ed. G.D. Rosenberg and S.K. Runcorn), 253-83. London: Wiley.

Pannella, G. and MacClintock, C. 1968. Biological and environmental rhythms reflected in molluscan shell growth. *Journal of Paleontology* 42:64–80.

Rhoads, D.C. and Lutz, R.A. 1980. Skeletal growth of aquatic organisms. New York: Plenum Press.

Rhoads, D.C. and Pannella, G. 1970. The use of molluscan growth patterns in ecology and paleoecology. *Lethaia* 3:143–61.

Richardson, C.A. 1987a. Tidal bands in the shell of the clam *Tapes philippinarum* (Adams & Reeve 1850). *Proceedings of the Royal Society of London*. B230:367–87.

Richardson, C.A., 1987b. Microgrowth patterns in the shell of the Malaysian cockle *Anadara granosa* and their use in age determination. *Journal of Experimental Marine Biology and Ecology* 111:77–98.

Richardson, C.A. 1988a. Tidally produced growth bands in the subtidal bivalve *Spisula subtruncata* (Da Costa). *Journal of Molluscan Studies* 54:71–82.

Richardson, C.A. 1988b. Exogenous and endogenous rhythms of band formation in the shell of the clam *Tapes philippinarum* (Adams & Reeve, 1850). *Journal of Experimental Marine Biology and Ecology* 112:105–26.

Richardson, C.A. 1989. An analysis of the microgrowth bands in the shell of the mussel *Mytilus edulis* (L.). *Journal of the Marine Biological Association of the United Kingdom* 69:477–91.

Richardson, C.A. 1990. Tidal rhythms in the shell secretion of living bivalves. *Earth's Rotation from Eons to Days* (ed. Brosche and Sundermann), 215-26. Heidelberg: Springer-Verlag.

Richardson, C.A., Crisp, D.J., and Runham, N.W. 1979. Tidally deposited growth bands in the shell of the common cockle *Cerastoderma edule (L.)*. *Malacologia* 18:277–90.

Richardson, C.A., Crisp, D.J. and Runham, N.W. 1980a. An endogenous rhythm in shell deposition in *Cerastoderma edule*. *Journal of the Marine Biological Association of the United Kingdom* 60:991–1004.

Richardson, C.A., Crisp, D.J. and Runham, N.W. 1980b. Factors influencing shell growth in *Cerastoderma edule*. *Proceedings of the Royal Society of London* B210:513–31.

Richardson, C.A., Crisp, D.J., Runham, N.W. and Gruffydd, L.D. 1980c. The use of tidal growth bands in the shell of *Cerastoderma edule* to measure seasonal growth rates under cool temperate and subarctic conditions. *Journal of the Marine Biological Association of the United Kingdom* 60:977–89.

Richardson, C.A., Crisp, D.J. and Runham, N.W. 1981. Factors influencing shell deposition during a tidal cycle in the intertidal bivalve *Cerastoderma edule*. *Journal of the Marine Biological Association of the United Kingdom* 61:465–76.

Richardson, C.A., Seed, R. and Naylor, E. 1990. Use of internal growth bands for measuring individual and population growth rates in *Mytilus edulis* from offshore production platforms. *Marine Ecology Progress Series* 66:259–65

Richardson, C.A. and Walker, P. 1991. The age structure of a population of the hard-shell clam *Mercenaria mercenaria* from Southampton Water, England, derived from acetate peel replicas of shell sections. *ICES Journal of Marine Science* 48:229–36

Ropes, J.W. 1987. Procedures for preparing acetate peels and evidence validating the annual periodicity of growth lines formed in the shells of ocean quahogs, *Arctica islandica*. *Marine Fisheries Review* 46:27–35.

Seed, R. and Richardson, C.A. 1990. *Mytilus* growth and its environmental responsiveness. In: *Neurobiology of Mytilus edulis* (ed. G.B. Stefano), 1-37. Manchester: Manchester University Press.

Tanabe, K. and Oba, T. 1988. Latitudinal variation in shell growth patterns of *Phacosoma japonicum* (Bivalvia: Veneridae) from the Japanese Coast. *Marine Ecology Progress Series* 47:75–82.

Thompson, I. 1975. Biological clocks and shell growth in bivalves. In *Growth Rhythms and the History of the Earth's Rotation* (ed. G.D. Rosenberg and S.K. Runcorn), 149-61. London: John Wiley & Sons.

ECOLOGY
SESSION PAPERS

SACOGLOSSA (MOLLUSCA: OPISTHOBRANCHIA) — SPECIALIST HERBIVORES AND PARTIAL PREDATORS: INTEGRATING ECOLOGICAL, PHYSIOLOGICAL AND MORPHOLOGICAL DATA

Kathe R. Jensen

Zoologisk Museum, Universitetsparken 15, DK-2100 Copenhagen Ø, Denmark

ABSTRACT

Sacoglossan opisthobranchs are almost exclusively stenophagous herbivores, feeding suctorially on the cell sap of marine algae or seagrasses. All shelled sacoglossans feed exclusively on the siphonalean green algal genus *Caulerpa*. Ability to retain algal chloroplasts and sequester algal secondary metabolites evolved prior to losing the shell. Radiation of diets is closely related to evolutionary changes in morphology and function of radular teeth and pharyngeal musculature. Two important changes have occurred in the pharyngeal musculature of the shell-less Sacoglossa. A shift in importance from the ascending limb to the descending limb of the radula has been accomplished by increasing the size of the ascus-muscle. A distinct layer of transverse muscles divides the odontophore of most non-shelled Sacoglossa, separating the ascending and descending limbs of the radula. These changes have made the radiation in diets possible. Buccal regurgitation and blade-shaped radular teeth are other important features increasing the efficiency of suctorial feeding on coenocytic algae. Most species have retained narrow food spectra even after the adaptive radiation of diets. This may be in order to cope with noxious algal metabolites.

INTRODUCTION

A comprehensive understanding of the intricate relationships between marine mesograzers and their food plants has not yet been developed. In fact, investigations in one field of research, e.g., ecology, tend to consider factors from other fields, e.g. physiology, as 'fixed constraints'. Also, the various fields use a completely different vocabulary, so that results from different fields cannot be immediately compared, and often seem incompatible. For example, an ecologist will talk about 'food handling', a physiologist about 'ingestion'. Usually, different experimental animals will be used in different fields. This further impedes comparisons between results from different fields.

Sacoglossan opisthobranchs are suctorial feeders. The majority are stenophagous herbivores feeding on the liquid contents of marine algae or seagrasses. Siphonalean green algae constitute the food of the majority of sacoglossans, and all shelled sacoglossans feed exclusively on algae of the genus *Caulerpa* (Jensen 1980a). These algae yield large amounts of cell sap with one piercing of the cell wall, but the cytoplasm is usually viscous. Also, many siphonalean green algae produce noxious secondary metabolites, which are found in only one or a few closely related algal species. These secondary metabolites deter most generalist herbivores (Paul and Fenical 1986; Paul and Hay 1986; Hay and Fenical 1988). Combined with often complex thallus structure (Womersley 1984), efficient suctorial feeding on these algae requires morphological as well as physiological adaptations. These factors all favour dietary specializations (Hughes 1980; Clark and DeFreese 1987).

The interactions between sacoglossans and their food plants have been studied by the present author from a number of different aspects, e.g. chemoreception (Jensen 1982, 1988), kleptoplasty (= chloroplast symbiosis) (Clark *et al.* 1981, 1990), feeding methods and selectivity (Jensen 1975, 1981a,b, 1983, 1986, 1989), and functional morphology of feeding apparatus (Jensen 1980a, 1991a). The present paper presents additional observations on functional morphology of the sacoglossan pharynx. Behavioural and physiological adaptations to diet are reviewed, and it is attempted to clarify how evolution and dietary specialization are closely interrelated.

MATERIALS AND METHODS

Collection data for the Hong Kong Sacoglossa used in the present study, have been published previously (Jensen 1985, 1990a). The pharynx of five species of Hong Kong Sacoglossa, *Lobiger sagamiensis* Baba, *Elysia chilkensis* Eliot, *E. leucolegnote* Jensen, *E. trisinuata* Baba, and *Ercolania emarginata* Jensen, was dissected out and drawn with the aid of a camera lucida. The pharynx was then cut sagittally, stained with aceto-carmine, and mounted with Canada balsam. The cut pharynx was also drawn with a camera lucida.

RESULTS

Functional morphology of the feeding apparatus

The alimentary system of sacoglossans is suctorial. Basically, it consists of a pumping, tubular, muscular section (pharynx, esophagus, intestine) and a finely branching 'reservoir' (digestive gland) (Fig. 1). There are usually two structurally differentiated muscular 'pumps'. The barrel-shaped pharynx is the most characteristic suctorial organ. In some species it is equipped with a muscular pharyngeal pouch, which may also have pumping function (Jensen 1991a). The second pump is the esophageal pouch. This is usually a spherical, muscular structure located rather close to the entrance of the esophagus into the stomach. The esophagus, dorsal stomach wall, and intestine have muscular walls and probably assist in 'pumping' by peristaltic movements. In the ventral part of the

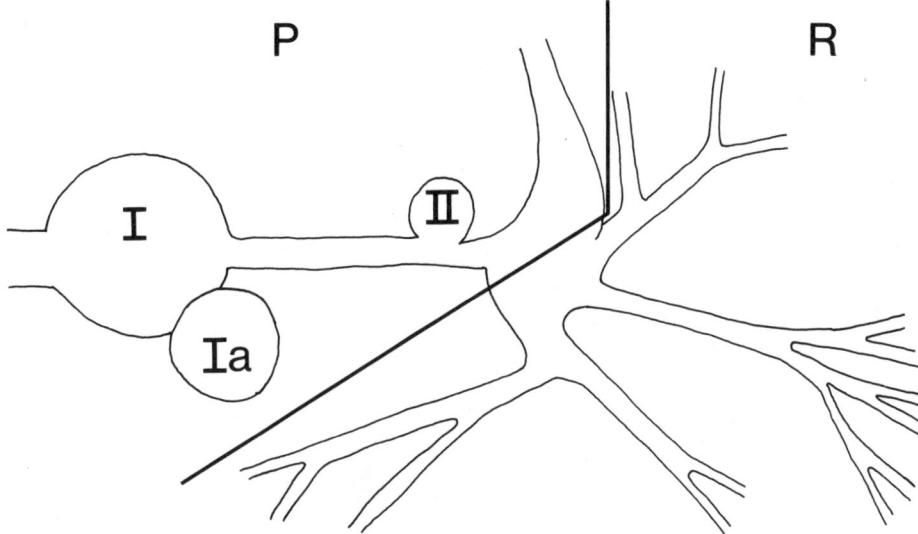

Fig. 1. Diagrammatic representation of the alimentary system in the Sacoglossa. P, pumping section; R, 'reservoir' section; I, first muscular pump (= pharynx); Ia, accessory pump (= pharyngeal pouch); II, second muscular pump (esophageal pouch).

stomach and the branches of the digestive gland, movement is solely by ciliary propulsion. This may be assisted by rhythmic contractions in the tissues surrounding the digestive gland. This is seen for example in pulsating cerata, where contents of digestive gland is seen to move when the ceras contracts and dilates (Rasmussen 1973; Gascoigne and Sordi 1980; Jensen 1981a).

The sacoglossan pharynx is of rather uniform shape throughout the group. It consists of a thick dorsal 'septate' muscle composed of alternating layers of (semi)circular and radial muscles (Gascoigne 1979; Jensen 1991a), a muscular odontophore containing the radular sac (= ascending or upper limb of the radula), and a more or less prominent ventral longitudinal muscle layer (= ascus-muscle) surrounding the descending or lower limb of the radula (Fig. 2). In some species the posteroventral surface of the pharynx is surrounded by a more or less prominent muscular collar or pouch (Jensen 1991a).

The sacoglossan pharynx functionally consists of four cylinders, one inside the other (Fig. 3). The largest, external cylinder is the outer pharynx wall which is most prominent dorsally where it forms the 'septate' muscle. Inside this cylinder and fastened ventrally and, in part, laterally, is the odontophore which is more or less solid muscle. The third cylinder is external to the outer pharynx wall, but attached to the ventral surface of the pharynx. This is the ascus-muscle. The fourth cylinder is formed by the radula. This bends abruptly at the anterior tip of the odontophore, and thus forms a small cylinder inside the odontophore, the ascending limb, as well as inside the ascus-muscle, the descending limb.

The pharyngeal musculature of several species of Sacoglossa has been described elsewhere (Jensen 1992, in press). In the present study the pharyngeal musculature of

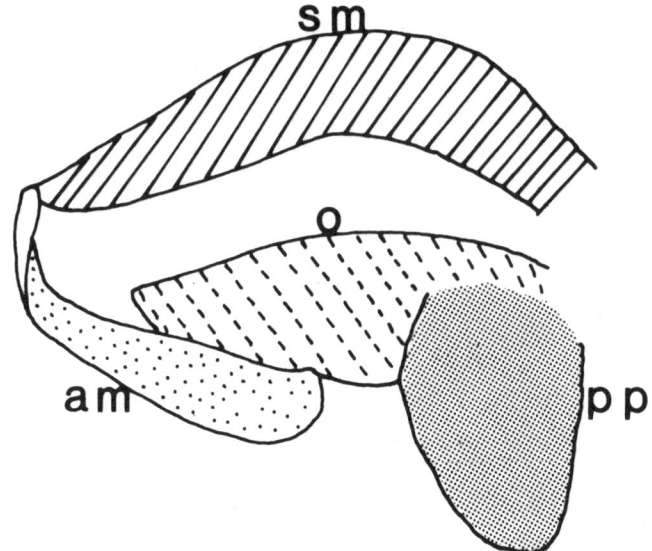

Fig. 2. Schematic drawing of the pharynx in the Sacoglossa. am, ascus-muscle; o, odontophore; pp, pharyngeal pouch; sm, dorsal septate muscle.

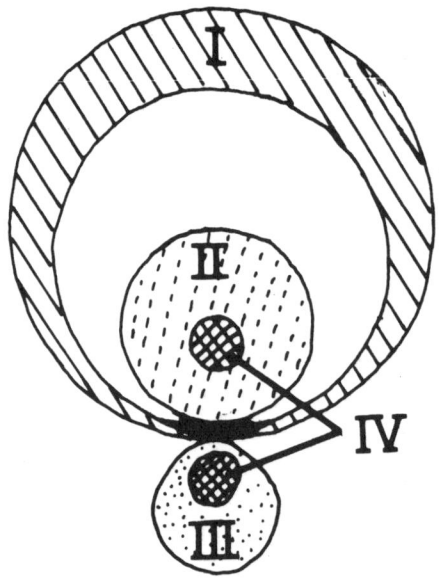

Fig. 3. Diagrammatic section through the sacoglossan pharynx. I, outer cylinder (dorsal septate muscle); II, odontophore (second cylinder); III, ascus-muscle (third cylinder); IV, radula (fourth cylinder).

five Hong Kong sacoglossans is described. Combined with the results of the above studies (Jensen, in press) and recent species descriptions (Gascoigne 1978, 1979; Jensen 1980b, 1993a; Jensen and Wells 1990), a functional-evolutionary interpretation is proposed.

Lobiger sagamiensis (Oxynoidae) has a moderately tall pharynx and an enormously long, coiled muscular pharyngeal pouch which is attached to the pharynx posteroventrally (Fig. 4). The ventral longitudinal ascus-muscle forms a thick layer anteriorly and extends posteriorly to the level of attachment of the pharyngeal pouch. The descending limb of the radula is rather steeply inclined in relation to the ventral pharynx surface. Three teeth are located at the free anterior tip of the odontophore. The radular teeth are large relative to the size of the pharynx, and the ascending limb of the radula forms a conspicuous median cylinder in the dorsal part of the odontophore (Fig. 5). Only a few short muscles (radula suspending muscles) connect the ascending limb of the radula and the dorsal surface of the odontophore. The ventral radula suspending muscles attach to the epithelium surrounding the descending limb over most of its length. This means that the transverse muscles separating the ascending and descending limbs of the radula are weakly developed. Dorsoventral muscles (odontophore depressor muscles) fill out most of the odontophore lateral to the ascending limb. The radular teeth are blade-shaped with lateral denticles and a bifid tip (Jensen 1985).

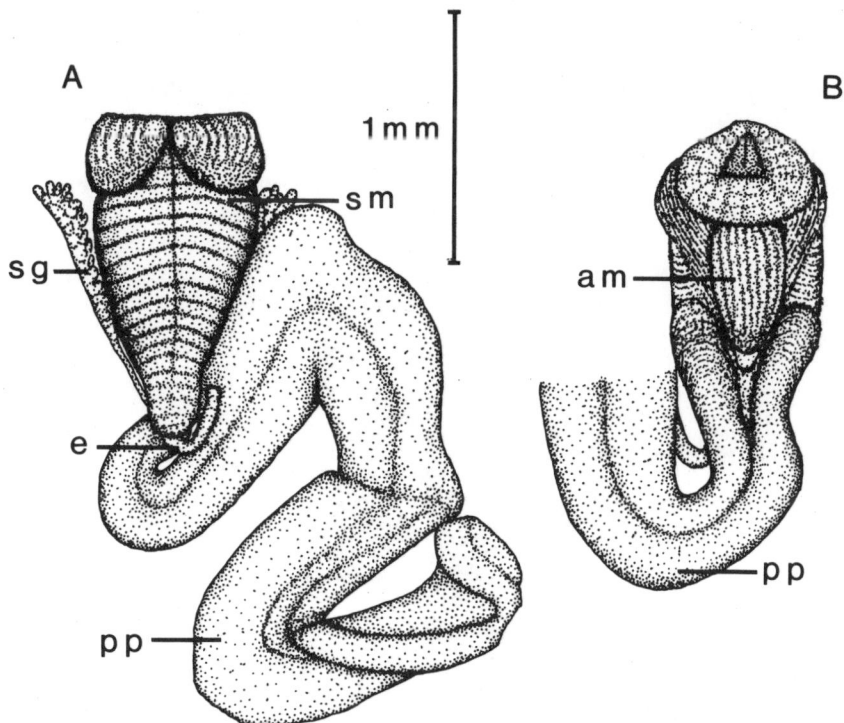

Fig. 4. The pharynx of *Lobiger sagamiensis*. A, dorsal view; B, ventral view. am, ascus-muscle; e, esophagus; pp, pharyngeal pouch; sg, salivary gland; sm, dorsal septate muscle.

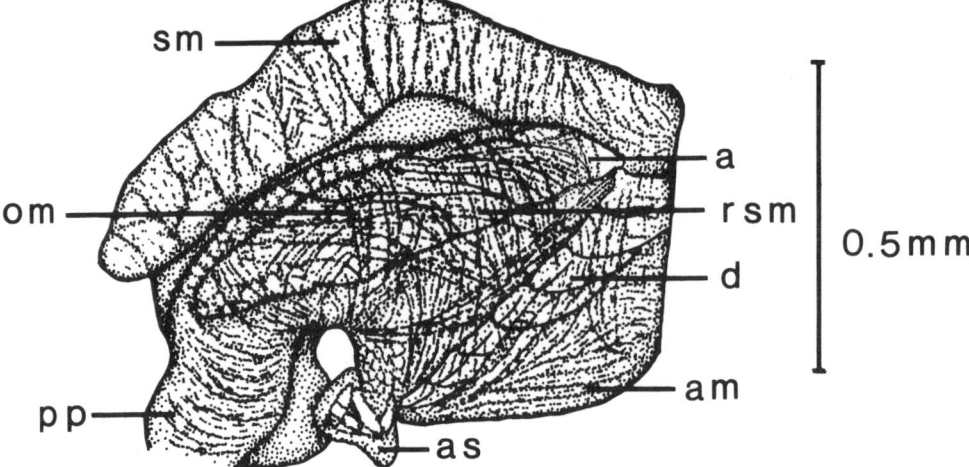

Fig. 5. Sagittal section through the pharynx of *Lobiger sagamiensis*. a, ascending limb of radula; am, ascus-muscle; as, ascus; d, descending limb of radula; om, odontophore muscles; rsm, radula suspending muscles; sm, dorsal septate muscle.

The pharynx of *Elysia chilkensis* (Elysiidae) is rather small and has a tall domed dorsal septate muscle (Fig. 6). This is very similar to the pharynx of *E. australis* (Quoy and Gaimard) (Jensen and Wells 1990), and in this connection it should be mentioned that *E. chilkensis* was collected in shallow, intertidal rock-pools containing Enteromorpha (Bleakney pers. comm.), which is one of the food plants of *E. australis* (Hinde 1980; Jensen and Wells 1990). Also, the pharyngeal lips are prominent, and the external demarcation of the odontophore forms a triangular area. These characters are also seen in

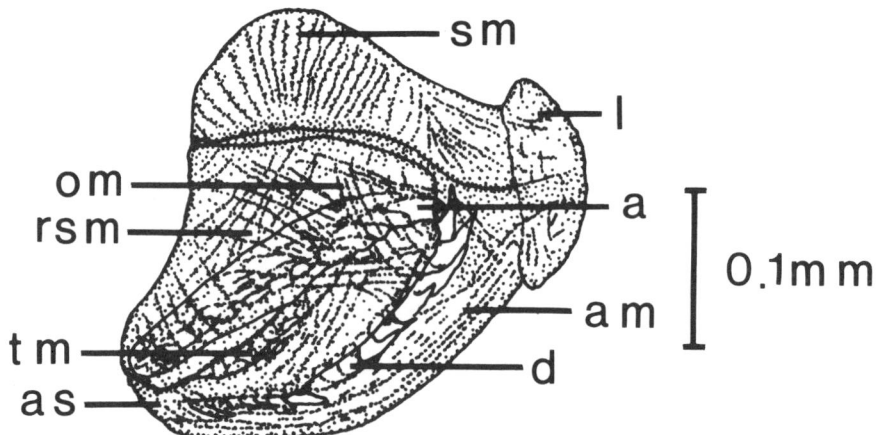

Fig. 6. Sagittal section through the pharynx of *Elysia chilkensis*. a, ascending limb of radula; am, ascus-muscle; as, ascus; d, descending limb of radula; l, pharyngeal lips; om, odontophore muscles; rsm, radula suspending muscles; sm, dorsal septate muscle; tm, transverse muscles.

E. australis. The odontophore does not extend into the anterior snout-like part of the pharynx. The longitudinal ventral ascus-muscle is as long as the pharynx, and it is attached to the pharynx throughout its length. The ventral radula suspending muscles attach only to the 3 anteriormost teeth of the descending limb. Behind this a distinct layer of transverse muscles separates the ascending and descending limbs of the radula. Posteriorly the bulk of musculature is located dorsal to the ascending limb of the radula. The radular teeth are blade-shaped with median denticles (Jensen 1985).

The pharynx of *Elysia leucolegnote* (Elysiidae) is extremely small for such a big animal (Jensen 1990a). The dorsal septate muscle is rather thick, and the ascus-muscle is almost as long as the pharynx (Fig. 7). The ascending limb of the radula is located rather centrally in the odontophore. Dorsally, are a few wide bands of radula suspending muscles running anteriorly and posteriorly from the ascending limb of the radula. Transverse muscles form a distinct layer behind the ventral radula suspending muscles. Behind the tip of the ascending limb the odontophore musculature is loosely organized, and hemocoelic spaces are conspicuous. The radular teeth are blade-shaped with median denticles (Jensen 1990a).

Elysia trisinuata (Elysiidae) has a large pharynx with a thick dorsal septate muscle

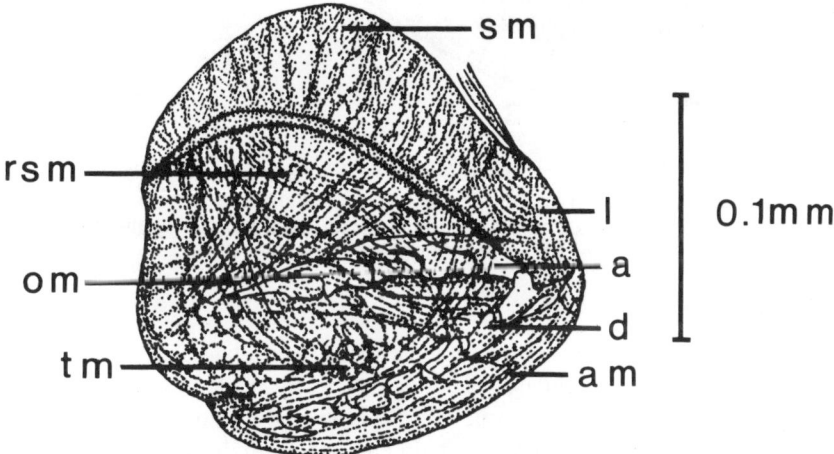

Fig. 7. Sagittal section through the pharynx of *Elysia leucolegnote*. a, ascending limb of radula; am, ascus-muscle; d, descending limb of radula; l, pharyngeal lips; om, odontophore muscles; rsm, radula suspending muscles; sm, dorsal septate muscle; tm, transverse muscles.

(Fig. 8). The odontophore is large and muscular, and the ascending limb of the radula ascends from the posterior ventral end towards the anterior dorsal surface. The ascus-muscle is as long as the pharynx, and there may be several small asci lined up posteriorly. Two teeth of the descending limb are visible at the free anterior tip of the odontophore. The transverse muscles separating the ascending and descending limbs form a distinct layer behind the third tooth in the descending limb. The ventral radula suspending muscles attach to the epithelium surrounding these teeth and also apparently to the transverse muscles. The radular teeth are blade-shaped with median denticles (Jensen 1985).

The pharynx of *Ercolania emarginata* (Stiligeridae) is large and elongate. The dorsal septate muscle is thick, and the odontophore musculature also appears 'septate'. The

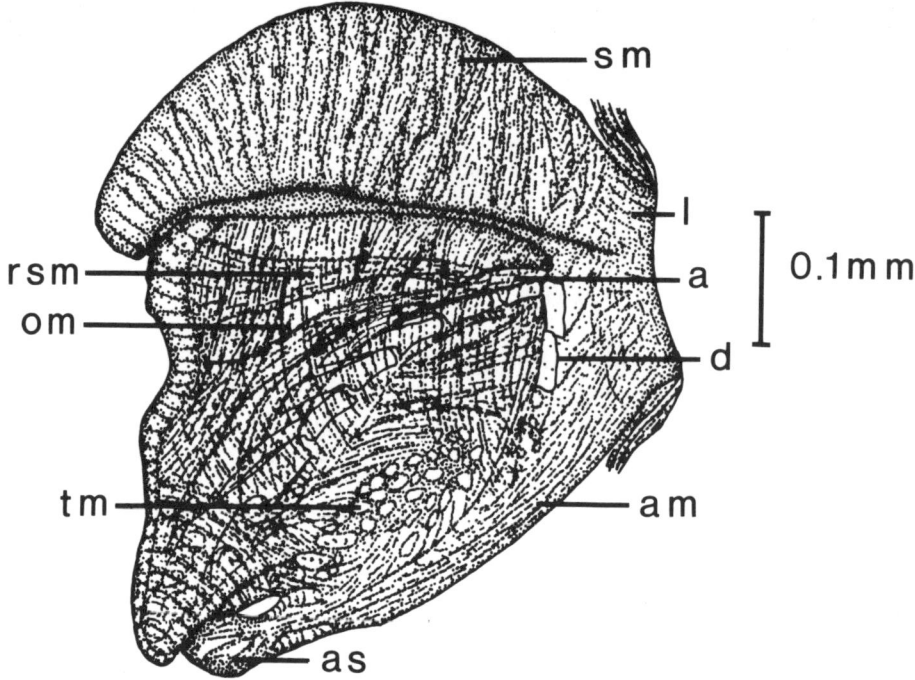

Fig. 8. Sagittal section through the pharynx of *Elysia trisinuata*. a, ascending limb of radula; am, ascus-muscle; as, ascus; d, descending limb of radula; l, pharyngeal lips; om, odontophore muscles; rsm, radula suspending muscles; sm, dorsal septate muscle; tm, transverse muscles.

pharynx contains four radular muscles: (1) Dorsal (dorso-lateral) oblique radula suspending muscles (= dorsal radula suspending muscles); (2) Ventral, longitudinal radula retractor muscle (= ventral radula suspending muscle); (3) Dorso-ventral, radiating muscles, which may be tensor muscles connecting ascending limb and ascus-muscle. These muscles probably maintain distance between ascending and descending limb; (4) Ventral, longitudinal ascus-muscle. The ascus-muscle is rather steeply inclined relative to the ventral surface of pharynx, and posteriorly it is completely separate from the pharynx wall (Fig. 9). Only one tooth in the descending limb, the 'leading tooth', is attached to the anterior, free tip of the odontophore. The radular teeth are sabot-shaped with smooth edges (Jensen 1985). The used teeth form an irregular heap behind the descending limb of the radula.

Comparison of the pharyngeal musculature of the above species shows that *Lobiger sagamiensis* differs from the others by the dorsal position of the ascending limb of the radula within the rather flat odontophore, and also by the presence of a pharyngeal pouch. In *Ercolania emarginata* the odontophore is also rather flat, but the ascending limb is located closer to the ventral surface of the odontophore. In the three species of *Elysia*, the ascending limb of the radula traverses the odontophore from the postero-ventral edge to the antero-dorsal tip, and there is a thick layer of musculature dorsal to the ascending limb. The ascus-muscle shows similar differences between the species studied here.

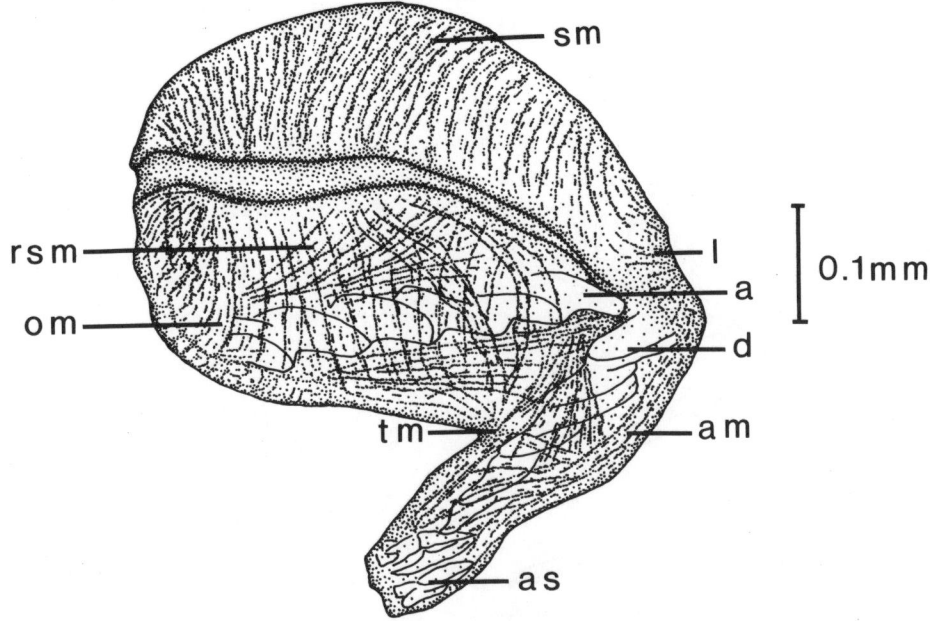

Fig. 9. Sagittal section through the pharynx of *Ercolania emarginata*. a, ascending limb of radula; am, ascus-muscle; as, ascus; d, descending limb of radula; l, pharyngeal lips; om, odontophore muscles; rsm, radula suspending muscles; sm, dorsal septate muscle; tm, transverse muscles.

In *L. sagamiensis* the ascus-muscle is slightly more than half as long as the pharynx, and it is attached to the ventral surface of the pharynx throughout its length. It only surrounds the descending limb of the radula ventrally and laterally. In the three *Elysia* species the ascus-muscle is as long as the pharynx and attached throughout its length. The descending limb of the radula is completely surrounded by the ascus-muscle in the posterior end. In *Ercolania emarginata* the ascus-muscle is about half as long as the pharynx. Its longitudinal axis is at a steep angle to the pharynx, and it is only attached anteriorly.

The odontophore contains two major groups of musculature. One group, the odontophore depressor muscles, run dorso-ventrally and radially from the dorsal surface of the odontophore to the lateral and ventral pharynx wall (Fig. 10). These muscles move the odontophore up and down during the sucking phase of feeding, and may also function during the rasping phase (see later). The second group of musculature is the radula suspending muscles. These radiate in all directions from the ascending limb of the radula to the dorsal surface of the odontophore and to the lateral and ventral pharynx wall (Fig. 10). In the species studied here at least one of the ventral radula suspending muscles attach to the epithelium surrounding the teeth of the descending limb of the radula. In *L. sagamiensis* most of the teeth in the descending limb are thus connected to the ascending limb of the radula. In the other species only the anteriormost two or three teeth have a branch of a radula suspending muscle attached. In these species this muscle probably functions as a radula retractor muscle. In the three species of

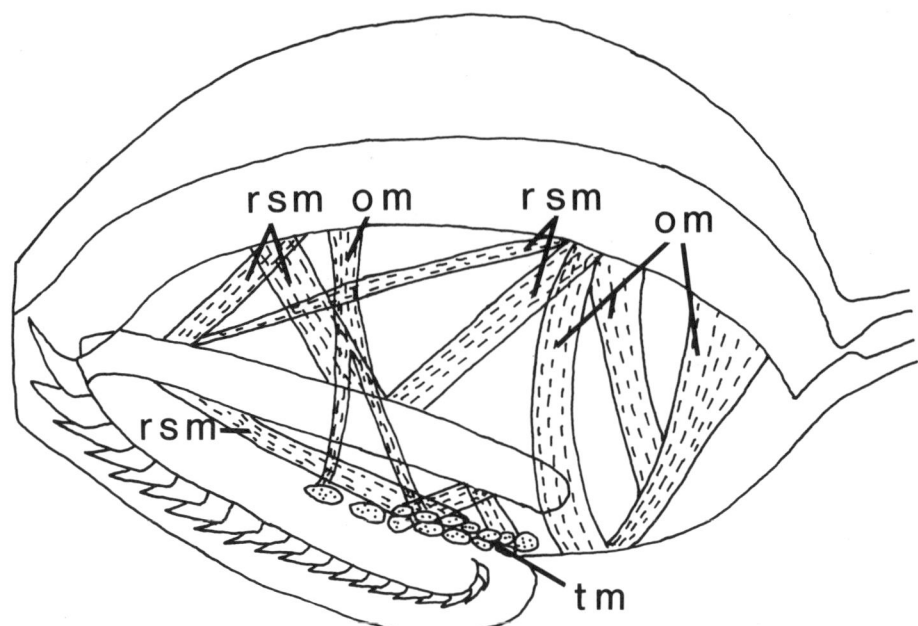

Fig. 10. Schematic figure of the sacoglossan pharynx showing odontophore musculature. om, odontophore depressor muscles; rsm, radula suspending muscles; tm, transversal muscles.

Elysia the remaining ventral radula suspending muscles attach to the layer of transverse muscles separating the ascending and descending limbs of the radula. In *Ercolania emarginata* the radula retractor muscle is parallel to the ventral surface of the pharynx (Fig. 9). The radula suspending muscles in all species protract and retract the ascending limb of the radula, and the fan-shaped arrangement probably allows very precise positioning of the radula.

The radula of the Sacoglossa is uniseriate and the teeth are large and interlocking. The radula consists of an ascending (upper) limb corresponding to the radular sac of other gastropods, a descending (lower) limb of about the same length, and a thin-walled ascus in which the used teeth are accumulated either rolled up in a spiral or densely packed in an irregular heap (Gascoigne 1979; Jensen 1991a). The bases of the radular teeth are stout and squarish, and articulate with the teeth in front and behind. There appears to be three basic shapes of the cusps (Jensen 1991a). The correlations between tooth shape and diets have been described elsewhere (Jensen 1993b).

The presence of pharyngeal pouches is usually associated with a weakly developed ascus-muscle, and also the transverse division of the odontophore separating the ascending and descending limbs of the radula, is weakly developed (Jensen 1992, in press, present study). The pharyngeal pouch is attached to the pharynx so that it surrounds the posteroventral part of the odontophore, including the posterior end of the ascending limb of the radula (Fig. 5). This suggests that in these species the ascending limb is more important than the descending limb in piercing the cell wall of the food plant. Most of these species have radular teeth with triangular cusps and lateral denticles. These teeth probably function in a 'rasping' manner (Jensen 1993b). Some species with pharyngeal pouches, e.g., *Lobiger sagamiensis* and *Oxynoe viridis* (Pease), have blade-shaped teeth with lateral denticles (Jensen and Wells 1990, present study). Very few species with pharyngeal pouches, e.g., *Caliphylla mediterranea* Costa, have smooth blade-shaped teeth (Gascoigne 1979). It is proposed that the odontophore functions in combination with the pharyngeal pouch. Contraction of the dorso-ventral muscles of the pharyngeal pouch causes elongation of the tip of the odontophore due to displaced hemolymph. The descending limb of the radula is held rigid by isometric contraction of the ascus-muscle (Fig. 11A). The second stage is contraction of the odontophore

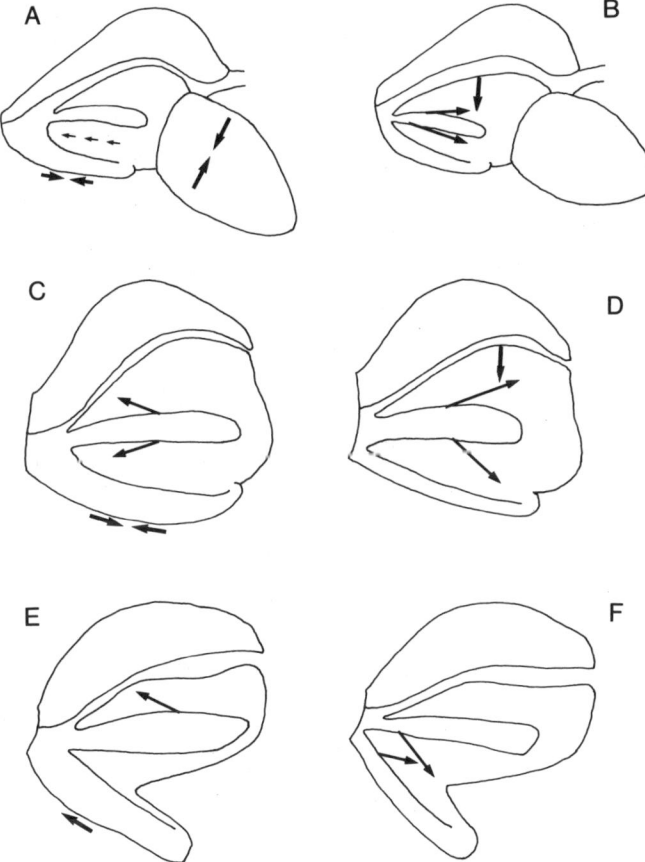

Fig. 11. Schematic drawings of proposed methods of functioning of the radula and pharyngeal musculature during rasping/ piercing phase of feeding in different groups of sacoglossans. A–B, Sacoglossans having pharyngeal pouches and triangular radular teeth. C–D, Sacoglossans having a long attached ascus-muscle and blade–shaped teeth. E–F, Sacoglossans having a short, posteriorly free ascus-muscle and sabot-shaped teeth. Heavy arrows indicate contractions of odontophore and ascus-muscles; light arrows indicate contraction of radula suspending muscles; small, thin arrows indicate flow of haemolymph in muscular hydrostat.

depressor muscles and a retraction of the ascending limb of the radula by contraction of posteriorly directed radula suspending muscles (Fig. 11B).

In the species without a pharyngeal pouch the ascus-muscle is strongly developed (Figs. 6–9). Some species, notably the genus *Elysia*, have a long ascus-muscle, i.e., more than half the total length of the pharynx, which is attached to the ventral surface of the pharynx through most of its length (Jensen and Wells 1990, present study). In these species the descending limb of the radula is completely surrounded by the longitudinal ascus-muscle, and a prominent layer of transverse muscles separates the ascending and descending limbs of the radula (Jensen 1991a, present study). These species have blade-shaped teeth with or without median denticles. These teeth probably function in a cutting manner (Jensen 1993b). It is proposed that in these species the curved ascus-muscle contracts to straighten out the descending limb of the radula, holding it as a rigid rod against the cell wall of the food plant. The ascending limb is protracted by anteriorly directed radula suspending muscles (Fig. 11C). The leading tooth eventually penetrates the cell wall of the food plant during one of these forwards movements. The second step is contraction of the odontophore depressor muscles and retraction of the ascending limb (Fig 11D). This causes the leading tooth to 'clip' against the anteriormost tooth in the ascending limb, thus cutting a slit in the algal cell wall from the inside (Jensen 1993b).

In the remaining species the ascus-muscle is also well developed, but it is short, i.e., shorter than or equal to half of the total length of pharynx. It is connected to the pharynx anteriorly at a rather steep angle, and posteriorly unattached (Fig. 9). All the species having sabot-shaped teeth have this type of pharynx, but also some species having blade-shaped teeth (Gascoigne 1978, 1979; Jensen 1991a, present study). In these species the transverse muscles separating the ascending and descending limbs of the radula form a tall, narrow 'stalk'. The function is probably as described by Gascoigne (1979), i.e., the ascus-muscle contracts driving the descending limb of the radula forwards as a lancet (Fig. 11E). Ascending and descending limbs of the radula are then both retracted (Fig. 11F), and these two steps are repeated until the cell wall of the food plant is pierced (Jensen 1993b).

REVIEW OF BEHAVIOURAL AND PHYSIOLOGICAL INTERACTIONS BETWEEN SACOGLOSSANS AND THEIR FOOD

Chemoreception

The first interaction between a sacoglossan and its food plant is the detection of chemical cues released from the food. These cues may be photosynthetic products, secondary metabolites, or wound plug components. All sacoglossans tested show some degree of 'arousal' when presented with homogenates of their food plants (Jensen 1982, 1988). The role of chemoreception is primarily that of 'arousal'. The aroused animal shows increased locomotory activity. Undamaged food plants can only be detected over very short distances (1–2 times animal length), and physical contact is necessary to recognize food (Jensen, 1980c, 1983). Removal of rhinophores has indicated that they are important in locating food (Jensen 1980c, 1982).

Feeding methods

Feeding methods differ in species feeding on filamentous algae and species feeding on planar food, and very few sacoglossans include both kinds of food in their diets (Jensen 1983, 1989, 1993b). Thus two functional groups of sacoglossan food plants can be distinguished. In species feeding on filamentous food, the filament is grasped between oral and pedal lobes, and the filament usually bends when the cell wall is pierced (Usuki 1977; Gascoigne 1978; Jensen 1980b, 1989). In species feeding on planar food oral and pedal lobes are spread out to form a seal surrounding the protracted pharyngeal opening (Jensen 1981a,b, 1989).

Feeding can be divided into 'rasping' and 'sucking' phases (Jensen 1981a, 1989, 1990b). In the former phase the radular teeth are active piercing the cell wall of the food plant, and in the latter phase the muscular pharynx pumps in the cell sap of the food plant.

A number of sacoglossans have been observed to reverse the flow of food so that cell sap which has been sucked into the pharyngeal cavity and anterior esophagus is returned to the algal siphon. This process is called buccal regurgitation (Jensen 1981a; Gascoigne 1983). It is suggested that this process mixes the algal cytoplasm with saliva to reduce viscosity and thus facilitate suction (Jensen 1981a). A precursor of buccal regurgitation may occur in the bivalved species *Julia japonica* Kuroda and Habe, in which suction is momentarily released and then resumed, but cell sap is apparently not regurgitated (Kawaguti and Yamasu 1966).

Feeding selectivity

Most sacoglossans are stenophagous and cannot be induced to change diet (Jensen 1981a, 1983, 1990b). Some are relatively euryphagous (Clark and Busacca 1978; Jensen 1983, 1989, 1991b; Brandley 1984; Bleakney 1989, 1990). In choice experiments many euryphagous sacoglossans show distinct preferences for one particular food plant, and usually this is correlated with higher growth rates on the preferred food (Jensen 1975, 1981b, 1983). Thallus morphology of the food plants is very important in food preference (Jensen 1981b, 1983). There is a distinct correlation between filament diameter and foot width of the sacoglossan predator in species feeding on filamentous algae, and in species feeding on planar food items, there is a correlation between length or diameter of radular teeth and dimensions of utricles or cells of food plants (Jensen 1981a,b, 1983, 1990b). Neither food preference nor growth are correlated with caloric contents of food plants or with ash content (Jensen 1983).

It has been suggested that differences in structural cell wall components, and also calcification, are important in determining which plants can be included in the diet of a sacoglossan (Jensen 1980a, 1981a). Sacoglossans feeding on filamentous algae will not feed on any alga having a suitable diameter. Usually only algae with similar cell wall structure will be eaten (Jensen 1975, 1980a, 1983).

One of the few species which naturally occurs in populations having different diets, including planar as well as filamentous algae, is *Elysia viridis* (Montagu). In this species changing from one type of food to the other requires a 'learning' period of up to two weeks. Some specimens are unable to change diet. 'Learning' involves increased efficiency in the process of piercing the algal cell wall as well as in sucking out the cell sap. Food preference changes as the animals 'learn' to cope with the new food, and it requires a new 'learning' period when the animals are transferred back to their original food (Jensen 1989).

The marked correlation between evolution and radiation of diets within the Sacoglossa has been noted previously (Kay 1968; Clark and Busacca 1978; Jensen 1980a). All shelled Sacoglossa feed on the siphonalean genus *Caulerpa*. Some shelled sacoglossans feed on several species of *Caulerpa*, and preference is based on relative filament diameter (Jensen 1981b). Others, notably the bivalved species, feed on only one species of *Caulerpa* (Burn 1960; Kawaguti and Yamasu 1966; Jensen 1980a, 1993a). In the non-shelled Sacoglossa several species are also restricted to feeding on *Caulerpa* spp. (Clark and Busacca 1978; Jensen 1980a; Clark and DeFreese 1987). It is usually assumed that loss of the shell preceded radiation to food plants other than *Caulerpa* (Clark and DeFreese 1987; Clark *et al.* 1990).

The majority of species of Sacoglossa feed on green algae of the orders Caulerpales, Codiales, and Derbesiales (formerly all included in the order Siphonales — see Taylor [1972]) (Jensen 1980a), and it is usually assumed that diet radiation was from fleshy species of *Caulerpa* to other fleshy siphonalean algae, e.g. *Codium*, and then to either highly calcified siphonalean algae, e.g., *Halimeda*, or filamentous, septate algae, e.g., *Chaetomorpha* (Clark and Busacca 1978; Jensen 1980a; Clark and DeFreese 1987; Clark *et al.* 1990). A few sacoglossans have highly deviating diets, such as diatoms, seagrasses, or opisthobranch eggs (Clark and Busacca 1978; Jensen 1980a, 1981a, 1983, 1986), and these species are considered the most advanced (Clark and DeFreese 1987; Clark *et al.* 1990).

Kleptoplasty ('Chloroplast symbiosis')

The Sacoglossa are probably best known for their ability to take up and maintain in the cells of their digestive gland, functional chloroplasts from their food algae. The extent to which this occurs has been discussed for many years (Greene 1970; Muscatine and Greene 1973; Hinde and Smith 1974; Trench 1975; Clark and Busacca 1978; Hinde; 1980; Clark *et al.* 1981, 1990; Brandley 1984). The actual mechanism of sorting and recognizing the chloroplasts in the alimentary system is unknown, but the chloroplasts are phagocytized by the cells of the digestive gland (McLean 1976). Subsequently the phagocytotic membrane dissolves, and the chloroplasts lie free in the cytoplasm of the digestive gland cells of the host (Trench 1975). The kleptoplastids are incapable of dividing and of synthesizing new chlorophyll (Muscatine and Greene 1973). The sacoglossan host produces a substance which induces the chloroplasts to release their photosynthates to the host cells (Gallop 1974).

It has been suggested that the ability to retain chloroplasts (non-functional) evolved earlier than the functional photosymbiosis, probably as a means of concealing the sacoglossan by nutritional homochromy (Clark *et al.* 1990). In the shelled family Volvatellidae the burrowing genus *Ascobulla* and also some species of *Volvatella* have white bodies and shells. Other species of *Volvatella* have a green periostracum, mantle fold, and visceral mass. The bivalved Juliidae and also the Oxynoidae, which have reduced shells, have more or less green bodies (Clark 1982; Gosliner 1987; Clark *et al.* 1990; Jensen and Wells 1990; Jensen 1991a). The shelled Sacoglossa and also a few non-shelled species have a massive ('holohepatic') digestive gland, which is probably unsuitable for photosymbiosis because of poor irradiance and gas exchange conditions

(Clark *et al.* 1981, 1990; Jensen 1991a). The most well-developed, long-term photosymbiosis occurs in species having a highly branched digestive gland with narrow tubular lumina, i.e., primarily elysiids, but medium-term functional retention has also been demonstrated in some caliphyllids and stiligerids (Clark *et al.* 1981, 1990). Retention time of functional chloroplasts ranges from less than 24 hours to more than 2 months (Muscatine and Greene 1973; Hinde and Smith 1974; Trench 1975; Clark and Busacca 1978; Hinde 1980; Clark *et al.* 1981, 1990).

The function of kleptoplasty has also been widely debated (Kay 1968; Hinde and Smith 1975; Thompson 1977; Clark and Busacca 1978; Jensen 1983; Waugh and Clark 1986; Thompson and Jarman 1989). Several levels of importance of the photosynthates in the nutrition of the sacoglossan host have been suggested: (1) Supplying a particular nutrient otherwise found only in *Caulerpa* (Kay 1968); (2) Supplying energy for mucus production (Trench *et al.* 1972); (3) Supplying an energy reserve during starvation periods (Jensen 1983; Thompson and Jarman 1989); (4) Being an important energy supplement during peak gametogenesis/reproduction (Waugh and Clark 1986); (5) Being the only energy source in adult animals (Ireland and Scheuer 1979; Thompson 1977). The fact is that somatic growth has not been detected in animals deprived access to feeding (Hinde and Smith 1975; Gallop *et al.* 1980; Jensen 1983).

It has been discussed whether only properties of the host animals influence the ability to form functional photosymbiosis, or whether properties of the chloroplasts are also involved (Muscatine and Greene 1973; Hinde and Smith 1974; Clark and Busacca 1978; Clark *et al.* 1981, 1990; Brandley 1984). It appears that the primitive reticulate chloroplasts of algae of the order Cladophorales are unsuitable for functional photosymbiosis, whereas the advanced chloroplasts of the Caulerpales and Codiales are particularly suitable, having tough outer membranes, banded or stacked thylakoids, and usually lacking a pyrenoid (Hori and Ueda 1967; Giles and Sarafis 1974; Jensen 1980a, Clark *et al.* 1990).

Chemical defense

Sequestration of noxious secondary metabolites from food algae has only been demonstrated in a few sacoglossans, but may be more widespread. Secondary metabolites with presumed feeding deterrent function have been recorded from many of the siphonaceous green algae which are included in the diets of sacoglossans (e.g., Norris and Fenical (1982), Paul and Fenical (1986), Paul (1987). At least one shelled sacoglossan, *Oxynoe panamensis* Pilsbry and Olsson, takes up and concentrates secondary metabolites from its food alga, *Caulerpa sertularioides* (Gmelin) Howe (Doty and Aguilar-Santos 1970). It also secretes a defensive mucus which is toxic to fish (Lewin 1970). Among the shell-less sacoglossans, *Elysiella pusilla* Bergh (= *Elysia halimedae* Macnae, see Jensen and Wells 1990), *Cyerce nigricans* (Pease), and *Costasiella ocellifera* (Simroth) sequester noxious secondary metabolites from their food plants (Paul and Van Alstyne 1988; Hay *et al.* 1989, 1990). *Mourgona germaineae* Marcus and Marcus also secretes a toxic defensive mucus, which is most likely derived from its food alga, *Cymopolia barbata* (L.) Lamouroux (Jensen 1984). The unique secondary metabolites found in *Tridachiella diomedea* (Bergh), *Tridachia crispata* Ørsted in Mørch, and *Plakobranchus ocellatus* van Hasselt are not diet-derived, but are synthesized by the sacoglossans, with carbon fixed by the kleptoplastids (Ireland *et al.* 1978, 1979; Ireland and Scheuer 1979; Ireland and Faulkner 1981).

DISCUSSION

Most sacoglossans are stenophagous, but wide differences in diets are found among different species. Evolution within the Sacoglossa is obviously closely associated with radiation in diets (Kay 1968; Clark and Busacca 1978; Clark and DeFreese 1987). This radiation probably involved behavioural, physiological, and morphological changes. The present study attempts to integrate information from all these fields and to identify evolutionary changes related to the radiation of diets.

All shelled Sacoglossa feed exclusively on the genus *Caulerpa* (Jensen 1980a). Although most species will include a variety of *Caulerpa* species in their diets, some apparently feed on only a single species (Jensen 1980a). Thallus morphology is highly variable in the genus *Caulerpa*. Twelve morphological groups have been defined. Anatomically they are all strictly coenocytic, and thallus rigidity is maintained by a network of internal trabeculae (Calvert *et al.* 1976; Womersley 1984). Chloroplast structure is also highly variable in *Caulerpa* (Calvert *et al.* 1976), but wound plug formation is uniform (Dawes and Goddard 1978). Only a few secondary metabolites have been recorded, which occur in varying combinations and concentrations in the different species (Vest *et al.* 1983). As in other Caulerpales, the structural cell wall component is xylan (Womersley 1984). The shelled Sacoglossa comprises at least three families, Volvatellidae, Juliidae, and Oxynoidae, each comprising about a dozen species (Marcus 1982, Gascoigne 1985).

The important questions to ask about the evolution of the group are: (1) Why did they 'leave' *Caulerpa*? And did they leave it simultaneously with losing the shell, or after the shell was lost? (2) How was it possible to change diet? The answers to the first question are purely speculative. It could be because of species packing (Clark and DeFreese 1987) or because of predation pressure (Hay *et al.* 1989).

The loss of the shell may have been necessary for the sacoglossans to occupy epiphytic habitats. The rigid thalli of some *Caulerpa* species may support rather large, shelled sacoglossans such as *Oxynoe* and *Lobiger*. It is characteristic that many shelled sacoglossans have been collected from rhizomes of *Caulerpa* spp. (Gascoigne and Sartory 1974; Thompson 1979; Jensen and Wells 1990), and also, the epifaunal forms are either very small, e.g. *Berthelinia*, or have a reduced shell, e.g., *Lobiger*. The shell has been lost several times independently within the Opisthobranchia (Gosliner and Ghiselin 1984), often in connection with transition from burrowing to epifaunal mode of life. The shell, though offering some protection, is energetically expensive to maintain. If protection can be gained from other sources, it may be profitable to get rid of the shell. Nutritional homochromy as well as sequestration of noxious algal metabolites are seen in shelled sacoglossans (Doty and Aguilar-Santos 1970; Clark *et al.* 1990). Thus, the protective value of the shell was diminished prior to the evolution of shell-less species.

The first evolutionary change thus appears to have been a behavioural shift from burrowing to epifaunal mode of life. This occurred in the Volvatellidae, and involved the development of partial nutritional homochromy. In the Juliidae and Oxynoidae nutritional homochromy is complete, and sequestration of noxious algal metabolites also occurs (Doty and Aguilar-Santos 1970; Clark *et al.* 1990). Anatomically, the shape of the radular teeth changes from triangular with lateral denticles in the Volvatellidae to blade-shaped with lateral denticles or completely smooth in the Oxynoidae and Juliidae.

The Volvatellidae treat *Caulerpa* siphons as planar food (Jensen 1981a) whereas the Juliidae and also the genus *Oxynoe* grasp the *Caulerpa* as filamentous food (Kawaguti and Yamasu 1966; Jensen 1980b). This indicates that feeding method has changed from rasping to cutting. However, the change in tooth shape was not accompanied by a marked change in pharyngeal musculature. All shelled sacoglossans have pharyngeal pouches. These range in size from short, horseshoe-shaped collars as in *Oxynoe*, to enormous spherical, as in *Volvatella*, or elongate, as in *Lobiger*, structures, much bigger than the pharynx itself (Jensen and Wells 1990; Jensen 1991a, present study). In the species studied so far, presence of pharyngeal pouches is associated with weak development of the transverse division of the odontophore separating the descending limb of the radula from the ascending limb (Jensen 1992, in press, present study). Thus the ascending limb must be more important than the descending limb of the radula, although the ascus-muscle of the Oxynoidae is more prominent than that of the Volvatellidae. In the shelled species the tip of the odontophore is rounded and several teeth are exposed during the 'rasping phase' of feeding (Jensen and Wells 1990; present study). Hence, cutting is not as efficient as in the Elysiidae in which only two teeth are functional at the tip of the odontophore. Cutting in *Lobiger* may be accomplished by contraction of the ventral radula suspending muscles (present study).

The development of the cutting feeding method may, however, have been the evolutionary step which enabled the diet radiation. The rasping feeding method of species having triangular, denticulate teeth requires that the algal siphon does not collapse when the plasmalemma is penetrated. Such rigid thalli are found in heavily calcified species such as *Halimeda* and also in the genus *Caulerpa*, in which the siphons are traversed by internal trabeculae (Womersley 1984). When the algal cell wall is cut from the inside, the incision only opens when suction is applied, and soft filaments as *Bryopsis* can be emptied by this method. This may also prevent wound plug formation which occurs in most coenocytic algae (Clark and DeFreese 1987).

If it is assumed that the shell has only been lost once in the Sacoglossa, i.e., the non-shelled Sacoglossa is a monophyletic group, then it seems most likely that the first shell-less species, like the shelled ones, had a holohepatic digestive gland, had non-functional kleptoplasty, triangular denticulate teeth, and a pharyngeal pouch. There are two major lines of evolution in the non-shelled Sacoglossa: the parapodia-bearing elysioid families and the cerata-bearing stiligeroid families (Clark and Busacca 1978; Gascoigne 1985; Clark and DeFreese 1987). In both lines species having pharyngeal pouches and triangular teeth with lateral denticles occur. None of these species feed on *Caulerpa*.

In the cerata-bearing Caliphyllidae, species of *Cyerce* feed on *Chlorodesmis* or *Penicillus*, for example, but other species feed on *Halimeda*. It has a holohepatic digestive gland, and functional kleptoplasty has not been detected (Clark et al. 1990). Probably the shift in pharyngeal musculature occurred at this stage as a response to less rigid algal filaments. It is also possible that buccal regurgitation developed at this stage, further facilitating withdrawal of the viscous algal cell sap. *Caliphylla mediterranea* Costa has smooth, blade-shaped teeth and large pharyngeal pouches. Also, the transverse division of the odontophore is well developed in this species (Gascoigne 1979; Jensen 1991a). It feeds on the soft filamentous alga *Bryopsis*. The lumina of the pharyngeal pouches are large, and they are used as a crop prior to buccal regurgitation (Gacoigne 1979, 1983). *Caliphylla mediterranea* has a digestive gland which sends branches into the cerata, and it has functional kleptoplasty (Clark et al. 1990).

In the elysioid line all species have cladohepatic (extensively branched) digestive gland, and functional kleptoplasty is widespread (Clark et al. 1990). Thus functional kleptoplasty in this group evolved prior to the shift in radular and pharyngeal morphology. The evolution of functional kleptoplasty may have given the Sacoglossa the capability of specializing on relatively rare food plants, because the nutrients provided by the chloroplasts enable the sacoglossans to tolerate starvation for extended periods.

The shift in importance from the ascending limb to the descending limb of the radula combined with evolution of blade-shaped teeth are probably the most important events in the evolution of shell-less sacoglossans. Blade-shaped teeth have apparently evolved in parallel in all three major lines of Sacoglossa. In the shelled Sacoglossa the blade-shaped teeth have lateral denticles, or, rarely, they are smooth. In the elysioid line the blade-shaped teeth have median denticles, or, in some species, they are smooth. In the stiligeroid line the blade-shaped teeth are most often smooth, but median or lateral denticles occur in a few species (Jensen 1980, 1993a; Marcus and Marcus 1967; Bleakney 1989). Hence this tooth shape must be considered the most successful within the Sacoglossa.

The well-developed transverse division of the odontophore separating the ascending limb from the descending limb of the radula has apparently evolved independently in the two lines of shell-less Sacoglossa. In both lines it is associated with the evolution of blade-shaped teeth. In the elysioid line it is also associated with loss of the pharyngeal pouch and the evolution of a long ascus-muscle. In the stiligeroid line the distinct transverse muscle layer is found in some species having pharyngeal pouches. In these species the ascus-muscle separated posteriorly from the ventral surface of the pharynx (Gascoigne 1979; Jensen 1991a). In both lines the transverse muscle layer is associated with greater development of the ascus-muscle, indicating that the descending limb can be moved independently of the odontophore, and conversely, the odontophore can be moved independently of the descending limb of the radula. This increases the efficiency of cutting through the algal cell wall, and very likely sucking is also facilitated. The elysiids feeding on *Caulerpa* do not have pharyngeal pouches.

The second major evolutionary change is the development of sabot-shaped teeth. This tooth shape evolved only in the stiligeroid line, and occurs only in species feeding on algae having cellulose cell walls (Jensen 1980a) Also, they all have a steeply inclined, posteriorly free ascus-muscle (Gascoigne 1978; Jensen 1991a). Very few species have functional kleptoplasty (Hinde and Smith 1974; Clark et al. 1990).

The present study has shown that radiation of diets is closely linked with morphological and functional changes in the radular teeth and pharyngeal musculature. Increased efficiency of the suctorial feeding method has enabled the shell-less Sacoglossa to utilize almost any marine plant which yields a sufficient amount of cell sap with one piercing. Functional kleptoplasty and sequestration of noxious algal secondary metabolites further enhanced the success of the Sacoglossa. However, the need for physiological adaptations to cope with the secondary metabolites has maintained stenophagy in the majority of species.

ACKNOWLEDGEMENTS

I would like to thank Prof. J. Sherman Bleakney, Acadia University, Canada, for donating specimens of *Elysia chilkensis* and copies of his field collecting notes. I would also like to thank the organisers of the International Workshops in Hong Kong, during which the other sacoglossans used in this study were collected.

REFERENCES

Bleakney, J.S. 1989. Morphological variation in the radula of *Placida dendritica* (Alder & Hancock, 1843) (Opisthobranchia: Ascoglossa/Sacoglossa) from Atlantic and Pacific populations. *Veliger* 32:171–81.

Bleakney, J.S. 1990. Indirect evidence of a morphological response in the radula of *Placida dendritica* (Alder & Hancock, 1843) (Opisthobranchia: Ascoglossa/Sacoglossa) to different algal prey. *Veliger* 33:111–5.

Brandley, B.K. 1984. Aspects of the ecology and physiology of *Elysia* cf. *furvacauda* (Mollusca: Sacoglossa). *Bulletin of Marine Science* 34:207–19.

Burn, R. 1960. Australian bivalve gastropods. *Nature* 187:44–6.

Calvert, H.E., Dawes, C.J. and Borowitzka, M.A. 1976. Phylogenetic relationships of *Caulerpa* (Chlorophyta) based on comparative chloroplast ultrastructure. *Journal of Phycology* 12:149–62.

Clark, K.B. 1982. A new *Volvatella* (Mollusca: Ascoglossa) from Bermuda, with comments on the genus. *Bulletin of Marine Science* 32:112–20.

Clark, K.B. and Busacca, M. 1978. Feeding specificity and chloroplast retention in four tropical Ascoglossa, with a discussion of the extent of chloroplast symbiosis and the evolution of the order. *Journal of Molluscan Studies* 44:272–82.

Clark, K.B. and DeFreese, D. 1987. Population ecology of Caribbean Ascoglossa (Mollusca: Opisthobranchia): A study of specialized algal herbivores. *American Malacological Bulletin* 5:259–80.

Clark, K.B., Jensen, K.R., Stirts, H.M. and Fermin, C.D. 1981. Chloroplast symbiosis in a non-elysiid mollusc, *Costasiella lilianae* Marcus (Hermaeidae: Ascoglossa (= Sacoglossa)): effects of temperature, light intensity, and starvation on carbon fixation rate. *Biological Bulletin* 160:43–54.

Clark, K.B., Jensen, K.R. and Stirts, H.M. 1990. Survey for functional kleptoplasty (chloroplast symbiosis) among West Atlantic Ascoglossa (= Sacoglossa) (Mollusca: Opisthobranchia). *Veliger* 33:339–45.

Dawes, C.J. and Goddard, R.H. 1978. Chemical composition of the wound plug and entire plants of the coenocytic green alga, *Caulerpa*. *Journal of Experimental Marine Biology and Ecology* 35:259–63.

Doty, M.S. and Aguilar-Santos, G. 1970. Transfer of toxic algal substances in marine food chains. *Pacific Science* 24:351–5.

Gallop, A. 1974. Evidence for the presence of a 'factor' in *Elysia viridis* which stimulates photosynthate release from its symbiotic chloroplasts. *New Phytology* 73:1111–7.

Gallop, A., Bartrop, J. and Smith, D.C. 1980. The biology of chloroplast acquisition by *Elysia viridis*. *Proceedings of the Royal Society of London, Series B* 207:335–49.

Gascoigne, T. 1978. The internal anatomy of *Stiliger fuscatus* (A. Gould, 1870) (Opisthobranchia: Sacoglossa). *Zoological Journal of the Linnean Society* 63:265–74.

Gascoigne, T. 1979. A redescription of *Caliphylla mediterranea* Costa, 1867 (Opisthobranchia: Ascoglossa). *Journal of Molluscan Studies* 45:300–11.

Gascoigne, T. 1983. Buccal regurgitation (Opisthobranchia: Ascoglossa). *Conchologists' Newsletter* 85:84–7.

Gascoigne, T. 1985. A provisional classification of families of the order Ascoglossa (Gastropoda: Nudibranchiata). *Journal of Molluscan Studies* 51:8–22.

Gascoigne, T. and Sartory, P.K. 1974. The teeth of three bivalved gastropods and three other species of the order Sacoglossa. With an appendix on *Calliopaea oophaga* n.sp., a new sacoglossan by H. Lemche. *Proceedings of the Malacological Society of London* 41:109–26.

Gascoigne, T. and Sordi, M. 1980. A redescription of *Placida viridis* Trinchese, 1873 (Gastropoda: Ascoglossa). *Journal of Conchology* 30:167–79.

Giles, K.L. and Sarafis, V. 1974. The importance of riescent integuments as a new structural feature of some algal chloroplasts. *Nature* 248:512.

Gosliner, T.M. 1987. *Nudibranchs of southern Africa. A guide to opisthobranch molluscs of southern Africa*. Monterey and El Cajon: Sea Challengers and Jeff Hamann.

Gosliner, T.M. and Ghiselin, M.T. 1984. Parallel evolution in opisthobranch gastropods and its implications for phylogenetic methodology. *Systematic Zoology* 33:255–74.

Greene, R.W. 1970. Symbiosis in sacoglossan opisthobranchs: symbiosis with algal chloroplasts. *Malacologia* 10:357–68.

Hay, M.E., Duffy, J.E., Paul, V.J., Renaud, P.E. and Fenical, W. 1990. Specialist herbivores reduce their susceptibility to predation by feeding on the chemically defended seaweed *Avrainvillea longicaulis*. *Limnology and Oceanography* 35:1734–43.

Hay, M.E. and Fenical, W. 1988. Marine plant–herbivore interactions: the ecology of chemical defense. *Annual Review of Ecology and Systematics* 19:111–45.

Hay, M.E., Pawlik, J.R., Duffy, J.E. and Fenical W. 1989. Seaweed-herbivore-predator interactions: host-plant specialization reduces predation on small herbivores. *Oecologia* 81:418–27.

Hinde, R. 1980. Chloroplast 'symbiosis' in sacoglossan molluscs. In *Endocytobiology, Endosymbiosis and Cell Biology. Vol. 1* (ed. W. Schwemmler and H.E.A. Schenk), 729–36. Berlin: Walter de Gruyter.

Hinde, R. and Smith, D.C. 1974. Chloroplast symbiosis and extent to which it occurs in Sacoglossa (Gastropoda - Mollusca). *Biological Journal of the Linnean Society* 6:349–56.

Hinde, R. and Smith, D.C. 1975. Role of photosynthesis in nutrition of mollusc *Elysia viridis*. *Biological Journal of the Linnean Society* 7:161–71.

Hori, T. and Ueda, R. 1967. Electron microscope studies on the fine structure of plastids in siphonous green algae with special reference to their phylogenetic relationships. *Science Reports of the Tokyo Kyoiku Daigaku Section B* 12:225–44.

Hughes, R.N. 1980. Optimal foraging theory in the marine context. *Oceanography and Marine Biology Annual Review* 18:423–81.

Ireland, C. and Faulkner, J. 1981. The metabolites of the marine molluscs *Tridachiella diomedea* and *Tridachia crispata*. *Tetrahedron* (Supplement) 37:233–40.

Ireland, C., Faulkner, D.J., Finer, J. and Clardy, J. 1979. Crispatone, a metabolite of the opisthobranch mollusc *Tridachia crispata*. *Journal of the American Chemical Society* 101:1275–6.

Ireland, C., Faulkner, D.J., Solheim, B.A. and Clardy, J. 1978. Tridachione, a propionate-derived metabolite of the opisthobranch mollusc *Tridachiella diomedea*. *Journal of the American Chemical Society* 100:1002–3.

Ireland, C. and Scheuer, P.J. 1979. Photosynthetic marine molluscs: in vivo ^{14}C incorporation into metabolites of the sacoglossan *Placobranchus ocellatus*. *Science* 205:922–3.

Jensen, K. 1975. Food preference and food consumption in relation to growth of *Limapontia capitata* (Opisthobranchia, Sacoglossa). *Ophelia* 14:1–14.

Jensen, K.R. 1980a. A review of sacoglossan diets, with comparative notes on radular and buccal anatomy. *Malacological Review* 13:55–77.

Jensen, K.R. 1980b. *Oxynoe azuropunctata* n.sp., a new sacoglossan from the Florida Keys (Mollusca: Opisthobranchia). *Journal of Molluscan Studies* 46:282–92.

Jensen, K.R. 1980c. Factors affecting feeding selectivity in herbivorous sacoglossans. Ph.D. Dissertation, Florida Institute of Technology, 144 pp.

Jensen, K.R. 1981a. Observations on feeding methods in some Florida ascoglossans. *Journal of Molluscan Studies* 47:190–9.

Jensen, K.R. 1981b. Influence of filament diameter on food preference and growth in *Oxynoe azuropunctata* Jensen, 1980 and *Elysia cauze* Marcus, 1957 (Opisthobranchia: Ascoglossa). *Ophelia* 20:127–35.

Jensen, K.R. 1982. Chemoreception as a factor in food location of *Elysia cauze* Marcus (Opisthobranchia, Ascoglossa). *Marine Behaviour and Physiology* 8:205–18.

Jensen, K.R. 1983. Factors affecting feeding selectivity in herbivorous Ascoglossa (Mollusca: Opisthobranchia). *Journal of Experimental Marine Biology and Ecology* 66:135–48.

Jensen, K.R. 1984. Defensive behavior and toxicity of ascoglossan opisthobranch *Mourgona germaineae* Marcus. *Journal of Chemical Ecology* 10:475–86.

Jensen, K.R. 1985. Annotated checklist of Hong Kong Ascoglossa (Mollusca: Opisthobranchia), with descriptions of four new species. In *Proceedings of the Second International Workshop on the Malacofauna of Hong Kong and Southern China, Hong Kong, 1983* (ed. B. Morton and D. Dudgeon), 77–107. Hong Kong: Hong Kong University Press.

Jensen, K.R. 1986. Observations on feeding, copulation and spawning of the ascoglossan opisthobranch *Calliopaea oophaga* Lemche. *Ophelia* 25:97–106.

Jensen, K.R. 1988. Chemoreception in six species of Florida Ascoglossa (Mollusca: Opisthobranchia), a comparative study of responses to homogenates of food and non-food plants. *Ophelia* 28:231–42.

Jensen, K.R. 1989. Learning as a factor in diet selection in *Elysia viridis* (Montagu) (Mollusca, Opisthobranchia). *Journal of Molluscan Studies* 55:79–88.

Jensen, K.R. 1990a. Three new species of Ascoglossa (Mollusca, Opisthobranchia) from Hong Kong, and a description of the internal anatomy of *Costasiella pallida* Jensen, 1985. In *Proceedings of the Second International Marine Biological Workshop: The Marine Flora & Fauna of Hong Kong & Southern China, Hong Kong 1986* (ed. B. Morton), 419–32. Hong Kong: Hong Kong University Press.

Jensen, 1990b. Feeding behaviour of some Hong Kong Ascoglossa (Mollusca, Opisthobranchia). In *Proceedings of the Second International Marine Biological Workshop: The Marine Flora & Fauna of Hong Kong & Southern China, Hong Kong 1986* (ed. B. Morton), 961–77. Hong Kong: Hong Kong University Press.

Jensen, K.R. 1991a. Comparison of alimentary systems in shelled and non-shelled Ascoglossa (Mollusca, Opisthobranchia). *Acta Zoologica* 72:143–50

Jensen, K.R. 1991b. Foraging behaviour of two Australian species of *Elysia* (Mollusca, Opisthobranchia). In *Proceedings of the Third International Marine Biological Workshop: The Marine Flora and Fauna of Albany, Western Australia* (ed. F.E. Wells, D.I. Walker, H. Kirkman and R. Lethbridge), 541–51. Perth: Western Australian Museum.

Jensen, K.R. 1992. Anatomy of some Indo-Pacific Elysiidae (Opisthobranchia: Sacoglossa (=Ascoglossa)) with a discussion of the generic division and phylogeny. *Journal of Molluscan Studies* 58:257–96.

Jensen, K.R. 1993a. Sacoglossa (Mollusca, Opisthobranchia) from Rottnest Island and central Western Australia. In *Proceedings of the Fifth International Marine Biological Workshop: The Marine Flora and Fauna of Rottnest Island, Western Australia* (ed. F.E. Wells, D.I. Walker, H. Kirkman and R. Lethbridge), 207–53. Perth: Western Australian Museum.

Jensen, K.R. 1993b. Morphological adaptations and plasticity of radular teeth of the Sacoglossa (= Ascoglossa) (Mollusca: Opisthobranchia) in relation to their food plants. *Biological Journal of the Linnean Society* 48:135–55.

Jensen, K.R. In press. Evolution of buccal apparatus and diet radiation in the Sacoglossa (Opisthobranchia). *Bolletino Malacologico, Milano*.

Jensen, K.R. and Wells, F.E. 1990. Sacoglossa (= Ascoglossa) (Mollusca, Opisthobranchia) from southern Western Australia. In *Proceedings of the Third International Marine Biological Flora and Fauna of the Albany Area* (ed. F.E. Wells, D.I. Walker, H. Kirkman and R. Lethbridge), 297–331. Perth: Western Australian Museum.

Kawaguti, S. and Yamasu, T. 1966. Feeding and spawning habits of a bivalved gastropod, *Julia japonica*. *Biological Journal of Okayama University* 12:1–9.

Kay, E.A. 1968. A review of the bivalved gastropods and a discussion of evolution within the Sacoglossa. *Symposia of the Zoological Society of London* 22:109–34.

Lewin, R.A. 1970. Toxin secretion and tail autotomy by irritated *Oxynoe panamensis* (Opisthobranchia; Sacoglossa). *Pacific Science* 24:356–8.

Marcus, E. de B.-R. 1982. Systematics of the genera of the order Ascoglossa (Gastropoda). *Journal of Molluscan Studies* (Supplement) 10:1–31.

Marcus, E. and Marcus, E. 1967. Opisthobranchs from the Gulf of California. *Studies in Tropical Oceanography* 6:141–248.

McLean, N. 1976. Phagocytosis of chloroplasts in *Placida dendritica* (Gastropoda: Sacoglossa). *Journal of Experimental Zoology* 197:321–30.

Muscatine, L. and Greene, R.W. 1973. Chloroplasts and algae as symbionts in molluscs. *International Review of Cytology* 36:137–69.

Norris, J.N. and Fenical, W. 1982. Chemical defense in tropical marine algae. In *The Atlantic*

Barrier Reef Ecosystem at Carrie Bow Cay, Belize, I. Structure and Communities (ed. K. Rutzler and J.G. Macintyre), 417–31. Smithsonian Contributions to Marine Science. Vol. 12. Washington, D.C.: Smithsonian Institution Press.

Paul, V.J. 1987. Feeding deterrent effects of algal natural products. *Bulletin of Marine Science* 41:514–22.

Paul, V.J. and Fenical, W. 1986. Chemical defense in tropical green algae, order Caulerpales. *Marine Ecology Progress Series* 34:157–69.

Paul, V.J. and Hay, M.E. 1986. Seaweed susceptibility to herbivory: chemical and morphological correlates. *Marine Ecology Progress Series* 33:255–64.

Paul, V.J. and Van Alstyne, K.L. 1988. Use of ingested algal diterpenoids by *Elysia halimeda* Macnae (Opisthobranchia: Ascoglossa) as antipredator defenses. *Journal of Experimental Marine Biology and Ecology* 119:15–29.

Rasmussen, E. 1973. Systematics and ecology of the Isefjord marine fauna (Denmark). *Ophelia* 11:1–507.

Taylor, W. 1972. *Marine algae of the eastern tropical and subtropical coasts of the Americas.* Ann Arbor: University of Michigan Press.

Thompson, T.E. 1977. Jamaican opisthobranch molluscs I. *Journal of Molluscan Studies* 43:93–140.

Thompson, T.E. 1979. Biology and relationships of the South African sacoglossan mollusc *Volvatella laguncula. Journal of Zoology, London* 189:339–47.

Thompson, T.E. and Jarman, G.M. 1989. Nutrition of *Tridachia crispata* (Mörch) (Sacoglossa). *Journal of Molluscan Studies* 55:239–44.

Trench, R.K. 1975. Of 'leaves that crawl': functional chloroplasts in animal cells. *Symposia of the Society of Experimental Biology* 29:229–65.

Trench, R.K., Trench, M.E. and Muscatine, L. 1972. Symbiotic chloroplasts; their photosynthetic products and contribution to mucus synthesis in two marine slugs. *Biological Bulletin* 142:335–49.

Usuki, I. 1977. Effects of food algae on the nutrition of *Ercolania boodleae* (Baba) (Opisthobranchia, Gastropoda). *Japanese Journal of Ecology* 27:103–10.

Vest, S.E., Dawes, C.J. and Romeo, J.T. 1983. Distribution of caulerpin and caulerpicin in eight species of the green alga *Caulerpa* (Caulerpales). *Botanica Marina* 26:313–6.

Waugh, G.R. and Clark, K.B. 1986. Seasonal and geographic variation in chlorophyll level of *Elysia tuca* (Ascoglossa: Opisthobranchia). *Marine Biology* 92:483–7.

Womersley, H.B.S. 1984. *The Marine Benthic Flora of Southern Australia. Part I.* South Australia: Government Printer.

The Marine Biology of the South China Sea
(ed. B. Morton). Proceedings of the First
International Conference on the Marine
Biology of Hong Kong and the South China Sea,
Hong Kong, 28 October – 3 November 1990.
Hong Kong: Hong Kong University Press, 1993.

THE RELATIONSHIP BETWEEN HERBIVOROUS MOLLUSCS AND ALGAE ON MODERATELY EXPOSED HONG KONG SHORES

Gray A. Williams

The Swire Marine Laboratory, The University of Hong Kong,
Cape d'Aguilar, Hong Kong

ABSTRACT

The zonation patterns of intertidal herbivorous molluscs and their algal food supply are described for the summer of 1990 on two Hong Kong rocky shores. Both shores were characterized by an increase in herbivore species at mid to low tide, the upper levels being dominated by littorines. The standing crop of algae increased in a down shore direction; the mid and lower levels being dominated by encrusting species and blue-green algae. Erect macroalgae were only found very low on the shore and were rare in the summer months. Herbivore distribution is probably limited by physical constraints and species are limited to crevices and pools during low water; few were found on open rock surfaces.

Exclusion of herbivores from areas of the mid shore did not affect microalgal abundance suggesting that physical as opposed to biological factors control the production of algae at this level during the summer months. Macroalgal sporelings did settle in herbivore exclosures at this level, although they did not flourish. On the low shore microalgae increased in herbivore exclusions and small turfs of green and blue-green algae developed. The effect of herbivore removal at this level suggests that lower on the shore biological factors are important in structuring the community during the summer months.

INTRODUCTION

There have been relatively few detailed investigations of tropical or sub-tropical shores, the notable exception being the study of the Panamanian Coast (see Menge *et al.* 1986a, b and references therein). These shores often appear barren of life, especially macroalgae, on casual inspection (Menge and Lubchenco 1981; Menge *et al.* 1986a). Closer inspection, however, reveals the presence of encrusting algae, numerous herbivorous molluscs (often hiding in crevices and cracks; Menge *et al.* 1983, 1985) and highly mobile predators, although zonation patterns tend to be less clearly delimited than on temperate rocky shores (Garrity and Levings 1981; Menge and Lubchenco 1981). Patterns on tropical, Panamanian, shores show little seasonal variation, primarily due to the constant physical conditions experienced in these regions (Menge and Lubchenco 1981).

Being sub-tropical, Hong Kong experiences seasonal variation in physical conditions which are reflected by the communities inhabiting the shores (Morton and Morton 1983). During the winter months erect forms of macroalgae, e.g., *Bangia*, *Porphyra* and *Sargassum*, appear on the shore. These species are only found between November and March and the algal flora is dominated by perennial encrusting forms and microalgal films for the rest of the year (Morton and Morton 1983; Hodgkiss 1984; Ho 1986). The seasonal variation in algal species and abundance is not reflected by the herbivores on the shore. These species (mostly molluscs) are dominant throughout the year, although there is evidence for seasonal variation in their behaviour and vertical distribution (J. Liu unpublished data; personal observation).

Physical stress has been suggested as limiting algal abundance and diversity during the summer months (May to September, Hodgkiss 1984). During these months low water spring tides occur at midday and the seas are usually calm, resulting in high temperatures and associated desiccation stress on the shore (Moore 1972). During winter months conditions are more benign for algae and wave action ensures little physical stress from high temperatures on the shore. The flora on Panamanian shores is thought to be controlled indirectly by the predictability of the tropical environment (Menge and Lubchenco 1981; Lubchenco *et al.* 1984; Menge *et al.* 1986a) promoting high predation pressure which does not allow prey species (especially algae) to attain the escapes, either in space or time, which are available in more physically variable temperate systems. The physical environment experienced on Hong Kong shores is less extreme than these tropical shores, and more seasonally variable; consequently escapes from predation may be more likely on these shores than on the tropical shores discussed by Lubchenco *et al.* (1984) where erect macroalgae are rarely found. Therefore, shores in sub-tropical regions may be directly structured by biological factors acting seasonally, as well as by physical factors.

This paper investigates the zonation patterns of algae and herbivorous molluscs on two moderately exposed Hong Kong shores during the summer months and describes some preliminary experiments to investigate the role of grazing molluscs in structuring the algal assemblage. Molluscs were the dominant herbivores found on these shores, although other grazers such as the grapsid crab *Grapsus albolineatus* Lamarck and the urchin *Anthocidaris crassispina* (A. Agassiz) were also present.

MATERIALS AND METHODS

Sites and timing

All experiments and surveys were carried out on two rocky shores (A and B) at Cape d'Aguilar, Hong Kong (Fig. 1) during the summer (June–August) of 1990. Both shores were situated on the peninsula of Hok Tsui and had similar aspects, although their topographies were not identical (Fig. 2).

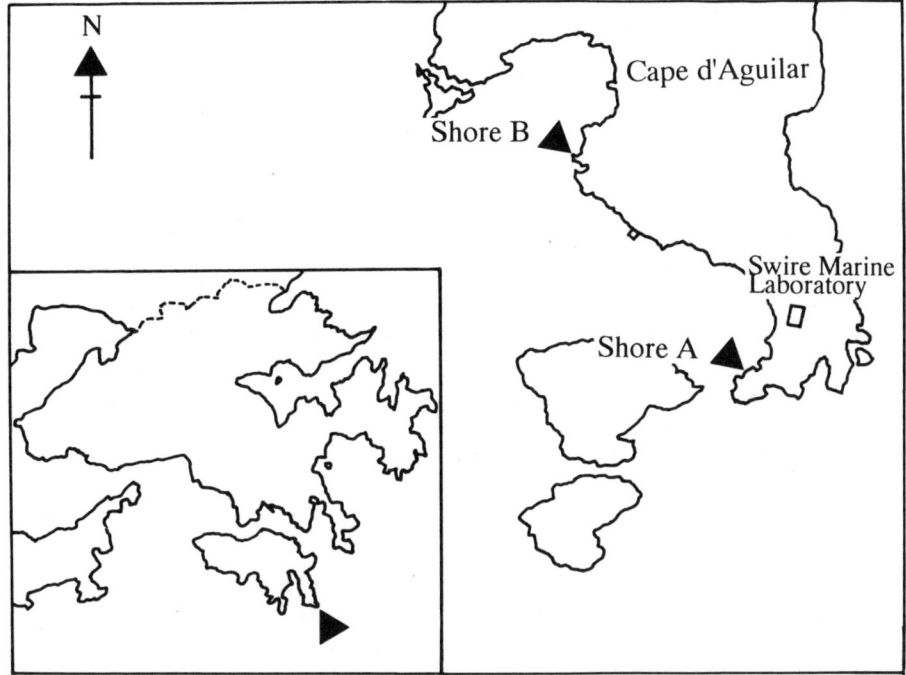

Fig. 1. Map of Hong Kong and the Cape d'Aguilar peninsula showing the location of the shores investigated.

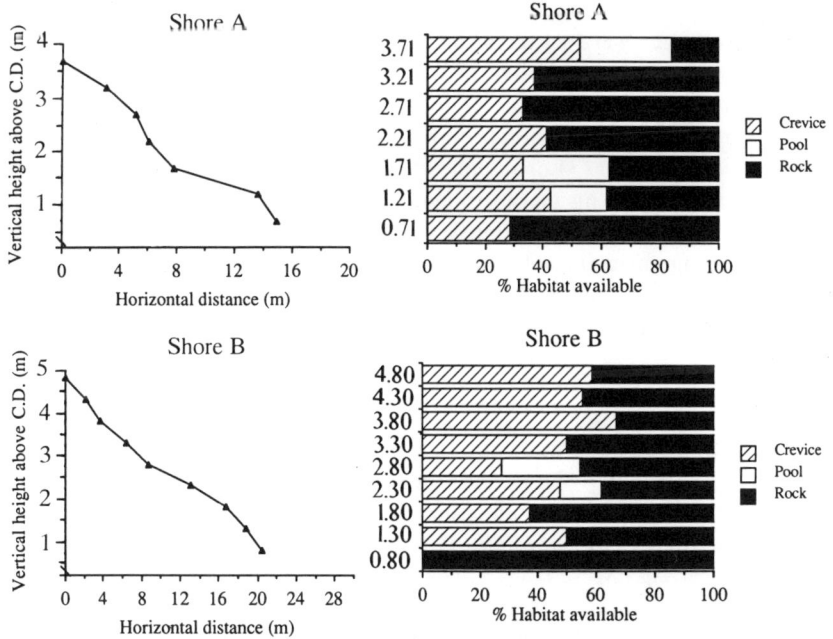

Fig. 2. Shore profiles and microhabitat availability.

Vertical zonation patterns

At both sites a stratified random sampling regime was adopted at each 0.5 m vertical drop in the shore. The vertical gradient was levelled (to C.D.) and a fixed point was marked at each height interval. On inspection the microhabitats of both shores could be divided into three main categories: open rock; rock pools and crevices (cracks deeper than 5 mm). At each height ten 25 x 25 cm quadrats were sampled for each habitat present (therefore if two habitat types were present twenty quadrats were sampled), except at the lowest site on Shore B where wave action only allowed seven quadrats to be sampled. The location of quadrats was determined randomly and thus allowed an assessment of the overall habitat composition at each height (Fig. 2). In each quadrat the abundance and species of herbivores present was recorded and the percentage cover of algae scored using a double strung 100-point quadrat (Jones *et al.* 1980). At each height, 10 random areas of rock (approximately 5 cm^2) were removed, using a hammer and chisel, for chlorophyll analysis.

Chlorophyll analysis

Rock fragments were transported back to the laboratory and analysed for chlorophyll using the hot methanol method (HMSO 1986; Hill and Hawkins 1990). Often, replicates were lost due to high turbidity readings (especially high shore samples) and these were either resampled or removed from the analysis (the number of replicates from each height was never less than 7).

Exclusion experiments

To investigate the effect of molluscan herbivores on the abundance and distribution of algae, exclusion cages were set up on Shore A. Cages (25 x 25 cm) made from chicken wire (mesh size 5 x 5 mm) were set up at two heights, about 1.5 and 1.0 m above C.D. The experimental design involved six replicates of three treatments at each height. The treatments were: (1) total exclusion (- herbivores, + cage); (2) cage control (partial cage, + herbivores, + cage) and (3) open control (no cage, + herbivores, - cage). The cages effectively excluded grazing molluscs and were frequently examined, no other herbivores were seen in the cages. In the initial two months pieces of rock were chipped from the cage (removing about 0.5% [2–3 cm^2] of the surface area at each sample date) and analysed for chlorophyll. After this period percentage cover of algae in the treatments was recorded in a similar manner to the vertical transect.

Note on taxonomy

Taxonomic descriptions of a number of species are unclear in tropical and sub-tropical regions (Garrity 1984). For the purpose of this paper certain species have been given generic names or identified as collections of species. Therefore *'Lithophyllum'* refers to pink crustose algae; *Hildenbrandia* is probably *H. prototypus* Nardo and *Ralfsia* is probably *R. verrucosa* (Aresch) J.Ag. The blue-green algae are at least three species in the genera *Anacystis*, *Calothrix* (?) and *Oscillatoria*; *Brachytrichia maculans* (Gom) has been described as *Kyrtuthrix maculans* Umezaki. The littorinids are named following Morton and Morton (1983). Reid (in press) has recently reviewed this genus and considers *Nodilittorina pyramidalis* Quoy and Gaimard to be a junior synonym of *N. trochoides* (Gray), *N. exigua* Dunker that of *N. radiata* (Eydoux and Souleyet) and *N. millegrana* Philippi that of *N. vidua* Gould. For convenience, however, the old names have been retained prior to publication of Reid's work.

RESULTS

The vertical distribution of species was similar on shores A and B (Figs. 3 and 4). The upper shore, higher than 2.0 m above C.D., was dominated by the littorinids *N. pyramidalis* and *N. exigua* (a few *N. millegrana* were also found). No macroalgae were present at this height, although lichens were found above 3.5 m on shore B and blue-green algae were recorded on both shores below 3.0 m. A conspicuous band of the colonial blue-green *Brachytrichia maculans* was recorded between 1.5–2.5 m on shore A and was also present in lower densities at the same level on shore B.

The greatest diversity of herbivores and algae was found at midshore (about 1.5 m above C.D.): eleven grazers being found on shore A, 9 on shore B and three species of encrusting algae on both shores. The dominant grazers were *Monodonta labio* L. and *Liolophura japonica* Lischke on shore A and *Patelloida saccharina* L., *Cellana toreuma* Reeve, *Liolophura japonica* and the two *Siphonaria* species on shore B (Figs. 3 and 4). The abundance of these species was, in general, higher on shore B than on shore A and on both shores greatest abundance was between about 1.0–1.5 m. The encrusting algae increased in abundance below 1.5 m with *Ralfsia*, *Hildenbrandia* and *Lithophyllum* being dominant (although some of the *Lithophyllum* was bleached). On shore B erect macroalgal species such as *Gymnogyrus flabelliformis* Harvey (holdfasts only) and *Corallina sessilis* Yendo were recorded low on the shore (below about 1.0 m above C.D.).

Analysis of microhabitat occupation by herbivores revealed that all species were patchily distributed being absent from open rock surfaces, preferring crevices or rock pools (Table 1). Active selection depends on habitat availability, and due to variation in this (Fig. 2) no firm conclusions concerning herbivore preference of pools over crevices at different tidal levels can be made. Some species, however, did seem to prefer pools if given a choice, e.g., *N. pyramidalis* (personal observation).

Total algal abundance (i.e., including macro / microalgae and endolithic algae), as estimated using chlorophyll analysis, was greater lower on the shore (Fig. 5; One Way Analysis of Variance [log transformed data] for Shore A: $F = 9.82$; $d°f = 6,62$; $P < 0.01$; Shore B: $F = 12.16$; $d°f = 8,74$; $P < 0.01$). Variation was quite high on Shore A both within and between tidal heights emphasizing the patchy distribution of the algae. Values at 1.71 m above C.D. on shore A were especially variable; the mean value at this height should be considered with some caution as it was associated with three very high replicate values suggesting a highly patchy distribution. The large increase in chlorophyll at the lowest height on shore B was associated with the inclusion of the holdfasts of *Gymnogyrus*, an erect macroalga, at this level.

Exclusion experiments

There was no significant difference in the chlorophyll content of any of the treatments at the mid shore site (at about 1.50 m above C.D.) (Fig. 6, Table 2). Variation was quite

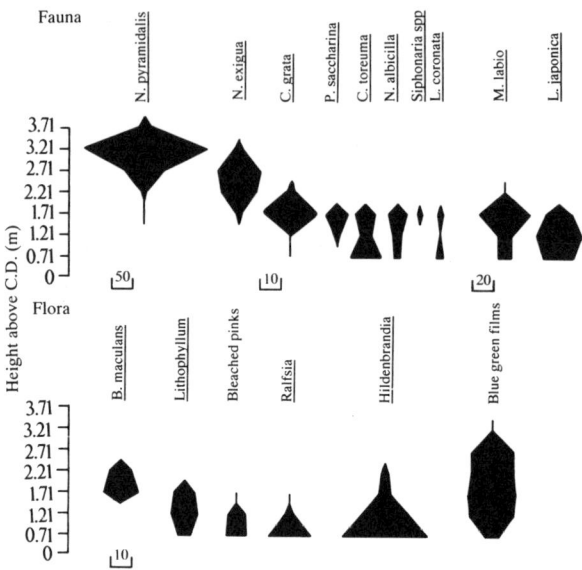

Fig. 3. Vertical distribution patterns of dominant molluscan herbivores and algae on shore A. Values are mean densities·m^{-2} for herbivores and mean (arc-sine transformed) percentage cover for algae. Note the different scales for herbivore abundance. *Chlorostoma rustica* and *Nodilittorina millegrana* were also found in small numbers. Bleached algae refers to algae bleached white by the sun.

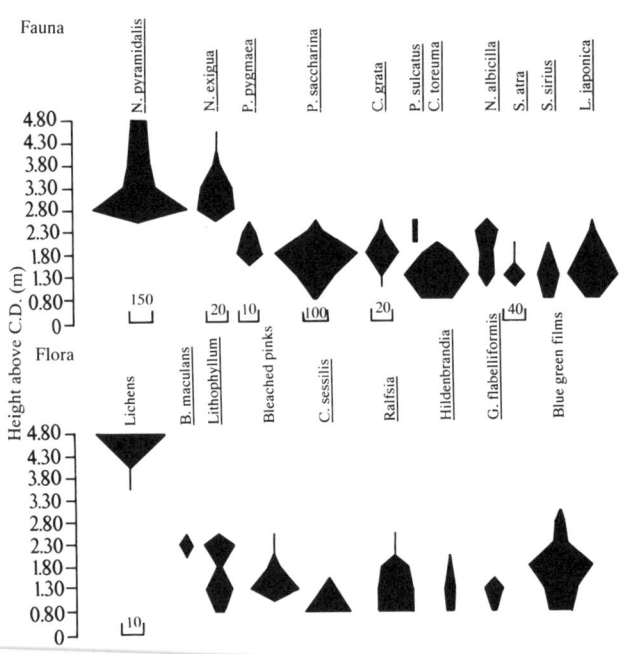

Fig. 4. Vertical distribution patterns of dominant molluscan herbivores and algae on shore B. Values as in Figure 3. (Mean values for the lowest site are from 7 quadrats.) Note the different scales for herbivore abundance. *Monodonta labio* and *Nodilittorina millegrana* were also found in small numbers. Bleached algae refers to algae bleached white by the sun.

Table 1
Habitat selection by herbivores. Habitat preferences are given (where significant after a Chi-square analysis). Only species which had an abundance greater than 10.m^2·height^{-1} were used in the analysis. Those species which did not exhibit a preference are not shown.

Species preferences	Shore and height
Pools:	
N. pyramidalis	A @ 3.21 – 3.71 m
	B @ 2.80 m
L. coronata; M. labio	A @ 1.71 m
C. toreuma	A @ 0.71 – 1.21 m
P. saccharina; L. japonica	A @ 1.71 m
N. albicilla	B @ 2.30 m
Crevices:	
N. pyramidalis	A @ 1.71 – 2.71 m
	B @ 3.30 – 4.80 m
N. exigua	A @ 1.71 – 2.71 m
	B @ 2.30 – 2.80 m
C. toreuma	A @ 0.71 m
M. labio	A @ 0.71 – 1.21 m
P. saccharina; P. pygmea	B @ 2.30 m
N. albicilla	B @ 1.30 – 1.80 m
L. japonica	A @ 0.71 – 1.21 m
	B @ 1.30 – 1.80 m
Siphonaria spp	B @ 1.30 m

All species avoided open rock surfaces

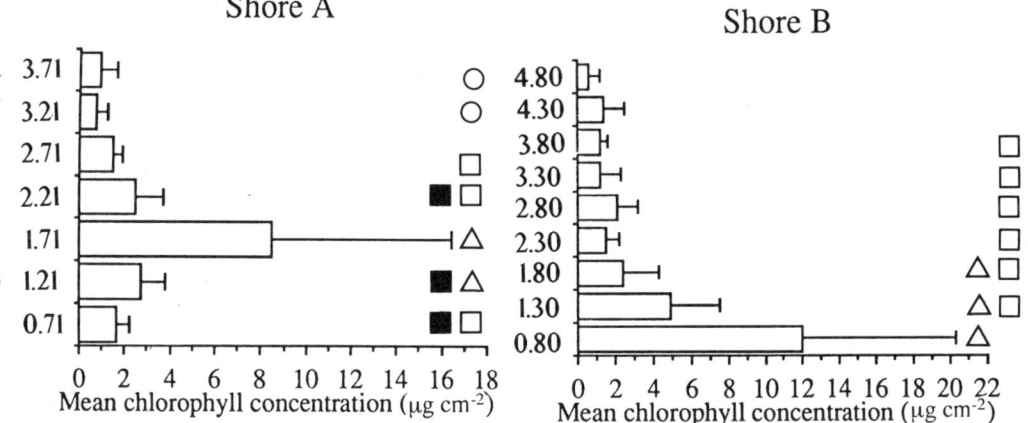

Fig. 5. Mean chlorophyll concentrations (± S.D.) along the vertical gradient of shores A and B. Heights linked with the same symbol were not significantly different (SNK Test after One Way Analysis of Variance).

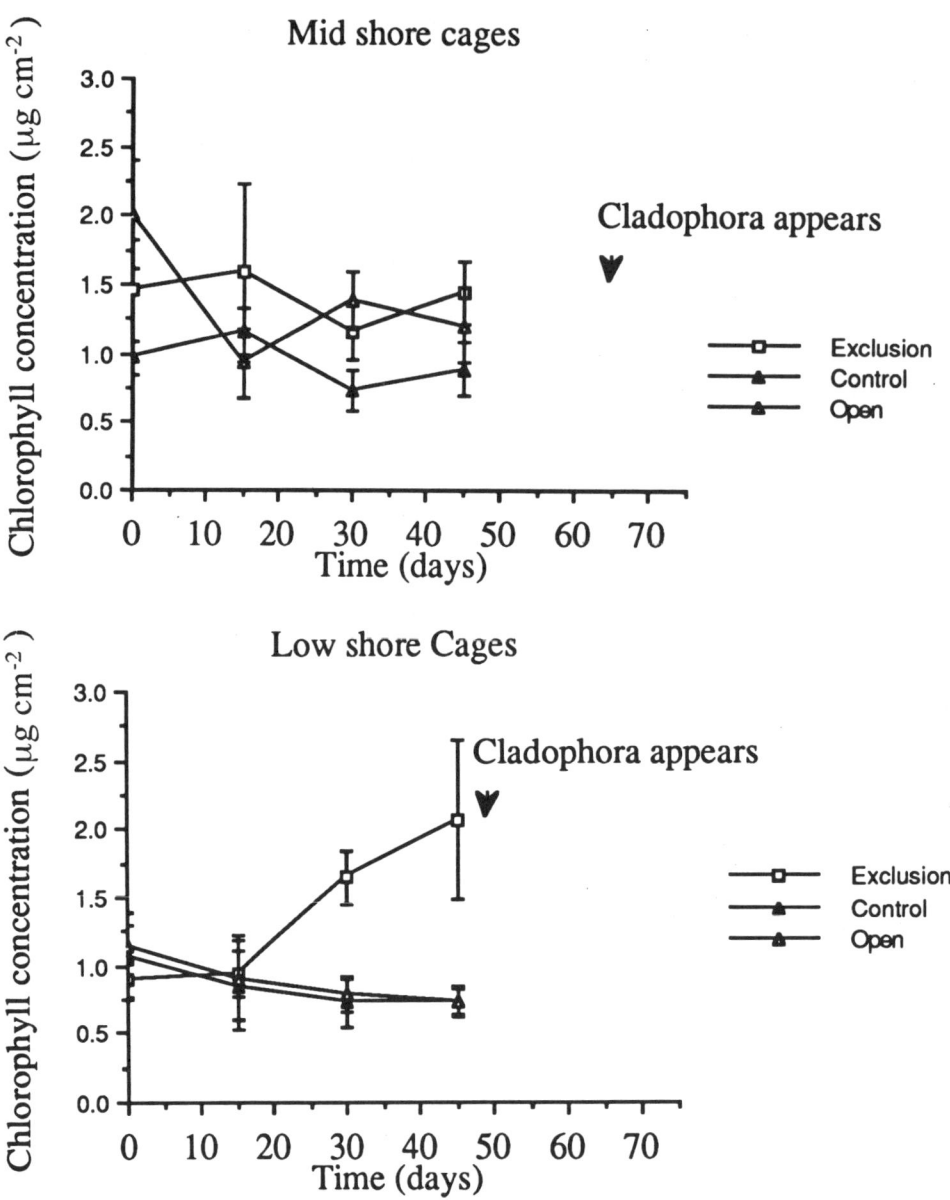

Fig. 6. Mean chlorophyll content (± S.E.) and time of appearance of macroalgae in experimental treatments at ~ 1.5 and 1.0 m above C.D. on shore A. Chlorophyll values are lower than values for the vertical transect as this survey did not include encrusting algae.

high, however, within the treatments. Variation was far less at the low shore site (at about 1.0 m above C.D.) (Fig. 6, Table 2) and the herbivore exclosure treatment had a significantly higher chlorophyll value than control treatments (Table 2). At both heights the control treatments had stable chlorophyll levels for the first two months.

Table 2
Two Way Analyses of Variance (data are log transformed) to investigate the effects of the factors time and treatment on chlorophyll concentration at mid and low shore (NS = not significant; * * $P < 0.05$).

Mid Shore

Source	D°f	Mean Square	F	Significance
Time	3	0.2618	0.95	NS
Treatment	2	0.8485	3.08	NS
Interaction	6	0.4154	1.51	NS
Error	60	0.2755		

Low shore

Source	D°f	Mean square	F	
Time	3	0.2783	1.02	NS
Treatment	2	1.8924	6.96	* *
Interaction	6	0.5248	1.93	NS
Error	60	0.2719		

After 46 days (in August) sporelings of *Cladophora* spp. and the development of a blue-green and green algal turf was noted in the low shore cages (mean cover 15%, Fig. 6). *Cladophora* sporelings were recorded at the mid shore site 19 days after the low shore site. These did not develop into the low turfs found on the low shore and often appeared bleached at low water (G.A. Williams unpublished data). At the low shore site the encrusting alga *Ralfsia* colonized herbivore exclusions after 65 days (September) and later in the year grew rapidly in some cages. Small patches (3–4 mm^2) of *Lithophyllum* were also noted at a higher level than normally found on bare rock, although *Lithophyllum* is found higher on the shore in rock pools. The development of the algal turf continued into the autumn-winter months and the mid shore site showed similar patterns but at later times than the lower shore site (G.A. Williams unpublished data). The important point to note is that low shore exclusions allowed the settlement and development of small algal turfs in the summer months.

DISCUSSION

The first description, though somewhat incomplete, of the molluscan fauna at Cape d'Aguilar was made in 1957 (Adal 1958) and these shores have been qualitatively reviewed by Morton and Morton (1983). During the summer months (June–August) these shores are very similar to those described from tropical regions (Menge and Lubchenco 1981). Both shores surveyed in this study had similar zonation patterns, although shore B had a greater variety of algal species and higher abundances of some grazing species, e.g., *P. saccharina*, although *M. labio* was more dominant on shore A. Causes of these differences between shores are not understood but may simply reflect natural variation between shores on this scale. There were few large mobile predators observed during the course of the study (including underwater observations), which is in contrast to the situation recorded for Panamanian tropical shores (Menge and Lubchenco 1981; Menge et al. 1985, 1986a).

In general, algal diversity and abundance increased down shore, a pattern recorded by other researchers in temperate and tropical regions (Raffaelli 1979; Menge and Lubchenco 1981; Underwood 1981; Hawkins and Hartnoll 1983) The abundance of chlorophyll showed a clear trend on shore B (but was less clear on shore A), of decreasing in an up shore direction as recorded on other shores (Underwood 1984). The high variability in the samples was due to the inclusion of encrusting algae on some of the rock chips and illustrates the patchy nature of the algal resource on these shores. Values for chlorophyll were within the ranges noted for other areas e.g., Australia (Underwood 1984; MacLulich 1986) (although note the correction for rock weight in their estimates) and the United Kingdom (Hill 1990).

Molluscan herbivore diversity peaked at mid–low shore. The high shore was characteristically dominated by littorinids. Similar patterns have been noted on shores world wide (Lewis 1964; Stephenson and Stephenson 1972; Raffaelli 1979; Underwood 1981; Menge and Lubchenco 1981). These patterns have been associated with changes in physical and biological factors and often the availability of microhabitat refuges (Raffaelli and Hughes 1978; Menge and Lubchenco 1981; Menge *et al.* 1983). Microhabitat selection has been shown to be of great importance in the present study: all species avoiding open rock surfaces and seeking refuge in the crevices and rock pools during low water. This type of behaviour is especially prevalent on shores where physical factors are harsh (Moore 1972; Garrity 1984). Gastropod species have been shown to exhibit a number of behavioural strategies to reduce these stresses and returning to spatial refuges is common in these animals (Wolcott 1973; Garrity and Levings 1981; Garrity 1984). The role of spatial refuges, either from physical factors or biological factors such as predation has long been recognized as important in structuring communities (Lubchenco and Gaines 1981; Menge *et al.* 1983, 1985). It would appear that these refuges are important to herbivore species on Hong Kong shores affecting their distribution, behaviour, their effect on algal assemblages (Levings and Garrity 1983) and perhaps ultimately their survival (large numbers of animals are killed high on the shore during periods of calm weather and high summer temperatures, G.A. Williams unpublished data and personal observation; see also Garrity 1984).

The grazer exclusion experiment revealed that low on the shore grazers reduce the production of the biofilm, prevent the development of a low turf of blue-green and green algae during the summer and also the settlement and growth of *Ralfsia* and *Lithophyllum* in the autumn (G.A. Williams unpublished data). Higher on the shore, however, grazers did not affect biofilm production but did affect settlement of green algal sporelings. Sporelings at this level did not form the felt-like turfs found at low shore and often appeared bleached at low water suggesting that physical factors were ultimately limiting at this level. It would appear that low on the shore grazers are having a significant effect on growth and production at both the micro- and macro-algal level in the summer months. Higher on the shore physical factors appear more important and although macroalgae do settle they do not develop in the summer months. Few escapes by algae are allowed by grazers at low shore, but when there is an escape the algae can utilize this reduction in grazer predation.

During the summer months, when influenced by the Hainan current from the South China Sea (Morton and Morton 1983), the shores of Hong Kong are similar to more tropical shores in the patterns seen. Refuges from physical factors appear the most important factors controlling the fauna and flora during these months although at lower levels on the shore biological factors such as escapes from grazing are important. In the winter months Hong Kong is influenced by the Kurish current from China bringing cooler, more temperate waters. Sea conditions are usually high and waves cover much of the shore, reducing desiccation stress (G.A. Williams personal observation). During these months erect macroalgae do occur on Hong Kong's shores, possibly due to escapes from herbivory, reduced physical stresses or the introduction of algal propagules from the north (the paucity of algae in the summer may simply represent the lack of propagules available). It would appear, therefore, that seasonal variation in the relative importance of physical and biological factors on Hong Kong shores allows the existence of different algal assemblages during the year.

ACKNOWLEDGEMENTS.

This work was supported by a Hong Kong University Research Grant. Thanks to Billy Hau Chi Hang for excellent field assistance and Dr Andy Hill for advising on chlorophyll extraction and investigation of the biofilm. Dr Colin Little commented on the manuscript.

REFERENCES

Adal, M.N. 1958. A collection of molluscs from Cape D'Aguilar. *Hong Kong University Fisheries Journal* 2:125–7.
Garrity, S.D. 1984. Some adaptations of gastropods to physical stress on a tropical rocky shore. *Ecology* 65:559–74.
Garrity, S.D. and Levings, S.C. 1981. A predator-prey interaction between two physically and biologically constrained tropical rocky shore gastropods: direct, indirect and community effects. *Ecological Monographs* 51:267–86.
Hawkins, S.J. and Hartnoll, R.G. 1983. Grazing of intertidal algae by marine invertebrates. *Oceanography and Marine Biology Annual* Review 21:195–282.
Hill, A.S. 1990. The ecology of microbial films on moderately exposed shores on the Isle of Man. Unpublished Ph.D. Thesis, University of Liverpool.
Hill, A.S. and Hawkins, S.J. 1990. An investigation of methods for sampling microbial films on rocky shores. *Journal of the Marine Biological Association of the United Kingdom* 70:77–88.
HMSO 1986. The determination of chlorophyll *a* in aquatic environments, Vol. 4. In *Methods for the examination of water and associated materials, Section 2*. London: HMSO.
Ho, Y.B. 1986. Common intertidal algae of the southern part of Hong Kong Island. *Memoirs of the Hong Kong Natural History Society* 17:103–6.
Hodgkiss, I.J. 1984. Seasonal patterns of intertidal algal distribution in Hong Kong. *Asian Marine Biology* 1:49–57.
Jones, W.E., Bennell, S., Beveridge, C., McConnell, B., Mack-Smith, S. and Mitchell, J. 1980. Methods of data collection and processing in rocky intertidal monitoring. In *The shore environment Volume 1: Methods* (ed. J.H. Price, D.E. Irvine and W.F. Farnham), 137–70. London: Academic Press.
Levings, S.C. and Garrity, S.D. 1983. Diel and tidal movement of two co-occurring neritid snails; differences in grazing patterns on a tropical rocky shore. *Journal of Experimental Marine Biology and Ecology* 67:261–78.
Lewis, J. 1964. *The ecology of rocky shores*. London: English Universities Press.
Lubchenco, J. and Gaines, S.D. 1981. A unified approach to marine plant-herbivore interactions. I. Populations and communities. *Annual Review of Ecology and Systematics* 12:405–37.

Lubchenco, J., Menge, B.A., Garrity, S.D., Lubchenco, P.J., Ashkenas, L.R., Gaines, S.D., Emlet, R., Lucas, J. and Strauss, S. 1984. Structure, persistence, and role of consumers in a tropical rocky intertidal community (Taboguilla Island, Bay of Panama). *Journal of Experimental Marine Biology and Ecology* 78:23–73.

MacLulich, J.H. 1986. Experimental evaluation of methods for sampling and assaying intertidal epilithic microalgae. *Marine Ecology Progress Series* 34:275–80.

Menge, B.A. and Lubchenco, J. 1981. Community organization in temperate and tropical rocky intertidal habitats: prey refuges in relation to consumer pressure gradients. *Ecological Monographs* 51:429–50.

Menge, B.A., Ashkenas, L.R. and Matson, A. 1983. Use of artificial holes in studying community development in cryptic marine habitats in a tropical intertidal region. *Marine Biology* 77:129–42.

Menge, B.A., Lubchenco, J. and Ashkenas, L.R. 1985. Diversity, heterogeneity and consumer pressure in a tropical rocky intertidal community. *Oecologia* 65:394–405.

Menge, B.A., Lubchenco, J., Ashkenas, L.R. and Ramsey, F. 1986a. Experimental separation of effects of consumers on sessile prey in the low zone of a rocky shore in the bay of Panama: direct and indirect consequences of food web complexity. *Journal of Experimental Marine Biology and Ecology* 100:255–69.

Menge, B.A., Lubchenco, J., Gaines, S.D. and Ashkenas, L.R. 1986b. A test of the Menge-Sutherland model of community organization in a tropical rocky intertidal food web. *Oecologia* 71:75–89.

Moore, H.B. 1972. Aspects of stress in the tropical marine environment. *Advances in Marine Biology* 10:217–69.

Morton, B. and Morton, J. 1983. *The seashore ecology of Hong Kong*. Hong Kong: Hong Kong University Press.

Raffaelli, D. 1979. The grazer-algae interaction in the intertidal zone on New Zealand rocky shores. *Journal of Experimental Marine Biology and Ecology* 38:81–100.

Raffaelli, D. and Hughes, R.G. 1978. The effects of crevice size and availability on populations of *Littorina rudis* and *Littorina neritoides*. *Journal of Animal Ecology* 47:71–83.

Stephenson, T.A. and Stephenson, A. 1972. *Life between tidemarks on rocky shores*. San Francisco: W.H. Freeman and Co.

Underwood, A.J. 1981. Structure of a rocky intertidal community in New South Wales: Patterns of vertical distribution and seasonal changes. *Journal of Experimental Marine Biology and Ecology* 51:57–85.

Underwood, A.J. 1984. The vertical distribution and seasonal abundance of intertidal microalgae on a rocky shore in New South Wales. *Journal of Experimental Marine Biology and Ecology* 78:199–220.

ACTIVITY RHYTHMS AND 'HOMING' BEHAVIOUR BY TWO PAIRS OF HIGH AND LOW-ZONED INTERTIDAL LIMPETS IN HONG KONG

J.H. Liu

The Swire Marine Laboratory, The University of Hong Kong,
Cape d'Aguilar, Hong Kong

ABSTRACT

Activity rhythms and 'homing' behaviour exhibited by two pairs of high-zoned, i.e., *Cellana grata* and *C. toreuma*, and low-zoned, i.e., *Siphonaria sirius* and *Patelloida saccharina*, intertidal limpets, have been investigated over diurnal and tidal cycles in a tide tank. *C. grata* and *C. toreuma* were found to be active only while submerged and during both the day and the night. Exhibiting no homing behaviour, periods of inactivity were spent on the vertical or under-surfaces of rocks. *Siphonaria sirius* and *Patelloida saccharina* both homed to a scar and were active while submerged and during both the day and the night. *C. grata* was found to be more active at night than during the day ($P < .001$). The others showed no significant difference between the probability of animals moving at night and the probability of animals moving in the day.

When removed to a tideless environment, from both the tide tank and the field, both pairs of limpets lost their tidal cycle but retained a diurnal cycle of activity and inactivity. *Cellana grata* and *C. toreuma* were active during both the day and the night but more so at night ($P < .001$) one day after removal from the tidal environment. A stronger pattern of activity at night was, however, evident after two weeks. *Siphonaria sirius* and *Patelloida saccharina* lost their homing abilities and were either continuously active or inactive one day after removal from the field but were active only at night and homed to a scar after two weeks. When transferred from the tide tank on their 'home' rocks, however, they retained their homing ability and were active only at night. Clearly, one day is insufficient time for these species to establish a new home.

After ten days removal of the same species to 24 hours photoperiods experiencing either constant darkness or constant light, both *Cellana grata* and *C. toreuma* lost their normal rhythm of light and dark regulated phases of activity and inactivity, resulting in random activity. Both *Siphonaria sirius* and *Patelloida saccharina*, however, remained inactive during periods of what would be daylight but were active during periods of what would be night, and continued to home. It appears that both *Siphonaria sirius* and *Patelloida saccharina* possess an endogenous cycle of activity and inactivity entrained by the diurnal cycle whereas *Cellana grata* and *C. toreuma* do not.

INTRODUCTION

Many marine invertebrates show rhythmic behaviour in response to the periodicity of the tides and to the diurnal cycle (Naylor 1958,1985,1988), even when removed to the uniform and tideless environment of the laboratory (Enright 1972; Klapow 1972) or when the light-dark cycle is altered (Morton 1979). Such studies have been reviewed by Brown et al. (1970), Lofts (1970) and Saunders (1977).

Morton (1969,1970,1971,1976) has suggested that many, if not all, lamellibranch bivalves have clearly defined cycles of feeding and digestion in relation to both tidal and diurnal rhythms. An endogenous rhythm of locomotor activity, regulated by the tide is implied from field experiments undertaken on the gastropods *Hydrobia ulvae* (Newell 1962) and *Cerithium* spp. (Moulton 1962), as well as from laboratory experiments upon the mud-snail *Ilyanassa obsoleta* (Stephens et al. 1954). Circatidal rhythms have also been recorded with regard to the migration, shell adduction and metabolism of various bivalves (Mori 1950; Bennett 1954; Brown 1954; Rao 1954). The snail *Nodilittorina exigua* remains stationary when dry on rock surfaces and only begins to move when splashed. They are thus more active when splashed than either when emersed or immersed (Ohgaki 1985), as is apparently the case with *Cellana toreuma* in Japan (Hirano 1979).

Endogenous circadian rhythms have been investigated for many plants and animals (Brown 1959; Harker 1964; Sollberger 1965). Most work has attempted to prove that rhythms are less dependent on environmental factors and are regulated by a so-called 'internal clock'. Beeston et al. (1979) have found that the freshwater prosobranch *Melanoides tuberculata*, entrained to a L:D 12:12 regimen, exhibited a crepuscular pattern of locomotor activity which persisted for 6 or 7 days in both constant light and constant relative darkness at a period which deviated only slightly from 24-hours, showing the rhythm to be endogenous. The free running period varied in different light intensities, being < 24-hours in constant light and > 24-hours in constant darkness, but remained about the same in constant light at different ambient temperatures. The slug *Deroceras caruanae* possesses an endogenous cycle of activity and inactivity entrained by the cycle of night and day. The slugs forage only at night. In constant darkness, *D. caruanae* loses its normal rhythm of light and dark regulated phases of activity and inactivity. The rhythm was, however, retained under conditions of constant illumination (Morton 1979).

A diurnal rhythm has been found for the unionid clam *Ligumia subrostrata* with respect to valve activity and oxygen consumption. Statistically significant rhythms of activity were identified, with higher activity levels occurring during the dark phase. No rhythm of valve activity was found in animals experiencing 24-hours light, but rhythms of oxygen consumption were retained. The activity rhythm is therefore probably exogenous, whereas the oxygen consumption rhythm was thought to be endogenous (McCorkle et al. 1979). Salanki (1964) and Salanki and Vero (1969) have shown that a diurnal periodicity can be demonstrated in the valve movements of freshwater mussels.

Salanki (1966) has shown that the daily rhythm of the marine bivalves *Pecten jacobaeus* and *Lithophaga lithophaga* depends on illumination changes and can be shifted by lengthening the light or dark periods. This author pointed out that in many cases the rhythms which do not change under constant conditions, will change when the rhythm of the controlling factor is altered, e.g., the light-dark regimen. A daily rhythm helps the organism to adapt to major environmental factors and is one of the ways of maintaining homeostasis.

Activity patterns, including foraging and homing, have been investigated for many prosobranch and pulmonate limpets, (Hewatt 1940; Galbraith 1965; Cook 1969,1971,1976; Cook and Cook 1975,1978,1981; Thomas 1973; Hartnoll and Wright 1977; Hirano 1979; Bertness et al. 1981; Verderber et al. 1983; Hulings 1985; Little 1985; Kunz and Connor 1986; Little et al. 1988, 1990; Branch 1988). The pattern of foraging and homing has been found to be variable as to when and under what conditions the various components of the pattern occur. Most limpets feed at a fixed time in relation to both the tidal and diurnal cycles. The patterns conform to the concept that feeding rhythms are geared to reduce desiccation (Cook and Cook 1978) and predation (Wells 1980). It is, however, difficult to generalize with regard to these patterns since different ones are recorded not only between closely related species, but also between individuals of the same species under different conditions or in different areas.

Limpet homing ability has been thought to be related to desiccation avoidance (Verderber et al. 1983; Kunz and Connor 1986) and a necessary consequence of the need both to forage and return to a home site where the shell accurately matches the contours of the rock. Since they lack an operculum, limpets depend upon the exactness of this match to reduce desiccation (Hartnoll and Wright 1977; Verderber et al. 1983). The home may also provide protection against wave action (Lindberg and Dwyer 1983; Branch and Cherry 1985) and predators (Underwood 1979; Branch 1981; Garrity and Levings 1983).

Homing behaviour is likely to have more functions than mentioned above. Mackay and Underwood (1977) have studied homing behaviour in the intertidal patellid limpet *Cellana tramoserica*. The controlled field experiments showed that the proportion of animals which homed was not affected by the height on the shore, force of wave action, the cover of macroalga, nor the irregularity of the substratum. Small limpets, however, homed more than large ones. Close proximity to other homing limpets causes individuals to stop homing and move away. More limpets emigrate from areas of increased density and more immigrate into areas of decreased density, when compared with control areas. Homing behaviour is an adaptation which regulates local density and dispersion to maximize utilization of food resources and, thus, to reduce intraspecific competition for food at high limpet densities.

On the rocky shore at Cape d'Aguilar, macroalgae occupy the substrata at low and high tidal levels during late autumn and winter but are sparse or absent during summer (Liu, unpublished data). At mid-shore levels, where the primary substratum is occupied by sessile animals and the encrusting algae *Ralfsia verrucosa* (Aresch.) J. Ag., *Hildenbrandtia prototypus* Nardo and *Brachytrichia quoyi* Bornet and Flahault. Here, grazing limpets are abundant. Both *Cellana grata* (Gould, 1859) and *Cellana toreuma* (Reeve, 1855) have a wide vertical distribution from mid to high shore between September and May, but only occur on the middle shore in summer (Liu, unpublished data). *Siphonaria sirius* (Pilsbry, 1894) and *Patelloida saccharina* (Linnaeus, 1758) occur low on the shore, year round. Hirano (1979) has studied the habits and activity of a field population of *Cellana toreuma* in Japan. Activity was observed during the ebb and flood tide in both the day and at night. No homing behaviour was, however, evident. Duration of movement and distance moved increased with limpet size. Apart from this study, little is known about the activity and homing behaviours of the limpets herein discussed.

MATERIALS AND METHODS

Specimens of two pairs of high-zoned, i.e., *Cellana grata* and *C. toreuma*, and low-zoned, i.e., *Siphonaria sirius* and *Patelloida accharina* were collected from Cape d'Aguilar, Hong Kong between February and March 1990 and returned to the laboratory where they were maintained in a tide tank containing aerated sea water. The tide tank design has been described by Bones *et al*. (1984). The experiments were conducted in a constant environment laboratory containing both the tide tank and the tideless aquarium and where water temperatures are maintained at 20 ± 1°C and salinities at between 30–33‰.

Individual limpets were tagged using glue-on polyethylene mollusc tags with a protective coating of Aron Alpha instant glue. Using this procedure, shells did not have to be removed from the rocks. The positions of the resting limpets were marked using paints and on graph paper. A line was painted on the shell of the animal and on the rock so that when the animal was exactly attached to its home scar the line was continuous. Activity could be detected when the line was broken.

Tidal conditions were divided into two categories: exposed and submerged (but without 'awash'). Two cycles were set up, i.e., a diurnal cycle (dark/light = 12/12 hours), and a tidal cycle (high/low/high/low = 6/6/6/6 hours).

The positions of the individual limpets on the rocks were recorded every hour and plotted on graph paper. A red light was used at night to avoid affecting the animals.

Between 11–35 individuals of *Cellana grata*, of shell length 25–35 mm; 9–25 individuals of *Cellana toreuma*, of shell length 20–30 mm; 10–20 individuals of *Siphonaria sirius*, of shell length 15–25 mm; and 8–15 individuals of *Patelloida saccharina*, of shell length 10–15 mm, were used in each experiment.

The laboratory tide tank

The tank measuring 183 x 91 x 46 cm, is constructed of 5 mm transparent perspex. The tidal rhythm is maintained by a tidal variation simulator which automatically controls the on/off operation of a seawater pump. The tide tank was designed to provide an automatic tidal system, which could be set 'in phase' with natural field conditions. The tank is illuminated and warmed by four Philips 220–230 V 150 W Comptalux 'daylight' bulbs (12318E/44), set for 12:12 light/dark illumination by a National (TB318) 24 hour timer. Thus, an automatic 12:12 light/dark system of artificial 'daylight' illumination and darkness was provided (Bones *et al*. 1984).

Food supply

Rocks covered with algae were transferred either to the tide tank or the aquarium from Cape d'Aguilar. The available food supply for foraging limpets in terms of the microflora, encrusting algae and young stages of macroalgae colonising the rock surface were examined using a light microscope.

Effects of diurnal and tidal cycles on the rhythm of activity of limpets in the tide tank

The effects of diurnal and tidal cycles on the rhythm of activity /inactivity of limpets in the tide tank were determined using the methods described above. Animals were maintained in the tide tank for at least three days before the experiments were begun. Observations upon activity were made over two separate 24 h periods.

Effects of a tideless environment

Observations on the movements of limpets were made over 24-hours periods upon rocks contained in each of four experimental perspex aquaria with running aerated sea water to determine whether or not the four limpet species possess an endogenous cycle of activity and inactivity entrained by the tidal cycle.

Two sets of animals were used in the experiments. One set was moved to the aquarium from the field; the other was removed to the aquarium from the tide tank by transfer of their 'home' rocks.

Effects of either constant darkness or constant light

Limpets used in these experiments were subjected to constant darkness or constant light for ten days to determine whether or not they possess an endogenous cycle of activity and inactivity entrained by the diurnal cycle. Constant dark conditions were created with black polyethylene bags which could be opened, in the darkened aquarium, when required. Constant light conditions of 700 lux were achieved by two lights positioned 30 cm above the experimental aquarium.

Three-dimensional chi-square test

It is hypothesized that if animals move at random over a 24-hours period, the experimental data should result in a 1:1 ratio, with regard to a 12:12 light:dark period. That is, the probability of animals moving at night is equal to the probability of animals moving in the day. This is referred to as the null hypothesis (Ho), and means that the probability of animals moving at night is not different from the probability of animals moving in the day, in a 1:1 ratio. The question to be asked, then, is whether the observed frequencies deviate significantly from the frequencies expected if the hypothesis is true. If it is concluded that Ho can be rejected, then an alternate hypothesis (H_A) will be assumed to be true, i.e., the probability of animals moving at night, might not be of equal probability to animals moving during the day.

A chi-square test was used as an overall measure of deviation using the formula:

$$X^2 = \sum_{i=1}^{r} \sum_{j=1}^{c} \sum_{e=1}^{t} \frac{(O_{ije} - E_{ije})^2}{E_{ije}}$$

Where O_{ije} is the frequency observed in row i, column j, and tier e; E_{ije} is the frequency expected in row i, column j, and tier e if the null hypothesis is ture. The number of rows, columns, and tiers are represented by r, c, and t, respectively.

Figure 1 shows the three-dimensional contingency table, where the two rows are night and day, the two columns are numbers of moved and not-moved animals, and the six (or twelve) tiers are hours.

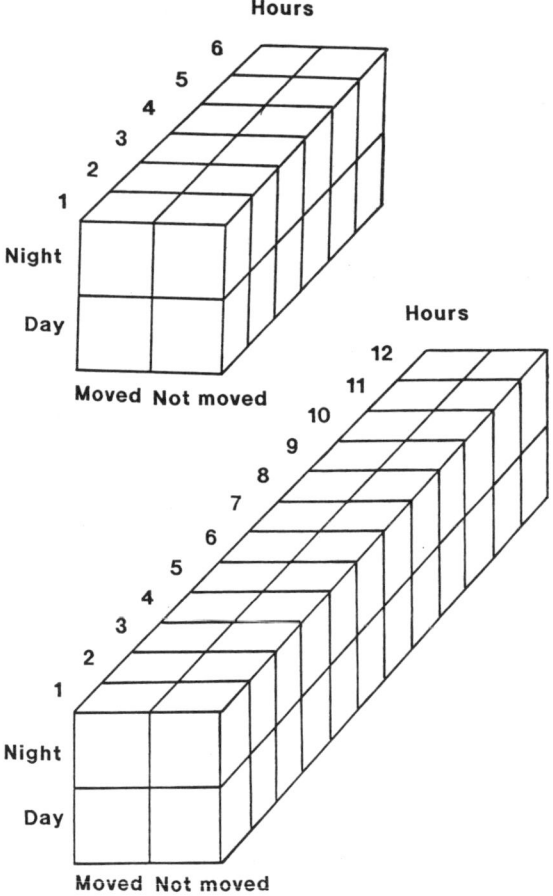

Fig. 1. A three-dimensional contingency table, where the two rows are night and day, the two columns are numbers of moved and not-moved animals, and the six or twelve tiers are hours.

In the tide tank experiments, there are six tiers of data, i.e., hours 23, 24, 1, 2, 3, and 4 for the moved and not-moved animals at night, and six tiers of data, i.e., hours 11, 12, 13, 14, 15, and 16 for the moved and not-moved animals in the day. In the tideless experiments, there are twelve tiers of data, i.e., hours 20, 21, 22, 23, 24, 1, 2, 3, 4, 5, 6, and 7 for the moved and not-moved animals at night, and twelve tiers of data, i.e., hours 8, 9, 10, 11, 12, 13, 14, 15, 16, 17, 18, and 19 for the moved and not-moved animals in the day. A table can be created for the chi-square calculations (Table 1). The observed frequencies of movement classified by: night/day, moved/not-moved and hours are shown; the expected frequency, of each class is calculated by multiplying the total number of observations for that tier by the proportion of this total that the null hypothesis predicts for the class.

In a two-dimensional chi-square test, the degrees of freedom are as follows:

$$d.f. = (r - 1) \times (c - 1)$$

where r is the rows, c is the columns. Since each tier has $r = c = 2$, there is one degree of freedom for each tier. The degrees of freedom for this three-dimensional chi-square test are the sums of the degrees of freedom for each tier. Thus, for the experiments in the tide tank, d.f. = 6; for the experiments in tideless conditions, d.f. = 12.

Table 1
Observed frequencies of animals movement classified by night/day, moved/not-moved and hours, and subsequent X^2 calculations.

Hour	Night						Hour	Day						
	Moved			Not moved				Moved			Not moved		
	O	E	$\frac{(O-E^2)}{E}$	O	E	$\frac{(O-E^2)}{E}$		O	E	$\frac{(O-E^2)}{E}$	O	E	$\frac{(O-E^2)}{E}$
23							11						
24							12						
1							13						
2							14						
3							15						
4							16						
20							8						
21							9						
22							10						
23							11						
24							12						
1							13						
2							14						
3							15						
4							16						
5							17						
6							18						
7							19						

O: Observed frequency
E: Expected frequency

RESULTS

Effects of the diurnal and tidal cycles on the rhythm of activity of limpets in the tide tank

The number of active animals was counted every hour and the percentage activity, as well as the tidal and dark-light periods, are shown in Figure 2.

Cellana grata showed two peaks of activity in each 24-hours cycle and both of which occurred only when the limpets were submerged. The major peak occurred during the night, while a minor peak occurred during daylight hours. That the animals were more active at night ($P < .001$) is statistically significant. A summary of chi-square tests performed on the experimental data obtained from the tide tank and tideless conditions is shown in Table 2. The percentage number of active individuals fluctuated from 0 to 100% but with two peaks of activity matching the tidal cycle. The animals were inac-

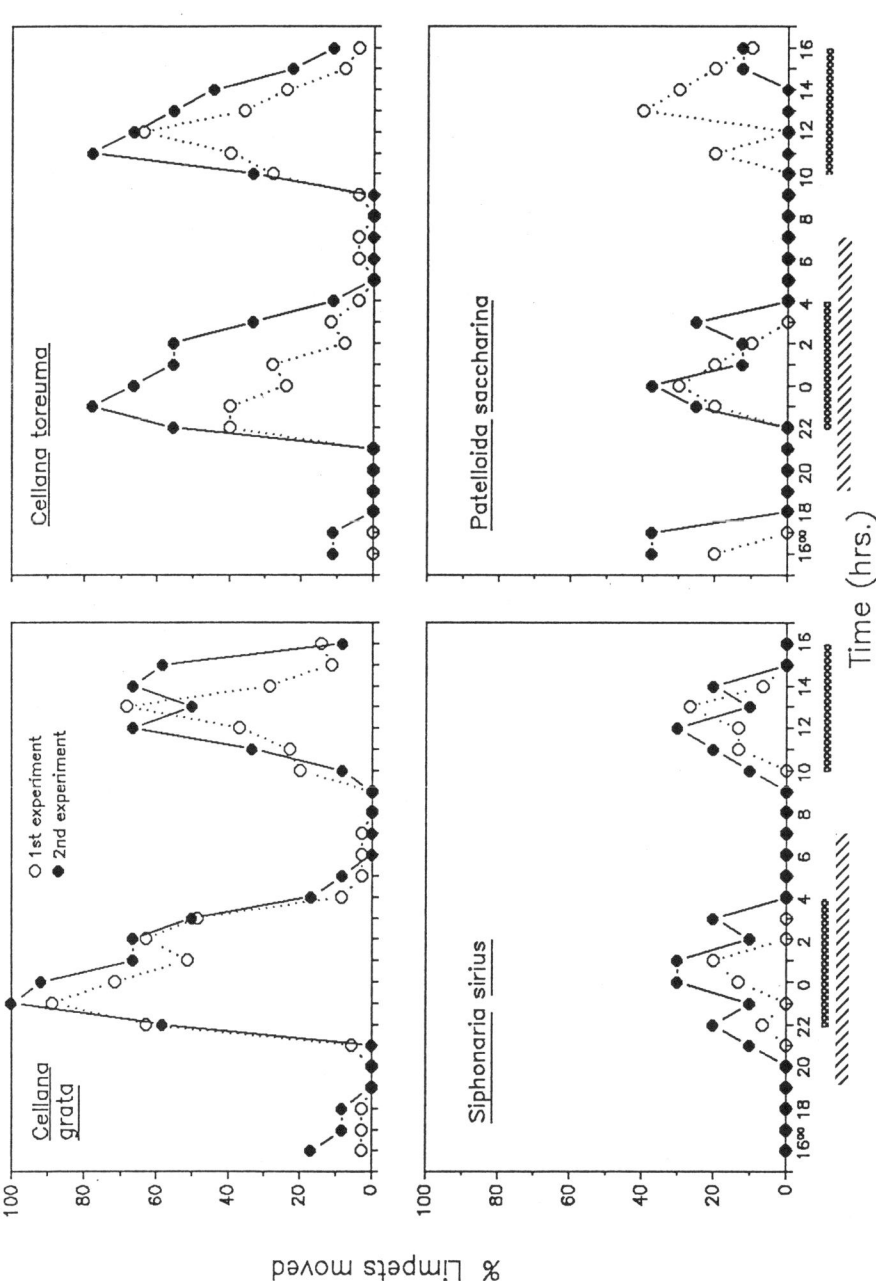

Fig. 2. The activity patterns of limpets in a tide tank. The hatched bar indicates darkness; the dotted bar indicates submersion.

Table 2
A summary table of the chi-square test performed on data obtained from experiments in the tide tank and under tideless conditions.

Species	Experimental conditions	d.f.	x^2	P – value
Cellana grata	In the tide tank, 1st experiment	6	61.42	< .001
C. grata	In the tide tank, 2nd experiment	6	15.14	< .025
C. toreuma	In the tide tank, 1st experiment	6	11.1	> .05
C. toreuma	In the tide tank, 2nd experiment	6	0.52	> .995
Siphonaria sinus	In the tide tank, 1st experiment	6	3.36	> .75
S. sirius	In the tide tank, 2nd experiment	6	4.48	> .50
Patelloida saccharina	In the tide tank, 1st experiment	6	9.02	> .10
P. saccharina	In the tide tank, 2nd experiment	6	9.58	> .10
C. grata	Tideless, after 1 day's removal from the field	12	39.6	< .001
C. grata	Tideless, after 2 weeks removal from the field	12	87.38	< .001
C. toreuma	Tideless, after 1 day's removal from the field	12	61.38	< .001
C. toreuma	Tideless, after 2 weeks removal from the field	12	96.46	< .001
C. grata	Tideless, after 1 day's removal from the tide tank	12	74.34	< .001
C. grata	Tideless, after 2 weeks removal from the tide tank	12	102.84	< .001
C. toreuma	Tideless, after 1 day's removal from the tide tank	12	72.00	< .001
C. toreuma	Tideless, after 2 weeks removal from the tide tank	12	89.26	< .001

tive when exposed to the air during low tide. Activity began either one hour before or shortly after the animals were submerged by the tide, and lasted for a maximum of seven hours. Activity of the majority of the animals ceased well in advance of the animals becoming exposed to air. The period of inactivity was spent on the vertical or undersurfaces of rocks. *C. grata* showed no homing behaviour.

The activity pattern of *Cellana toreuma* was similar to that of *Cellana grata* in that they were only active when submerged during both the day and the night. The first experiment showed that the percentage number of active individuals varied from 0 to 64.0%. When the experiment was repeated, the percentage number of active individuals fluctuated from 0 to 77.8%. *C. toreuma* was less active than *C. grata*, overall (Fig. 2) and showed no homing behaviour. The experiments showed there to be no significant difference between the probability of animals moving at night and the probability of animals moving in the day ($P > .05$ or $P > .995$) (Table 2).

Siphonaria sirius and *Patelloida saccharina* also showed two peaks of activity in each 24-hours cycle. There is no significant difference between the peaks formed at night and in the day for those two species in the four experiments (Table 2). All the peaks of activity were associated with the tidal cycle, i.e., they only occurred during high tide submergence. The percentage number of active individuals fluctuated from 0 to a maximum of 50%. In comparison with both *C. grata* and *C. toreuma*, therefore, *S. sirius* and *P. saccharina* were both much less active, overall (Fig. 2). Both species homed to a scar.

Effects of a tideless environment

Animals removed from the field.

The percentage number of active individuals and the dark-light conditions are shown in Figure 3. Both *Cellana grata* and *C. toreuma* lost their tidal cycle but retained a diurnal cycle of activity and inactivity. The pattern of activity recorded was stronger at night one day after removal from the tidal environment (*C. grata*, $X^2 = 39.6$, $P < .001$; *C. toreuma*, $X^2 = 61.38$, $P < .001$) A stronger pattern of activity was recorded after 2 weeks (*C. grata*, $X^2 = 87.38$, $P < .001$; *C. toreuma*, $X^2 = 96.46$, $P < .001$) (Table 2).

The percentage number of active *Cellana grata* fluctuated from 30.77% to 100%. The three times when they were most active, i.e., 100%, occurred between 2000–2200 h but no clear peak of activity was apparent one day after removal to the aquarium. The percentage number of active individuals ranged from 9.09% to 100%. Two weeks after removal to the aquarium, the rhythm was more clearly defined and a noticeable increase in the number of limpets active followed the approach of night and remained high until 'lights on' at 07:00 h.

Cellana toreuma was active during both night and day in each 24-hours cycle, one day after removal from the tidal environment, and a peak of activity occurred during the night. The percentage number of active individuals fluctuated from 6.25% to 93.75%. Two weeks after removal from the tidal environment, the percentage number of active individuals ranged from 0 to 86.67%. Individuals were, however, much less active during daylight hours and were more active at night.

Siphonaria sirius lost their homing ability and were continuously active after one day's removal from the field. The percentage number of active individuals varied from 7.14% to 42.86%. Animals were only active at night and showed homing behaviour after two weeks when the percentage number of active individuals ranged from 0 to 21.43%.

Like *Siphonaria sirius*, *Patelloida saccharina* also lost its homing ability and individuals were inactive for most of the time after one day's removal from the field but showed a nocturnal pattern of activity and a homing ability after two weeks. The percentage number of active individuals varied from 0 to 25.00%.

Animals removed from the tide tank.

The percentage number of active individuals and the experimental dark-light conditions are shown in Figure 4.

Cellana grata and *C. toreuma* lost their tidal cycle but retained a diurnal cycle of activity and inactivity. They were active during both the night and the day but more so

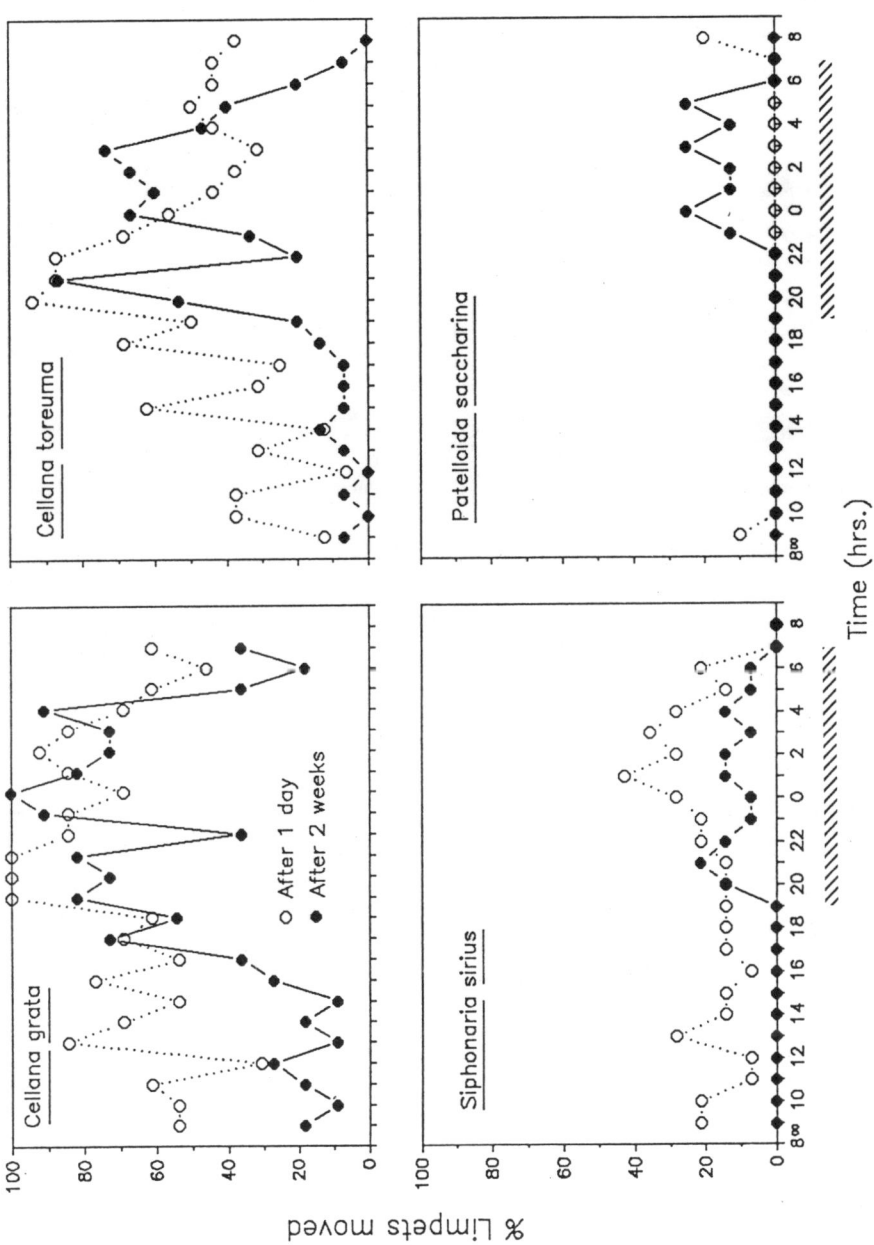

Fig. 3. The activity patterns of limpets removed from the field in a tideless environment. The hatched bar indicates darkness.

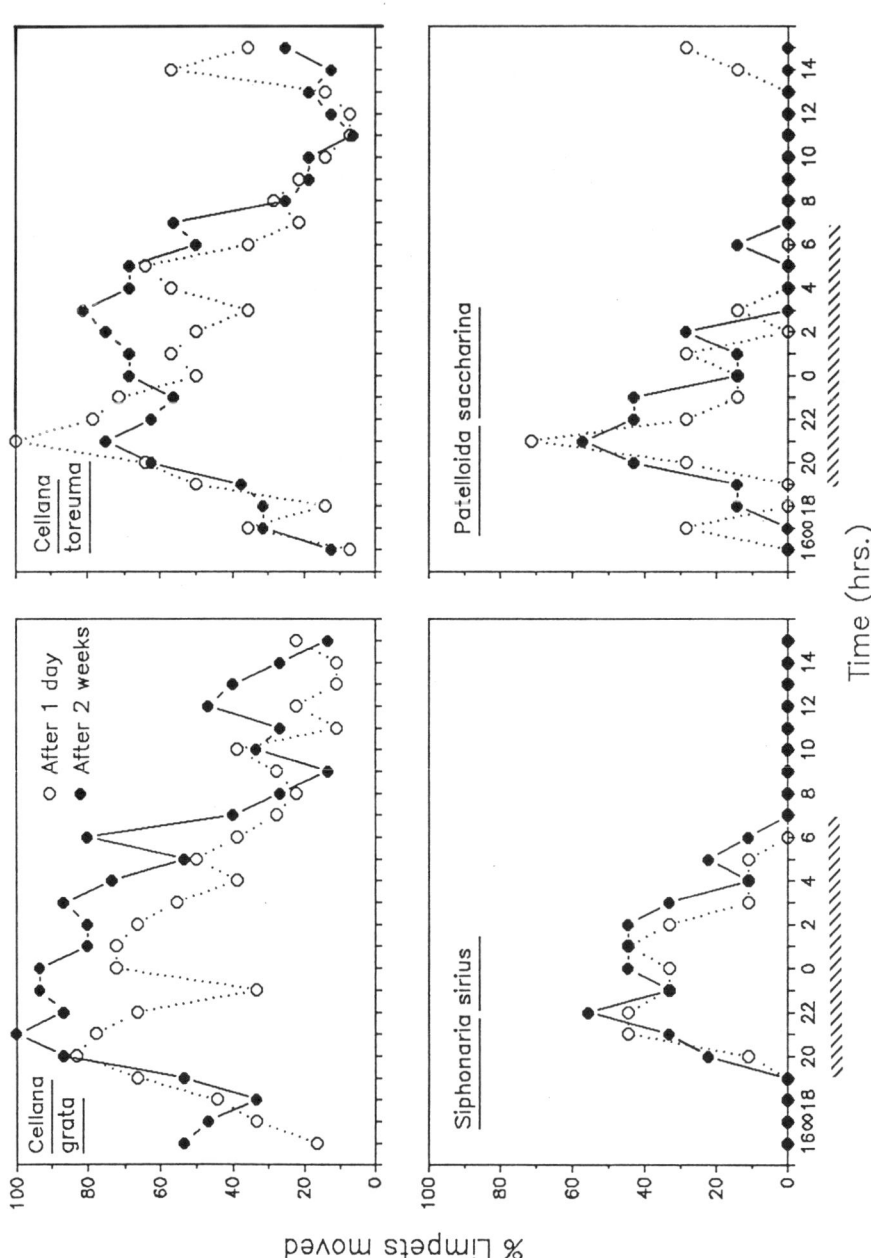

Fig. 4. The activity patterns of limpets removed from the tide tank in a tideless environment. The hatched bar indicates darkness.

at night 1 day after removal from the tide tank (*C.grata*, $X^2 = 74.34$, $P< .001$; *C. toreuma*, $X^2 = 72.00$, $P < .001$) (Table 2). A stronger rhythm of movement at night was recorded after two weeks (*C. grata*, $X^2 = 102.84$, $P< .001$, *C. toreuma*, $X^2 = 89.26$, $P < .001$) (Table 2).

The percentage number of active *Cellana grata* fluctuated from 11.11% to 83.33% after one day's removal from the tide tank. There were two peaks of activity formed and both occurred during the night. After two weeks removal, the percentage number of active individuals fluctuated from 13.33% to 100%.

Cellana toreuma demonstrated a peak of activity during the night but was also active during daylight hours after one day's removal from the tide tank. The percentage number of active individuals fluctuated from 7.14% to 100%. The nocturnal pattern became stronger after two weeks and when the percentage number of active individuals varied from 6.25% to 81.25%.

Siphonaria sirius and *Patelloida saccharina* retained their homing ability and were both active only at night after one day and two weeks removal from the tide tank. The percentage number of active *S. sirius* ranged from 0 to 44.44% after one day's removal and from 0 to 55.56% after two weeks removal from the tide tank.

The percentage number of active individuals of *P. saccharina* varied from 0 to 71.43% after one day's removal, to 0 to 57.14% after two weeks removal from the tide tank.

Effects of either constant darkness or constant light

The percentage numbers of active individuals in the experiment experiencing constant light conditions are shown in Figure 5.

Cellana grata and *C. toreuma* lost their normal rhythm of light and dark regulated phases of activity and inactivity resulting in a random pattern of activity. The percentage number of active *C. grata* individuals fluctuated from 25.00% to 91.67% and from 16.67% to 66.67% for *C. toreuma*.

Siphonaria sirius and *Patelloida saccharina* remained inactive in constant light during what would be daylight but became active during what would be night. They also continued to home. The percentage number of active individuals of *S. sirius* ranged from 0 to 60.00% and from 0 to 50.00% for *P. saccharina*.

The percentage number of active individuals in the experiment experiencing conditions of constant darkness is shown in Figure 6.

As in the constant light experiment, both *Cellana grata* and *C. toreuma* lost their normal rhythm of light and dark regulated phases of activity and inactivity resulting in random activity.

The percentage number of active individuals of *C. grata* ranged from 5.56% to 61.11% and from 0 to 66.67% for *C. toreuma*. *Siphonaria sirius* and *Patelloida saccharina* were only active during what would be night, for short periods, and continued to home.

Food supply

The available food supply for the limpets grazing on the surfaces of the experimental rocks was examined regularly over the course of the experiments. The available food

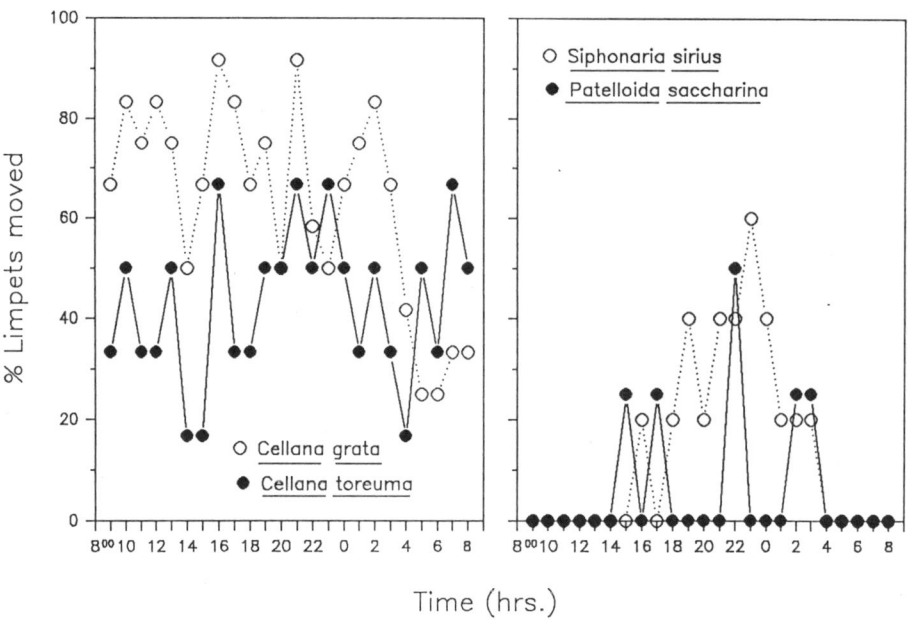

Fig. 5. The activity of limpets in conditions of permanent light.

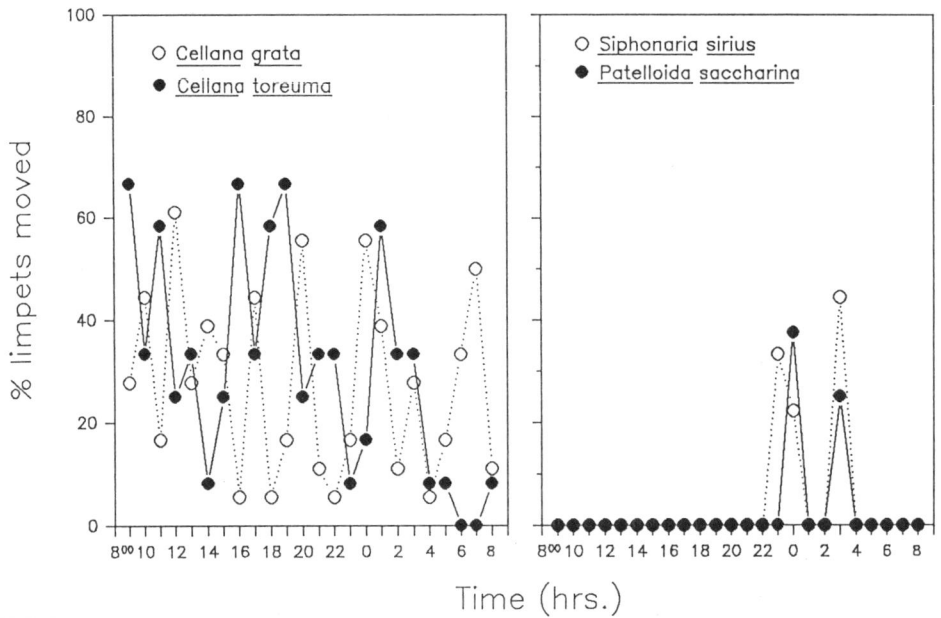

Fig. 6. The activity of limpets in conditions of permanent dark.

mainly comprised encrusting algae, i.e., *Branchytrichia maculans*, *Hildenbrandtia prototypus*, and *Ralfsia verrucosa*, and young stages of macroalgae, i.e., *Ulva* sp., *Enteromorpha* sp., and *Cladophora divergens*, plus diatoms and algal spores. Algae were present on the rocks even after ten day's constant darkness.

DISCUSSION

Animals and plants living in the intertidal zone are subjected to alternating periods of inundation and exposure. These tidal cycles bring with them associated fluctuations in temperature, pressure, mechanical agitation due to the pounding of waves, food supply and, possibly, light intensity and salinity. Some organisms may be more active when covered by water, others are more active when the tide recedes. The duration and onset of such activity patterns depends on the vertical position of the organism on the shore (Saunders 1977).

The researches of Hirano (1979) have described a population of *Cellana toreuma* to be active at ebb and flood tide in both daylight and at night, with no homing behaviour. The present work shows that the activity of *C. toreuma* in the laboratory tide tank does not precisely match the findings of Hirano obtained from the field. Animals in these experiments were active while submerged in both daylight and at night, whereas the individuals represented upon by Hirano were active when the tide was flooding or ebbing, i.e., when they were awash. The tide tank experiences no real ebbing and flooding tides with splash and spray, and it is not therefore surprising that the two sets of results differ somewhat but still show a similar underlying pattern. It appears that the tidal cycle plays an important role in the activity rhythm of limpets but not the diurnal cycle. Desiccation seems to be a danger to both *C. toreuma* and *C. grata* during emersion thus the animals were active only while submerged.

Activity rhythms have been reported upon for a number of siphonariid limpets (Bertness *et al.* 1981; Branch and Cherry 1985; Hulings 1985). The rhythms of activity of *Siphonaria normalis* and *S. alternata*, both of which home to a scar, have been found to be correlated with the duration of the period of turbulence accompanying the tide at a particular site (Cook and Cook 1978). In general, siphonariids are either active during high tide, or during the ebbing or flooding period when they are awash. Only one species, *S. capensis* which are confined to high-shore intertidal pools, has been recorded as being active during low tide (Branch and Cherry 1985). The activity pattern of *S. sirius* in the tide tank matches those obtained for other species of *Siphonaria* in the field, i.e., animals were active during high tide periods both in the daylight and at night. Desiccation is possibly the most important factor affecting the activity rhythms of both pairs of limpets because all species were active only while submerged.

Branch (1981) has summarized the records of foraging activity by limpets, and shown that there are five patterns: (1) species that feed while submerged at both day and night; (2) those that move while awash during the rising and falling tides but not while exposed or immersed (also during day and night); (3) those that move only at night and at low tide; (4) those that move only during submergence and only at night and (5) those that move during low tide, in both the day and the night. The first three patterns conform to the concept that activity rhythms are geared to reduce desiccation, but if desiccation dictates the pattern of rhythmicity expected, why should there be no

Table 3
A summary of activity rhythm records for limpets
[*Refer to Branch (1981) for these publications].

Species	Reference
A. Movement while awash, usually day and night.	
Cellana toreuma	Hirano 1979
Siphonaria alternata	Cook 1976
S. normalis	Cook 1976
S. pectinata	Thomas 1973
Patelloida saccharina	* Ohgushi 1954
Notoacmea scutum	* Rogers 1968
Collisella limatula (only at night)	Wells 1980
C. scabra (only in daylight)	Wells 1980
B. Movement when submerged, day and night.	
Patella cochlear	* Branch 1971
P. vulgata	* Punt 1968
Cellana ornata	* Beckett 1968
C. exarata	* Kay and Magruder 1977
C. radians	* Beckett 1968
C. radiata	* Balaparameswara Rao & Ganapati 1971; Hulings 1985
Collisella limatula	* Connor 1975; * Eaton 1968
C. pelta	* Craig 1968
C. Movement when exposed at low tide, and only at night.	
Collisella pelta	* Connor 1975
Patella vulgata: low shore	* Cook *et al.* 1969
P. vulgata: high shore	Little *et al.* 1985, 1988, 1990
P. depressa: low shore	* Cook *et al.* 1969
P. vulgata	* Dearnaley *et al.* 1969; Funke 1968
P. granularis	* Stephenson, in Thorpe 1962
D. Movement mainly when submerged, and mainly at night.	
Patella vulgata (only move during days)	Hartnoll and Wright 1977
P. vulgata; high shore (only moves at night)	* Cook *et al.* 1969
P. depressa: high shore	* Cook *et al.* 1969
P. coerulea	Funke 1968
Cellana nigrolineata	Hirano 1979
Acmaea dorsuosa	* Abe 1931
Patelloida virginea	* Clokie and Norton 1974
Siphonaria laciniosa	Hulings 1985
E. Movement when exposed at low tide, day and night.	
Siphonaria thersites	Branch 1988
Patella vulgata: low shore	Little *et al.* 1985, 1988, 1990
P. vulgata: mid shore (mainly at night)	

movement during the daytime period of submergence in the fourth pattern? The fifth pattern is unusual, but occurs in populations of *Siphonaria capensis* that are confined to high-shore intertidal pools where there is little or no threat of desiccation. Table 3 summarizes the records of activity rhythms in limpets and is based upon references quoted by Branch (1981) with the addition of subsequent publications.

Homing behaviour has been proposed as an adaptation to reduce desiccation during periods of low tide (Wolcott 1973; Cook 1976; Verderber et al. 1983; Kunz and Connor 1986), to reduce vulnerability to dislodgement by strong wave action (Orton 1929; Lindberg and Dwyer 1983; Branch and Cherry 1985), to avoid predators (Underwood 1979; Branch 1981; Garrity and Levings 1983), and to maximize utilization of food resources (Mackay and Underwood 1977). Branch (1981) has pointed out that homing is best developed in high-shore species and high-shore individuals. There are, however, low-shore and even subtidal species that have well-developed scars and exhibit homing behaviour. In contrast to the above observation, the present work shows that the high-zoned, i.e., *Cellana grata* and *C. toreuma* have no homing behaviour whereas the low-zoned, i.e., *Siphonaria sirius* and *Patelloida saccharina* have well-developed scars and homing behaviour. Table 4 shows the incidence of homing trips of *S. sirius* and *P. saccharina*. Desiccation may not, therefore, be the only factor promoting such behaviour. Homing behaviour is likely to have more functions, as one of the

Table 4
The incidence of homing trips by limpets within 24 hours.

Species	Conditions	No. of limpets	No. of homing trips	Time spent on a homing trip (hours) (mean ± SD)	No. of homing trips by an individual within 24-h.
Siphonaria sirius	Tideless	46	26	1.50 (0.71)	0–2
Patelloida saccharina	Tideless	32	7	2.14 (1.22)	0–1
Siphonaria sirius	Tide tank	25	8	2.13 (0.64)	0–1
Patelloida saccharina	Tide tank	18	4	1.75 (1.50)	0–1

Table 5
A summary of homing behaviour records for limpets.
[* Refer to Branch (1981) for these publications].

Species	Position on the shore	Reference	Homing vs not homing
Patella depressa	Low to mid	* Cook et al. 1969	Rigid homing
P. aspera *P. vulgata*	Mid to high	* Morgan 1894	Rigid homing
		* Russell 1907	Small animals do not home
		* Loppens 1922	Changes scar if food is short or rock crumbles
		Orton 1929	Smooth or wet substratum reduces homing

Table 5 (continued)

Species	Position on the shore	Reference	Homing vs not homing
		* Bree 1959	Rigid homing
		* Cook et al. 1969	Rigid homing and tidal rhythms of movement
P. granularis	Mid to high	* Stephenson 1936	Homing occurs
		* Branch 1971	Homing most rigid on high shore
P. granatina	Mid	* Branch 1971	Homing
P. oculus	Mid	* Branch 1971	Large animals have a home scar
P. longicosta	Low	* Branch 1971, 1975	Rigid homing
P. tabularis	Subtidal	* Stephenson 1936	Rigid homing
P. cochlear	Very low	* Branch 1971, 1975	Rigid homing
P. argenvillei	Low	* Branch 1971	Well-developed scar
P. barbara	Low to subtidal	* Branch 1971	Poorly defined scar
P. miniata	Subtidal	* Branch 1971	Poorly defined scar and only in adults
P. compressa	Subtidal	* Branch 1971, 1975	Homing well-developed in adults on kelp stipes
Notoacmea persona	Low to mid	* Richardson 1934; * Villee and Groody 1940	Not homing
N. petterdi	Very high	* Creese 1980	Rigid homing
Collisella testudinalis	Low	* Wells 1917	Indefinite results
C. scabra	High	* Villee and Groody 1940	Large animals home rigidly
		Hewatt 1940	Rigid homing
		* Wells 1917	Indefinite results
		* Jessee 1968	95% homed rigidly
	Low	Wells 1980	Homed to a scar
		Lindberg and Dwyer 1983	Homed to a scar
	High	Kunz and Connor 1986	Homed to a scar
C. limatula	Low	Wells 1980	No homing
C. digitalis	High	* Gailbraith 1965	54% homing
		* Frank 1964	No homing to a scar but a 'homing range'
		* Villee and Groody 1940	No homing
C. pelta	Low-mid	* Villee and Groody 1940	No homing
Cellana tramosenca	Low-high	* Underwood 1977	Both homers and non-homers in the population
		Mackay and Underwood 1977	Proportion homing related to food availability
C. exarata	Mid-high	* Kay and Magruder 1977	high-shore animals home; low-shore animals do not

Table 5 (continued)

Species	Position on the shore	Reference	Homing vs not homing
C. nigrolineata	Mid-high	Hirano 1979	Homing more rigid on exposed rocks than in crevices
C. toreuma	Mid	Hirano 1979	No home scar
C. ornata	High	* Beckett 1968	Animals > 12 mm home to scar
C. radians	Low-mid	* Beckett 1968	No homing
C. radiata	Mid	Hulings 1985	Temporary homer
C. grata	Mid-high	This study	No homing
C. toreuma	Mid-high	This study	No homing
Siphonaria laciniosa	Mid	Hulings 1985	Rigid homer
S. normalis		Cook 1969	Homing occurs
S. alternata		Cook 1971	Homing occurs
		Verderber et al. 1983	Homed to a scar
S. sirius	Low-mid	This study	Homed to a scar
Patelloida saccharina	Low-mid	This study	Homed to a scar

species herein discussed, i.e., *Siphonaria sirius*, largely occurs in intertidal pools on the middle shore where there is reduced desiccation and wave action stress. Probably homing behaviour in this species is a mechanism to avoid predation thus predation may be an important factor promoting homing behaviour in the low-zoned limpets. Table 5 summarizes the records of homing behaviour in limpets and is based upon references quoted by Branch (1981) with the addition of subsequent publications.

Morton (1979) recognized that the slug *Deroceras caruanae* had an endogenous rhythm which is entrained by light to correspond to the normal 24 hour cycle of night and day. In the absence of light this rhythm is not maintained. Salanki (1966) has also found that illumination levels play a significant role in the regulation of the rhythmic activity of the bivalves *Pecten jacobaeus* and *Lithophaga lithophaga*. The work of Funke (1968) upon laboratory populations of *Patella vulgata* showed that activity was based on an endogenous rhythm, entrained by two 'zeitgebers', i.e., light to dark and emersion to submersion changes. The present work shows that the activity patterns of all the species in the tide tank is primarily entrained by tidal conditions rather than the time of day, but that activity patterns of the animals in tideless conditions depend strongly on the time of day. *Cellana grata* and *C. toreuma* do not possess an endogenous rhythm of activity and inactivity entrained by either tidal or diurnal cycles. Both *Siphonaria sirius* and *Patelloida saccharina*, on the other hand, possess an endogenous rhythms of activity and inactivity entrained by the diurnal cycle but not the tidal cycle.

ACKNOWLEDGEMENTS

I would like to thank my supervisors Professor Brian Morton and Dr I.J. Hodgkiss for their advice on this study and for the former's critical reading of the first drafts of the manuscript of this paper. I also thank Professor Richard Cowan for his help with the statistical analysis of the data. This work forms a part of the thesis submitted to The University of Hong Kong for the degree of Doctor of Philosophy.

REFERENCES

Beeston, D.C. and Morgan, E. 1979. A crepuscular rhythm of locomotor activity in the freshwater prosobranch, *Melanoides tuberculata* (Müller). *Animal Behaviour* 27:284–91.

Bennett, M.F. 1954. The rhythmic activity of the Quahog *Venus mercenaria* and its modification by light. *Biological Bulletin* 107:174–9.

Bertness, M.D., Garrity, S.D. and Levings, S.C. 1981. Predation pressure and gastropod foraging: a tropical-temperate comparison. *Evolution* 35:995–1007.

Blankley, W.O. 1982. Feeding ecology of three inshore fish species at Marion Island (Southern Ocean). *South African Journal of Zoology* 17:164–70.

Bones, L., Cornish, L.S. and Wong, T.T. 1984. An electronically-controlled tide tank for use in a marine biology laboratory. *Asian Marine Biology* 1:125–33.

Branch, G.M. 1978. The responses of South African patellid limpets to invertebrate predators. *Zoologica Africana* 13:221–32

Branch, G.M. 1979. Aggression by limpets against invertebrata predators. *Animal Behaviour* 27:408–10.

Branch, G.M. 1981. The biology of limpets: physical factors, energy flow, and ecological interactions. *Oceanography and Marine Biology Annual Review* 19:235–380.

Branch, G.M. 1988. Activity rhythms in *Siphonaria thersites*. In *Behavioral Adaptations to Intertidal Life* (ed. G. Chelazzi and M. Vannini), 27–44. New York: Plenum Press.

Branch, G.M. and Cherry, M.I. 1985. Activity rhythms of the pulmonate limpet *Siphonaria capensis* Q. and J. as an adaptation to osmotic stress, predation and wave action. *Journal of Experimental Marine Biology and Ecology* 87:153–68.

Brown, F.A. 1954. Persistent activity rhythms in the oyster. *American Journal of Physiology* 178:510–4.

Brown, F.A. 1959. The rhythmic nature of animals and plants. *American Scientist* 47:147–68.

Brown, F.A., Hastings, J.W. and Palmer, J.D. 1970. *The Biological Clock*. New York: Academic Press.

Cook, S.B. 1969. Experiments on homing in the limpet *Siphonaria normalis*. *Animal Behaviour* 17:679–82.

Cook, S.B. 1971. A study of homing behavior in the limpet *Siphonaria alternata*. *Biological Bulletin* 141:449–57.

Cook, S.B. 1976. The role of the 'home scar' in pulmonate limpets. *Bulletin of the American Malacological Union* 42:34–7.

Cook, S.B. and Cook, C.B. 1975. Directionality in the trail-following response of the pulmonate limpet *Siphonaria alternata*. *Marine Behaviour and Physiology* 3:147–55.

Cook, S.B. and Cook, C.B. 1978. Tidal amplitude and activity in the pulmonate limpets *Siphonaria normalis* (Gould) and *S. alternata* (Say). *Journal of Experimental Marine Biology and Ecology* 35:119–36.

Cook, S.B. and Cook, C.B. 1981. Activity patterns in *Siphonaria* populations: heading choice and the effects of size and grazing interval. *Journal of Experimental Marine Biology and Ecology* 49:69–79.

Enright, J.T. 1972. A virtuoso isopod: circa-lunar rhythms and their tidal fine structure. *Journal of Comparative Physiology* 77:141–62

Frank, P.W. 1982. Effects of winter feeding on limpets by black oystercatchers, *Haematopus bachmani*. *Ecology* 63:1352–62.

Funke, W. 1968. Heimfindevermogen und Ortstreue bei *Patella L.* (Gastropoda Prosobranchia). *Oecologia* 2:19–142.

Galbraith, R.T. 1965. Homing behaviour in the limpets *Acmaea digitalis* and *Lottia gigantea*. *American Midland Naturalist* 74:245–6.

Garrity, S.D. and Leving, S.C. 1983. Homing to scars as a defense against predators in the pulmonate limpet *Siphonaria gigas* (Gastropoda). *Marine Biology* 72:319–24.

Harker, J.E. 1964. *The Physiology of Diurnal Rhythms*. Cambridge: Cambridge University Press.

Hartnoll, R.G. and Wright, J.R. 1977. Foraging movements and homing in the limpet *Patella vulgata* L. *Animal Behaviour* 25:806–10.

Hawkins, S.J. and Hartnoll, R.G. 1982. The influence of barnacle cover on the numbers, growth and behaviour of *Patella vulgate* on a vertical pier. *Journal of the Marine Biological Association of the United Kingdom* 62:855–67.

Hewatt, W.G. 1940. Observations on the homing limpet *Acmaea scabra* Gould. *American Midland Naturalist* 24:205–8.

Hirano, Y. 1979. Studies on activity pattern of the patellid limpet *Cellana toreuma* (Reeve). *Journal of Experimental Marine Biology and Ecology* 40:137–48.

Hockey, P.A.R. and Branch, G.M. 1983. Feeding of birds on rocky shores: competition or facilitation? In *Proceedings of the Fifth National Oceanographic Symposium* Rhodes University.

Hulings, N.C. 1985. Activity patterns and homing in two intertidal limpets, Jordan Gulf of Aqaba. *The Nautilus* 99:75–80.

Klapow, L.A. 1972. Natural and artifical rephasing of a tidal rhythm. *Journal of Comparative Physiology* 79:233–58.

Kunz, C. and Connor, V.M. 1986. Roles of the home scar of *Collisella scabra* (Gould). *The Veliger* 29:25–30.

Lindberg, D.R. and Dwyer, K.R. 1983. The topography, formation and role of the home depression of *Collisella scabra* (Gould) (Gastropoda: Acmaeidae). *The Veliger* 25:229–34.

Lindberg, D.R., Warheit, K.I. and Estes, J.A. 1987. Prey preference and seasonal predation by oystercatchers on limpets at San Nicolas Island, California, USA. *Marine Ecology* 39:105–13.

Little, C. 1985. Patterns of foraging activity in the limpet *Patella vulgata* L.—A preliminary study. *Journal of Experimental Marine Biology and Ecology* 89:283–96.

Little, C., Williams, G.A., Morritt, D., Perrins, J.M. and Stirling, P. 1988. Foraging behaviour of *Patella vulgata* L. in an Irish sea-lough. *Journal of Experimental Marine Biology and Ecology* 120:1–20.

Little, C., Morritt, D., Paterson, D.M., Stirling, P. and Williams, G.A. 1990. Preliminary observations on factors affecting foraging activity in the limpet *Patella vulgata*. *Journal of the Marine Biological Association of the United Kingdom* 70:181–95.

Lofts, B. 1970. A*nimal Photoperiodism*. London and Beccles: William Clowes and Sons, Ltd.

Mackay, D.A. and Underwood, A.J. 1977. Experimental studies on homing in the intertidal patellid limpet *Cellana tramoserica* (Sowerby). *Oecologia* 30:215–37.

McCorkle, S., Shirley, T.C. and Dietz, T. H. 1979. Rhythms of activity and oxygen consumption in the common pond clam, *Ligumia subrostrata* (Say). *Canadian Journal of Zoology* 57:1960–4.

Mori, S. 1950. Characteristic tidal rhythmic migration of a mussel, *Donax semigranosus*, and the experimental analysis of its behaviour. *Dobutsugaku Zasshi* 59:87–9.

Morton, B. 1969. Studies on the biology of *Dreissena polymorpha* Pall. II. Correlation of the rhythms of adductor activity, feeding, digestion and excretion. *Proceedings of the Malacological Society of London* 38:401–15.

Morton, B. 1970. The tidal rhythm and rhythm of feeding and digestion in *Cardium edule*. *Journal of the Marine Biological Association of the United Kingdom* 50:499–512.

Morton, B. 1971. The diurnal rhythm and tidal rhythm of feeding and digestion in *Ostrea edulis*. *Biological Journal of the Linnean Society* 3:329–42.

Morton, B. 1976. The tidal rhythm of feeding and digestion in the Pacific oyster *Crassostrea gigas* (Thunberg). *Journal of Experimental Marine Biology and Ecology* 26:135–51.

Morton, B. 1979. The diurnal rhythm and the cycle of feeding and digestion in the slug *Deroceras caruanae*. *Journal of Zoology, London* 187:135–52.

Moulton, J.M. 1962. Intertidal clustering of an Australian gastropod. *Biological Bulletin* 123:170–8.

Naylor, E. 1958. Tidal and diurnal rhythms of locomotor activity in *Carcinus maenas* (L.) *Journal of Experimental Biology* 35:602–10.

Naylor, E. 1985. Tidally rhythmic behaviour of marine animals. *Symposia of the Society for Experimental Biology* 39:63–93.
Naylor, E. 1988. Clock-controlled behaviour in intertidal animals. In *Behavioural Adaptations to Intertidal Life* (ed. G. Chelazzi and M. Vannini), 1–14. New York: Plenum Press.
Newell, R. 1962. Behavioural aspects of the ecology of *Peringua* [*Hydrobia*] *ulvae* (Pennant) (Gastropoda Prosobranchia). *Proceedings of the Zoological Society of London* 138:49–75.
Ohgaki, S. 1985. Field observations on the rhythmic up-and-down movement of *Nodilittorina exigua* (Gastropoda: Littorinidae). *Journal of Ethology* 3:49–58.
Orton, J.H. 1929. Observations on *Patella vulgata*. III. Habitats and habits. *Journal of the Marine Biological Association of the United Kingdom* 16:277–88.
Rao, K.P. 1954. Tidal rhythmicity of the rate of water propulsion in *Mytilus* and its modifiability by transplantation. *Biological Bulletin* 106:353–9.
Salanki, J. 1964. Contributions to the problem of daily rhythm in the activity of the fresh water mussel An*odonta cygnea* L. *Annales Institutum biologicum Academiae Scientarium Hungaricae, Tihany* 31:109–16.
Salanki, J. 1966. Daily activity rhythm of two mediterranean lamellibranchia (*Pecten jacobaeus* and *Lithophaga lithophaga*) regulated by light-dark period. *Annales Institutum biologicum Academiae Scientarium Hungaricae, Tihany* 33:135–42.
Salanki, J. and Vero, M. 1969. Diurnal rhythm of activity in freshwater mussel (*Anodonta cygnea* L.) under natural conditions. *Annales Institutum biologicum Academiae Scientarium Hungaricae, Tihany* 36:95–107.
Saunders, D.S. 1977. *An Introduction to Biological Rhythms*. Glasgow and London: Blackie Press.
Sollberger, A. 1965. *Biological Rhythm Research*. Amsterdam, London, and New York: Elsvier.
Stephens, G.C., Sandeen, M.I. and Brown, F.A. 1954. Persistent daily and tidal rhythms of oxygen consumption in two species of marine snail. *Physiological Zoology* 27:350–6.
Thomas, R.F. 1973. Homing behavior and movement rhythm in the pulmonate limpet, *Siphonaria pectinata* Linnaeus. *Proceedings of the Malacological Society of London* 40:303–11.
Underwood, A.J. 1979. The ecology of intertidal gastropods. *Advances in Marine Biology* 16:111–210.
Verderber, G.W., Cook, S.B. and Cook, C.B. 1983. The role of the home scar in reducing water loss during aerial exposure of the pulmonate limpet *Siphonaria alternata* (Say). *The Veliger* 25:235–43.
Wells, R.A. 1980. Activity pattern as a mechanism of predator avoidance in two species of acmaeid limpet. *Journal of Experimental Marine Biology and Ecology* 48:151–68.
Wolcott, T.G. 1973. Physiological ecology and intertidal zonation in limpets *Acmaea*: a critical look at 'limiting factors'. *Biological Bulletin* 145:389–422.

The Marine Biology of the South China Sea
(ed. B. Morton). Proceedings of the First
International Conference on the Marine
Biology of Hong Kong and the South China Sea,
Hong Kong, 28 October – 3 November 1990.
Hong Kong: Hong Kong University Press, 1993.

THE ORIENTATION OF CIRRIPEDES ON THEIR HOSTS FROM HONG KONG WATERS

Cai Ruxing

Biology Department, University of Hangzhou, China

and

Huang Zongguo

Third Institute of Oceanography, State Oceanic Administration, Xiamen, China

ABSTRACT

In Hong Kong, *Balanus amphitrite* attaches to *Xenostrobus atrata* (attachment frequency = 86%). *Chelonibia patula* attaches to *Charybdis cruciata* (27%) and *Portunus pelagicus* (14%). The locations and numbers of these cirripedes on their hosts are different. Such differences are related to water flow. *Balanus amphitrite* mainly attaches to the posterior end of the *Xenostrobus atrata* shell, individuals oriented at ±180°, i.e., with the cirri opposite the host's siphons. In this orientation, *Balanus amphitrite* has a higher rostrum and the ratio between carinal and rostrum height is 1.9:1. Conversely, an individual oriented at 0° increases its carinal height, allowing utilization of the currents created by the host's siphons during feeding. *Balanus amphitrite* mainly attaches to host shells as single individuals (74.57%). *Chelonibia patula* mainly attaches to the centre of the host carapace with some attachments at the front edge. This allows utilization of the currents created when the host moves or is feeding. Its occurrence at the centre of the carapace of *Charybdis cruciata* is 96.30% and on *Portunus pelagicus* 91.30%. *Chelonibia patula* on the carapace front of *Portunus pelagicus* and *Charybdis cruciata* mainly occur as single individuals, 13.04% and 33.96%, respectively. This may avoid competition among individuals and allow utilization of the feeding currents created by the host. The numbers of individuals settled on the centre of the carapace of *Charybdis cruciata* and *Portunus pelagicus* were between 4–11 and 5–29, respectively.

The orientation of *Balanus amphitrite* is usually ±180°, there being two major types: (a), left shell, $\theta = +39°10'$ and (b), right shell valve, $\theta = -41°43'$. When oriented at 0° with the cirri facing forwards, there are also two types: (a'), left shell valve, $\vartheta = +38°48'$ and (b'), right shell valve, $\theta = -37°30''$. The orientation at ±180° accounts for 93.75% of cases. *Chelonibia patula* attached to *Charybdis cruciata* and *Portunus pelagicus* also has two orientations, ±180° and 0°; the former occurs most frequently. This orientation allows utilization of the current by the host for feeding and avoids direct competition for food and oxygen with the hosts.

The orientation of *Chelonibia patula* facilitates feeding and avoids direct competition for food and oxygen with the host. The orientation of *Chelonibia patula* attached in other positions on the host carapace is ±90° – ±180°, this being related to the host's habits. The cirri of the barnacle can move through ±90°, allowing utilization of the currents created when the crabs move in different directions. Orientation on the *Charybdis cruciata* carapace was $\theta = -175° 37'$ ($R = 0.91$) whereas on the carapace of *Portunus pelagicus* it was $\theta = +172° 49'$ ($R = 0.82$).

INTRODUCTION

The orientation of marine cirripedes aids feeding (Moore 1935; Crisp 1955; Barnes and Reeve 1960; Bowers 1968; Ayling 1976) and growth (Crisp 1960). Orientated cirripedes can compete more effectively with unorientated species (Barnes and Reeve 1960; Ayling 1976) and occupy an advantageous position, becoming dominant species in the tidal zone and neritic waters. Investigations on orientation and other biological features of these animals provides a theoretical basis for hydrologists and palaeoecologists (Cai and Huang 1988).

Much work has been done on the orientation of marine cirripedes in relation to illumination and current flow (Moore 1935; McDougall 1943; Pyefinch 1948; Barnes *et al.* 1951; Crisp 1953, 1955; Crisp and Stubbings 1957; Forbes *et al.* 1971; Ayling 1976; Cai and Huang 1984, 1988) and to illumination and surface contours of the substratum (Moore 1935; Gregg 1948; Barnes *et al.* 1951; Barnes 1953; Crisp and Barnes 1954; Utinomi 1955; Hurley 1973; Cai and Huang 1988).

Investigations have been carried out on the orientation of marine cirripedes on a variety of hosts. Crisp and Stubbings (1957) and Briggs and Morejohn (1972) reported upon *Coronula diadema* orientation on whales. Hastings (1972) reported *Conchoderma virgatum* orienting commensally with *Nerocila acuminata* and *Alutera schoepfi* and Williams (1978) reported *C. virgatum* orienting on *Dinemoura latiforia*, which parasitises *Isurus oxyrhynchus*. Barnes (1953) reported *Balanus balanus* orienting on the shells of *Pecten maximus* and *Chlamys opercularis*. Cai and Huang (1984, 1988) reported *Balanus cirratus* orienting on *Anadara subcrenata*, *Anadara granosa*, *Scylla serrata*, *Matuta planipes* and *Portunus sanguinolentus*; *Chelonibia testudinaris* orienting on *Chelonia mydas*, *Caretta caretta* and *Eretmochelys imbricata*; *C. hunteri* orienting on *Hydrophis cyanocinctus*; *Chelonibia patula* orienting on *Portunus trituberculatus* and *M. planipes* and *B. trigonus* orienting on *Perna viridis* and *Mytilus crassitesta*, From Hong Kong waters, however, there no reports on the orientation of *Balanus amphitrite* on *Xenostrobus atrata* and of *Chelonibia patula* on *Charybdis cruciata* and *Portunus pelagicus*.

MATERIALS AND METHODS

Material examined in this paper was collected from April to August 1986 in Hong Kong.

Samples of *Balanus amphitrite* and *Xenostrobus atrata* were collected at Sai Kung pier. Some samples of *Chelonibia patula*, *Charybdis cruciata* and *Portunus pelagicus* were bought from aquatic product shops at North Point and Shau Kei Wan, others were obtained from shops at A Gung Ngam.

Statistical analysis of the numbers of cirripedes facing or opposing the current flow was used to investigate orientation. The schematic diagram is shown in Figure 1. The orientation angle is defined as the angle between the direction of cirral extension and contraction and the body axis of the host. Formulas for calculating the orientation angle are as follows:

$$A = \frac{1}{N} \sum_t \cos \theta_i$$

$$B = \frac{1}{N} \sum_t \sin \theta_i$$

$$\theta = \tan^{-1} \frac{B}{A}, \quad R = \sqrt{A^2 + B^2}$$

(N = number of individuals, R = vector)

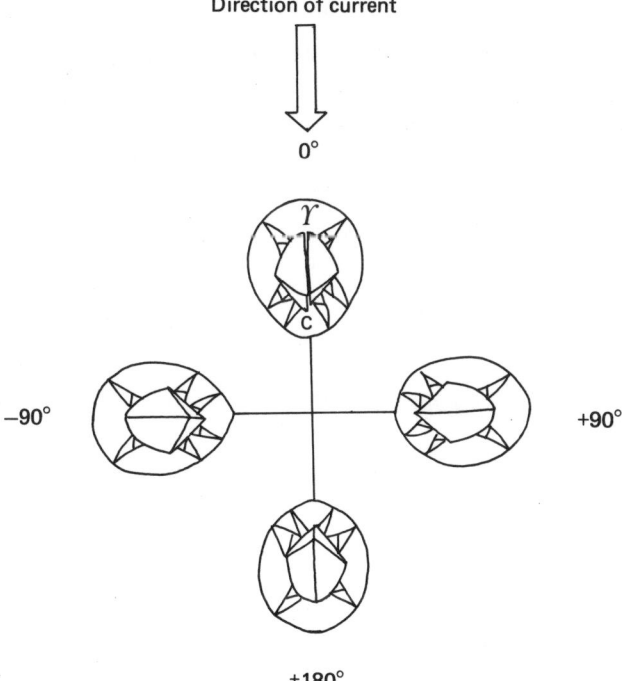

Fig. 1. Schematic diagram explaining the method of assessing barnacle orientation. c, carina; r, rostrum.

Observations have shown that barnacle cirral movements are related closely to current flow. In the current, cirri are expanded in a fan shape, rotating right and left by about ±90° towards the flow to catch food particles (Fig. 2).

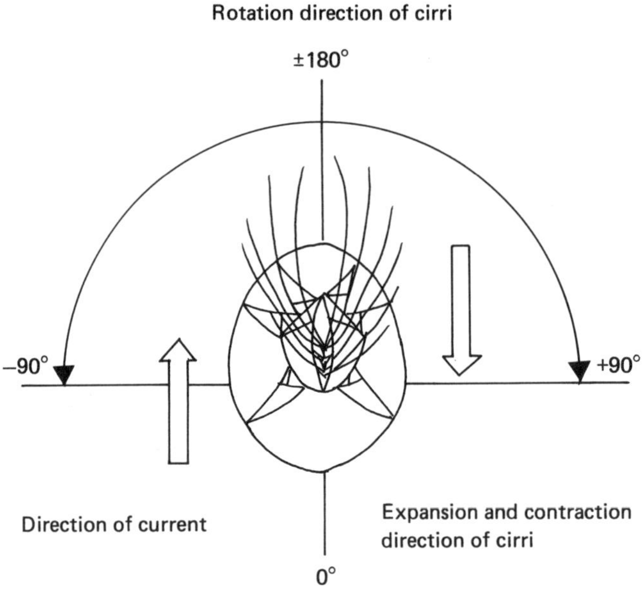

Fig. 2. Schematic diagram explaining cirral movement in barnacles.

To investigate morphological variation in the barnacles, heights of the rostrum and carina of individuals with different orientations were measured. Shell height was measured from the top of the shell to the base. For the measurement of the basal area, the maximum diameter and maximum cross shaft of the base were measured.

RESULTS

The orientation of *Balanus amphitrite* on hosts

Attachment frequency, attachment position and the number of attached individuals

The attachment frequency of *Balanus amphitrite* on *Xenostrobus atrata* was 86%. All attachments were at the posterior end of the host's shell (Plate IA). The number of attached individuals was between 1–4 ·host^{-1}. The frequency of singly attached individuals was highest, i.e., 74.57% (Table 1).

Modes and types of orientation

The orientation of *Balanus amphitrite* on the host shell has two modes:(±180° and 0°) and four types: a, (left shell valve); b, (the right shell valve); a', (left shell valve) and b', (right shell valve). Single individuals attached mainly in the mode of ±180° (92.93%), and the frequency of type b was the highest in this mode (53.42%). Individuals attached in groups of between 2–4 individuals had different orientation modes. Table 2 shows that individuals attached in groups of four occurred on the left valve more than the right; all other types occurred on the right more than the left valve.

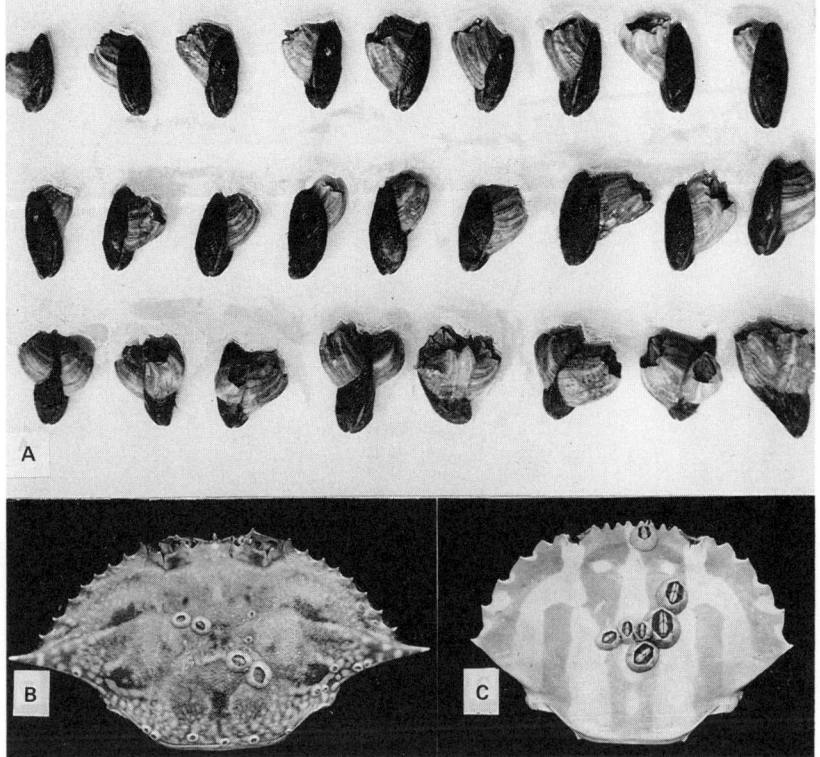

Plate 1. The orientations of barnacles on their hosts
  A. *Balanus amphitrite* attached to *Xenostrobus atrata* .
  B. *Chelonibia patula* attached to the carapace of *Portunus pelagicus.*
  C. *Chelonibia patula* attached to the carapace of *Charybdis cruciata.*

Orientation angle

Balanus amphitrite has two types of orientation on the shell of *Xenostrobus atra* in the mode of ±180°, there are also two types of orientation in the 0°mode (Table 3; Fig. 3). Comparisons between the occurrence of various orientations and orientation angles of *Balanus amphitrite* on host shells are shown in Figure 4.

Orientation and morphology

Morphological comparisons between unorientated *Balanus amphitrite* and those attached to *Xenostrobus atrata* (orientated individuals) show that orientated individuals have different carinal and rostral lengths. In the ±180° orientation mode, the rostral length increases, the ratio between carinal and rostrum length being 1:2.2. In the ϑ° orientation mode, the carinal length increases, the ratio between carinal and rostrum length being 2.1:1 (Table 4, Figs. 5 and 6). For individuals attached to host shells, shell height increases and basal area decreases.

Table 1
A comparison of attachment frequency, attachment position and numbers of barnacles on their hosts.

Barnacle (numbers of individuals)	Host	Barnacle			Attachment locations (no's of attached individuals)			
		Numbers with barnacles	Attachment frequency (%)	Numbers·shell⁻¹	Position	Number of individuals	Times	Frequency (%)
B. amphitrite (1518)	X. atrata	1357 (1167)	86	1–4	Posterior end of shell	1	1132	74.57
						2	316	20.82
						3	60	3.92
						4	10	0.66
	C. cruciata	197 (53)	27	4–11	Front edge of carapace	1	18	33.96
						2–3	11	20.75
					Anterior lateral margin	2–4	12	22.64
					Centre of carapace	4–11	51	96.23
					Posterior margin	2–3	2	3.77
					Posterior lateral margin	2–4	4	7.55
C. patula (371)	P. pelagicus	165 (23)	14	5–29	Front edge of carapace	1	11	47.83
						3–4	3	13.04
					Anterior lateral margin	2–4	15	65.22
					Centre of carapace	5–29	21	91.30
					Posterior margin	2–3	19	82.61
					Posterior lateral margin	3–7	17	73.91

Table 2
A comparison between orientation modes and orientation types of
Balanus amphitrite on shells of *Xenostrobus atrata*

Numbers of barnacles	Shell valve	Orientation type	Numbers present	Frequency (%)		Total
1	left	a	490	46.58	92.93	1132
	right	b	562	53.42		
		sum	1052	100		
	left	a'	23	28.75	7.07	
	right	b'	57	71.25		
		sum	80	100		
	total		1132			
2	left	a	110	42.15		316
		a'	42			
	sum		152			
	right	b	126	51.90		
		b'	38			
	sum		164			
	total	316	100			
3	left	a, b	26	43.33		60
	right	a, b, a'	34	56.67		
	total		60	100		
4	left	a, b, a'	7	70		10
	right	b, b'	3	30		
	total	10	100			

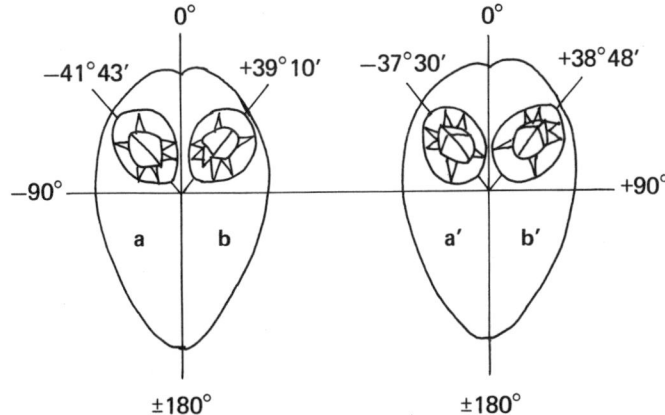

Fig. 3. Schematic diagram illustrating the orientation and orientation angles of *Balanus amphitrite* on *Xenostrobus atrata* shells.

Table 3
A comparison between orientation modes and orientation angles of barnacles on their hosts.

Barnacle (numbers of individuals)	Host	Attachment angle and position	Orientation modes and types (N=number of individuals)	$\vartheta°$	R	Deviation angle
B. amphitrite (1132)	X. atrata	±180° (1052)	a (490)	−41° 43'	0.98	−2°33' (average)
			b (562)	+39° 10'	0.97	
		0° (80)	a' (23)	−37° 30'	0.99	1° 18' (average)
			b' 57	+38° 48'	0.98	
C. patula	C. cruciata (138)	front edge (18)	±180° (11)	±180°	/	/
			0° (7)	0°	/	/
		carapace	±45° ±180° (120)	−175° 37'	0.91	(individual)
	P. pelagicus (individual numbers of barnacles) (268)	front edge (11)	±180° (8)	± 180°	/	/
			0° (3)	0°	/	/
		carapace	±90° ±180°(257)	+172° 49'	0.82	(individual)

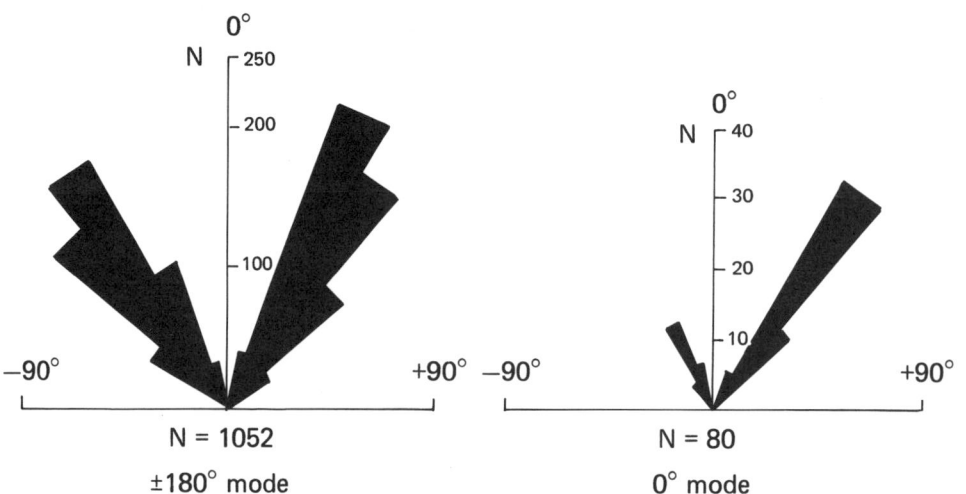

Fig. 4. A comparison of the occurrences of various orientations and orientation angles of *Balanus amphitrite* on *Xenostrobus atrata* shells. (N=numbers of individuals)

Table 4
A morphological comparison of unorientated barnacle individuals and individuals exhibiting various orientations.

Orientation	Number of individuals	plates	Height (mm)	Height ratio	Shell height (mm)	Substrate area (mm²)
unorientated	173	carina	6.08	1.3:1	5.26	52.01
		rostrum	5.12			
orientated ±180°	167	carina	4.04	1:2.2	7.55	31.49
		rostrum	8.67			
orientated 0° mode	80	carina	9.84	1.9:1	7.21	31.17
		rostrum	5.19	1.9:1	7.21	31.17

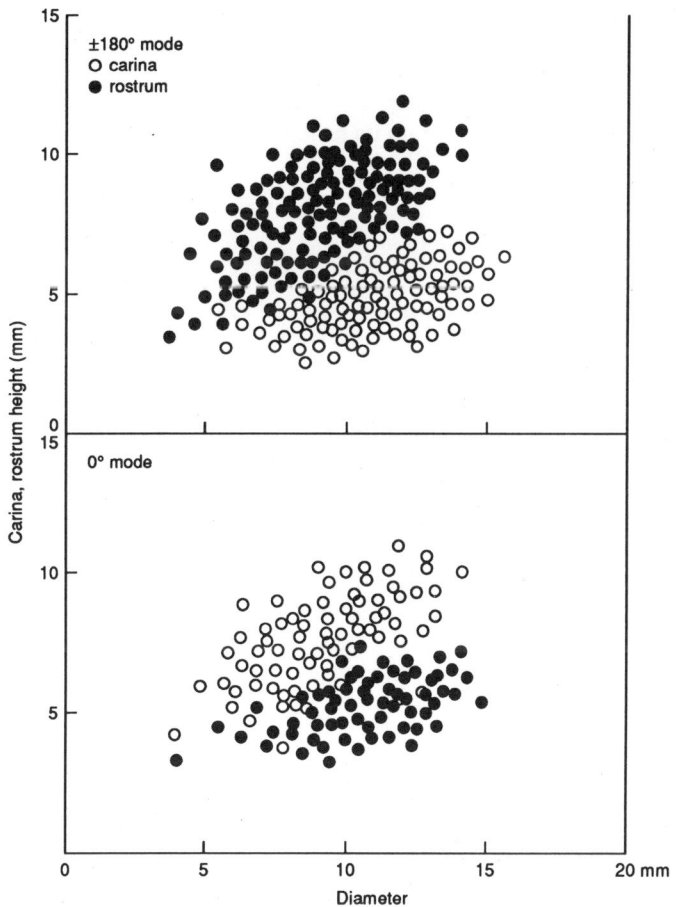

Fig. 5. A comparison of carina and rostral heights between various orientation modes of *Balanus amphitrite* on *Xenostrobus atrata* shells.

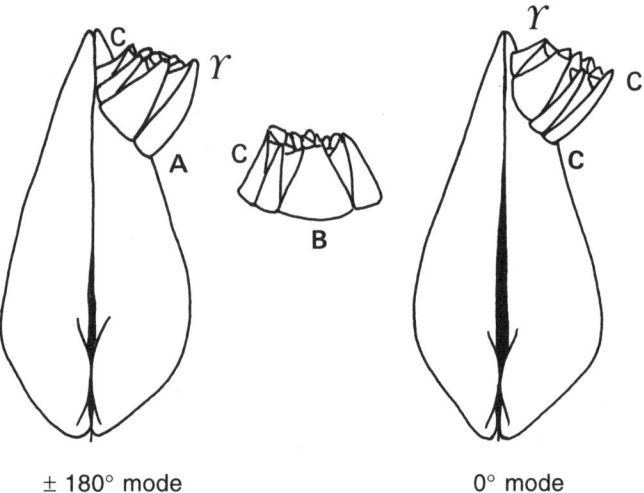

Fig. 6. A morphological comparison of various orientation modes of *Balanus amphitrite* on *Xenostrobus atrata* shells.

The orientation of *Chelonibia patula* on its hosts

Attachment frequency, attachment positions and numbers of attached individuals

The attachment frequency of *Chelonibia patula* on *Charybdis cruciata* was 27%, the number of attached individuals was 4–11 (Plate IC), and on *Portunus pelagicus*, 14% (between 5–29 attached individuals) (Plate IB). On both hosts, the barnacles were attached mainly in the centre of the carapace (96.23% and 91.30%, respectively). Individuals attaching to the front edge of the carapace were mainly single individuals; attachment rates were 33.96% and 47.83%, respectively (Table 1).

Orientation modes and orientation angles

Chelonibia patula is commensal on *Charybdis cruciata* and *Portunus pelagicus*. When attached to the front of either host, orientation is mainly in the mode of ±180°. Individuals attached on the carapace of *Charybdis cruciata* were in the mode of ±45° — ±180°, and ±90° – ±180° for *Portunus pelagicus*. In the former case, $\vartheta = 175° 37'$, $R = 0.91$ and the deviation angle was about ±45°; in the latter case $\vartheta = +172° 49'$, $R = 0.82$ and the deviation angle was about ±90° (Table 3). Differences in orientation angles are shown in Figure 7.

DISCUSSION

Attachment position

Barnacles have a determined attachment position on their host. This can be related to the need for current utilization. We believe that *Balanus amphitrite* attaching to the

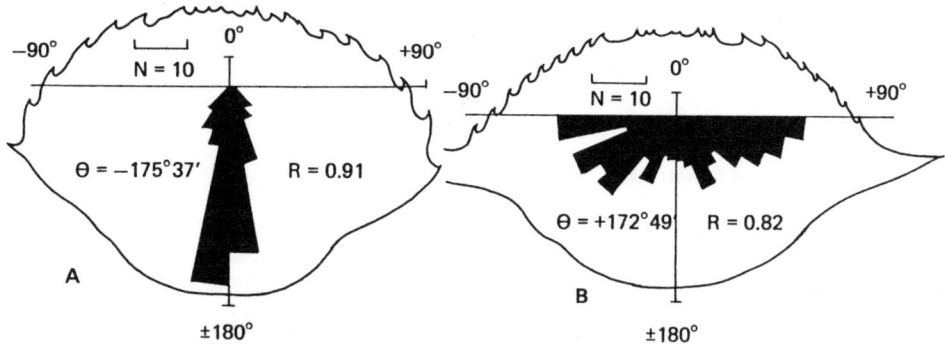

Fig. 7. Comparisons between orientations of *Chelonibia patula* on A: *Charybdis cruciata* and B, *Portunus pelagicus* (N = number of individuals).

posterior end of *Xenostrobus atrata* shell uses the currents created at the siphons for orientation. Cai and Huang (1984) found that all *B. cirratus* attached to the posterior ends of live *Anadara subcrenata* and *Anadara granosa*. Comparisons of cirral extension and contraction of *Balanus cirratus* on live hosts and dead hosts were made in the laboratory. Results showed that when the currents created by the siphons of live hosts are normal, cirral extension and contraction frequency was between 32–36 times·minute^{-1}. There are no currents on dead hosts and in this situation, *B. cirratus* evidently increases the frequency of extension and contraction to 44–49 times·minute^{-1}. This confirms the relationship between orientation and currents (Cai and Huang 1984). We also believe that *Chelonibia patula* orientated on the front edge of the crab carapace, can use the currents created by the host's mouthparts as well as the currents formed whilst the host advances. *Chelonibia patula*, attached to *Portunus trituberculatus* and *Matuta planipes*, exhibits the same phenomenon (Cai and Huang 1988). Barnacle orientation in relation to water currents created by the host has been recorded in a number of studies, e.g., Crisp and Stubbings (1975). Briggs and Morejohn (1972) reported oriented *Chelonibia diadema* attached to whales; Bowers (1968) on barnacles commensal with lobsters; Hastings (1972) reported commensalism of *Conchoderma virgatum* with *Nerocila acuminata* and *Alutera schoepfi*, and Williams (1978) reported commensalism of *C. virgatum* with *Dinemoura latiforia*.

Attachment frequency and numbers of attached individuals

The attachment frequency of *Balanus amphitrite* on host shells is extremly high (86%).The attachment rate of *Chelonibia patula* on the carapace of *Charybdis cruciata* is higher than that on *Portunus pelagicus* (Table 1). The numbers of attached individuals of *Chelonibia patula* on the carapace of *Portunus pelagicus* is twice or more than that on *Charybdis cruciata*. This may be related to the size of the hosts. *Balanus amphitrite* attaches gregariously to natural substrata (Cai and Huang 1988), but attaches to *Xenostrobus atrata* shells singly (74.5%). *Chelonibia patula* attaches to the host carapace gregariously, but single individuals attach to the front edge of the carpace (Table 1). We think this aversion phenomenon of barnacle larvae is advantageous in that it allows utilization of the limited feeding currents created by the host and avoids competition amongst individuals. *B. cirriatus* attaches mainly singly to the posterior ends of *Anadara subcrenata* and *Anadara granosa* shells and to the front edge of the carapace of *Scylla serrata* (Cai and Huang 1984).

Modes and types of orientation

The orientation of single individuals of *Balanus amphitrite* on hosts is mainly in the mode of ±180° (92.93%) (Table 1), with the occurence of orientation type b (right shell valve) highest (53.4%). We have found that single individuals of *Balanus cirratus* on *Anadara subcrenata* and *Anadara granosa* shells attach mainly to the hosts in the mode of ±180° with orientation type a (left shell valve) having the highest occurrence (Cai and Huang 1984). Because the edge of the posterior end of the *Xenostrobus atrata* shell is narrow and small, the two other orientation types found on *Anadara* shells are absent. The different attachment modes on different hosts may be related to the relative direction of tidal currents.

Differing orientation types are exhibited by multi-individual groups of *Balanus amphitrite* on host shells (Table 2). The directions of cirral movements of neighbouring individuals of various orientation types are either the same or opposite. Individuals rarely face each other, thereby avoiding competition for food. We have found a similar situation in the orientation of multi-individual groups of *Balanus cirratus* attached to hosts (Cai and Huang 1984).

The orientation of *Chelonibia patula* on the carapace of *Charybdis cruciata* and *Portunus pelagicus* is in the mode of ±180°. The individuals attached to the front edge of the carapace are orientated in two modes, 0° and ±180°, with the ±180° mode dominant (Table 3). The orientation of *Chelonibia patula* on the carapace of *Portunus trituberculatus* and *Matuta planipes* has similar modes (Cai and Huang 1988). The orientation of *Balanus amphitrite* on the posterior end of the host shell and of *Chelonibia patula* on the front edge of the host carapace are mainly in the mode of ±180°. This mode of orientation is advantageous as it can utilize the feeding currents formed by the host and thus avoid competition with the host for obtaining food and oxygen.

The orientation of cirripedes on hosts is related to water currents created by host movement (Moore 1935; Crisp 1935,1955; Utinomi 1955; Ayling 1978; Cai and Huang 1988). *Chelonibia patula*, attached to the carapace of *Chelonia mydas* and *Chelonia caretta*, uses the currents created as the host advances for feeding. Therefore, the cirri face towards the currents flowing over the host's body surface and orientation is in the mode of 0°. Sea snakes advance in a sinuous manner. Thus *Conchoderma hunteri* attached to the tail of *H. cyanocinctus* orients in the mode of 0° – ±90°. The orientation of *Balanus trigonus* on spiral shells is in the mode of 0° – ±180° to suit the irregular movement of the host (Cai and Huang, 1988). The orientation of *Chelonibia diadema* on the back of whales is in the mode of 0°, with the cirri facing towards the direction of the currents flowing over the host's body surface (Crisp and Stubbings 1957; Briggs and Morejohn 1972); the orientation of *Conchoderma virgatum* on *Dinemoura latiforia* is at an angle of 135° to the host body axis (Williams 1978).

McDougall (1943), Barnes *et al*. (1951) and Crisp and Stubbings (1957) pointed out that barnacle larvae are phototropic under direct light, orienting with the carina up and the rostrum down. Ayling (1978) proposed that water currents were the main factor determining the orientation of *Balanus trigonus*, but the direction of orientation may be changed when the direction of light changes. Moore (1935) thought that *Balanus balanoides* larvae showed orientation to the current, and rotation would occur when adults were at an angle to the current. Crisp and Stubbings (1957) confirmed that the cyprid larvae of *B. balanoides*, *B. crenatus*, and *Elminius modestus* showed orientation to direct light. Larval stages were vertical but, under the influence of a lateral current, individuals rotated during growth and adults were tilted in a direction appoximately at 0°. Cai and Huang (1988) found that in natural oceanic conditions, *Tetraclita squamosa squamosa*, *Chirona amaryllis*, *Balanus cirratus* and *Balanus uliginosus* showed orientation at a certain angle to the current. The orientation of these species is thus under the simultaneous influence of light and current.

Balanus amphitrite on the posterior end of *Xenostrobus atrata* shells and *Chelonibia patula* on the carapace of *Charybdis cruciata* and *Portunus pelagicus* show orientation with the rostrum facing downwards and the carina upwards (±180° mode); this may be related to illumination. However, Barnes (1953) pointed out that the orientation of *Semibalanus balanoides* populations on shells of *Pecten maximus* was related to gravity, with barnacles on *Chlamys opercularis* concentrated on the highest position of the host shell, because the upper part of the shell is curved. The negative reaction of this benthic animal to gravity is considered to have an important survival value.

Orientation angle

Single individuals of *Balanus amphitrite* orient themselves on *Xenostrobus atrata* shells in the mode of ±180°, orientation type a $\theta = -41° 43'$, $R = 0.98$, orientation type b $\theta = +39° 10'$, $R = 0.97$ and deviation angle $\theta = -2° 33'$ (Table 1). Orientation angles of *Balanus cirratus* on *Anadara subcrenata* shells with the same orientation type are as follows: $\theta = 27° 18'$ and $J = 25° 27'$, $R = 0.91$ and 0.85 and deviation angle $\vartheta = +1° 51'$ (Cai and Huang 1984). When the orientation of *B. amphitrite* on *Xenostrobus atrata* is in the mode of 0, orientation type a' $\theta = -37° 30'$, $r = 0.99$, deviation and orientation type b' $\theta = +38° 48'$, $R = 0.98$ and deviation angle $\vartheta = 1° 18'$. Orientation angles of *B. cirratus* on *A. subcrenata* with the same orientation type are: $\vartheta = 34° 11'$ and $48'$, $R = 0,89$ and 0.92 and deviation angle $J = 1° 23'$ (Cai and Huang 1984). These differences may be related both to the host's body size and to the contours of the posterior end of the host's shell, and may be advantageous to barnacles using the currents created by the host's siphons.

Orientation angles of *Chelonibia patula* on the carapace of *Charybdis cruciata* are $\theta = -175° 37'$, $R = 0.91$ and $\theta = +172° 49'$, $R = 0.82$ on *Portunus pelagicus* (Table 3). Orientation angles of *Chelonibia patula* on the carapace of *Portunus trituberculatus* are $\theta = 175° 46'$, $R = 0.087$ and on *Matuta planipes* $\theta = 150°-172°$, $R = 0.85$ (Cai and Huang 1988). Williams (1978) reported that *Conchoderma virgatum* on *Dinemoura latiforia* showed orientation at an angle of 135° to the host's body axis. Ayling (1978) found that under the action of the tide, *B. trigonus* showed orientation in a direction approximately at 90° to the wave axis. Evidently, the orientation of *C. patula* at 172°–175° on the crab's carapace allows the barnacle to utilize the currents created when the host moves in various directions.

Orientation and morphology

In comparison with the morphology of unorientated individuals, individuals of *Balanus amphitrite* orientated at ±180° show an increased rostral length; individuals orientated at 0° show was increased carinal length, whilst their basal area is reduced and their shell height increases simultaneously (Table 4, Figs. 5 and 6). These changes are also seen in *Balanus cirratus* on *Anadara subcrenata* and *Anadara granosa* at the posterior end of the shells, and in *Balanus trigonus* on *Mytilus crassitesta* also at the posterior end of the shells (Cai and Huang 1984, 1988). These changes allow the barnacle shell to be kept in an approximately horizontal position, thus utilizing the currents created by the host's siphons for feeding.

ACKNOWLEDGEMENTS

Sincere thanks are due to The University of Hong Kong and the Unesco Regional Office for Science and Technology for Southeast Asia for funding this research in Hong Kong and to Professor Brian Morton for the provision of research facilities and for correcting the drafts of the manuscript of this paper.

REFERENCES

Ayling, A.M. 1976. The strategy of orientation in the barnacle *Balanus trigonus*. *Marine Biology* 36:335–42.

Barnes, H. 1953. Orientation and aggregation in *Balanus balanoides* (L) da Costa. *Journal of Animal Ecology* 22:141–8.

Barnes, H. and Reeve, E.S. 1960. The behaviour of the stalked interidal barnacle *Pollicipes polymerus* J.B. Sowerby, with special reference to its ecology and distribution. *Journal of Animal Ecology* 29:169–86.

Barnes, H., Crisp, D.J. and Powell, H.T. 1951. Observations on the orientation of some species of barnacles. *Journal of Animal Ecology* 20:227–41.

Bowers, R.L. 1968. Observations on the orientation and feeding behaviour of barnacles associated with lobsters. *Journal of the Marine Biological Association of the United Kingdom* 35:631–9.

Briggs, K.T. and Morejohn, G.V. 1972. Barnacle orientation and flow characteristics in California Grey Whales. *Journal of Zoology, London* 167:287–98.

Cai, R.X. and Huang, Z.G. 1984. Studies on the orientation of cirripedes I, The orientation of *Balanus cirratus* on the hosts. *Oceanologia et Limnologia Sinica* 15:317–28.

Cai, R.X. and Huang, Z.G. 1988. Studies on the orientation of cirripedes II. Orientation on the hosts and natural habitats. *Oceanologia et Limnologia Sinica* 19:321–7.

Crisp, D.J. 1953. Changes in the orientation of barnacles of certain species in relation to water currents. *Journal of Animal Ecology* 22:333–43.

Crisp, D.J. 1955. The behaviour of barnacle cyprids in water movement over a surface. *Journal of Experimental Biology* 32:569–90.

Crisp, D.J. 1960, Factors influencing growth-rate in *Balanus balanoides*. *Journal of Animal Ecology* 29:95–116.

Crisp, D.J. and Barnes, H. 1954. The orientation and distribution of barnacles at settlement with particular reference to surface contour. *Journal of Animal Ecology* 23:142–62.

Crisp, D.J. and Stubbings, H.G. 1957. The orientation of barnacles to water currents. *Journal of Animal Ecology* 26:179–96.

Forbes, L., Seward, M.J.B. and Crisp, D.J. 1971. Orientation to light and the shading response in barnacles. *Proceedings of the European Marine Biological Symposium* 4:539–58.

Gregg, J.H. 1948. Replication of substrata detail by barnacles and some other marine organisms. *Biological Bulletin* 94:161–8.

Hastings, R.W. 1972. The barnacle, *Conchderma virgatum* (Spengler), in association with the isopod, *Nerocila acuminata* Schioedte and Meinert, and the orange filefish, *Alutera schoepfi* (Walbaum). *Crustaceana* 22:274–7.

Hurley, A.C. 1973, Larval settling behaviour of the acorn barnacle (*Balanus pacificus* Pilsbry) and its relation to distribution. *Journal of Animal Ecology* 42:508–609.

McDougall, K.D. 1943. Sessile marine invertebrates of Beaufort, North Carolina. *Ecological Monographs* 13:321–74.

Moore, H.B. 1935. The biology of *Balanus balanoides* in relation to environmental factors. *Journal of the Marine Biological Association of the United Kingdom* 20:263–307.

Pyefinch, K.A. 1948. Notes on the biology of cirripedes. *Journal of the Marine Biological Association of the United Kingdom* 27:464–503.

Utinomi, H. 1955. Studies on the Cirripedia of Japan III. Ecological evidences. *Bulletin of the Biogeographical Society of Japan* 16–19:124–34.

Williams, E.H. 1978. *Conchoderma virgatum* (Spengler) (Cirripedia Thoracica) in association with *Dinemoura latifolia* (Steenstrup and Lutken) (Copepoda, Caligidea), a parasite of the shortfin Mako, *Isurus oxyrhynchus* Rafinesque (Pisces, Chondrichthyes). *Crustaceana* 34:109–10.

SOME ASPECTS OF THE ECOLOGY OF SEDIMENT FAUNA IN BALINGASAY, BOLINAO, PANGASINAN (NORTHERN PHILIPPINES)

Helen T. Yap and Hildie Maria E. Nacorda

Marine Science Institute, University of the Philippines,
Diliman, Quezon City, Philippines

ABSTRACT

The distribution of sediment fauna along an inshore-offshore gradient was studied in Balingasay, Bolinao, Pangasinan (northern Philippines) in the months of January 1988, May 1988 and January 1989, representing roughly semi-annual sampling intervals. The study site is a moderate-sized river, so that the transect established also encompassed a salinity gradient. Four sampling stations were evenly spaced along this transect to cover a distance of approximately 2 km. The most dominant taxonomic groups studied included the polychaetes, crustaceans, molluscs and nematodes. With each monitoring visit, most of these groups were seen to vary in abundance and diversity along the transect. Overall, organismal abundance correlated significantly with measured organic carbon values in the sediment. Furthermore, a relatively coarse grain size was positively correlated with the abundance of crustaceans and molluscs, and with the diversity of polychaetes, crustaceans and molluscs. Silt, on the other hand, seemed to enhance nematode abundance. It appears that the composition and distribution of sediment fauna may be predicted by characteristics of the substrate. Another environmental variable seen to affect benthic fauna is salinity, which correlated significantly with diversity of polychaetes.

INTRODUCTION

In this paper, results are presented of a continuing effort to investigate the composition and spatial patterns of sediment fauna at selected sites in the Philippines. This study is significant as being one of the first in the country, and was initiated in 1988 under the ASEAN-Australia project Living Resources in Coastal Areas'. Initial findings, including a preliminary species list, have been presented in the paper by Yap *et al.* (in press).

The present work focuses on the study site off Balingasay, a moderate-sized river in Bolinao (province of Pangasinan) in the northwestern Philippines. A transect extending seaward from the river mouth was chosen for investigation because it was felt that the existence of an onshore-offshore gradient characterized by a progression in depth and salinity might produce patterns in the sediment fauna that would lend themselves more easily to analysis and interpretation.

The purpose of this study is to characterize faunal composition in terms of the major taxonomic groups, especially those that achieve dominance in this particular environmental setting. Associated physico-chemical factors were also measured and analysed, especially as they influence faunal patterns. Emphasis is given to the substrate-related parameters such as organic carbon content and sediment grain size distribution since these are known to affect benthic dwellers directly. If properly quantified, they may assume a predictive value in terms of the kinds of organisms that may be found in a particular sediment type.

MATERIALS AND METHODS

The study site is at Balingasay River in Bolinao, Pangasinan, located at 119°51'14"E and 16°21'31"N. Four stations (A–D), spaced approximately 500 m apart, were delineated from the river mouth going seaward (see figure in Yap *et al.* in press). The innermost station, A, was delimited by a land bridge.

In January 1988, May 1988 and January 1989 (representing roughly semi-annual intervals) 4 samples were taken at each of the 4 stations using a 15 cm^2 Ekman grab — 3 replicates for faunal composition and 1 for sediment analysis. After fixing and staining, the sediment for faunal analysis was passed through a series of large sieves (mesh sizes of 5, 3 and 2 mm) to separate the large macrofauna. The remaining sediment was processed through smaller sieves (mesh sizes of 0.85 and 0.3 mm) to catch the smaller organisms. Faunal samples were preserved in either 70% alcohol or 10% buffered formalin as considered appropriate.

Organic carbon content of the sediment was determined by drying to constant weight at 105°C, and then ashing at 550°C to constant weight. Sediment grain size distribution was determined based on Wentworth's size classification (Holme and McIntyre 1984). Further details are provided in Yap *et al.* (in press). During each sampling visit, routine measurements were made of surface and bottom temperature and salinity.

Community parameters determined were faunal abundance per unit area, total number of species (N), and species diversity (H') using the Shannon-Wiener index (Poole 1974). Data were analyzed using the analysis of variance (ANOVA) and simple correlation coefficients (Sokal and Rohlf 1981), including Spearman rank correlation analysis (Sachs 1984) where appropriate. Abundance values were normalized by the log (y+1) transformation, and percentage data by the arcsine transformation.

RESULTS

General environmental parameters Average depths ranged from 4 m at Station A, the shallowest site, to 17 m at Station D, the deepest site. Temperatures at all stations were similar and ranged from 27–32°C throughout the year. Bottom salinities, on the other hand, were always slightly lower at the two inner stations, ranging from 24–34‰ over an annual cycle. Values at the two outer stations, C and D, ranged from 30 to 34‰.

Faunal composition, abundance and diversity

An overview of the dominant faunal assemblages at all stations during each sampling time is given in Figure 1. The graphs depict mean numbers of individuals per square meter. It should be noted that the vertical scales increase from January 1988 to May 1988 to January 1989, implying that organismal abundance increased over time during the period of study.

As seen in Figure 1, the dominant groups were the polychaetes, crustaceans, molluscs and nematodes. In January 1988, the polychaetes were the largest single group at all stations. In May 1988, the overall dominance shifted to the crustaceans, except in Station D. This pattern did not carry over to January 1989, when crustaceans were dominant at Station A, and polychaetes at Station C.

Variation on a spatial scale was examined by an ANOVA (Table 1) performed for each major taxonomic group for each sampling time. According to the ANOVA results, variation in faunal abundance from station to station was in general highly significant. No trend, however, could be established for an inshore-offshore gradient, and no distinct patterns over a spatial or temporal scale could be detected with respect to diversity (Table 2).

SEDIMENT CHARACTERISTICS

Levels of organic carbon in the sediment were analyzed for samples taken in May 1988 and January 1989 (Fig. 2). No distinct trend could be seen, except that values were highest on both occasions in Station A. This station was subjected to a high degree of organic loading, being situated closest to the human settlements on shore. The organic input consisted of plant debris, domestic waste and a large amount of animal faeces.

Percentage organic matter at Station A ranged from near 20 to over 30% of the total sediment weight. At the other stations, it was generally below 10% (Fig. 2).

Another significant sediment parameter analyzed was grain size distribution, again for samples taken in May 1988 and January 1989 (Fig. 3). In May 1988, the dominant size fraction varied from coarse to fine sand, which is characteristic of exposed marine environments.

In January 1989, the fine sand fraction predominated at all stations except A. In general, the range was from medium to very fine sand. The predominant size fraction at Station A were the granules which indicate a deposition of coarse terrestrial material at this particular time, probably due to heavy rains.

Correlations between environmental factors and faunal characteristics

Abundance

The sediment parameters of organic carbon content and grain size distribution showed significant correlations with faunal abundance (Table 3). Total faunal abundance is the sum of all individuals in a station averaged over the three replicates. When this quantity was pooled for all stations and all sampling times, it correlated significantly with organic carbon levels in the sediment ($r = 0.80214$; $p < 0.05$).

The individual faunal groups also demonstrated significant positive correlations (p

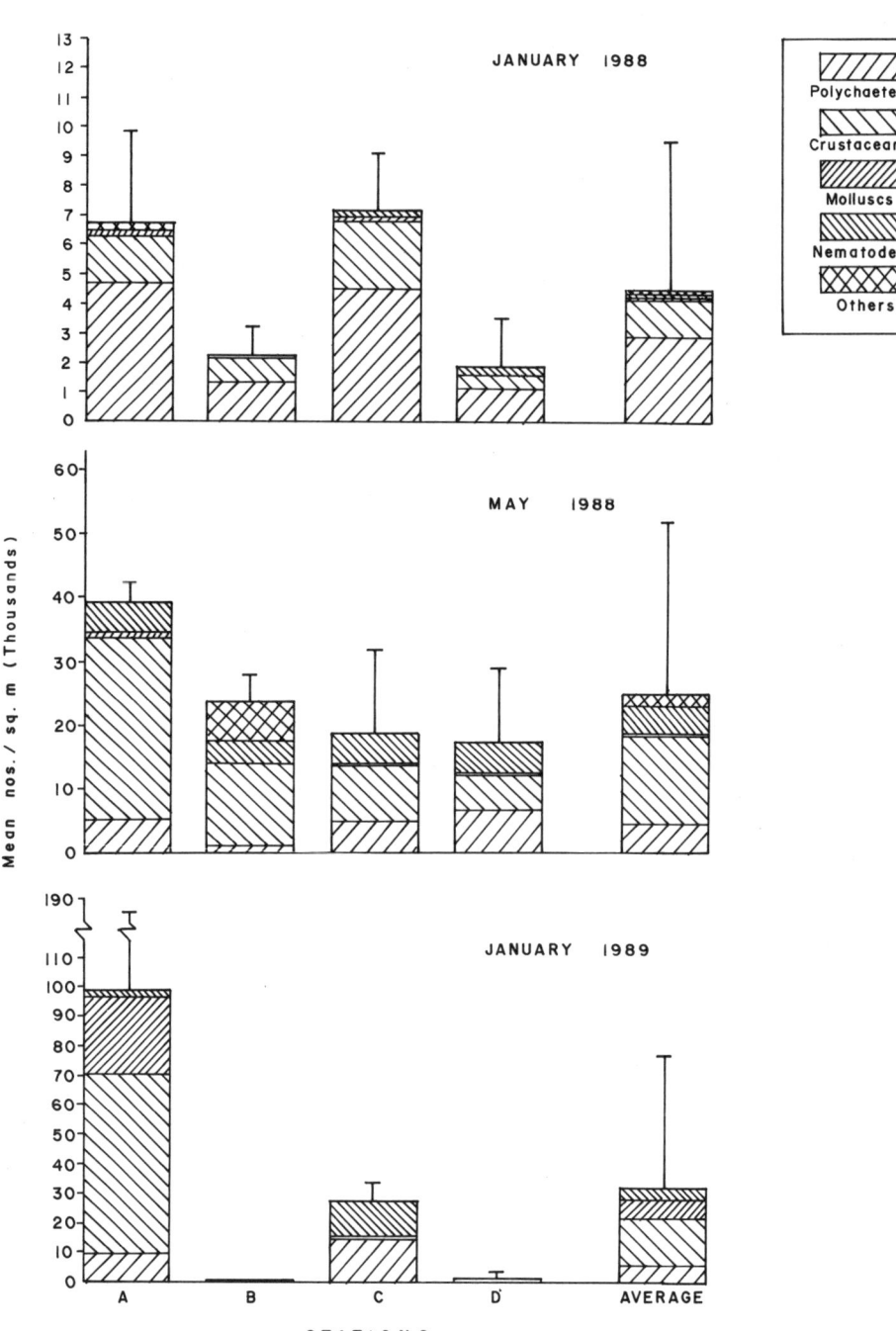

Fig. 1. Distribution of major taxonomic groups of sediment fauna along an onshore-offshore transect (Stations A–D) in January 1988, May 1988 and January 1989.

Table 1
Summary of one-way analyses of variance comparing faunal abundance (log-transformed) among stations (A–D). [$F_{0.05\,(3,8)} = 4.07$].

Date	Faunal groups	F value	d.f.	P
January 1988	Polychaetes	4.818	3, 8	3.35E–02
	Crustaceans	4.811	3, 8	3.36E–02
	Molluscs	3.883	3, 8	N.S.
	Nematodes	2.424	3, 8	N.S.
May 1988	Polychaetes	9.364	3, 8	5.39E–03
	Crustaceans	5.512	3, 8	2.39E–02
	Molluscs	16.012	3, 8	9.62E–04
	Nematodes	0.252	3, 8	N.S.
January 1989	Polychaetes	13.441	3, 8	1.72E–03
	Crustaceans	1.340	3, 8	N.S.
	Molluscs	24.134	3, 8	2.31E–04
	Nematodes	8.911	3, 8	6.11E–04

Table 2
Diversity indices (Shannon-Wiener, H') of the abundant taxa at the stations (A–D) at Balingasay, Bolinao, Pangasinan, in January and May 1988 and January 1989.

Month/ Stations ->	A	B	C	D
January 1988				
Polychaetes	2.38	1.77	2.43	1.19
Crustaceans	1.93	2.42	2.59	2.07
Molluscs	1.62	– *	1.36	– **
All groups combined	3.00	2.74	3.25	2.20
May 1988				
Polychaetes	2.29	2.28	2.86	2.87
Crustaceans	1.91	1.88	1.83	2.44
Molluscs	0.88	0.69	1.36	1.42
All groups combined	2.57	2.34	2.87	3.27
January 1989				
Polychaetes	0.98	0.36	1.99	1.44
Crustaceans	1.40	1.71	2.77	1.51
Molluscs	1.20	0.69	1.32	1.42
All groups combined	2.23	1.61	2.04	2.14

* 2species with similar importance values
** none recorded

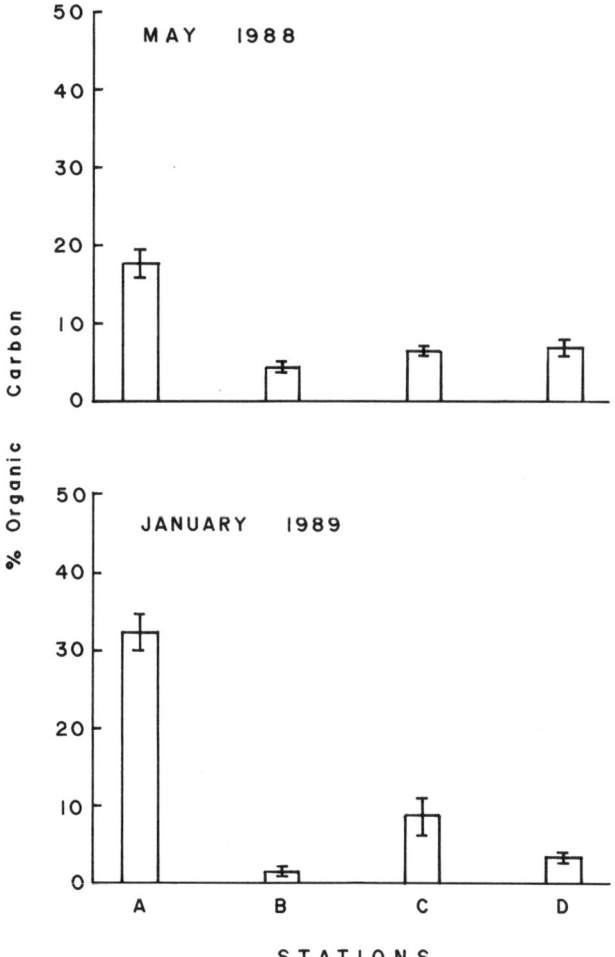

Fig. 2. Organic carbon levels (%) in the sediment along an onshore-offshore transect (Stations A–D) in May 1988 and January 1989.

< 0.05) with organic content of the sediment in terms of their abundance, as follows: polychaetes (r = 0.68052), crustaceans (r = 0.78165), and molluscs (r = 0.91383).

Possible significant trends with respect to sediment grain size were revealed when individual numbers of particular taxonomic groups were again pooled together for all stations and all sampling times. Crustacean abundance correlated positively with granules and very coarse sand, and negatively with fine sand (Table 3). Molluscs likewise appeared to increase in abundance with increasing amounts of granules. Nematodes, on the other hand, appeared to favour a higher silt content of the sediment.

It is of interest to note that organic carbon levels were positively correlated with the percentage amount of granules occurring in the sediment (r = 0.76115, p < 0.05).

Correlations of faunal abundance with other environmental factors such as depth, salinity and temperature were not significant.

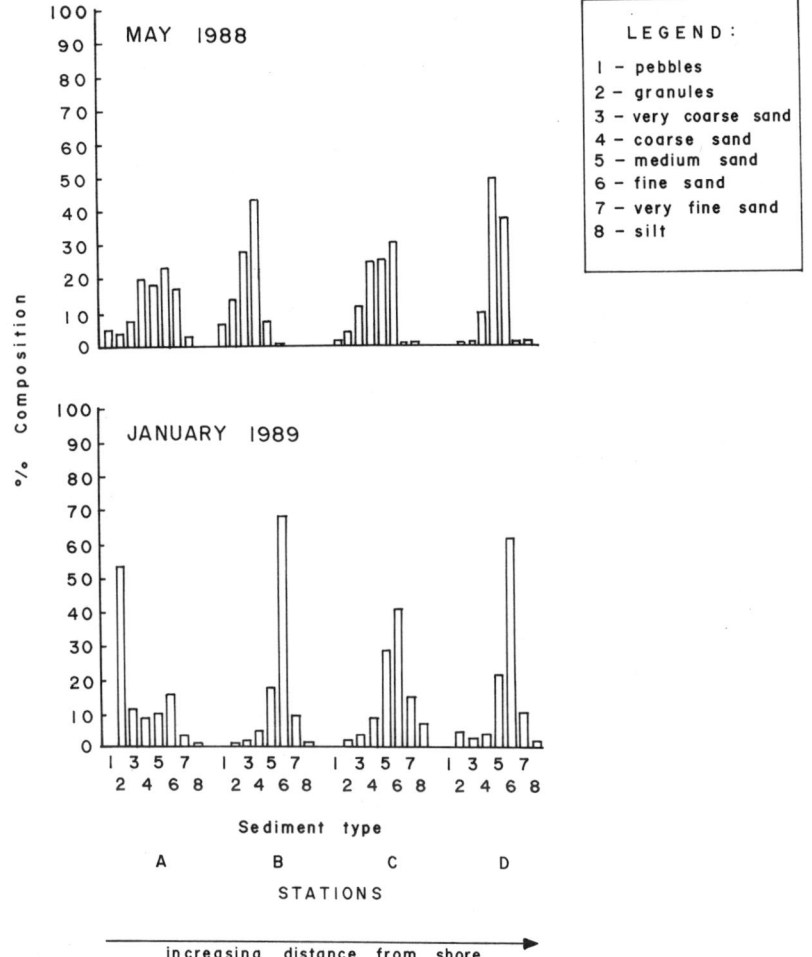

Fig. 3. Sediment grain size distribution (based on Wentworth's classification) of samples along an onshore-offshore transect (Stations A–D) in May 1988 and January 1989.

Diversity

Sediment size composition seemed to have a significant effect on the diversity of particular faunal groups (Table 4). Polychaete diversity increased with increasing levels of coarse sand in the sediment. The diversity of crustaceans correlated positively with the percentage of medium sand. Mollusc diversity likewise correlated significantly with increasing medium sand fractions. In addition, the total number of molluscan species (N) was found to correlate significantly with levels of granules and coarse sand. When all faunal groups were combined, total diversity was seen to be positively correlated with coarse sand, and negatively correlated with fine sand (Table 4).

Organic carbon in the sediment appeared to enhance the diversity of molluscs in terms of total number of species (Table 4).

A pattern seems to emerge with respect to a possible effect of salinity on diversity

Table 3

Significant r values obtained from correlation analyses of faunal abundance versus sediment characteristics (p < 0.05). Values for all stations and sampling dates pooled.

Variables in sediments	% Organic carbon	Sediment type
Total faunal abundance	0.80214	
Polychaete abundance	0.68052	
Crustacean abundance	0.78165	0.70715 (granules) 0.72791 (very coarse sand) 0.70414 (fine sand)
Mollusc abundance	0.91383	0.65999 (granules)
Nematode abundance		0.70712 (silt)

Critical values (1-tailed): ±0.62658
(2-tailed): ±0.70477
N = 8

Table 4

Significant r values obtained from correlation analyses of species diversity (H') and number of species (N) with sediment characteristics and salinity (p < 0.05). Values for all stations and sampling dates pooled.

Variables	% Organic carbon in sediments	Sediment type	Salinity
Species diversity (H')			
Total		0.77416 (coarse sand) −0.68719 (fine sand)	0.68410
Polychaetes		0.67421 (coarse sand)	0.90166
Crustaceans		0.65187 (medium sand)	
Molluscs*		0.802 (medium sand)	
Number of species (N)			
Total		0.68068 (coarse sand) 0.64103 (fine sand)	
Polychaetes		0.73774 (coarse sand) 0.65023 (fine sand)	0.73596
Molluscs*	0.804	0.664 (granules) 0.664 (coarse sand)	

Critical values (1-tailed) = ±0.62658
(2-tailed) = ±0.70477

N = 8

*Critical values (for Spearman rank correlation analysis)
(1-sided) = ±0.643
(2-sided) = ±0.738

(Table 4). Diversity of all organisms combined, as well as of the polychaete group alone, correlated significantly with salinity, i.e., diversity increased towards the more saline (seaward) stations.

DISCUSSION

Sediment fauna

The data show that either the polychaetes or the crustaceans were the most dominant groups in the sediment. This finding has been corroborated by numerous other studies in tropical nearshore areas, e.g., Hylleberg and Nateewathana (1984), Maurer et al. (1988), Riddle (1988), Shin (1989). Some studies in the temperate region reveal similar results (Young and Rhoads 1971; Yokoyama and Hayashi 1980; Eleftheriou et al. 1986; Carrasco et al. 1988). A tentative list of 86 species belonging to 63 families under 7 phyla is provided in Yap et al. (in press).

The ANOVA performed on the data demonstrates significant variation in abundance of individual taxonomic groups on the order of hundreds of metres. This well-known phenomenon of patchiness in benthic faunal distribution has been shown in a number of studies, e.g., Poore and Rainer (1979), Coull and Wells (1981), Thrush et al. (1989). Such spatial variation is a result of responses to local environmental factors, particularly those that are substrate-associated, as will be discussed below.

The data are as yet insufficient for an analysis of temporal variation. The preliminary picture that emerges is that individual numbers fluctuate markedly over time. Although part of the variability is certainly due to sampling error, i.e., the exact spots were not sampled by the grab each time, factors such as recruitment and mortality over a seasonal cycle certainly play a role.

The shift in dominance between polychaetes and crustaceans with each sampling may again reflect spatial variability, or real differences in recruitment to the sediment fauna over time.

Influence of sediment characteristics on benthic fauna

As shown by the present study, the amount of organic carbon in the sediment appears to positively influence the occurrence of most organisms. Levinton (1979, in Jones 1984) noted that organic matter can affect community variables, e.g., densities of deposit feeders. Thus, sediments with organic matter reaching 8% (by weight, largely plant matter) were found with high densities of organisms occurring throughout the year in the westernmost part of Wakasa Bay (Yokoyama and Hayashi 1980). Organic enrichment in the littoral sediments of the Gulf of Aqaba, mainly contributed by seagrass meadows, favoured meiofaunal settling and prominence (Grelet et al. 1987). Organic carbon values in the coastal areas of the Firth of Clyde (UK) correlated strongly with large densities of opportunistic polychaetes and nematodes (Eleftheriou et al. 1986). Organic carbon levels in the sediment may thus serve as one, albeit of many, predictors of the abundance of benthic assemblages in a locality.

A more reliable predictor of faunal composition may be the particular grain size that predominates in the sediment. As shown in this study, the abundance and/or diversity of certain faunal groups correlate significantly with the percentages of particular size fractions, i.e., polychaetes, crustaceans and molluscs with the coarser fractions and nematodes with the fine particles. Such a pattern may be a reflection of the particular habits of the organisms concerned. Thus, polychaetes, crustaceans and molluscs may prefer larger spaces between grain sizes which allow for greater movement and water circulation (see, for example, Coull 1985). Nematodes, on the other hand, with their narrow vermiform bodies are better adapted to the tight interstitial spaces which characterize silty substrata.

St. John *et al.* (1989) found polychaetes and harpacticoid copepods to be more abundant in coarse as opposed to fine sediments in the Great Barrier Reef. Jones (1984) established a significant correlation between median phi or particle diameter of the sediment and species richness of crustaceans, also in the Great Barrier Reef. On the other hand, a high relative abundance of nematodes was associated with very fine sediments in the Gulf of Aqaba (Grelet *et al.* 1987). Shin (1989) and Hylleberg and Nateewathana (1984) related low abundances of benthic fauna to high silt-clay fractions, while Lee (1976) detected a lower species diversity in fine sediments off the Busan coast of Korea.

In general, sandy bottoms seem to be associated with higher diversities than muddy bottoms because of the greater variety of microhabitats in the former (Sanders 1968 in Young and Rhoads 1971). This may be one reason for the significant positive correlations of the abundance and diversity of the above-mentioned groups with the coarser sediments.

Effect of salinity on diversity

The results of this study, though tentative, indicate a possible increase in diversity with higher salinity, especially for the polychaetes. This could mean that species tend to increase in number under more 'normal' oceanic conditions as compared to brackish water situations. This may be a reflection of the possible stress associated with the constant mixing of fresh and salt water which is ameliorated as one goes seaward. A similar finding is that of Jones *et al.* (1986) in the Hawkesbury Estuary where seaward transects supported more species as compared to the upstream transects. Salinity was postulated to be one of the two most important factors influencing polychaete distribution in coastal lagoons of the central Mediterranean (Gravina *et al.* 1988). According to Armonies and Armonies (1987), polychaetes, being a marine group, are expected to show a seaward increase. In addition to sediment characteristics, salinity is thus seen to play an important role in determining faunal distribution.

ACKNOWLEDGEMENTS

The authors are grateful to Mr Ben-Hur R. Viloria who contributed a major part in the field and taxonomic work. The study was funded by the Australian International Development Assistance Bureau (AIDAB) through the ASEAN-Australia project 'Living Resources in Coastal Areas'. This is contribution no. 217 of the Marine Science Institute, University of the Philippines.

REFERENCES

Armonies, W. and Hellwig-Armonies, M. 1987. Synoptic patterns of meiofaunal and macrofaunal abundances and specific composition in littoral sediments. *Helgolander Meeresuntersuchungen* 41:83–111.
Carrasco, F.D., Gallardo, V.A. and Medrano, S. 1988. Sublittoral macrobenthic infaunal assemblages of two nearby embayments from Central Chile. *Internationale Revue der Gesamten Hydrobiologie* 73:441–55.
Coull, B.C. 1985. Long-term variability of estuarine meiobenthos: an 11 year study. *Marine Ecology-Progress Series* 24:205–18.
Coull, B.C. and Wells, J.B.J. 1981. Density of mud-dwelling meiobenthos from three sites in the Wellington region. *New Zealand Journal of Marine and Freshwater Research* 15:411–5.
Eleftheriou, A., Robertson, M.R. and Murison, D.J. 1986. The benthic fauna of sandy bays, with particular reference to Irvine Bay. *Proceedings of the Royal Society of Edinburgh* 90B:317–27.
Gravina, M.F., Ardizzone, G.D. and Giangrande, A. 1988. Selecting factors in polychaete communities of Central Mediterranean coastal lagoons. *Internationale Revue der Gesamten Hydrobiologie* 73:465–76.
Grelet, Y., Falconetti, C., Thomassin, B.A., Vitiello, P. and Abu Hilal, A.H. 1987. Distribution of the macro- and meiobenthic assemblages in the littoral soft-bottoms of the Gulf of Aqaba (Jordan). *Atoll Research Bulletin* 308:1–14.
Holme, N.A. and McIntyre, A.D. (eds.). 1984. *Methods for the study of marine benthos.* 2nd ed. Oxford: Blackwell Scientific Publications.
Hylleberg, J. and Nateewathana, A. 1984. Responses of polychaete families to monsoon- and offshore mining- associated sediment disturbance. In *Proceedings of the First International Polychaete Conference, Sydney* (ed. P.A. Hutchings), 279–91. Linnean Society of New South Wales.
Jones, A.R. 1984. Sedimentary relationships and community structure of benthic crustacean assemblages of reef-associated sediments at Lizard Island, Great Barrier Reef. *Coral Reefs* 3:101–11.
Jones, A.R., Watson-Russell, C.J. and Murray, A. 1986. Spatial patterns in the macrobenthic communities of the Hawkesbury Estuary, New South Wales. *Australian Journal of Marine and Freshwater Research* 37:521–43.
Lee, J.H. 1976. A study on the benthic fauna along the Busan coast, Korea. *Publications of Institute of Marine Sciences, National Fisheries University of Busan* 9:49–70
Maurer, D., Vargas, J. and Dean, H. 1988. Polychaetous annelids from the Gulf of Nicoya, Costa Rica. *Internationale Revue der Gesamten Hydrobiologie* 73:43–59.
Poole, R.W. 1974. *An introduction to quantitative ecology.* Tokyo: McGraw-Hill Kogakusha.
Poore, G.C.B. and Rainer, S. 1979. A three-year study of benthos of muddy environments in Port Phillip Bay, Victoria. *Estuarine and Coastal Marine Science* 9:477–97.
Riddle, M.J. 1988. Patterns in the distribution of macrofaunal communities in coral reef sediments on the central Great Barrier Reef. *Marine Ecology-Progress Series* 47:281–92.
Sachs, L. 1984. *Applied statistics, a handbook of techniques.* New York: Springer-Verlag, Inc.
Shin, P.K.S. 1989. Natural disturbance of benthic infauna in the offshore waters of Hong Kong. *Asian Marine Biology* 6:193–207.
Sokal, R.R. and Rohlf, F.J. 1981. *Biometry.* 2nd ed. New York: W.H. Freeman and Co.
St. John, J., Jones, G.P. and Sale, P.F. 1989. Distribution and abundance of soft-sediment meiofauna and a predatory goby in a coral reef lagoon. *Coral Reefs* 8:51–7.
Thrush, S.F., Hewitt, J.E. and Pridmore, R.D. 1989. Patterns in the spatial arrangements of polychaetes and bivalves in intertidal sandflats. *Marine Biology* 102:529–35.
Yap, H.T., Viloria, B.H.R. and Nacorda, H.M.E. (in press). Comparison of soft bottom community profiles in two Philippine nearshore sites. In *'Living Resources in Coastal Areas'-Proceedings of the First Regional Symposium.* Marine Science Institute, Quezon City.
Yokoyama, H. and Hayashi, I. 1980. Zonation and species diversity of smaller macrobenthos in the westernmost part of Wakasa Bay (the Sea of Tango). *Journal of the Oceanographical Society of Japan* 36:46–58.
Young, D.K. and Rhoads, D.C. 1971. Animal-sediment relations in Cape Cod Bay, Massachusetts. I. A transect study. *Marine Biology* 11:242–54.

The Marine Biology of the South China Sea
(ed. B. Morton). Proceedings of the First
International Conference on the Marine
Biology of Hong Kong the South China Sea,
Hong Kong, 28 October – 3 November 1990.
Hong Kong: Hong Kong University Press, 1993.

THE CHEMICAL CHARACTERISTICS OF SOIL AND ITS ASSOCIATION WITH STANDING LITTER BIOMASS IN A SUBTROPICAL MANGROVE COMMUNITY IN HONG KONG

N.F.Y. Tam and L.L.P. Vrijmoed

Department of Biology and Chemistry, City Polytechnic of Hong Kong,
Tat Chee Avenue, Kowloon, Hong Kong

and

Y.S. Wong

Research Centre, The University of Science and Technology,
Clear Water Bay, Kowloon, Hong Kong

ABSTRACT

An ecological survey using transect lines was carried out to examine site variations in soil nutrient and trace metal concentrations, litter accumulation and plant coverage of a small mangal in Hong Kong. Transects 1 and 2, located in the north-eastern part of the mangal, traversed a relatively wide band of mangrove vegetation (greater than 80 m). Transect 3 was in the south-eastern region and had a narrow coverage of mangrove vegetation (less than 40 m). This transect was more disturbed by human activities. Soil samples collected from Transects 1 and 2 had larger amounts of organic carbon, phosphorus and potassium than Transect 3. All the three transects had relatively higher soil nutrient concentrations at the landward sites which decreased towards the sea. A significant correlation was obtained between soil nutrient levels and the amount of litter accumulated. On the other hand, trace metal levels, including Cu, Mn, Zn and Pb, did not show any specific trend of changes along each transect. The concentrations fluctuated from landward to seaward sites. The differences among the three transects varied with metal species. For example, Transect 3 had higher concentrations of Pb when compared with Transects 1 and 2 but a lower level of Mn was recorded. These results suggest that, even in a small mangrove stand (0.03 km^2), site variations in soil chemical characteristics and standing litter biomass are obvious. These spatial variations can be partially related to human activities.

INTRODUCTION

A mangal consists of a group of mangrove plants found along sheltered, estuarine, shores within the tropical and subtropical regions (Macnae 1968). They extend from 25°N to 25°S and fringe about 75% of the world's coastline at these latitudes. The mangal attains its greatest diversity and luxuriance in equatorial areas, especially on the west coast of Peninsula Malaysia where they grow up to 30 m high and merge at the back of the shore with the tropical rain forest (Hodgkiss 1986). Hong Kong, located in the subtropical region (22°N), is near the northern limit of mangal development. The local mangrove ecosystem is different from other tropical mangals in terms of environmental conditions, the flora and fauna. Yipp (1982) reported that both the micro- and macro-fauna are less diverse at Three Fathoms Cove mangrove stand, Hong Kong. Only a few species of mangrove plants are present which grow in isolated patches and are generally stunted (seldom taller than 2 m) (Hodgkiss 1986). Most of the literature on ecological studies of mangal are descriptions of species composition and zonation of the flora and fauna. Little information is available on the relationships between mangrove soils, plant coverage and standing litter biomass, especially in sub-tropical mangals. This knowledge is important in understanding the productivity of a mangrove community and its role in the detritus food web. It also provides baseline information on the capacity of a mangrove stand to assimilate nutrients and pollutants when the mangrove swamps are used as sites for the disposal of wastewater (Clough *et al.* 1983). Moreover, the relationship between soil characteristics and primary productivity within a mangal has been seldom studied although such information represents an important component of the data-base required for long-term policies on management and conservation. A survey was therefore undertaken to investigate site variations in chemical characteristics of mangrove soils, standing litter biomass and plant coverage in a small mangal in Hong Kong.

MATERIALS AND METHODS

The study was carried out in a mangal located at Sai Keng, Three Fathoms Cove (22.5°25'N, 114°16'E), Tolo Harbour, Hong Kong. The study site is about 0.6 km wide, covering an area of 0.03 km^2. The mangrove plants are located in an enclosed bay and the effects of wave action are relatively little. These plants are frequently inundated and spatial variations in strength and frequency of inundation are small. The substrata of the mangrove floor vary from hard to soft, comprising large pebbles and clay particles. The soft muddy floor of the mangrove is usually wetter and has a thicker soil depth than the pebbly part. Only a few plant species are present in this stand; it is dominated mainly by *Kandelia candel* (L.) Druce and *Aegiceras corniculatum* (L.) Blanco. Other mangrove plants such as *Avicennia marina* (Forsk.) Vierh., *Lumnitzera racemosa* Willd. and *Excoecaria agallocha* L. are not as common. They are clustered in sites with special environmental conditions. For example, *A. marina* grows along the small creeks where the substrata are soft and wet, while *L. racemosa* is mainly found at the back of the shore.

The distribution of mangrove plants, standing litter biomass and the associated soil characteristics were studied by running three transects perpendicular to the shore, stretching over the entire zone occupied by mangrove plants. Transects 1 and 2 were located in the northeastern part of the mangal. They transversed a relatively wide band of mangrove vegetation, and spanned both the pebbly and muddy sites. Transect 3 was located in the south-eastern region and had a narrow coverage by plants. The substratum was more muddy and wetter than Transects 1 and 2. This transect was adjacent to a recreational area and was the main access to the mangal under investigation. The mangrove plants and soils along Transect 3 would, thus, be more disturbed by human activities. In fact, a public toilet was located at the landward edge of Transect 3. This transect was selected specifically to explore the effects of human disturbance, (e.g., faecal contamination, on soil characteristics and plant coverage. Along each transect, the plant species were identified. The height and the percentage cover of each plant species were measured using the line intercept technique (Cox 1979). At regular intervals of 4 to 5 m, depending on the total length of the transect, the plant litter accumulated on the surface of the mangrove floor was collected using a 0.25 m^2 quadrat. The litter was then washed gently with deionized water and sorted into the following components: leaves, twigs (and bark), fruits and flowers. These components were oven dried at 50°C for at least two days and weighed separately. Two quadrats of standing litter biomass were measured for each sampling point.

Duplicate samples of surface soil (0 to 10 cm) were also collected at each interval. They were then air-dried, sieved through a 2 mm mesh sieve and analysed for organic carbon (Walkley and Black 1934), salinity (saturated solution, by an optical refractometer-salinometer), pH and conductivity (1:5 water:soil extract, by pH and conductivity meters, respectively), ammonium and nitrate nitrogen (extracted with 2N KCl followed by steam distillation, Keeney and Nelson 1982), total Kjeldahl nitrogen (Micro-Kjeldahl digestion using concentrated H_2SO_4 and Cu catalyst, followed by Markham distillation, Allen et al. 1974), total phosphorus (Murphy and Riley 1962) and available phosphorus (Olsen et al. 1954). For the measurement of total concentration of trace metals, the soil samples were digested in concentrated HNO_3 and H_2SO_4 at 160°C. The filtered digests were then analysed for total potassium (K) by flame photometry; and copper (Cu), zinc (Zn), manganese (Mn), lead (Pb), cadmium (Cd) and nickel (Ni) by flame atomic absorption spectrophotometry. The available trace metals were determined by extracting the soil samples with 1M ammonium acetate (pH = 7) at 1:5 soil:water ratio and the extracts analysed as described above.

RESULTS

Plant cover and standing biomass of litter

Figure 1 shows the distribution and cover of plant species along each of the three transects. Both Transects 1 and 2 covered a wider band of vegetation than Transect 3. In all the transects, *Kandelia candel* was the most dominant species, followed by *Aegiceras corniculatum*. In Transect 1, patches of grass and a few individuals of *Lumnitzera racemosa* and *Excoecaria agallocha* were also present at the back of the shore. As described before, *Avicennia marina* was found mainly on soft and wet substrata, near the creeks, This therefore, species was rarely recorded along the three transects. In general, the species variety was limited in this mangal and the distribution of the mangrove plants did not show any specific pattern. The vegetation zonation observed in many tropical mangals was not recorded in this study.

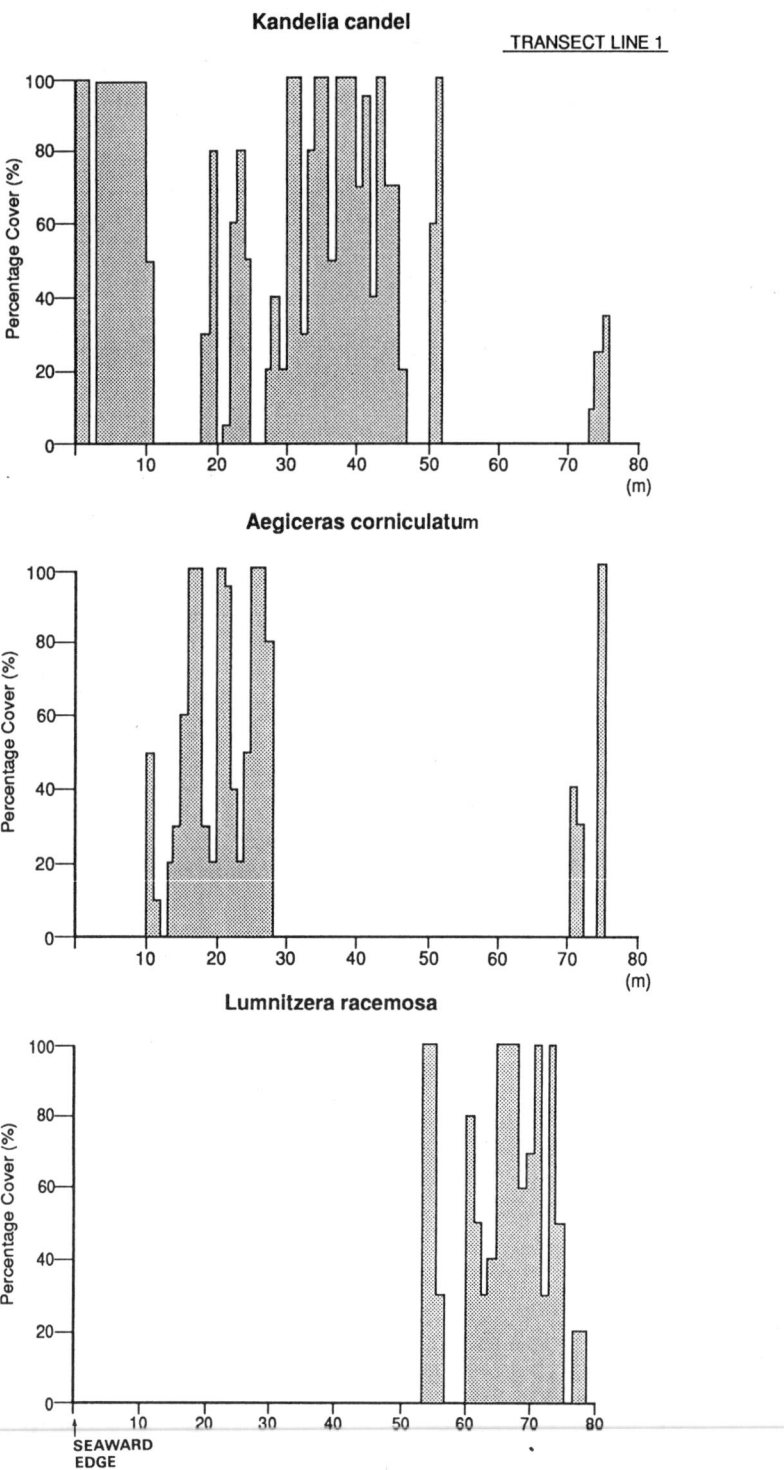

Fig. 1. Distribution and coverage of dominant plant species in Transects 1, 2 and 3.

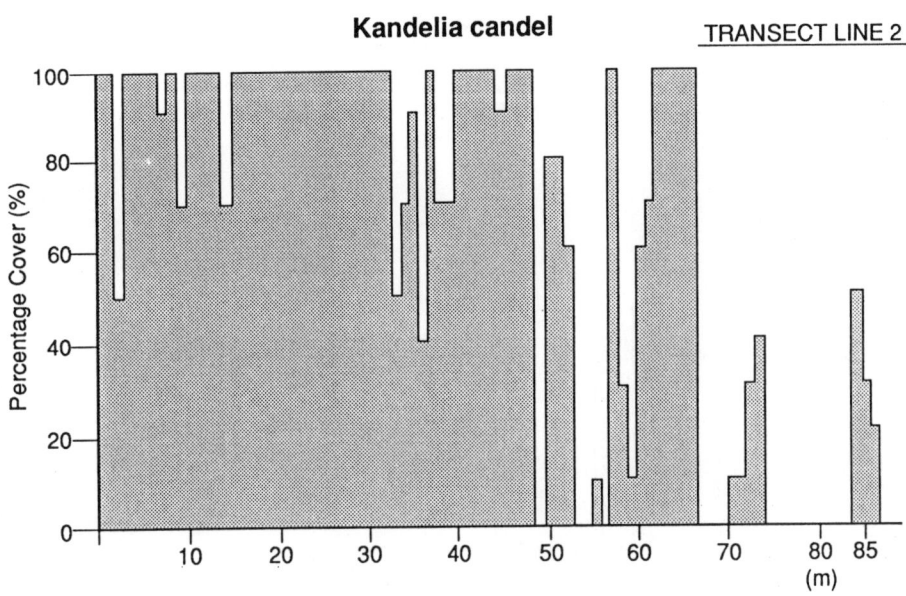

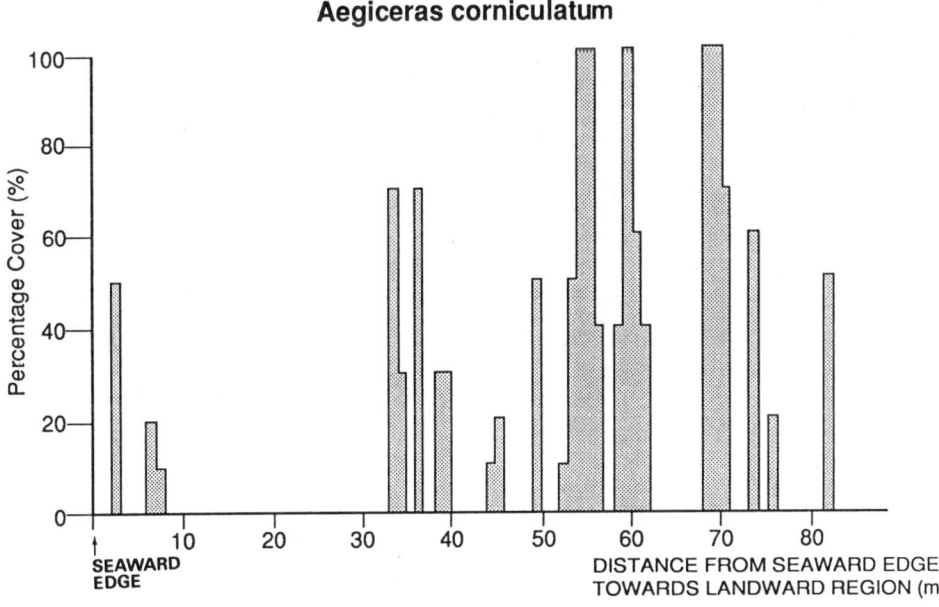

Fig. 1. (Continued).

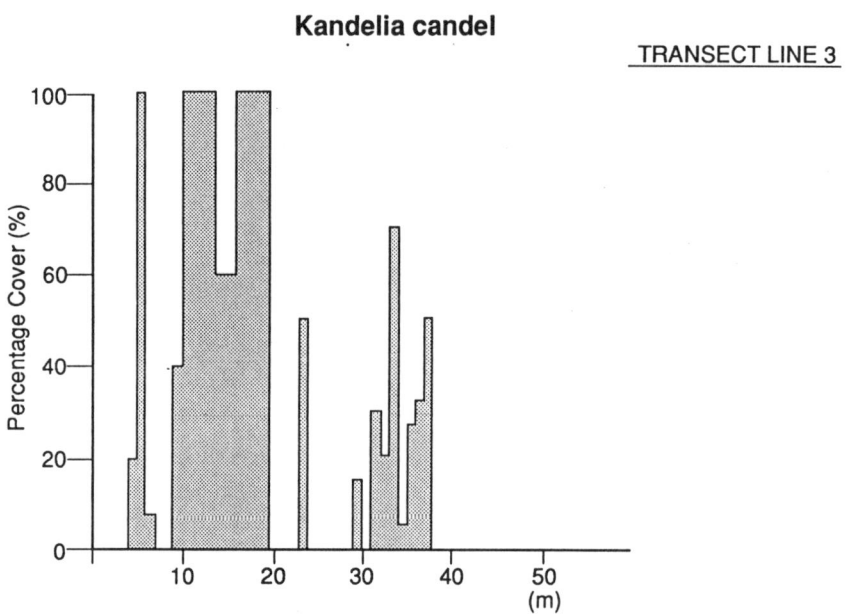

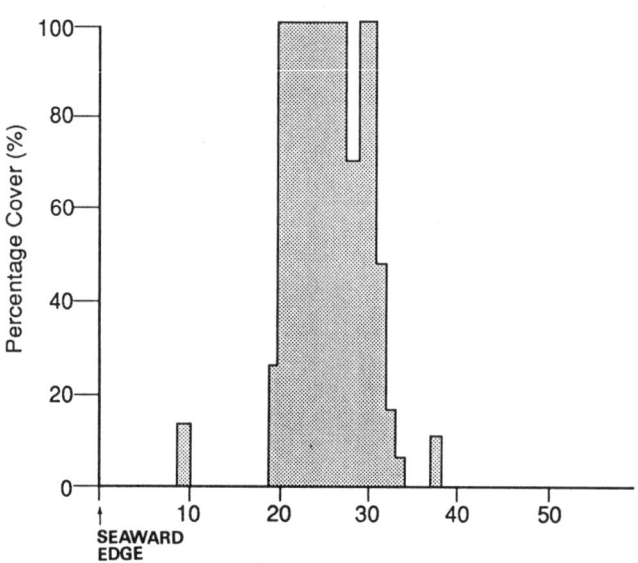

Fig. 1. (Continued).

Table 1
Percentage cover of plants and standing litter biomass ($g \cdot m^{-2}$) in three transects.

	Transect 1	Transect 2	Transect 3
Average % cover			
Kandelia	38.27	65.88	37.49
Aegiceras	16.00	15.76	32.24
Lumnitzera	15.73	2.78	nd
Excoecaria	4.93	nd	nd
Avicennia	nd	nd	1.14
Average standing litter biomass			
Leaf	73.9	78.6	5.1
Total	76.7	109.3	9.7

(nd: not detected)

The average percentage cover of the plant species along the three transects is summarized in Table 1. The plant distribution and cover varied from transect to transect. Both Transects 1 and 2 had more cover of *K. candel* than *A. corniculatum,* but relatively equal cover of these two species were found in Transect 3. In addition to cover, individuals of *Kandelia* and *Aegiceras* recorded along Transect 3 were taller than those found along Transects 1 and 2. The average heights of *Kandelia* and *Aegiceras* along Transect 3 were 1.2 and 1.8 m, respectively, while the average heights for the other two transects were 0.8 and 0.6 m. Yipp (1982) also reported that *Kandelia* in this mangal seldom grew higher than 1.5 to 1.8 m.

Litter accumulated on the mangrove floor varied from landward to seaward regions along each transect. Spatial variations were also found between transects (Fig. 2). Along all the transects, the standing litter biomass gradually increased towards the landward regions, as the seaward sites received more frequent tidal flushing which carried the litter away from the mangal. The seaward edge of Transect 3 had the lowest standing litter biomass (4.7 $g \cdot m^{-2}$) while the landward edge of Transect 2 showed the largest value (245 $g \cdot m^{-2}$) (Fig. 2). When are the three transects compared, Transect 2 had, in general, more litter accumulated (average value was 109.3 $g \cdot m^{-2}$), followed by Transect 1, and the least value was recorded from Transect 3 (an average of 9.7 $g \cdot m^{-2}$) (Table 1). As mentioned above, Transect 3 covered the narrowest band of vegetation and the entire transect received more frequent tidal flushing which exported more litter than the other two transects. In all the transects, leaf litter contributed a large proportion to the total standing litter biomass (Table 1). The contribution by leaf litter to Transects 1, 2 and 3 was 96.3%, 71.9% and 52.6%, respectively. Poovachiranon (1990) recorded an average standing leaf litter biomass in the Three Fathoms Cove mangrove of 9.93 g dry wt. m^{-2} (0.0993 t ha^{-1}), a quantity similar to the data obtained from Transect 3 of the present study.

Chemical properties of mangrove soils

Spatial variations in soil nutrients were found along each transect as well as between transects. The soil nutrient contents, in particular C and N, were relatively high in the landward sites but decreased gradually towards seaward regions (Fig. 3). In general,

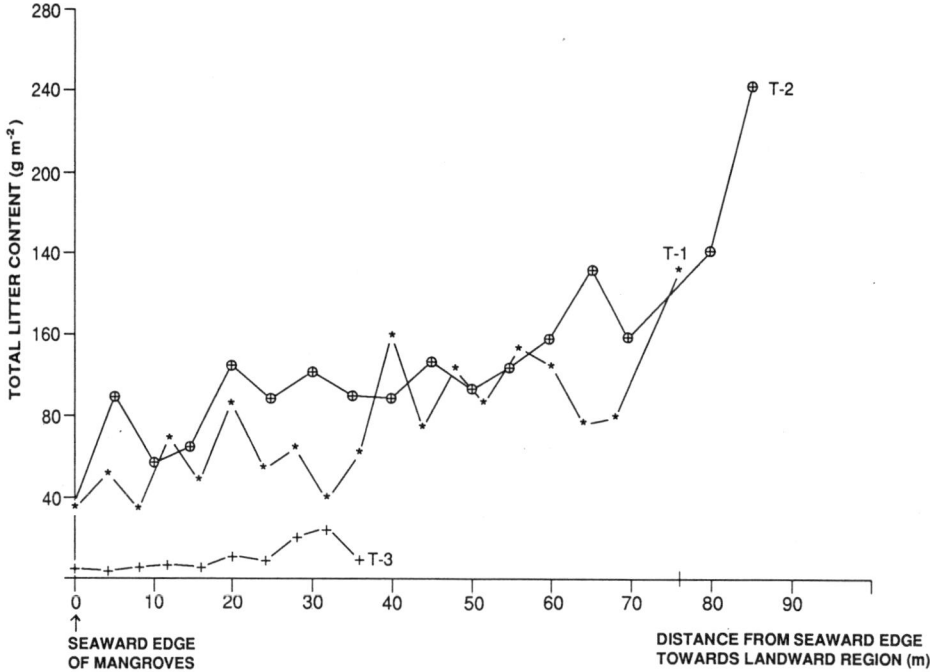

Fig. 2. The profile of total litter production along the three transects. (T–1: Transect 1; T–2: Transect 2; T–3: Transect 3).

Transect 3 had lower contents of soil organic C, total K, and P than the other two transects (Fig. 3). Table 2 summarizes the average nutrient contents in each transect and shows that the proportions of NH_4^+– and NO_3^-–N to total N, Olsen P to total P and extractable K to total K in all soil samples were very low. This suggests that most of the macronutrients present in the mangrove soils were organically bound.

The trace metal contents, including Cu, Zn, Mn and Pb, along the three transects fluctuated widely and did not exhibit any specific trend (Fig. 4). Transect 3 had higher levels of Zn and Pb while larger Mn contents were recorded in Transect 1 (Table 2). Deviations found between replicate samples were large and it is difficult to draw any meaningful conclusions from the present study. In general, only a very low percentage of these metals were extractable which implies their availability to plants was low (Table 2). Other trace metals such as cadmium, nickel and chromium in mangrove soils were not detected in the present study.

Correlations between soil, plant and litter

Simple correlation coefficients between soil chemical characteristics, standing litter biomass and plant coverage in each transect were calculated (Tables 3-5). Only very small correlations were found between plant coverage and soil chemical parameters, and these correlations varied from plant species to species. For example, in Transect 2, the percentage cover of *Aegiceras* (Aeg) was apparently associated with the total soil P, K

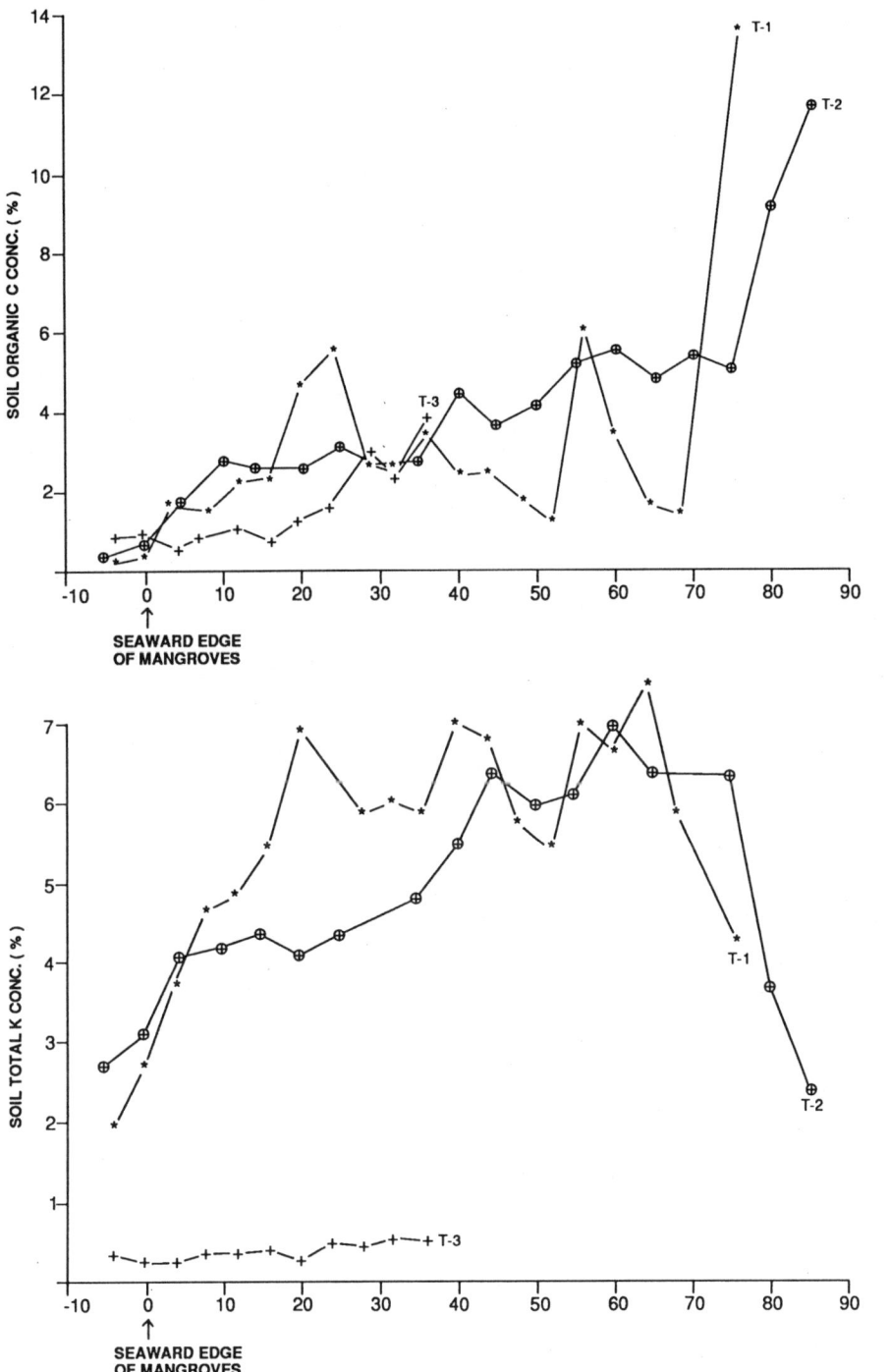

Fig. 3. The levels of organic carbon (C), total potassium (K), Kjeldhal nitrogen (N) and total phosphorus (P) contents of mangrove soil along the three transects. (T1 = Transect 1; T2 = Transect 2; T3 = Transect 3).

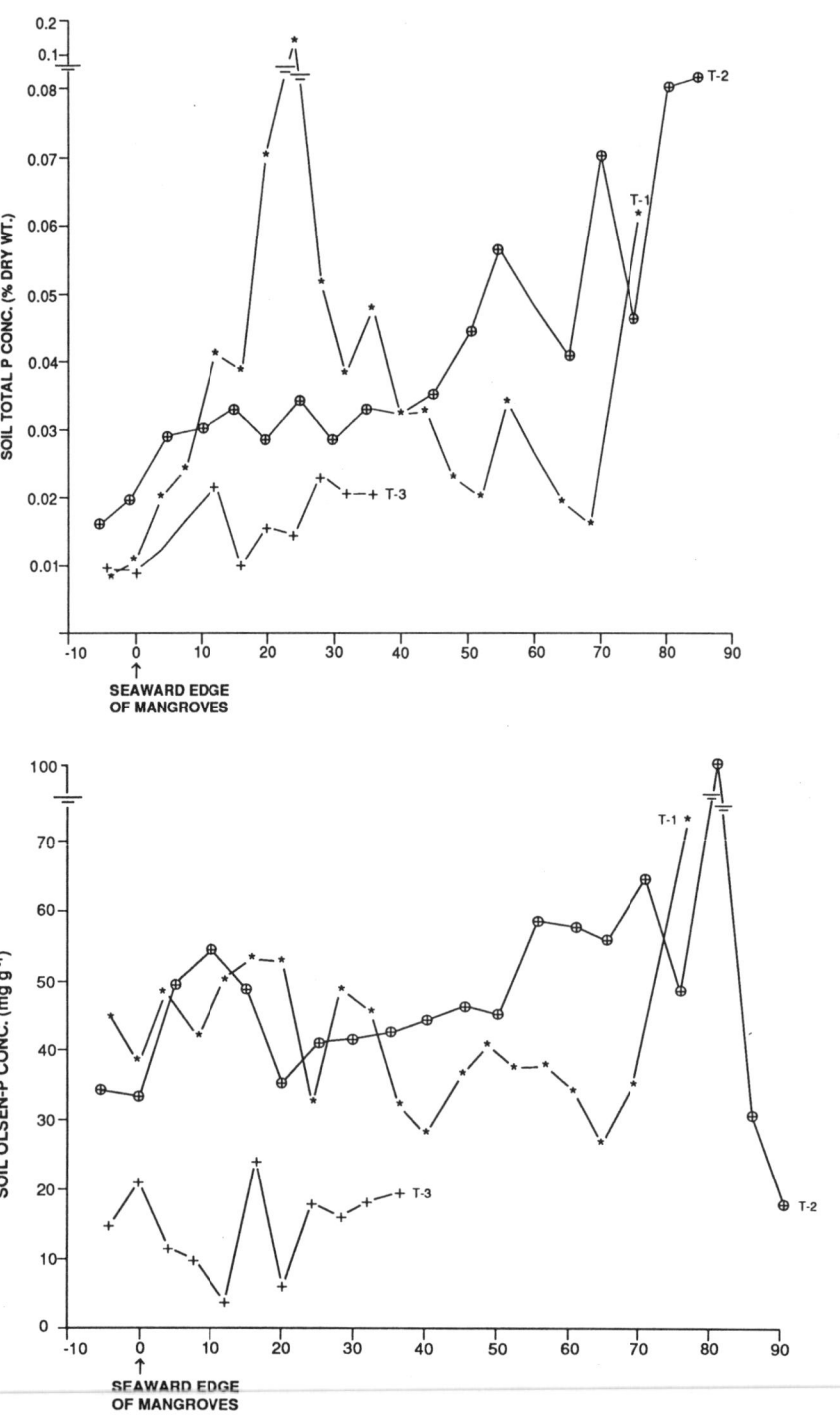

Fig. 3. (Continued).

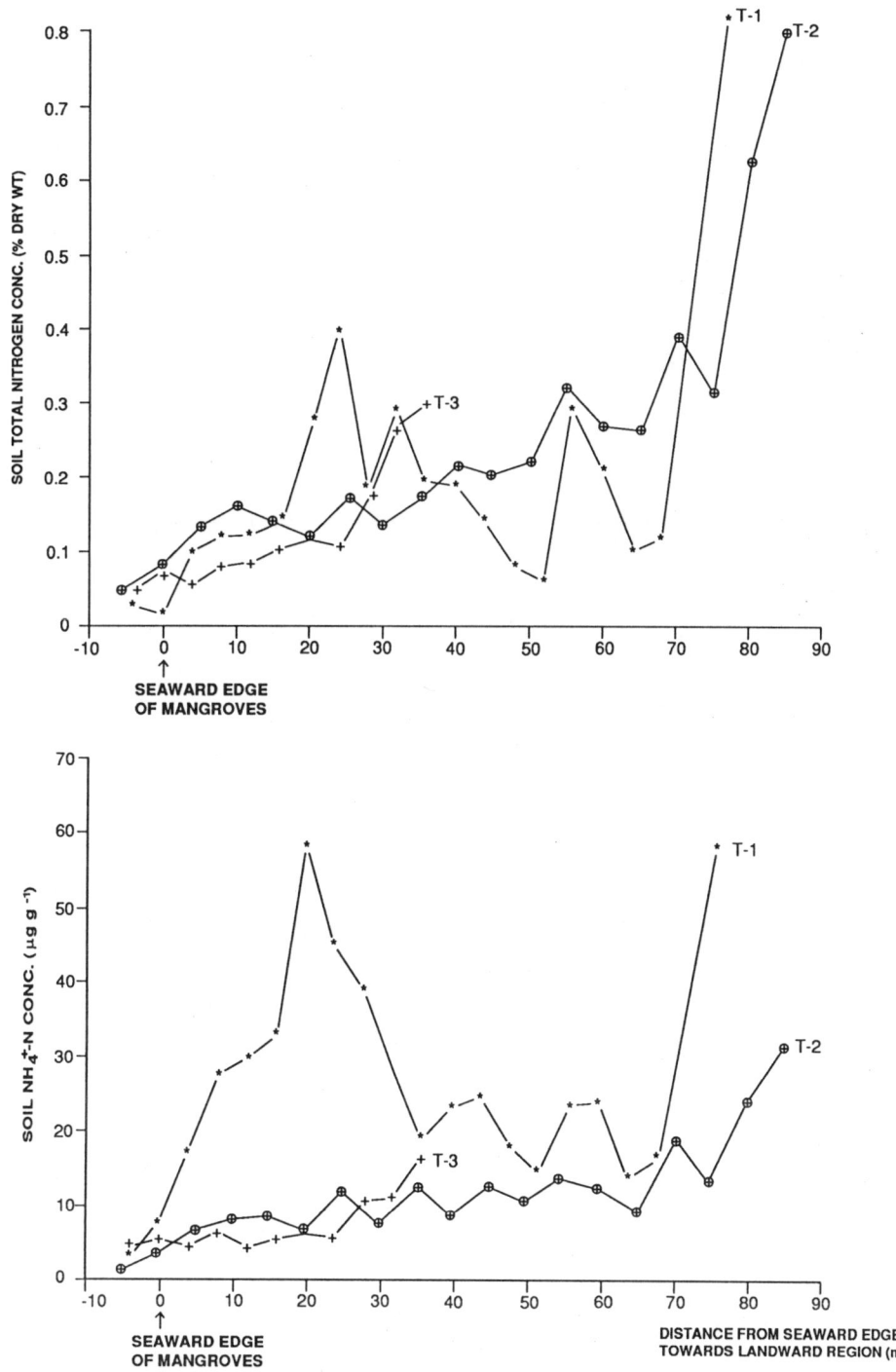

Fig. 3. (Continued).

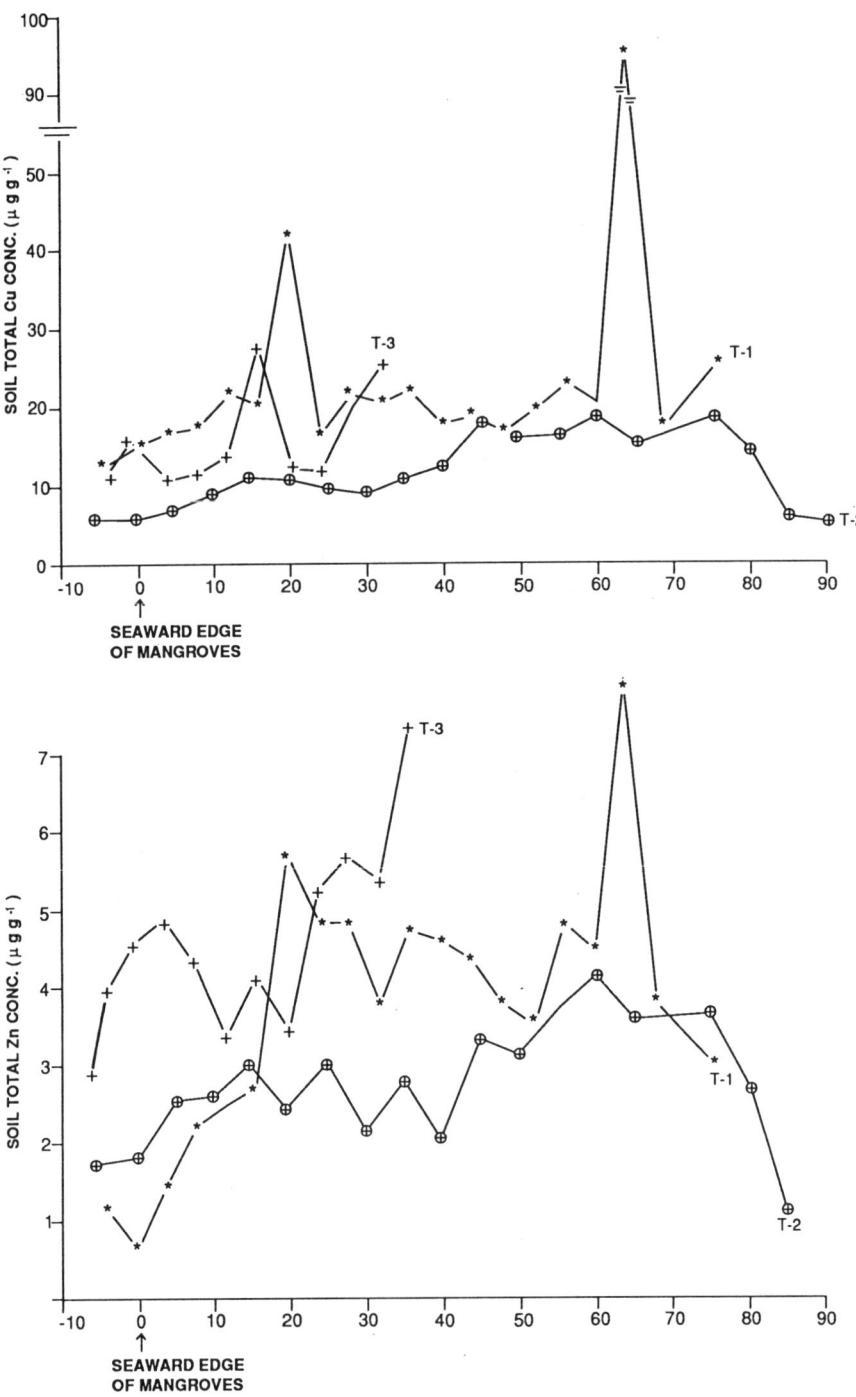

Fig. 4. The levels of total copper (Cu), zinc (Zn), manganese (Mn) and lead (Pb) in the mangrove soils along the three transects. (T1 = Transect 1; T2 = Transect 2; T3 = Transect 3).

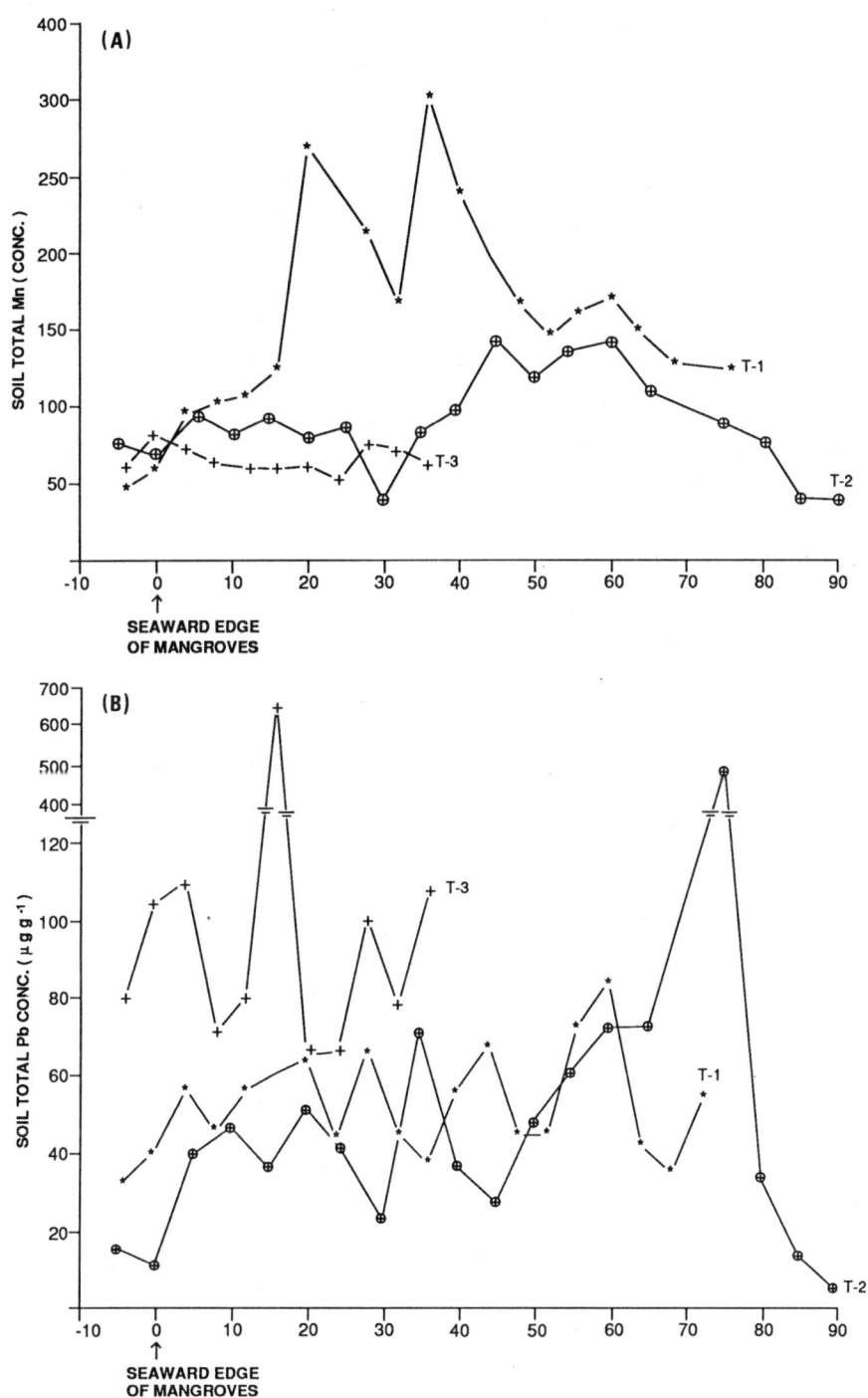

Fig. 4. (Continued).

Table 2
Chemical characteristics of the mangrove soils along the three transects

	Transect 1 mean (s.d.)		Transect 2 mean (s.d.)		Transect 3 mean (s.d.)	
pH	6.22	(0.24)	5.83	(0.69)	6.54	(0.54)
Conductivity (mmhos cm^{-1})	73.30	(26.47)	139.25	(46.04)	60.91	(20.07)
Organic C (%)	1.99	(1.03)	3.47	(1.990)	1.53	(1.06)
Total K (%)	5.43	(1.49)	5.02	(1.37)	0.37	(0.12)
Ext. K. (μg·g^{-1})	42.66	(18.75)	100.34	(41.06)	321.31	(150.50)
Total P (%)	0.028	(0.013)	0.040	(0.010)	0.016	(0.006)
Ols-P (μg·g^{-1})	39.63	(8.60)	47.13	(15.65)	21.66	(14.55)
Kjeld. N (%)	0.13	(0.07)	0.20	(0.11)	0.13	(0.09)
NH_4^+-N (μg·g^{-1})	20.92	(10.12)	9.39	(4.38)	7.32	(4.18)
NO_3^--N (μg·g^{-1})	3.08	(1.15)	1.12	(1.18)	3.18	(9.03)
Trace metals (μg·g^{-1})						
Total Mn	150.35	(65.19)	100.43	(28.68)	64.65	(11.35)
Ext. Mn	10.08	(10.01)	7.63	(5.31)	3.23	(2.17)
Total Zn	35.67	(18.94)	31.02	(9.51)	47.51	(12.48)
Ext. Zn	0.47	(0.35)	1.00	(1.50)	3.60	(2.39)
Total Cu	23.25	(26.42)	12.87	(5.48)	16.44	(7.76)
Ext.Cu	nd		nd		nd	
Total Pb	51.64	(14.99)	71.39	(99.84)	138.11	(243.1)
Ext. Pb	nd		nd		nd	

(nd: not detected; s.d.: standard deviation)

and Mn contents but such a correlation was not found for *Kandelia* (Table 4). Moreover, the plant cover was not related to soil nutrient content along Transects 1 and 3 (Tables 3 and 5). On the other hand, the amounts of litter accumulated on the mangrove floor had positive correlations with carbon, nitrogen, phosphorus, potassium and even some trace metals (Zn and Cu) in the soil (Tables 3-5). The correlation coefficients varied from transect to transect.

DISCUSSION

In the present study, only two dominant plant species (*K. candel* and *A. corniculatum*) were found and the vegetation zonation reported upon by Hodgkiss (1986) was not observed. The maximum tree height attained in the present study (< 2 m) was lower than those reported in the literature. Lee (1989) recorded that *K. candel* in the tidal shrimp ponds of the Mai Po Marshes, Hong Kong, had a height of 2.5-4.3 m with some individuals reaching a height of 6-7 m. The stunted growth of the mangrove plants and the paucity of plant species suggested that the mangrove community under investigation was apparently marginal. External factors, including tidal flushing, soil salinity, availability of freshwater and nutrient, and climate are the major environmental stresses contributing to the poor development of the plants. Unfavourable soil conditions (such

Table 3

Correlation coefficients between chemical parameters of the soil, plant cover and standing litter biomass along transect 1. (Correlations were based on 33 samples, * and ** indicate correlations significant at the 0.01 and 0.001 probability levels, respectively).

	Kan	Aeg	Leaf	Lit	pH	Cond	TotN	NH_4^+-N	OrgC	TotP	OlsP	TotK	TotMn	TotZn	TotCu
Kan															
Aeg	-.22														
Leaf	-.22	-.17													
Lit	-.22	-.13	.89**												
pH	.08	.09	-.20	-.17											
Cond	.08	.39	-.25	-.13	-.07										
TotN	-.07	.01	.28	.28	-.75**	.06									
NH_4^+-N	.02	.29	.16	.23	-.38	.23	.50*								
OrgC	.14	.06	.41	.48*	-.47	.03	.78**	.55*							
TotP	-.03	.22	.06	.15	-.42	.24	.65**	.74**	.72**						
OlsP	-.02	.39	-.49	-.36	-.03	.44	-.03	.32	-.12	.23					
TotK	-.26	-.01	.60**	.61**	-.56**	-.18	.60**	.42	.69**	.46*	-.46*				
TotMn	.01	-.11	.46*	.43	-.32	-.11	-.56**	.37	.69**	.68**	-.40	.69**			
TotZn	-.32	-.11	.36	.31	-.42	-.35	.39	.15	.46*	.31	-.43	.81**	.54*		
TotCu	-.17	-.03	-.06	-.11	-.17	-.18	-.04	-.13	-.01	-.05	-.21	.34	.01	.76**	
TotPb	-.01	.16	.32	.43	-.13	.13	.39	.54*	.62**	.36	.06	.38	.23	.01	-.16

(Kan: % cover of *Kandelia*; Aeg: % cover of *Aegiceras*; Lit: standing litter biomass).

Table 4

Correlation coefficients between chemical parameters of the soil, plant cover and standing litter biomass along transect 2. (Correlations were based on 33 samples, * and ** indicate correlations significant at the 0.01 and 0.001 probability levels, respectively).

	Kan	Aeg	Leaf	Lit	pH	Cond	TotN	NH_4^+-N	OrgC	TotP	OlsP	TotK	TotMn	TotZn	TotCu
Aeg	-.48*														
Leaf	-.28	-.20													
Lit	-.09	.19	.37												
pH	.14	-.01	-.28	-.46*											
Cond	.17	.30	.43	.45*	-.09										
TotN	-.49*	.35	.16	.64**	-.38	.43									
NH_4^+-N	.22	.36	.40	.57**	-.32	.65**	.82**								
OrgC	.41	.37	.28	.67**	-.46*	.50*	.97**	.81*							
TotP	-.42	.45*	.21	.57**	-.23	.54*	.96**	.85**	.92**						
OlsP	-.21	.24	-.02	.44	-.13	.49*	-.77**	.65**	-.70**	.82**					
TotK	-.14	.45*	.44	.64**	-.25	.65**	.69**	.69**	.75**	.73**	.63**				
TotMn	-.19	.54*	.32	.35	-.12	.46*	.54	.48*	.58**	.64**	.61	.81**			
TotZn	-.36	.34	.20	.56**	-.58**	.19	.72**	.56**	.73**	.70**	.50**	.67**	.62*		
TotCu	-.30	.37	.37	.58**	-.31	.45*	.79**	.67**	.81**	.80**	-.66**	.91**	.77**	.80**	
TotPb	-.41	.13	-.10	.34	-.18	.11	.32	.29	.28	.25	.10	.36	-.04	.22	-.36

(Kan: % cover of *Kandelia*; Aeg: % cover of *Aegiceras*; Lit: standing litter biomass).

Table 5

Correlation coefficients between chemical parameters of the soil, plant cover and standing litter biomass along transect 3. (Correlations were based on 33 samples, * and ** indicate correlations significant at the 0.01 and 0.001 probability levels, respectively).

	Kan	Aeg	Leaf	Lit	pH	Cond	TotN	NH$_4^+$-N	OrgC	TotP	OlsP	TotK	TotMn	TotZn	TotCu
Kan															
Aeg	-.41														
Leaf	-.15	.17													
Lit	-.17	.32	.73**												
pH	-.05	-.46	-.48	-.52											
Cond	-.12	.54*	-.15	.16	-.11										
TotN	-.01	.07	.78**	.58*	-.70**	-.29									
NH$_4^+$-N	-.11	.03	.65*	.44	-.62	-.22	.87**								
OrgC	-.15	.21	.55*	.48	-.77**	-.01	.88**	.83**							
TotP	.07	.20	.49	.52	-.66**	.09	.53**	.45	.57*						
OlsP	-.09	.05	.54*	.58*	-.48	.01	.66**	.72**	.65*	.21					
TotK	.10	.12	.52	.34	-.73**	-.07	.68**	.45	.63*	.42	.41				
TotMn	-.20	-.17	.23	.37	.23	.09	.15	.23	.15	.05	.44	-.37			
TotZn	-.21	-.02	.44	.27	-.45	-.23	.66**	.76**	.74**	.35	.71**	.39	.23		
TotCu	-.33	-.17	.30	.42	-.22	-.09	.47**	.29	.30	.13	.55*	.40	.29	.21	
TotPb	.44	-.17	-.17	-.02	.12	-.03	-.06	-.14	-.19	-.22	.13	.04	.08	-.16	.79**

(Kan: % cover of *Kandelia*; Aeg: % cover of *Aegiceras*; Lit: standing litter biomass).

as low nutrient levels, high contents of trace metals, stony substrata and shallow soil depth) combined with human disturbance (especially logging and pollution) are also important stresses.

Spatial variations in plant cover and standing litter biomass were obvious in this study. More litter was found at the back of the shore in each transect. Transect 3 had the lowest mean standing litter biomass. This may result from the influence of tide and substratum. Yipp (1982) and the present field observations on the particle size distribution indicate that the substrata of this mangal were not homogenous, Transects 1 and 2 had a dense, cover of stones and cobbles (diameter > 4 mm approximately) than Transect 3, especially at the back of the shore. The cobbles became less abundant towards the seaward edge. It was observed that during high tide, large amounts of leaf litter floated in the upper shore. When the tide ebbed, most litter was trapped among the pebbles and cobbles occurring in this area. This explains why more litter was found at the landward regions of all transects. Poovachiranon (1990) also recorded differences in the quantity of accumulated leaf litter of *K. candel* between the upper zone (14.306 g·m^{-2}) and the lower zone (4.091 g·m^{-2}) of Three Fathoms Cove mangrove. Such are smaller than other mangals in Hong Kong. For example, the mean standing litter biomass of *K. candel* stands in a Mai Po tidal shrimp pond was 9.587 t ha^{-1} (958.7 g·m^{-2}) (Lee 1989), nearly four times the highest standing litter biomass recorded in the present study. This is related to the fact that this mangal was normally inundated by tides and export was the major factor responsible for the low standing litter biomass (Yipp 1982; Poovachiranon 1990).

Similar microhabitat differences of soil nutrients along each transect as well as among the three transects were observed. The soil macronutrient levels decreased gradually from the landward towards the seaward regions. The extremely high levels of organic C, total P and Kjeldahl N at the landward edge may be explained by two possible factors: (1) the large amount of grass roots trapped within the soil were too fine to remove and (2) the accumulation of more litter at the back of the mangrove which undergoes decomposition and becomes a nutrient source. Furthermore, human activities at the back of the mangrove plants were more apparent. This area was often used as a refuse and sewage dumping site by adjacent residents and holiday visitors. Among the three transects, the mean contents of organic C, P and K in Transect 3 a lower than the other two transects. As described before, Transect 3 covered very narrow band of vegetation and had the lowest standing litter biomass. The nutrient input from litter detritus would thus be less than Transects 1 and 2. Moreover, because of its narrow vegetation zone, the soils at the landward edge of Transect 3 were submerged more often than that of the other two transects. This enhances nutrient exchange between soil and water and reduces the amounts of nutrients in the soil. Nevertheless, the mangal being studied is small, the seaward edges of each transect were so close to each other that any differences in degree and frequency of inundation were negligible.

When the soil nutrient concentrations obtained in the present study are compared with other mangrove stands, the mean organic C, Kjeldahl N and total P recorded in this mangal (Table 2) were lower. Liao (1990) found that the soils of the Solonchak mangrove in the northeast part of Hainan Island, China, had an average of 4.48% organic matter, 0.053% P_2O_5 and 0.77% K_2O. The mangal in the Jiulong River Estuary, China, had soil N and P levels of 0.34% and 0.05% dry weight, respectively (Lin 1989). Sasekumar (1974) found that organic C in a Malaysian mangrove forest was 5.2% while

0.15–0.4% Kjeldahl N and 0.05–0.1% total P was recorded by Henley (1978). On the other hand, the quantity of ammonium nitrogen and Olsen-phosphorus recorded in this study were slightly higher than the findings of Boto et al. (1984). These indicate that the mangal being investigated was less fertile. According to Henley (1978) and Boto and Wellington (1983), mangrove productivity could be enhanced by fertilizing the soils with either commercial fertilizers or sewage effluents. They concluded that mangrove ecosystems had a considerable capacity to accept and assimilate these nutrients. It might be possible to employ the mangrove ecosystem as a sink for receiving nutrients.

The soil trace metal contents varied from site to site (both between transects and along transect) and no specific trends could be detected. It is difficult to know whether the soils in this mangal were contaminated by trace metals or not because only very few data were available in the literature. Harbison (1986) reported the ranges of trace metals contents in mangrove soils of South Australian Gulfs and Barker Inlet were 30–80, 142–190 and 85–112 $\mu g \cdot g^{-1}$ for Cu, Zn and Pb, respectively. The levels of Cu and Zn recorded in the present study (Table 2) were lower than Harbison's study. However, Pb contents were extremely high in the present study. Moreover, certain microhabitats of this mangal exhibited elevated metal levels (Fig. 4). These findings suggest the local contamination and accumulation of trace metals have occurred. It is possible that the mangrove soils have an extraordinary capacity to accumulate metals (Harbison 1986).

In addition to spatial variations, seasonal fluctuations should not be neglected. Boto and Wellington (1983) suggested that large seasonal variations could be caused by flood deposition of nutrient rich silt during the summer (wet) season, with subsequent depletion by plant uptake and tidal leaching during the rest of the year. The present survey was carried out in the summer season (August 1989) and the findings are applicable to this period only. Another ecological study examined the temporal variations of the nutrient status of mangrove soil and its relationship with plant cover and litter accumulation has to be carried out to verify seasonality.

Significant correlations were obtained between soil nutrients and trace metals concentrations, between soil chemical parameters and standing litter biomass, but not with plant cover. These indicate the accumulated plant litter on the mangrove floor was one of the input sources for maintaining the nutrients and trace metals levels in mangrove soils. It has been documented that litter accumulation and its decomposition are important sources for soil nutrients in a mangrove stand (Knox 1986). With respect to the poor correlation between soil chemical characteristics and plant cover, it is suggested that ecological factors other than these soil parameters might be important in governing mangrove plant growth and distribution. These factors include the amount of stones/pebbles on the mangrove floor, the structure and redox potential of the soil, the exposure period, microtopography and human disturbance. Matilal and Mukherjee (1986) also reported that the differences in soil NPK ratio, salinity, pH, cation exchange capacity, and texture could only be partially responsible for the distribution of mangrove plants Knox (1986) argued that plant and soil formation represented a response to a complex of external forces including sedimentation, microtopography, estuarine hydrology and geochemistry. In the present study, as the mangal was small and only covered a narrow band of mangrove vegetation (less than 100 m in width), the differences in macroscopic factors, like estuarine hydrology, sea level change and climatic condition would be negligible. The differences in soil characteristics, plant cover and amount of litter accumulated might be related to more localized factors. The major ones include the impact of microtopography of the particular landforms, the substratum and soil physical properties (texture and structure, the amounts of stones/pebbles on the mangrove floor) and human disturbance.

ACKNOWLEDGEMENTS

The authors would like to thank Mr S.H. Li for his assistance in field and laboratory work. Financial support was obtained from the Research Committee of the Hong Kong Polytechnic.

REFERENCES

Allen, S.E., Grimshaw, H.M., Parkinson, J.A. and Quarmby, C. 1974. *Chemical Analysis of Ecological Materials*. Oxford: Blackwell Scientific Publications.
Boto, K.G. and Wellington, J.T. 1983. Nitrogen and phosphorus nutritional status of a northern Australian mangrove forest. *Marine Ecology Progress Series* 11:63–9.
Clough, B.F., Boto, K.G. and Attiwill, P.M. 1983. Mangroves and sewage: a re-evaluation. In *Biology and Ecology of Mangroves* (ed. H.J. Teas), Tasks for Vegetation Science Series. Vol. 8, 151—62. Lancaster: Dr. W. Junk Publishers.
Cox, G.W. 1979. *Laboratory Manual of General Ecology*. Dubuque, Iowa: Wm. C. Brown Company Publishers.
Harbison, P. 1986. Mangrove muds — a sink and a source for trace metals. *Marine Pollution Bulletin* 17:246–50.
Henley, D.A. 1978. An investigation of proposed effluent discharge into a tropical mangrove estuary. In *Proceedings of the International Conference on Water Pollution Control in Developing Countries, Bangkok 21–25 February*, 43–64.
Hodgkiss, I.J. 1986. Aspects of mangrove ecology in Hong Kong. *Memoirs of the Hong Kong Natural History Society* 17:107–16.
Keeney, D.R. and Nelson, D.W. 1982. Nitrogen — inorganic forms. In *Methods of Soil Analysis. Part 2 Chemical and Microbiological Properties* (ed. A.L. Page, R.H. Miller, and D.R. Keeney), 643–98. Wisconsin, U.S.A.: American Society of Agronomy, Inc.
Knox, G.A. 1986. *Estuarine Ecosystems: A Systems Approach .Vol. I*. Florida: CRC Press Inc.
Lee, S.Y. 1989. Litter production and turnover of the mangrove *Kandelia candel* (L.) Druce in a Hong Kong tidal shrimp pond. *Estuarine, Coastal and Shelf Science* 19:75–87.
Liao, J. 1990. The chemical properties of the mangrove Solonchak in the northeast part of Hainan Island. *Supplement to the Acta Scientiarum, Naturalium Universitatis Sunyatseni* 9:67–72.
Lin, P. 1989. Biomass and element cycle of *Kandelia* forest, China. In *Mangrove Research Papers (1980–1989)* (ed. P. Lin), 143–9. Xiamen: Xiamen University Press.
Macnae, W. 1968. A general account of the fauna and flora of mangrove swamps and forests in the Indo-West-Pacific region. *Advances in Marine Biology* 6:73–270.
Matilal, S. and Mukherjee, B.B. 1986. Studies on soil-vegetation of mangrove forests of Sunderbans. *Indian Journal of Marine Sciences* 15:181–4.
Murphy, J. and Riley, J.P. 1962. A modified single solution method for the determination of phosphate in natural wastes. *Analytical Chemistry Acta* 27:31–6.
Olsen, S.R., Cole, C.V., Watanabe, F.S. and Dean, L.A. 1954. Estimation of available phosphorus in soils by extraction with sodium bicarbonate. *U.S. Department of Agriculture Circular* 939:1–19.
Poovachiranon, S. 1990. The food of *Chiromanthes bidens* (De Haan, 1835) and *C. maipoensis* (Soh, 1978) (Decapoda:Sesarminae) in Hong Kong mangroves. In *The Marine Flora and Fauna of Hong Kong and Southern China II* (ed. B. Morton), Proceedings of the Second

International Workshop on the Marine Flora and Fauna of Hong Kong and southern China, Hong Kong, 1986. 723–35. Hong Kong: Hong Kong University Press.

Sasekumar, A. 1974. Distribution of macrofauna on a Malayan mangrove shore. *Journal of Animal Ecology* 43:51–69.

Walkley, Y.A. and Black, I.A. 1934. An examination of the Detjareff method for determining soil organic matter and a proposed modification of the chromic acid titration method. *Soil Science* 37: 29–38.

Yipp, M.W. 1982. The distribution of ground-dwelling gastropods in a small mangrove stand in Hong Kong. In *The Marine Flora and Fauna of Hong Kong and South China*. Proceedings of the First International Marine Biological Workshop: The Marine Flora and Fauna of Hong Kong and Southern China, 18 April–10 May 1980, Hong Kong (ed. B. Morton and C.K. Tseng), 705–20. Hong Kong: Hong Kong University Press.

IMPACT OF EUTROPHICATION ON MARINE PLANKTON IN TOLO HARBOUR, 1988-89

Alice L.C. Chan and C. Kim Wong

Department of Biology, The Chinese University of Hong Kong,
Shatin, New Territories, Hong Kong

ABSTRACT

Tolo Harbour is an almost land-locked water body with an area of about 50 km^2, polluted by treated sewage from more than 500,000 people. The hydrography and marine plankton of Tolo Harbour were studied at four stations between November 1987 and January 1990. Surface seawater temperature reflected seasonal air temperature variations. Overall water quality was poor. Eutrophication was most pronounced in the inner harbour where water transparency was low and oxygen depletion in the bottom was severe. Intense algal blooms, as indicated by chlorophyll a concentrations > 50 µg·L^{-1}, were recorded throughout the study period.

Chlorophyll a concentration and zooplankton dry weight showed spatial variation with highest values observed in the inner harbour. However, neither variable showed significant correlation with temperature and no clear seasonal patterns were found. Equally marked spatial and temporal variations were observed in the populations of crustacean zooplankton. Densities were higher in the inner harbour than in the channel. Significant correlation was found between the abundance of crustacean zooplankton and temperature, but no obvious seasonal patterns could be identified. The increase dominance of toxic or inedible dinoflagellates may affected the crustacean zooplankton. The population densities of both copepods and cladocerans decreased markedly during 1989.

INTRODUCTION

Tolo Harbour is an almost land-locked water body with an area of aproximately 50 km^2. The outlet, Tolo Channel, opens towards the Pacific Ocean in the north-east and has an average width of about 1.5 km. Mean depth of the harbour and channel is about 12 m. Maximum depth is around 20 m. Because of the semi-enclosed bay topography, flushing rates are low and average water residence time was estimated to be at 35 days (Oakley and Cripps 1972).

Since the mid-1970s, urban development in the catchment has proceeded rapidly.

The population increased from 70,000 in 1973 to nearly 500,000 in 1988, and a figure of over 1 million is projected for the 1990s. While there has been a steady decline in agricultural activities, sewage discharge from the expanding population is still causing a net overall increase in organic and nutrient loading (Lam and Ho 1989). Two sewage treatment plants were commissioned in the early 1980s to provide secondary treatment for most of the human sewage from the new towns of Shatin and Tai Po, but this has not reduced the risk of eutrophication from increased nutrient input.

Many authors (Trott and Fung 1973; Hodgkiss and Chan 1983; Wear et al. 1984) have reported on the deteriorating water quality in Tolo Harbour. In general there has been a dramatic increase in nutrient concentration in the entire water column and a gradual decrease in dissolved oxygen level in the bottom waters. Hodgkiss and Chan (1987) reported a tenfold increase in dissolved inorganic phosphorus concentration and a fivefold increase in dissolved inorganic nitrogen concentration from 1978 to 1985 in the surface water of Tai Po Hoi. Because of the well established thermocline and halocline in Tolo Harbour, anoxia of bottom waters is common in the summer. Very low (24.7% saturation) dissolved oxygen levels were measured in the bottom waters in 1975, before eutrophication became a serious problem (Wear et al. 1984). Since then dissolved oxygen values have tended to decrease. (Environment Protection Department 1989).

Increase in nutrient loading and decrease in dissolved oxygen level have imposed considerable stress upon the biological communities. Increases in abundance of phytoplankton and dominance of dinoflagellates have been related to increasing nutrient levels in the harbour (Wear et al. 1984; Chan and Hodgkiss 1987; Hodgkiss and Chan 1987; Lam and Ho 1989). During the 1980s, oxygen depletion in the summer has been implicated in periodic large scale fishkills at mariculture sites in the harbour (Holmes and Lam 1985). At the same time, the abundance, biomass and species diversity of fish in Tolo Harbour and Channel have all steadily declined (Wu 1988). Similarly, mass mortalities of benthic organisms have been attributed to summer depletion of oxygen (Wu and Richards 1979; Horikoshi and Thompson 1980; Wu 1982).

Despite regular monitoring of water quality and phytoplankton, relatively little attention has been given to marine zooplankton in Tolo Harbour. Chen (1982) reported that micro-crustaceans such as copepods and cladocerans are the most important zooplankters in the shallow coastal waters of Hong Kong in terms of abundance and diversity. A more recent survey by Wear et al. (1984) provided information on zooplankton biomass in Tolo Harbour, yet no investigation of the relationship between eutrophication and zooplankton dynamics has been carried out. Information on zooplankters is important because they are major components of the marine food web and changes in their abundance and species composition may ultimately affect the trophic structure. A detailed survey was initiated in 1987 to study the impacts of hydrography and eutrophication on the abundance, composition, seasonal dynamics and spatial distribution of the marine zooplankton in Tolo Harbour. Part of the results are presented in this paper.

MATERIALS AND METHODS

Sampling was carried out at four stations (Fig. 1) at roughly monthly intervals from November 1987 to January 1990, but analyses for chlorophyll did not begin until May 1988. All samplings were done between 0900 h and 1300 h.

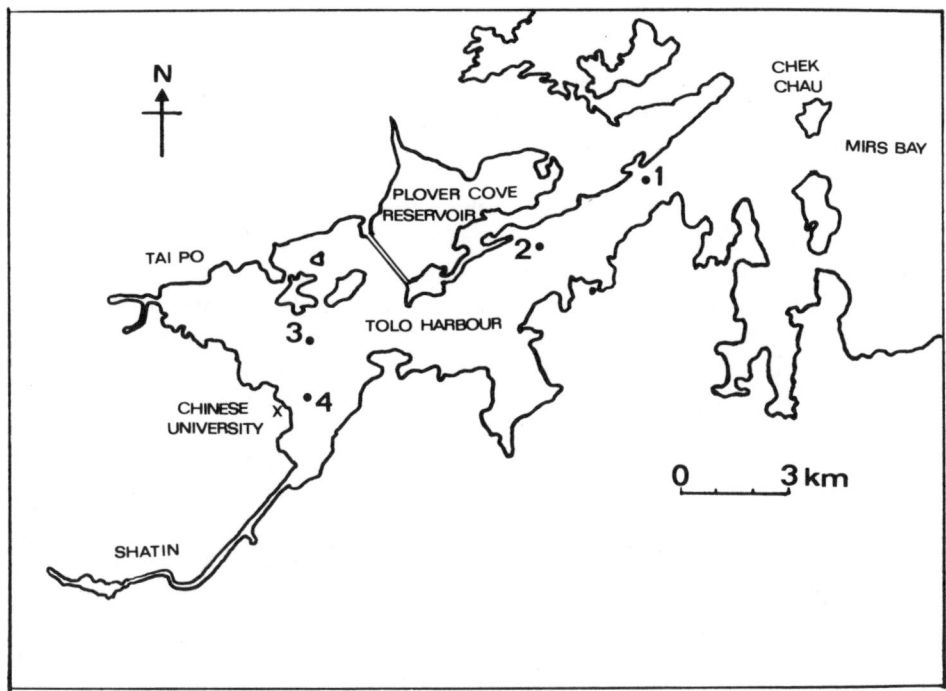

Fig. 1. Map of Tolo Harbour showing the location of sampling stations.

Water temperature and dissolved oxygen in the surface and bottom were measured *in situ* with an electronic oxygen meter (YSI Model 57). Salinity of surface water was determined by a refractometer. Water transparency was estimated with a 30–cm diameter Secchi disc.

Zooplankton was sampled by making duplicated vertical hauls from bottom to surface with a conical net of 50–cm mouth diameter and 125–µm mesh size. The contents of each net haul were concentrated in 100 mL of filtered (125 µm) seawater and preserved immediately in 4% formaldehyde. In the laboratory, densities of crustacean zooplankton were estimated by counting subsamples under a stereomicroscope. At least two 3–mL subsamples were counted for each sample. For dry weight determination, a 50–mL subsample of each sample was rinsed with distilled water and dried to constant weight at 60°C. It should be noted, however, that formaldehyde preservation may introduce slight errors into dry weight determination (Wear *et al.* 1984).

At each station, seawater samples were collected 1 m below the surface with a Van Dorn water sampler. Two subsamples of 500 mL each were preserved immediately in Lugol's iodine for phytoplankton identification and counting. A third 500–mL subsample was stored in a dark polyethylene bottle for chlorophyll *a* analysis. In the laboratory, phytoplankton samples were allowed to settle in glass cylinders. Aliquots of condensed samples were transferred to a Sedgewick Rafter counting chamber and examined under an inverted microscope. For measurement of chlorophyll *a* concentrations, aliquots of 1 or 2 mL were filtered with 0.45 µm Millipore filters. The filters were extracted for at least 5 h in 90% aqueous acetone. Chlorophyll *a* concentration of extracted samples was measured with a Turner Model-112 fluorometer (Parsons *et al.* 1984).

RESULTS

Seawater temperature in Tolo Harbour ranged from 14°C in January 1989 to 31°C in August 1989 (Fig. 2). Water temperatures in the winter were typically around 15–19°C. Gradual warming of the water column began in March and a thermocline appeared at all stations at the beginning of May. Summer temperatures ranged between 27–31°C at the surface and fell to between 17–29°C at the bottom. Water temperature began to drop after September. Thermoclines at all stations started to break down in October when seawater temperature at the surface fell to around 25°C.

Dissolved oxygen levels in the seawater fluctuated considerably throughout the study period, although no clear trend of spatial variation was observed (Fig. 3). Differences between surface and bottom waters were greatest in the summer. Surface waters of the entire area of Tolo Harbour and Channel were supersaturated with dissolved oxygen. In contrast, much lower levels of dissolved oxygen were measured in the bottom waters. Oxygen depletion was particularly serious during the summer of 1988 when bottom dissolved oxygen fell to < 10% saturation at all stations. Oxygen depletion in the bottom waters was detected again at stations 1 and 2 during the summer of 1989, but bottom waters at the shallower stations 3 and 4 remained relatively saturated with oxygen (> 100% saturation). Spatial and temporal variations in Secchi disc value were large (Fig. 4). At Station 1, the outermost station, values were usually around 6 m. On the other hand, values at stations 3 and 4, the two inner stations, never exceeded 4 m. The highest value of 12.5 m was observed at Station 1 in January 1989 and the lowest value of 0.75 m was observed in November 1988 at the same station. Temporal variations in Secchi disc transparency were much greater at stations 1 and 2 than at stations 3 and 4.

Variation in chloropyll a concentration among stations was high (Fig. 5). Mean values at stations 3 and 4 over the study period were 49.4 and 50.3 $\mu g \cdot L^{-1}$, respectively. In fact, values above 50 $\mu g \cdot L^{-1}$ were frequently observed at both stations. Chlorophyll a levels at stations 1 and 2 were somewhat lower, but still high compared to unpolluted oceanic waters. Mean concentrations over the study period were 11.3 $\mu g \cdot L^{-1}$ at Station 1 and 17.9 $\mu g \cdot L^{-1}$ at Station 2. Marked temporal variation was observed at all stations, although no clear seasonal trends could be detected.

Spatial variation in the relative contribution of diatoms and dinoflagellates to the total phytoplankton is presented in Figure 6. The population density was only measured in the summer of 1989. In 1989 the average percentage contribution of dinoflagellates to the total phytoplankton was 41.2% at stations 3 and 4 and 64.2% at stations 1 and 2.

Marked spatial and seasonal variations in zooplankton dry weight were recorded (Fig. 7). With the exception of a single peak of 0.36 $g \cdot m^{-3}$ at Station 1 in December 1988, zooplankton dry weights at stations 1 and 2 were generally lower than 0.1 $g \cdot m^{-3}$. Values in the inner harbour were somewhat higher, with a number of peaks above 0.1 $g \cdot m^{-3}$. Mean values at stations 1, 2, 3 and 4 were 0.05, 0.04, 0.08 and 0.08 $g \cdot m^{-3}$, respectively.

The most important zooplankters in Tolo Harbour and Channel numerically were crustaceans, principally copepods and cladocerans. Cyclopoid copepods constituted the largest proportion of the crustacean zooplankton in terms of number. The most dominant genera were *Oithona* and *Corycaeus*. Calanoid copepods were the most important component of the zooplankton in terms of species number (Chen 1982). Dominant genera

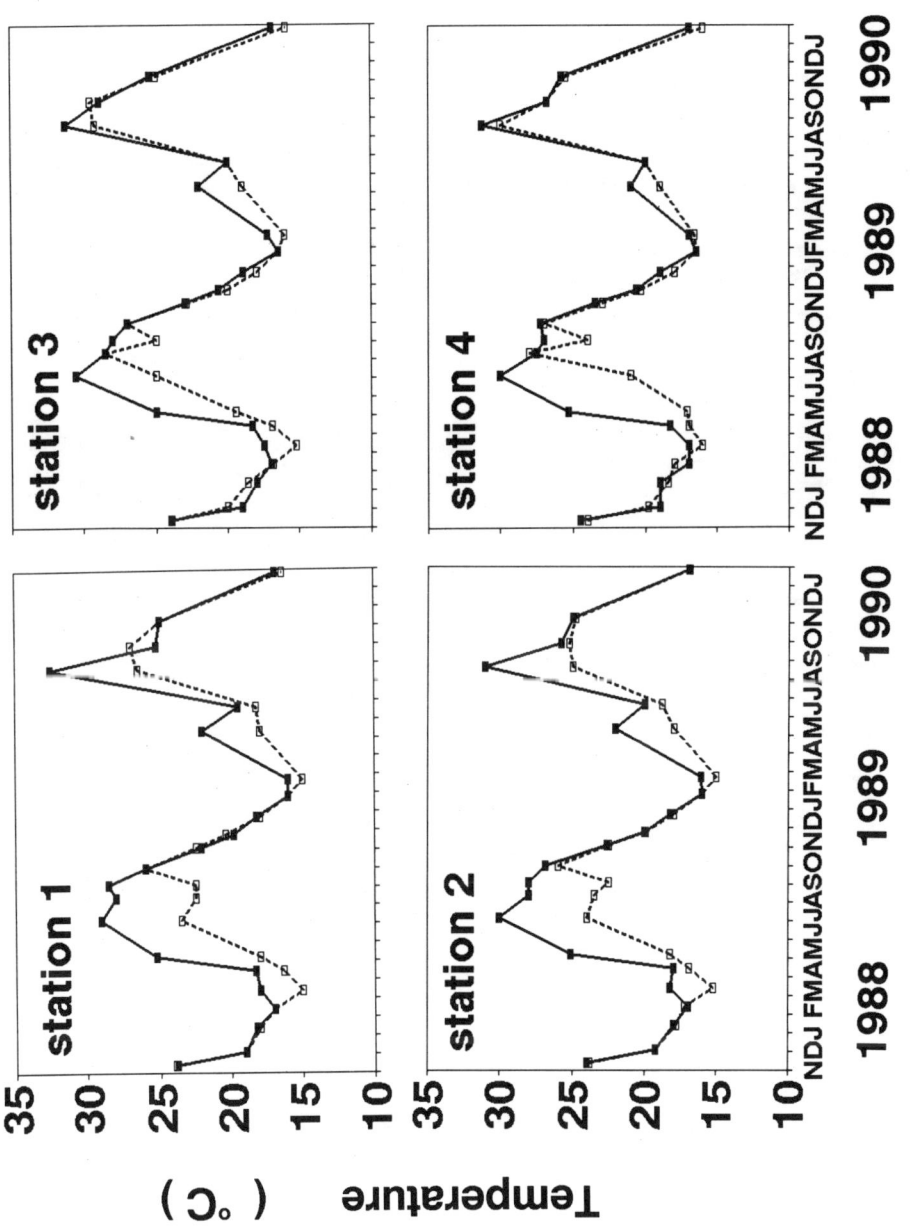

Fig. 2. Water temperature at the surface (■) and bottom (□) of stations 1–4.

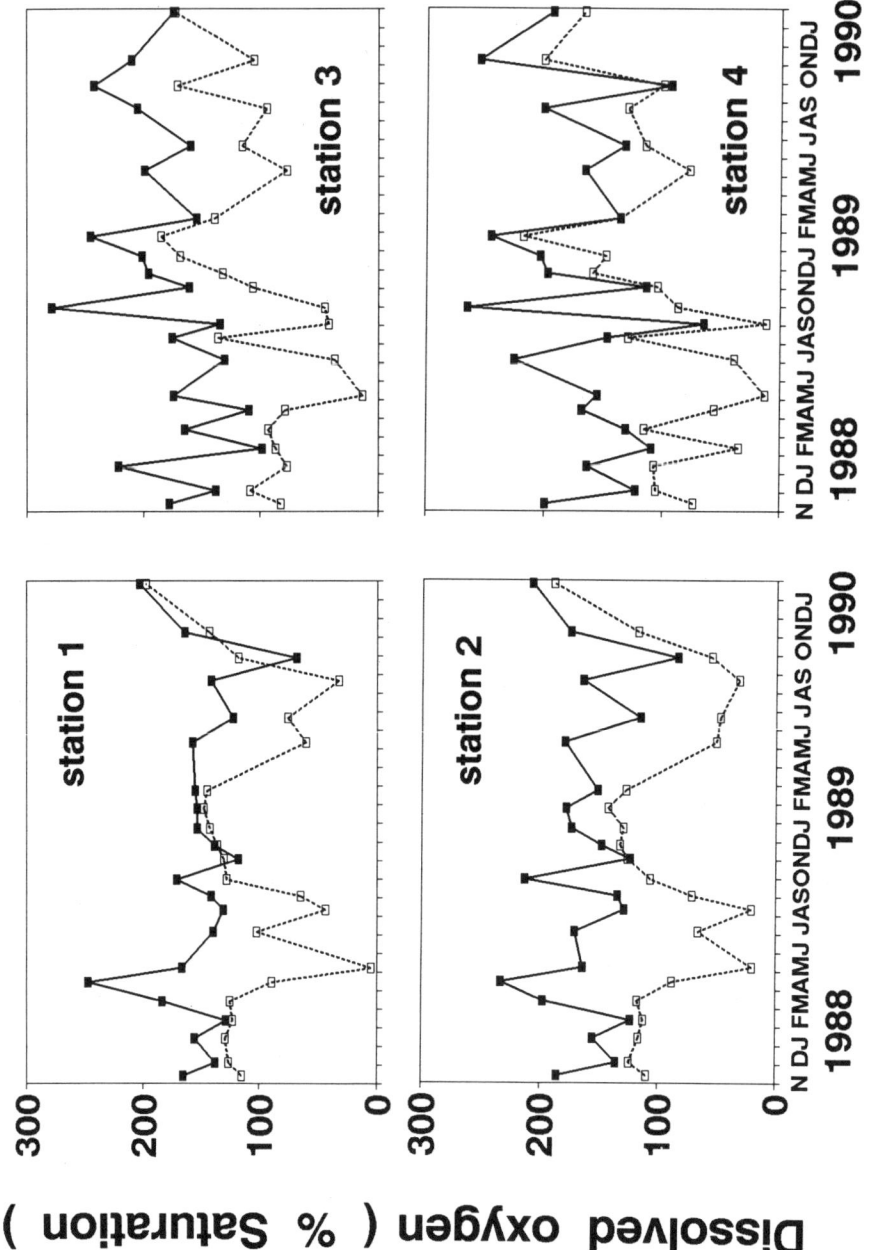

Fig. 3. Dissolved oxygen at the surface (■) and bottom (□) of stations 1–4.

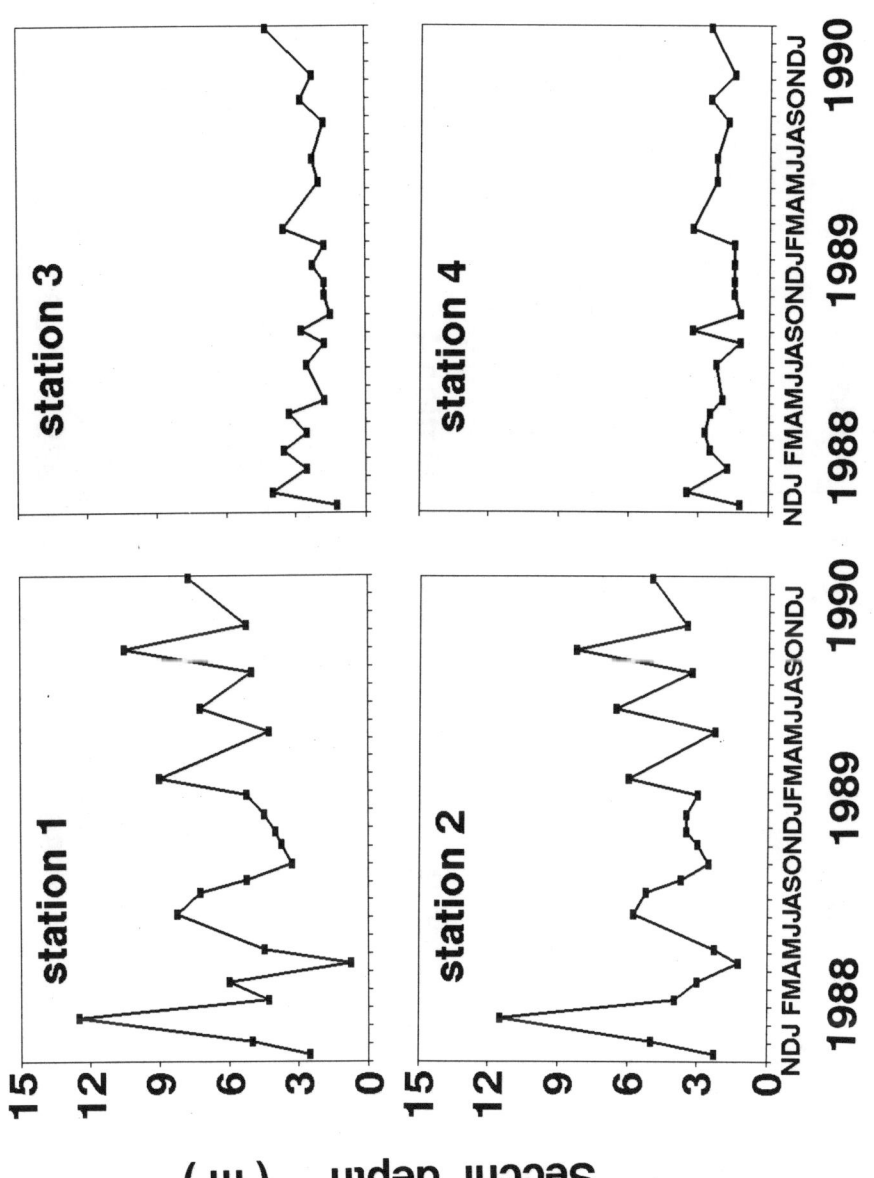

Fig. 4. Secchi disc transparency at stations 1–4.

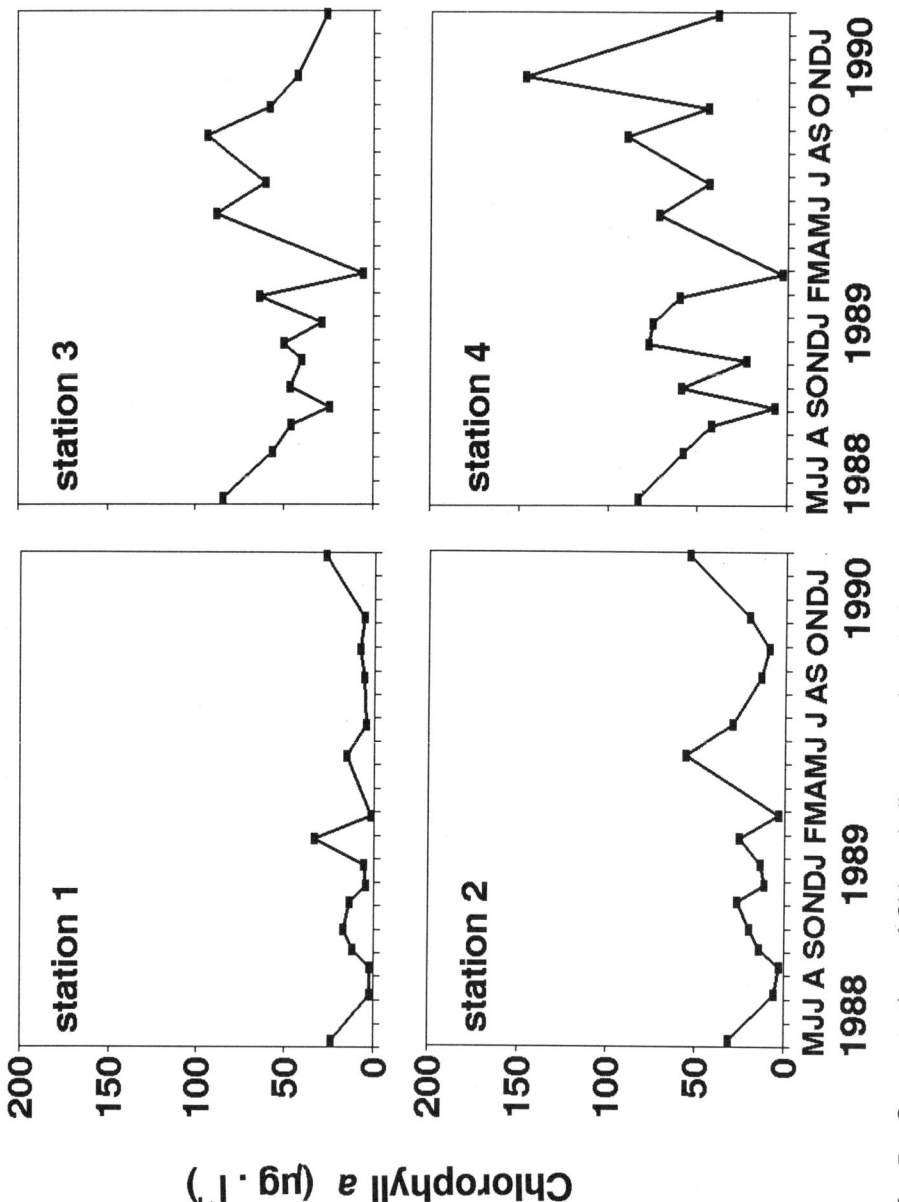

Fig. 5. Concentrations of Chlorophyll a at stations 1–4.

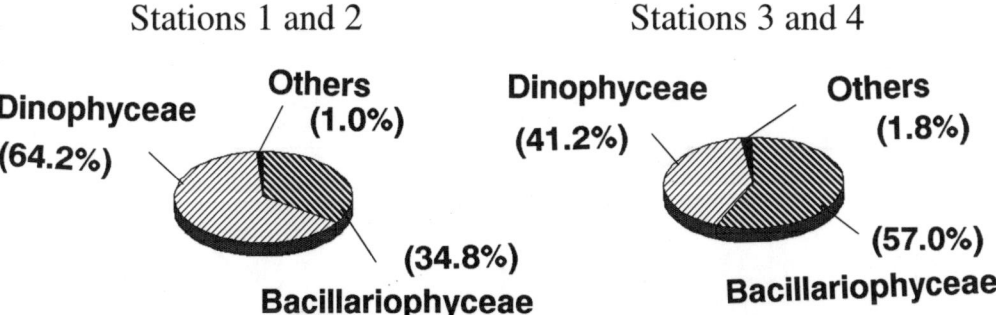

Fig. 6. Percentage contribution of diatoms and dinoflagellates to the phytoplankton in Tolo Harbour during the summer of 1989.

included *Paracalanus*, *Acartia* and *Temora*. Three species of cladocerans, *Penilia avirostris*, *Evadne tergestina* and *Podon* sp., were found. Cladocerans, making up less than 10% of the crustacean zooplankton, sometimes accumulated in dense patches near the surface.

Population densities of crustacean zooplankton at various stations provided further evidence of landward increase of zooplankton abundance from Station 1 to Station 4 (Fig. 8). Much of the increase could be accounted for by the dramatic increase in the abundance of Cyclopoida which accounted for 66.7% of the crustacean zooplankton in the inner harbour (Fig. 9). Time series of population densities showed several seasonal outbursts of cyclopoid copepods at stations 3 and 4. Calanoida constituted a smaller proportion of the crustacean zooplankton, but their importance increased towards the mouth of the channel and their population cycle appeared to coincide with that of cyclopoid copepods at stations 3 and 4. Cladocerans constituted about 7% of the zooplankton in Tolo Harbour and Channel. Population densities in the inner harbour were slightly higher than at the channel.

No clear seasonal patterns in zooplankton population could be discerned (Fig. 8). Population cycles of cyclopoid and calanoid copepods tended to coincide, especially at stations 3 and 4. Population patterns of cladocerans did not appear to follow those of copepods. Zooplankton abundance appeared to decrease at all stations in 1989. No major population outbursts in marine copepods were recorded in the inner harbour after January 1988. An increase in the abundance of calanoid copepods was recorded at all stations during our last sampling in January 1990, but the population densities of Calanoida and Cladocera remained at very low levels.

DISCUSSION

In Tolo Harbour, the difference in surface and bottom seawater temperature during summer frequently exceeds 5°C. When the thermally induced density stratification is strengthened by a vertical gradient in salinity, mixing of the entire water column is largely prevented and difference in dissolved oxygen level between surface and bottom

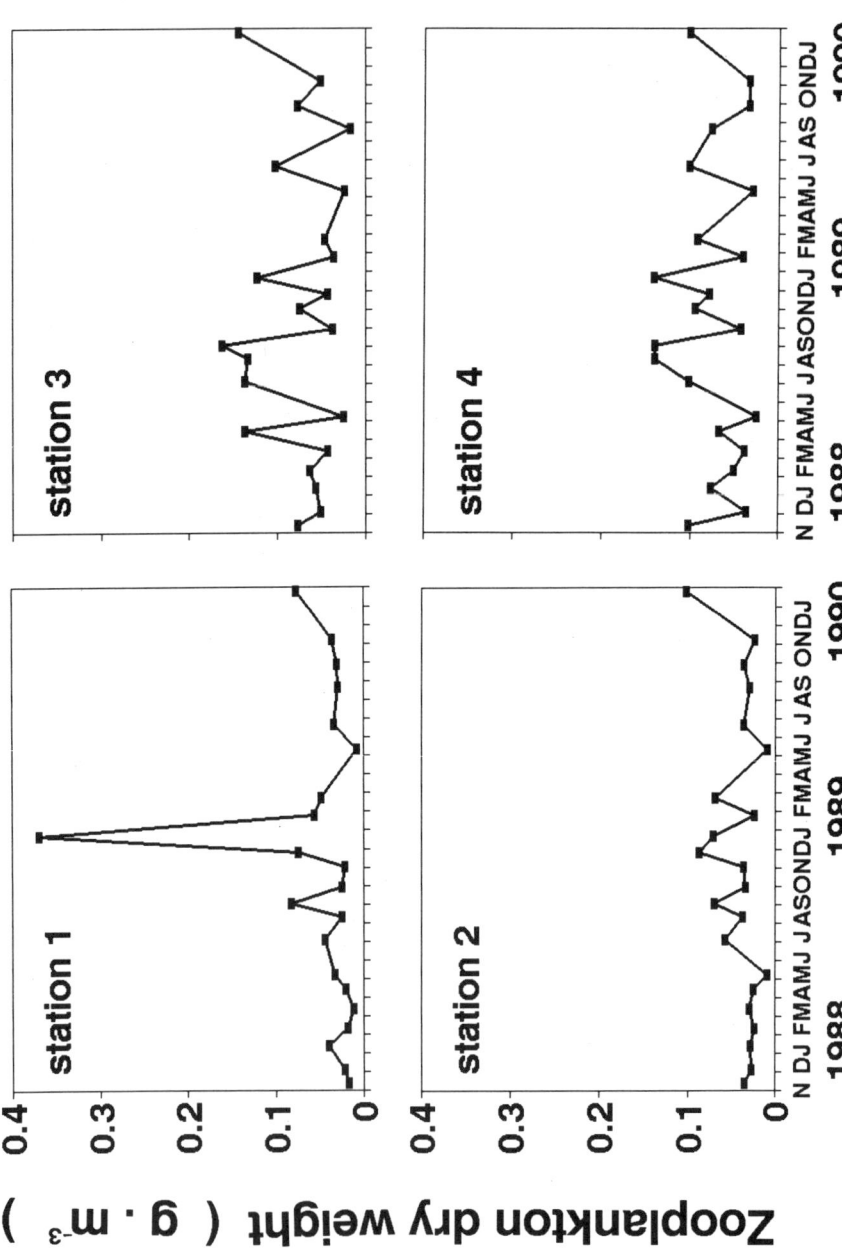

Fig. 7. Zooplankton dry weights at stations 1–4.

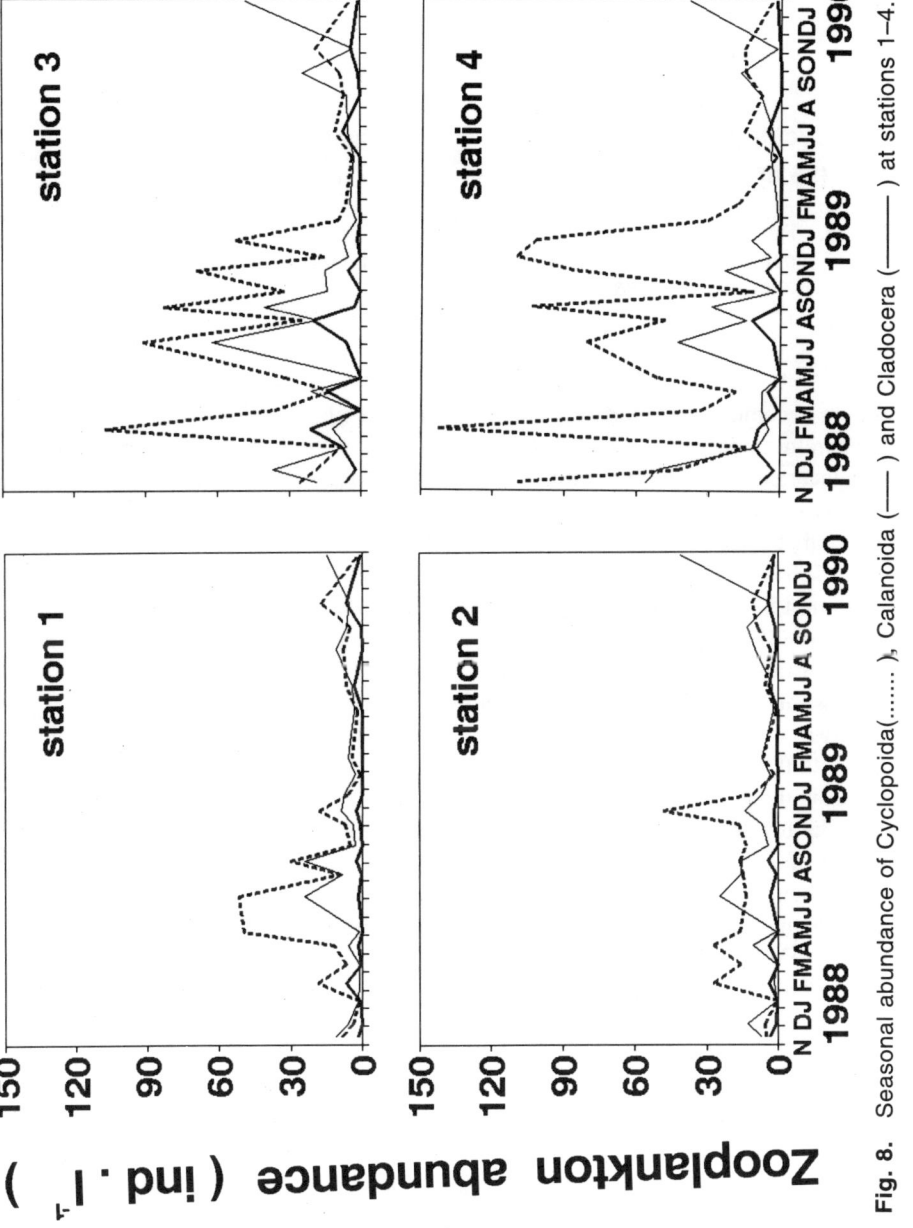

Fig. 8. Seasonal abundance of Cyclopoida (······), Calanoida (– – –) and Cladocera (———) at stations 1–4.

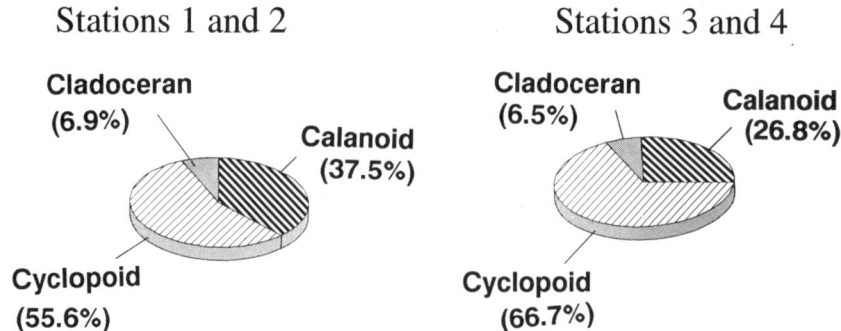

Fig. 9. Percentage contribution of Copepoda, Calanoida and Cladocera to the crustacean zooplankton of Tolo Harbour and Tolo Channel. Values represent the average of 21 sampling dates.

waters becomes particularly pronounced. In September and early October, declining air temperature cools the surface water. This results in the loss of the thermocline and the disappearance of density stratification. Eventually, wind-induced circulation produces a fairly homogeneous water mass in terms of dissolved oxygen. Wear et al. (1984) reported that dissolved oxygen values in the surface waters of Tolo Harbour were generally about 100% saturation between 1974 and 1976. Dissolved oxygen values of about 200% saturation have been recorded in Tai Po Hoi by the Environmental Protection Department (1988). Extremely high levels of dissolved oxygen (> 200% saturation) measured in the surface waters during the course of this study indicate a continuing trend of gradual increase in dissolved oxygen level in Tolo Harbour. Good correlation ($r = 0.58$, $P < 0.001$, $n = 64$) between chlorophyll a concentration and dissolved oxygen level suggests that supersaturation of oxygen in the surface waters is related to active photosynthesis of the large algal biomass.

The lowest dissolved oxygen value reported by Wear et al. (1984) for the bottom waters of Tolo Harbour was 24.7% saturation. This was recorded in September 1975. Since then, oxygen depletion in the bottom waters of the whole area of Tolo Harbour and Channel has become more severe. Extremely low levels of less than 10% saturation were measured at all stations in May 1988, and the situation is believed to be largely caused by the decomposition of organic matter. Large differences (> 5 mg·L^{-1}) in the amount of oxygen present in bottom waters at the beginning and at the end of stratification indicate very high rates of oxygen utilization in the bottom and, therefore, reflect a serious environmental problem.

Concentration of chlorophyll a in seawater provides an indirect estimate of the amount of phytoplankton in the water. Wear et al. (1984) reported upon high chlorophyll a concentrations in waters close to Plover Cove in 1975. A single peak of 13.5 mg·L^{-1} was recorded in August, although concentrations during the rest of the year were always below 10 µg·L^{-1}. Considerably higher concentrations were measured by Chan and Hodgkiss (1987) several years later. In waters close to the Tai Po Sewage Treatment Plant, mean concentrations of 14.36 µg·L^{-1} and 17.12 µg·L^{-1} were recorded in 1983 and 1984, respectively. In the channel where nutrient concentrations were lower, mean chlorophyll a concentrations only reached 2.69 µg·L^{-1} in 1983 and 4.12 µg·L^{-1} in 1984.

Organic pollution stands as the most important cause for the dramatic increase in phytoplankton biomass in Tolo Harbour. Studies carried out in the 1970's revealed that concentrations of nutrients had already increased in surface waters of Tolo Harbour (Trott 1973; Kueh 1974; Wear et al. 1984). Since that time, input of nutrients into Tolo Harbour has increased substantially (Morton 1982; Lam and Ho 1989). In 1984 Hodgkiss and Chan (1987) found that the levels of inorganic phosphate and inorganic nitrogen in the inner harbour were 118.8 µg·L^{-1} and 103.9 µg·L^{-1}, respectively. Wear et al. (1984) argued that nitrogen was the most important limiting nutrient for phytoplankton. Higher nitrogen levels and N/P ratios would thus promote more active algal growth. Indeed, Wu (1988) found good correlation between nitrogen level and phytoplankton standing crop in Tolo Harbour. Significant increase in nutrients concentration would also explain the dramatic increase in phytoplankton biomass. In 1988 and 1989 chlorophyll a concentrations in the surface waters reached mean values of 50 µg·L^{-1} in the inner harbour and 14 µg·L^{-1} in the channel. Compared to the earlier studies, these results indicate that eutrophication and intense algal blooms have affected the whole area of Tolo Harbour and Channel.

Chlorophyll a levels in the water fluctuated considerably throughout the study period, but no obvious seasonal patterns can be discerned. Lam and Ho (1989) suggested that the relatively high winter temperatures in Hong Kong may not suppress algal growth. Correlation between chlorophyll a concentration and temperature is poor ($r = 0.1$, $0.20 < P < 0.50$, $n = 64$). A similar lack of seasonal patterns in chlorophyll a concentrations was also reported by Wear et al. (1984).

Shifted species composition and increased dominance of dinoflagellates is evident when our results are compared to those of earlier studies. Wear et al. (1984) found that the diatom *Chaetoceros* was the dominant phytoplankter in Tolo Harbour in 1975. Several years later, Hodgkiss and Chan (1983) reported that diatoms still accounted for 80–90% of the phytoplankton in 1978 and 1979. Since those earlier studies, however, a gradual and steady decline in the dominance of the diatoms has begun. From 1983 to 1984 the percentage contribution of dinoflagellates increased from 11.4% to 25.8% in the inner harbour and from 20.5% to 65.7% in the channel (Hodgkiss and Chan 1987). The increasing dominance of dinoflagellates was accompanied by a progressive decline of the diatoms. Between 1983 and 1984, the percentage contribution of diatoms ranged from 73.4–88.4% in the inner harbour and 32.7–79.0% in the channel. By 1989 the values had declined to 57% in the inner harbour and 34.8% in the channel. Associated with increased dominance of the dinoflagellates is a notable increase in the occurrence of red tide and oxygen depletion (Wu 1988; Lam and Ho 1989).

Evaluation of long term population trends for various groups of crustacean zooplankton is difficult because no regular zooplankton sampling has been conducted in Tolo Harbour. Abundance of crustacean zooplankton showed considerable spatial and temporal variations. Abundance of both phytoplankton and zooplankton were lowest near the mouth of the channel and increase towards Station 4, the inner most station. To some extent, accumulation of phytoplankton and zooplankton in the inner harbour is the result of currents. However, high nutrient supply and slow water movement may also play a role by allowing a zone of high phytoplankton standing crop to develop. Since increased primary production by phytoplankton is expected to eventually give rise to higher zooplankton abundance, it can be speculated that the distribution of herbivorous zooplankton is determined by the availability of their principal food. There was, however, no good correlation between chlorophyll a concentration and zooplankton biomass (r = 0.08, P > 0.50, n = 64). While phytoplankton standing crop has increased dramatically during the last several years, comparison with earlier results (Wear et al. 1984) indicates only a slight increase in zooplankton dry weight biomass.

An obvious explanation for the poor correlation between chlorophyll a concentration and zooplankton biomass is that much of the measured zooplankton dry weight can be accounted for by the dinoflagellate *Noctiluca scintillans* which occasionally dominated the plankton community. However, correlations between the densities of crustacean zooplankton and chlorophyll a concentration were equally poor (r = 0.03, P > 0.5, n = 64). As discussed earlier, much of the increase in chlorophyll a concentrations in the waters of Tolo Harbour can be attributed to a dramatic rise in the abundance of dinoflagellates. Certain dinoflagellate species are known to produce toxic metabolites (Loeblich and Loeblich 1979; Shimizu 1982). Many zooplankton herbivores are known to avoid dense patches of toxic dinoflagellates (Fiedler 1982) and reject cells of certain dinoflagellates as food (Huntley et al. 1986). In addition, even dinoflagellate species which are not known to be toxic may not be suitable food for zooplankton herbivores. For instance, Kim et al. (1988) observed that while some marine cladocerans occur in dinoflagellates blooms, their feeding was largely restricted to diatoms. Similarly, Huntley et al. (1987) found that some dinoflagellates do not contain nutritional factors essential for survival and development of marine copepods.

In Tolo Harbour, an increased dominance of toxic or inedible dinoflagellates may have already adversely affected the crustacean zooplankton. The population densities of both copepods and cladocerans decreased markedly during 1989. To date, it is not known whether the decrease was part of natural population fluctuation or the beginning of a long term decline triggered by deteriorating water quality and competitive dominance of dinoflagellates. However, since oxygen depletion in the bottom waters was not particularly severe in 1989, it is probable that the competitive edge of dinoflagellates is at least partly responsible.

Significant correlation was found between zooplankton density and temperature (r = 0.23, P < 0.05, n = 64), but no clear seasonal patterns in zooplankton abundance can be indentified. While the zooplankton community in Tolo Harbour is diverse, seasonal succession of individual species is not apparent. The occurrence of large populations of zooplankton in the winter is mostly due to warm temperature and high levels of primary production (Chan and Hodgkiss 1987). Marine cladocerans, which have been observed to occur most frequently during the warmer seasons in the northwestern Pacific (Yoo and Kim 1987), displayed no clear seasonal patterns in the sub-tropical waters of Tolo Harbour.

This study represents the latest in a series of attempts to document the biological impacts of organic pollution in Tolo Harbour. The results confirm that water quality has continued to deteriorate and eutrophication has impacted the marine plankton. While the small size and transient nature of plankton patches may account for the lack of distinctive seasonal trends, long term changes including increases in phytoplankton standing crop, decreases in zooplankton abundance and changes in species composition are clearly identifiable.

ACKNOWLEDGEMENTS

We thank G. Lau, K.C. Chung, M.K. Cheung and Y.C. Tam for assistance in the field and laboratory. We also thank P.K.S. Lam for comments on the manuscript. Financial support was provided by a Messrs. Ho Tim and Ho Yin Research Grant and UPGC Direct Grants.

REFERENCES

Chan, B.S.S. and Hodgkiss I.J. 1987. Phytoplankton productivity in Tolo Harbour. *Asian Marine Biology* 4:79–90.
Chen, Q.C. 1982. The marine zooplankton of Hong Kong. In *Proceedings of the First International Marine Biological Workshop: The Marine Flora and Fauna of Hong Kong and Southern China, Hong Kong, 1980* (ed. B. Morton and C.K. Tseng), 789–99. Hong Kong: Hong Kong University Press.
Environmental Protection Department. 1988. *Marine Water Quality in Hong Kong, 1988.* Hong Kong.
Environmental Protection Department. 1989. *Marine Water Quality in Hong Kong, 1989.* Hong Kong.
Fiedler, P.C. 1982. Fine-scale spatial pattern in the coastal epiplankton: Description and functional significance. Ph.D. thesis, University of California, San Diego. 94 pp.
Hodgkiss, I.J. and Chan, B.S.S. 1983. Pollution studies on Tolo Harbour, Hong Kong. *Marine Environmental Research* 10:1–44.
Hodgkiss, I.J. and Chan, B.S.S. 1987. Phytoplankton dynamics in Tolo Harbour. *Asian Marine Biology* 4:103–12.
Holmes, P.R. and Lam, C.W.Y. 1985. Red tides in Hong Kong waters—response to a growing problem. *Asian Marine Biology* 2:1–10.
Horikoshi, M. and Thompson, G.1980. Distribution of subtidal molluscs collected by trawling in Tolo Harbour and Tolo Channel, Hong Kong, with special reference to habitat segregation in two venerid bivalves. In *Proceedings of the First International Workshop on the Malacofauna of Hong Kong and Southern China, Hong Kong, 1977* (ed. B. Morton), 149–62. Hong Kong: Hong Kong Univeristy Press.
Huntley, M.E., Ciminiello, P. and Lopez, M.D.G. 1987. Importance of food quality in determining development and survival of *Calanus pacificus* (Copepoda:Calanoida). *Marine Biology* 95:103–13.
Huntley, M., Sykes, P, Rohan, S. and Marin, V. 1986. Chemically-mediated rejection of dinoflagellate prey by the copepods *Calanus pacificus* and *Paracalanus parvus* : mechanism, occurrence and significance. *Marine Ecology Progress Series* 28:105–120.
Kim, S.W., Yoo, Y.H., Onbe, T. and Endo, T. 1988. Is grazing of marine cladocerans important for the occurrence of red tide? In *Red tide: biology, environmental science and toxicology.* (ed. T. Okaichi, D.M. Anderson and T. Nemoto), 259–62. New York: Elsevier.
Kueh, C.S.W. 1974. An investigation on the nutrients, coliform bacteria and other indicators of marine pollution in Tolo Harbour, Hong Kong. *Hong Kong Fisheries Bulletin* 4:115–24.
Lam, C.W.Y. and Ho, K.C. 1989. Phytoplankton characteristics of Tolo Harbour. *Asian Marine Biology* 6:5–18.
Loeblich, III, A. and Loeblich, L.A. 1979. The systematics of *Gonyaulax* with special reference to the toxic species. In *Toxic Dinoflagellate Blooms* (ed. D.L. Taylor and H.H. Seliger), 235–8. New York: Elsevier/North Holland.
Morton, B. 1982. An introduction to Hong Kong's marine environment with special reference to the north-eastern new territories. In *Proceedings of the First International Marine Biological Workshop: The Marine Flora and Fauna of Hong Kong and Southern China, Hong Kong, 1980* (ed. B. Morton and C.K. Tseng), 25–35. Hong Kong: Hong Kong University Press.
Oakley, H.R. and Cripps, T. 1972. Marine pollution studies at Hong Kong and Singapore. In *Marine pollution and sea life* (ed. M.J. Ruivo), 83–91. Surrey: Fishing News.

Parsons, T.R., Maita, Y. and Carol, M.L. 1984. *A manual of chemical and biological methods for seawater analysis*. Oxford: Pergamon Press.

Shimizu, Y. 1982. Recent progress in marine toxin research. *Pure Application Chemistry* 54:1973–80.

Trott, L.B. 1973. Preliminary hydrographic studies of Tolo Harbour, Hong Kong. *Journal of The Chinese University of Hong Kong* 1:255–69.

Trott, L.B. and Fung, A.Y.C. 1973. Marine pollution in Hong Kong. *Marine Pollution Bulletin* 4:13–5.

Wear, R.G., Thompson, G.B. and Stirling, H.P. 1984. Hydrography, nutrients and plankton in Tolo Harbour. *Asian Marine Biology* 1:59–75.

Wu, R.S.S. 1982. Periodic defaunation and recovery in a sub-tropical epibenthic community, in relation to organic pollution. *Journal of Experimental Marine Biology and Ecology* 64:253–69.

Wu, R.S.S. 1988. Marine pollution in Hong Kong: a review. *Asian Marine Biology* 5:1–23.

Wu, R.S.S. and Richards, J. 1979. *Mass Mortality of Benthos in Tolo Harbour*. Hong Kong Fisheries Occasional Paper No. 21. Agriculture & Fisheries Department, Hong Kong.

Yoo, K.I. and Kim S.W. 1987 Seasonal distribution of marine cladocerans in Chinhae Bay, Korea. *Journal of the Oceanological Society of Korea* 22:80–6.

THE PHYSIOLOGICAL ECOLOGY OF *PERNA VIRIDIS* (BIVALVIA: MYTILIDAE) FROM CONTRASTING ENVIRONMENTS IN HONG KONG

S.G. Cheung

Department of Zoology, The University of Hong Kong, Pokfulam Road, Hong Kong*

ABSTRACT

Seasonal variations in respiration rate, excretion rate and O:N ratio of *Perna viridis* were monitored at four sites in Hong Kong. Respiration was found to be positively correlated with temperature at Tai Lam Chung and Tolo Harbour while excretion rate was positively correlated with temperature at Kat O Fisheries Research Station (KOF) and Tolo Harbour. Positive correlations between excretion and respiration rates were shown at all sites. O:N ratio was negatively correlated with ammonia excretion rate at all sites but was not correlated with temperature, salinity or total particulate matter, except at KOF where a negative correlation was obtained with temperature and a positive correlation with salinity.

INTRODUCTION

Mussels, like many other littoral invertebrates (Prosser 1955; Newell 1973), are able to vary their respiratory and feeding rates in such a way as to maintain them relatively independent of ambient temperature. Immediate compensation to acute temperature change and long term acclimation responses of *Mytilus edulis* have been reviewed by Bayne *et al.* (1976a). Ammonia is the dominant excretory product in marine mussels (Bayne *et al.* 1976b). Unlike the rate of respiration (Widdows and Bayne 1971), no compensation for temperature increase was evident in the rate of protein catabolism. These responses result in a decline in the O:N ratio at high temperatures (Bayne 1975), as the mussels rely more heavily on the catabolism of protein than of non-protein substrates to meet the increased demand for energy (Bayne and Scullard 1977).

Many mussels are considered to be euryhaline. *Mytilus edulis* has an extremely wide estuarine and marine distribution, ranging from salinities of 4–5‰ to fully marine con-

---

* Present address: Department of Biology and Chemistry, City Polytechnic of Hong Kong, Tat Chee Avenue, Kowloon, Hong Kong.

ditions (Bayne et al. 1976a). *Modiolus demissus* occurs in waters with salinities of as low as 8–9‰ (Vernberg et al. 1963). *Perna viridis* in Hong Kong is reported to tolerate salinities as low as 12‰ (Lam 1987). Increased oxygen uptake in response to reduced salinity is common among invertebrates (Newell 1979). Similar results have also been reported upon for *P. viridis* and *P. indica* by Hawkins et al. (1987). An acclimation response was, however, obtained by Remane and Schlieper (1971) for *M. edulis*. An increase in ammonia excretion with a reduction in salinity was reported upon by Tedengren and Kautsky (1986) for *M. edulis* and associated with an osmotic adjustment. Hawkins et al. (1987) also reported an increase in the excretion rate at reduced salinities in *P. viridis* and *P. indica*.

The rate of metabolism in *Mytilus edulis*, including respiration and excretion, was found to vary with season. Such variation persisted even after removing temperature and body size effects. This 'residual seasonal pattern' was attributed to the gametogenic cycle and the availability of body reserves (Bayne and Scullard 1977) and is reflected in the seasonal change in O:N ratio.

Compared with the considerable amount of work undertaken on *Mytilus edulis*, little work is reported upon for *Perna viridis*. Only a few laboratory studies on respiration (Shafee 1976; Davenport 1983; Mathew and Menon 1983; Hawkins et al. 1987) and ammonia excretion (Hawkins et al. 1987) have been published. The physiological ecology of *P. viridis* has not been undertaken in Hong Kong, though it is a dominant intertidal species on most polluted rocky shores. The present study is the first attempt to understand the physiological ecology (including respiration, excretion and O:N ratio) of *P. viridis* in Hong Kong.

MATERIALS AND METHODS

Bimonthly samples of *Perna viridis* were collected from the Tolo Harbour (Fig. 1) from May 1987 to September 1988. In order to study the plasticity of the physiological responses, variable sizes of the mussels were transplanted from Tolo Harbour to three sites along the hydrographic gradient typical of Hong Kong's coastal waters using nylon net bags. These three sites, namely Kat O (KOF), Tai Tam (TT) and Tai Lam Chung (TLC), are located in the eastern oceanic, transition and western zones, respectively (Fig. 1), receiving different degrees of influence from the Pearl River and the currents of the South China Sea. The hydrographic parameters of each site including water temperature, salinity, dissolved oxygen, particulate organic matter and total particulate matter were determined.

Respiration

Forty mussels of sizes ranging from 15 mm to 80 mm were brought into the laboratory from the intertidal population in Tolo Harbour at each bimonthly sampling from July 1987 to September 1988 to study respiration. From the three transplantation sites, monthly samples of 20–40 individuals were collected from January 1986 to January 1987. Mussels were cleaned of epibionts and placed in a 10 L tank containing seawater obtained from the respective stations. The tank was maintained at the corresponding field temperature by placing it in a temperature controlled water bath. The experiments

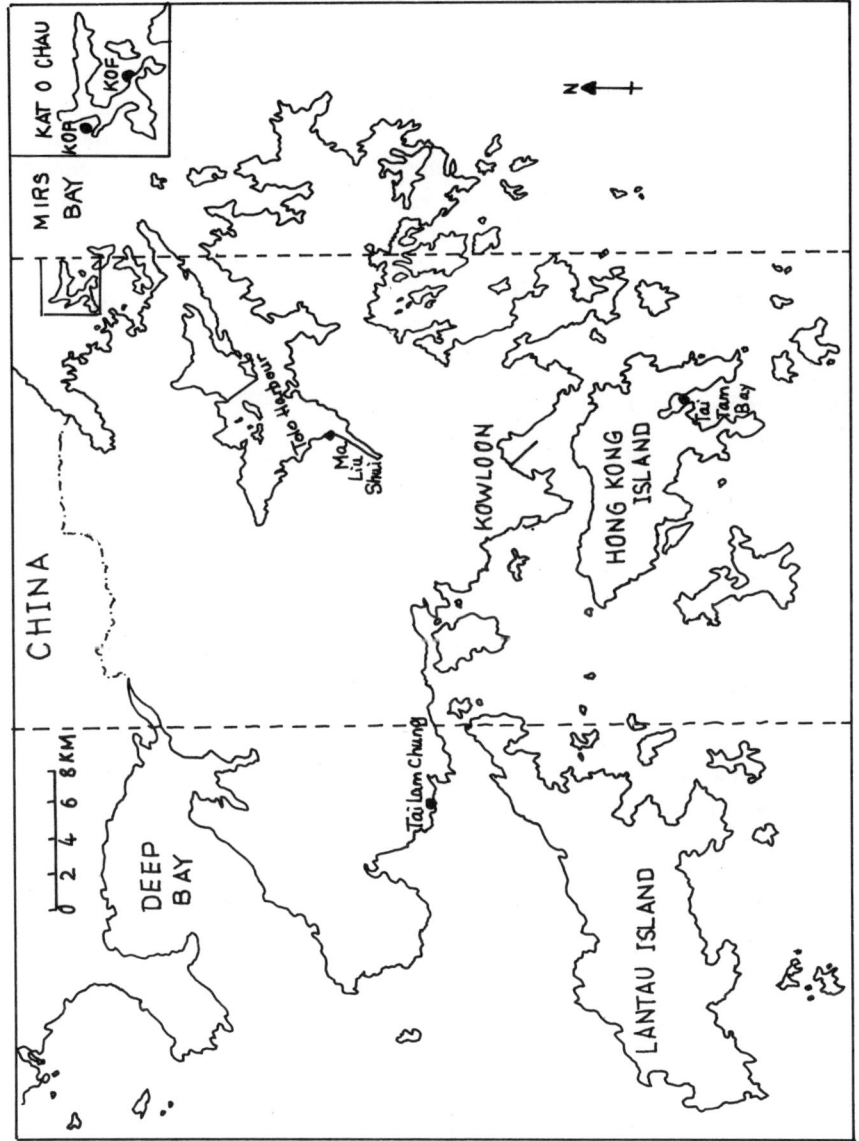

Fig. 1 Map of Hong Kong showing the location of the 4 study sites.

were undertaken at least 3 hours after the animals were returned to the laboratory and not later than 48 hours to prevent the animals acclimating to laboratory conditions. Before the start, each animal was placed in a glass bottle containing between 200 to 1200 mL of seawater obtained from each site, depending upon the size of the animal. These glass cylinders were sealed, taking care not to trap air bubbles, and placed in the water bath at the prevailing site temperature. Two more bottles were filled with seawater without animals and served as experimental controls. The experiment lasted for approximately one hour and started when the siphons of the mussels were protruded. As the respiration rate of *Perna viridis* is known to remain relatively independent of oxygen tension in seawater down to 20% air saturation (Hawkins *et al.* 1987), the timing of the experiment was selected to prevent a lowering of respiration rate by anoxic conditions. Dissolved oxygen levels in the cylinders were measured by a YSI 51 model oxygen meter at the start and at the end of the experiment. The amount of oxygen consumed within that period was calculated as the difference between the two readings after adjustment of the control values. Respiration rate was then expressed as mg O_2 consumed·hour^{-1}.

Ammonia excretion

After determination of respiration rate, the ammonia excretion rates of individuals from the Tolo Harbour population and the transplanted populations were measured. Individuals were placed in a wide mouth glass cylinder with between 200–500 mL of seawater obtained from the respective stations maintained at the prevailing site temperature. The wide–mouth cylinder provided a large surface area for gaseous exchange between the air and water interface to meet the oxygen demands of the animal. The seawater was first filtered through a preheated (450°C for 24 hours) Whatman 4.7 cm glassfibre filter (GF/C) to remove suspended particles (Worrall *et al.* 1983).

The amount of ammonia in the experimental pots and two controls were determined at the start and the end (1 hour) of the experiment. The ammonia excretion rate of each individual was then computed after correction of control values and expressed as µg NH_4–N·hr^{-1}. Ammonia levels were determined by the phenol-hypochlorite method (Parsons *et al.* 1984).

The O:N ratio, which is defined as the atomic equivalents of oxygen consumed to those of ammonia-nitrogen excreted, was also calculated to indicate the proportion of protein, relative to carbohydrate and lipid, that is catabolised for energy metabolism.

Data analysis

Linear regression was applied to relate respiration and excretion rates with body size in the form of the allometric equation:

$$\log y = \log a + b \log x$$

where y = respiration rate (mg O_2·hr^{-1}) or excretion rate (µgNH_4–N·hr^{-1}),
x = dry flesh weight (g),
and a and b are coefficient constants.

Temporal variation in respiration and excretion rates of a standard animal of 0.5 g dry flesh weight were computed from the monthly regression equations. Differences in the annual mean rates of physiological responses of a standard animal of 0.5 g between sites were compared by one way ANOVA using log-transformed variables performed on a VAX/SPSSX system.

To compare seasonal differences in physiological rates between sites, the months were grouped into four seasons: January to March were considered as winter with a mean sea temperature of 16.9°C, April to June and July to September were considered as spring (25.8°C) and summer (29.7°C) respectively. Autumn included the months of October to December with a mean sea temperature of 21.7°C. Data within a particular season were pooled for each site to calculate new regression lines. As the experimental animals from each site differed in size because of differential growth rates, the physiological parameters were recalculated to remove the confounding effects of body size. Separate slopes with different regression lines were used to recalculate the physiological variables (Packard and Boardman 1987) using a grand mean size computed from all sites in each season. Adjusted values were then compared using non-parametric Kruskal-Wallis one way ANOVA. Effects of environmental factors including temperature, salinity and total particulate matter and internal factor such as the dry condition index (expressed as ratio of dry tissue weight to shell weight) on respiration, excretion and O:N ratio at each site were determined using correlation analysis.

RESULTS

Hydrography

Values of some of the more important physical hydrographical parameters at the three experimental sites are summarised in Table 1.

The hydrographical characteristics of the three experimental sites (KOF, TT and TLC) are representative of the major marine environments found in Hong Kong, i.e., estuarine, transitional, oceanic (Morton 1982). Tolo Harbour is, however, somewhat peculiar. It is considered to be a polluted eutrophic embayment arising from poor water circulation and dispersion rates (Wu 1988). Its hydrology is influenced by local events rather than the bigger effects of ocean currents and the Pearl River.

Located in the extreme northeast, KOF is strongly influenced by ocean currents, i.e., the Hainan, the Kuroshio and the Taiwan Currents, which maintain high salinities year round. TLC is at the other, estuarine, extreme of the hydrographical conditions encountered in Hong Kong. The salinity fluctuates widely and is governed by the seasonal discharge of silt-laden and polluted freshwater from the Pearl River, especially in summer (Morton and Wu 1975; Mak 1982). TT in the central transition zone of Hong Kong experiences a minor decrease in salinity in summer when the influence of the Pearl River is more prominent. Tolo Harbour, with its outlet connecting to Mirs Bay in the northeast of Hong Kong, maintains stable high salinities of 28‰ year round. The salinity is, however, slightly lower than at KOF in Mirs Bay because of the constant freshwater input into it from the catchment population through the two sewage treatment plants and streams discharging into the harbour.

All the above sites show a high annual mean dissolved oxygen level of over 90% saturation. In Tolo Harbour, the monthly variation of dissolved oxygen level was great.

Table 1

Summary of the hydrographic conditions prevailing at the three experimental sites in 1986 and 1987. Values given are the mean ± S.D. Bracketed values are the range.

Parameter	Kat O 1986	Kat O 1987	Tai Tam 1986	Tai Tam 1987	Tai Lam Chung 1986	Tai Lam Chung 1987
Temperature (°C)	24.6 ± 5.1 (15.0 , 31.9)	24.1 ± 4.9 (17.3 , 30.6)	23.7 ± 5.3 (15.0 , 30.0)	24.3 ± 1.4 (16.0 , 30.4)	22.7 ± 5.5 (14.5 , 30.6)	24.3 ± 4.2 (17.6 , 30.6)
Salinity (‰)	31.4 ± 2.9 (26.0 , 37.0)	31.7 ± 2.8 (26.0 , 35.0)	29.7 ± 2.9 (22.0 , 33.0)	30.4 ± 3.1 (23.0 , 33.0)	27.1 ± 6.6 (12.0 , 35.0)	25.1 ± 6.5 (12.0 , 32.5)
Dissolved oxygen ($mg \cdot L^{-1}$)	7.4 ± 1.1 (6.2 , 9.6)	7.1 ± 0.8 (6.1 , 8.6)	7.0 ± 1.2 (5.4 , 8.9)	6.7 ± 1.0 (5.2 , 8.4)	7.6 ± 0.8 (6.4 , 8.6)	7.1 ± 1.4 (5.3 , 10.1)
Particulate organic matter ($mg \cdot L^{-1}$)	1.56 ± 0.67 (0.80 , 3.40)	1.31 ± 0.56 (0.80 , 2.90)	2.32 ± 0.61 (1.67 , 3.56)	1.77 ± 0.76 (1.10 , 3.70)	1.94 ± 0.69 (0.70 , 2.50)	2.88 ± 1.36 (0.88 , 5.70)
Total particulate matter ($mg \cdot L^{-1}$)	4.86 ± 1.63 (1.80 , 8.80)	3.51 ± 1.41 (1.70 , 7.90)	7.46 ± 2.36 (3.00 , 11.70)	6.55 ± 2.75 (3.60 , 4.10)	12.66 ± 8.93 (3.30 , 32.30)	11.02 ± 4.26 (4.90 , 19.80)
POM/TPM ratio	0.32	0.37	0.31	0.27	0.15	0.26

The maximum difference measured between months was 7.42 mg·l⁻¹. This was attributed to oxygen supersaturation caused by the active growth of algae. Oxygen depletion occurred when the algae died and decayed in this eutrophic site (Environmental Protection Department 1988).

Both TPM and POM levels showed a gradient from east to west. KOF in the extreme northeast had the lowest levels of TPM and POM indicating that the site is relatively free from the effects of the Pearl River and pollution. TT in the transition zone had median values. TLC in the west had the highest levels of both, presumably due to silty water brought down by the Pearl River which also resulted in a lower POM/TPM ratio. TPM and POM in Tolo Harbour, though located in the northeast, were about five times higher than that obtained from KOF. This is attributed to poor flushing and the heavy organic loading of the harbour from the surrounding catchment population.

Respiration

All the allometric equations relating oxygen uptake rates to dry body weight for log-transformed variables at the four sites were significant at the 95% probability level except for September at TLC with an insignificant value of $P = 0.36$. Probably this can be attributed to the small sample size used. The regression coefficient b varied between months for all sites, with mean values of 0.74, 0.68, 0.70 and 0.79 for Tolo Harbour, KOF, TT and TLC respectively. These are comparable to the results obtained for *Perna viridis* in India by Hawkins *et al.* (1987) (b = 0.789).

Temporal variations in respiration rates at the four sites are presented in Figure 2 A–D. High values were generally obtained in summer at all sites when water temperature was high. This seasonal trend was, however, less obvious at TT though high values were still obtained in summer, i.e., 1.78 and 1.18 mg O_2·hr⁻¹ in June and August 1986 when prevailing temperatures of 29°C and 29.5°C were recorded, respectively. Low values were, however, also obtained in summer between the high values of 0.55 mg O_2·hr⁻¹ recorded in both July and September 1986. The absence of winter data from January to March 1986, when temperatures of between 15–17°C prevailed, further obscured the seasonal pattern.

No significant difference was found in annual mean respiration rates between sites ($P > 0.05$) using one-way ANOVA. An *a-priori* t-test for comparison between two sites at each time also revealed no significant difference between any two sites. Significant seasonal differences were, however, found between sites. Out of 12 regression lines relating log oxygen uptake rates to log dry tissue weight for the four seasons at three experimental sites (KOF, TT and TLC), winter and autumn samples at TT were found to be insignificant, possibly due to the large variation in the samples. Comparison of autumn and winter samples were, therefore, possible only for KOF and TLC. The rest of the regressions were highly significant with $P < 0.0001$. The adjusted respiration rates, after removing the confounding effect of body size, were compared using the non-parametric Kruskal-Wallis ANOVA test. Of the four seasons, significant differences were found between sites in winter, spring and summer (Table 2). No significant difference was found between KOF and TLC in autumn but a higher value was recorded from KOF in winter. Similarly, the highest value was obtained from KOF and the lowest from TLC in spring. In contrast, the highest value was measured from TLC in summer, followed by KOF and TT respectively.

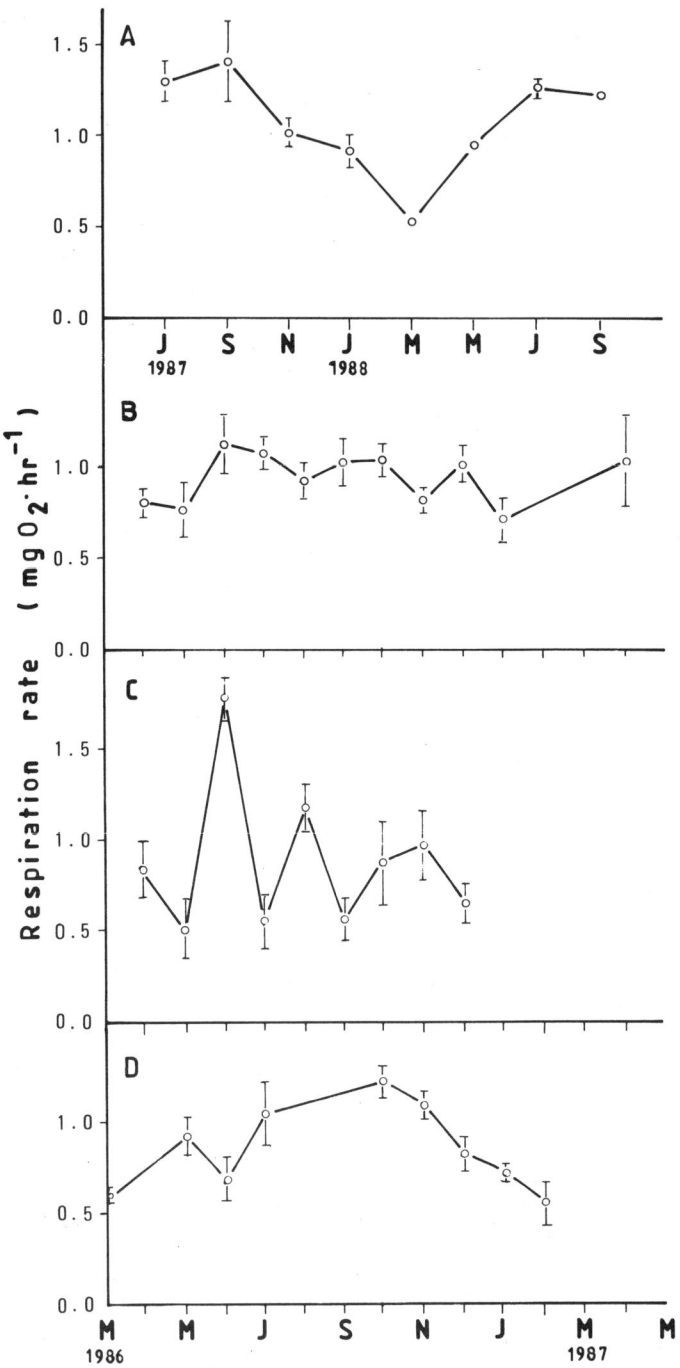

Fig. 2. *Perna viridis.* Temporal variation in respiration rate (±95% confidence level) of a standard 0.5 g dry weight individual at four sites. A, Tolo Harbour; B, Kat O; C, Tai Tam; D, Tai Lam Chung.

Table 2
Perna viridis. A comparison of respiration rate (mg $O_2 \cdot hr^{-1}$) between sites during four seasons using Kruskal-Wallis one-way ANOVA.

		Kruskal-Wallis 1-way ANOVA		
Winter Jan–Mar 1986		Mean rank 100.78 62.36	cases 73 86	site KOF TLC
cases 159	chi-square 27.4923	significance 0.0000	corrected for ties chi-square 27.4923	significance 0.0000
Spring Apr–Jun 1986		Mean rank 128.77 91.33 84.98	cases 106 69 41	site KOF TT TLC
cases 216	chi-square 22.1687	significance 0.0000	corrected for ties chi-square 22.1687	significance 0.0000
Summer Jul–Sep 1986		Mean rank 129.03 50.16 147.14	cases 117 67 28	site KOF TT TLC
cases 212	chi-square 84.5874	significance 0.0000	corrected for ties chi-square 84.5874	significance 0.0000
Autumn Oct–Dec 1986		Mean rank 100.56 106.90	cases 126 79	site KOF TLC
cases 205	chi-square 0.5552	significance 0.4562	corrected for ties chi-square 0.5552	significance 0.4562 N.S.

N.S. Not significant at the 95% probability level.

KOF = Kat O.
TT = Tai Tam.
TLC = Tai Lam Chung.

A correlation matrix, relating respiration rate to three environmental factors and the condition index, are presented in Table 3. Salinity, total particulate matter and condition index did not correlate with respiration rate at any of the four sites. Temperature was a major controlling factor in Tolo Harbour and at TLC as shown by the significant positive correlation values. The relationship was not significant at KOF ($P = 0.056$). As shown in Figure 2B, the highest and lowest rates obtained corresponded to the highest and lowest temperatures measured. The insignificant relationship was possibly due to a smaller difference between the maximum and minimum values which were more obvious in Tolo Harbour and at TLC. The respiration rate at TT was not correlated with any of the environmental variables considered or with condition index. No seasonal pattern in oxygen uptake was discernible, as shown by the great fluctuation in monthly values.

Table 3

Perna viridis. Correlations between respiration rate (OXY) and temperature (T), salinity (S), total particulate matter (TPM) and condition index (CI) at the four sites.

		T	S	TPM	CI
OXY	(Tolo)	0.880	-0.433	-0.081	-0.790
		(n = 8)	(n = 8)	(n = 8)	(n = 8)
		P = 0.002*	P = 0.142	P = 0.424	P = 0.010*
	(KOF)	0.507	-0.215	0.073	-0.608
		(n = 11)	(n = 11)	(n = 11)	(n = 11)
		P = 0.056	P = 0.263	P = 0.415	P = 0.024*
	(TT)	0.218	0.115	0.060	0.529
		(n = 9)	(n = 9)	(n = 9)	(n = 9)
		P = 0.287	P = 0.384	P = 0.439	P = 0.071
	(TLC)	0.733	-0.222	0.629	-0.498
		(n = 9)	(n = 8)	(n = 7)	(n = 9)
		P = 0.012*	P = 0.299	P = 0.065	P = 0.086

* Significant at the 95% probability level.

Tolo = Tolo Harbour.
KOF = Kat O.
TT = Tai Tam.
TLC = Tai Lam Chung.

Ammonia excretion

Of 41 regressions relating log transformed variables of excretion rate to dry tissue weight at the four sites, three were found to be insignificant. Others were significant at $P < 0.005$ except for April 1987 at KOF where $P < 0.05$. All sites showed inter-month variations in exponent b. The annual means of b values from Tolo Harbour, KOF, TT and TLC were 0.71, 0.65, 0.76 and 0.69, respectively.

The rates of ammonia-nitrogen excreted by a 0.5 g dry flesh weight mussel at the four sites are presented in Figure 3A–D. Seasonal variation in excretion rate was obvious at all sites with high values recorded in summer except at TLC, where a low value

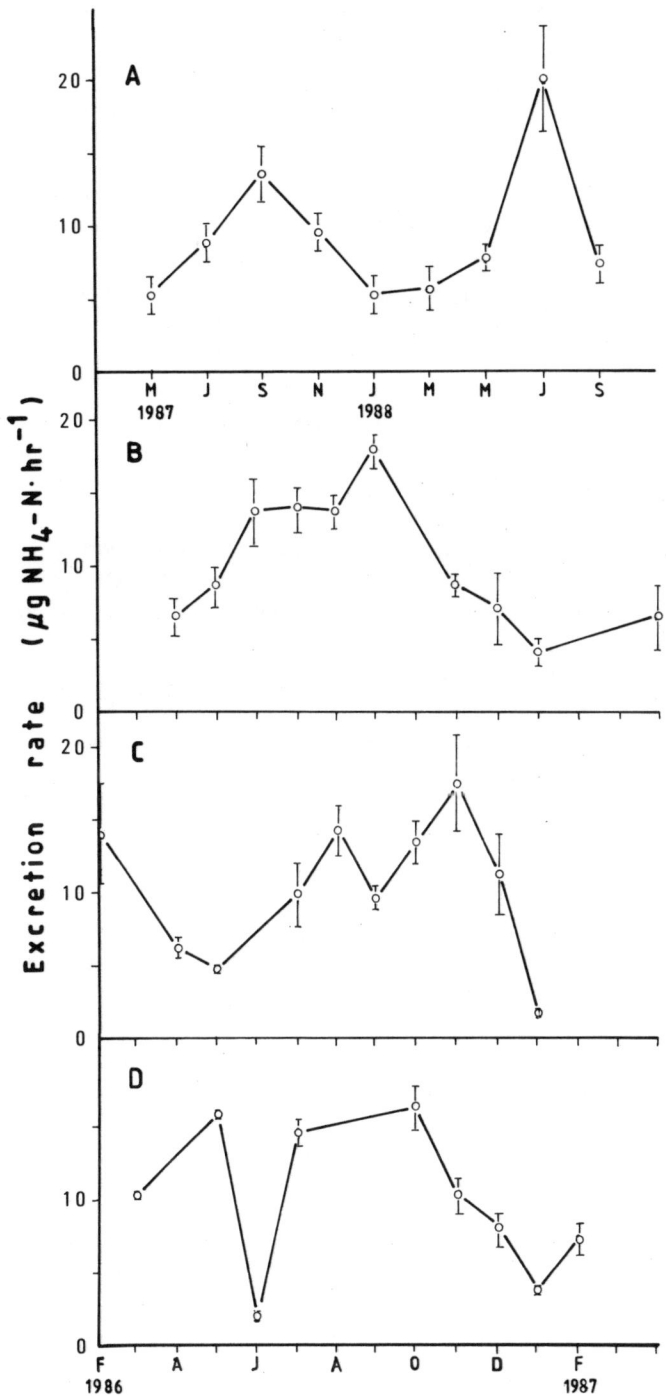

Fig. 3. *Perna viridis*. Temporal variation in excretion rate (±95% confidence level) of a standard 0.5 g dry weight individual at four sites. A, Tolo Harbour; B, Kat O; C, Tai Tam; D, Tai Lam Chung.

of 1.9 µg NH_4–N·hr^{-1} was recorded in June 1986. This was the lowest value recorded from TLC.

No significant difference in annual mean excretion rates was recorded between the four sites ($P > 0.05$). A contrast coefficient matrix of the data revealed no significant difference between any two sites. In regressions relating log excretion rates to log dry flesh weight during the four seasons at KOF, TT and TLC, two occasions, out of a total of twelve, there was no significant relationship at the 95% probability level; the others were all highly significant, with $P < 0.0001$. These two occasions were the winter sample from KOF and the spring sample from TLC. As a consequence, comparisons were only available between two sites in winter and spring. Comparisons of excretion rates between sites during different seasons were tested by non-parametric Kruskal-Wallis analysis of variance. Results of this analysis are presented in Table 4. No significant difference was found between TT and TLC in winter and KOF and TT in spring. A significantly higher rate was recorded from TLC in summer; the lowest was from TT. In contrast, TT had the highest value in autumn, followed by TLC and KOF, respectively.

Correlations between excretion rate with three environmental variables and the condition index are presented in Table 5. A positive correlation was obtained between temperature and excretion rates from Tolo Harbour and KOF but not from TT and TLC. Nevertheless, all sites showed positive correlations between respiration rate and excretion rate, indicating that an increase in metabolism is associated with an increase in the amount of metabolic wastes produced, at least in the form of ammonia. Condition index also showed a negative correlation with ammonia excretion from KOF and TT. Salinity and TPM were not significantly correlated with excretion rate at any site.

O:N ratio

Temporal variations in the O:N ratio obtained from the four sites are presented in Figure 4A–D. High values were obtained in winter especially in January from Tolo Harbour, KOF and TLC. The O:N ratio remained high year round in Tolo Harbour with values > 100, except on two occasions, i.e., March 1988 (93.8) and July 1988 (63.1). An exceptionally high value of 323.8 was, however, identified at TLC in June 1986 and was contributed to by an extremely low excretion rate (2.1 µg NH4–N·hr–1). Consistently low O:N values were measured at TT from July till December 1986 with most values < 90. No significant difference was obtained in annual mean values of O:N ratio from the four sites using the non-parametric Kruskal-Wallis test (n = 35, $P = 0.11$).

In regression equations relating log O:N to log dry flesh weight during the four seasons at the three experimental sites, three occasions, out of twelve, showed no significant relationship between O:N ratio and dry tissue weight. Others were significant at $P < 0.005$ except for the autumn sample (October–December 1986) from TT ($P < 0.05$). The relationships were, however, highly variable, with small r^2 values. Of nine significant regressions, only two had r^2 values > 0.2. Nevertheless, positive slopes were obtained from all significant relationships at KOF and TLC. Negative b values were obtained from the spring and autumn samples from TT.

A Pearson correlation analysis relating O:N ratio to environmental and physiological variables is presented in Table 6. O:N ratio was negatively correlated with ammonia excretion rate at all sites showing that an increase in ammonia excretion is associated

Table 4
Perna viridis. A comparison of excretion rate (μg NH_4-N·hr^{-1}) between sites during four seasons using a Kruskal-Wallis one-way ANOVA.

	Kruskal-Wallis 1-way ANOVA				
Winter Jan–Mar 1986		Mean rank	cases	site	
		73.93	59	TT	
		73.21	87	TLC	
				corrected for ties	
cases	chi-square	significance	chi-square	significance	
146	0.0103	0.9190	0.0103	0.9190	N.S.
Spring Apr–Jun 1986		Mean rank	cases	site	
		93.22	104	KOF	
		79.00	70	TT	
				corrected for ties	
cases	chi-square	significance	chi-square	significance	
174	3.3346	0.0678	3.3346	0.0678	N.S.
Summer Jul–Sep 1986		Mean rank	cases	site	
		125.02	116	KOF	
		70.19	70	TT	
		131.21	29	TLC	
				corrected for ties	
cases	chi-square	significance	chi-square	significance	
215	38.5800	0.0000	38.5800	0.0000	
Autumn Oct–Dec 1986		Mean rank	case	site	
		111.21	141	KOF	
		226.81	85	TT	
		148.18	79	TLC	
				corrected for ties	
cases	chi-square	significance	chi-square	significance	
305	91.4467	0.0000	91.4467	0.0000	

N.S. Not significant at the 95% probability level.

KOF = Kat O.
TT = Tai Tam.
TLC = Tai Lam Chung.

Table 5

Perna viridis. Correlations between excretion rate (Ammo) and temperature (T), salinity (S), total particulate matter (TPM), condition index (CI) and respiration rate (Oxy) at the four sites.

		T	S	TPM	Oxy	CI
Ammo	(Tolo)	0.700 (n = 9) P = 0.018*	-0.036 (n = 9) P = 0.464	-0.262 (n = 9) P = 0.248	0.687 (n = 8) P = 0.030*	-0.350 (n = 9) P = 0.178
	(KOF)	0.867 (n = 10) P = 0.001*	-0.488 (n = 10) P = 0.076	0.089 (n = 10) P = 0.403	0.608 (n = 10) P = 0.031*	-0.836 (n = 10) P = 0.001*
	(TT)	0.201 (n = 10) P = 0.289	-0.010 (n = 10) P = 0.489	-0.340 (n = 10) P = 0.168	0.656 (n = 8) P = 0.039*	-0.538 (n = 10) P = 0.055
	(TLC)	0.312 (n = 9) P = 0.207	-0.279 (n = 8) P = 0.252	0.037 (n = 7) P = 0.469	0.702 (n = 9) P = 0.018*	-0.462 (n = 9) P = 0.105

* Significant at the 95% probability level.
Tolo = Tolo Harbour.
KOF = Kat O.
TT = Tai Tam.
TLC = Tai Lam Chung.

Table 6

Perna viridis. Correlations between O:N ratio (ON) and temperature (T), salinity (S), total particulate matter (TPM), respiration rate (Oxy), excretion rate (Ammo) and condition index (CI) at the four sites.

		T	S	TPM	Oxy	Ammo	CI
ON	(Tolo)	−0.265 (n = 8) P = 0.263	−0.579 (n = 8) P = 0.067	−0.245 (n = 8) P = 0.280	−0.079 (n = 8) P = 0.426	−0.705 (n = 8) P = 0.026*	0.201 (n = 8) P = 0.316
	(KOF)	−0.864 (n = 10) P = 0.001*	0.581 (n = 10) P = 0.039*	−0.112 (n = 10) P = 0.379	−0.328 (n = 10) P = 0.178	−0.893 (n = 10) P = 0.000*	0.796 (n = 10) P = 0.003*
	(TT)	−0.173 (n = 8) P = 0.341	0.310 (n = 8) P = 0.228	0.230 (n = 8) P = 0.292	0.090 (n = 8) P = 0.416	−0.658 (n = 8) P = 0.038*	−0.458 (n = 8) P = 0.127
	(TLC)	0.233 (n = 9) P = 0.274	−0.021 (n = 8) P = 0.481	−0.009 (n = 7) P = 0.492	−0.292 (n = 9) P = 0.223	−0.779 (n = 9) P = 0.007*	0.2723 (n = 9) P = 0.239

* Significant at the 95% probability level.
Tolo = Tolo Harbour.
KOF = Kat O.
TT = Tai Tam.
TLC = Tai Lam Chung.

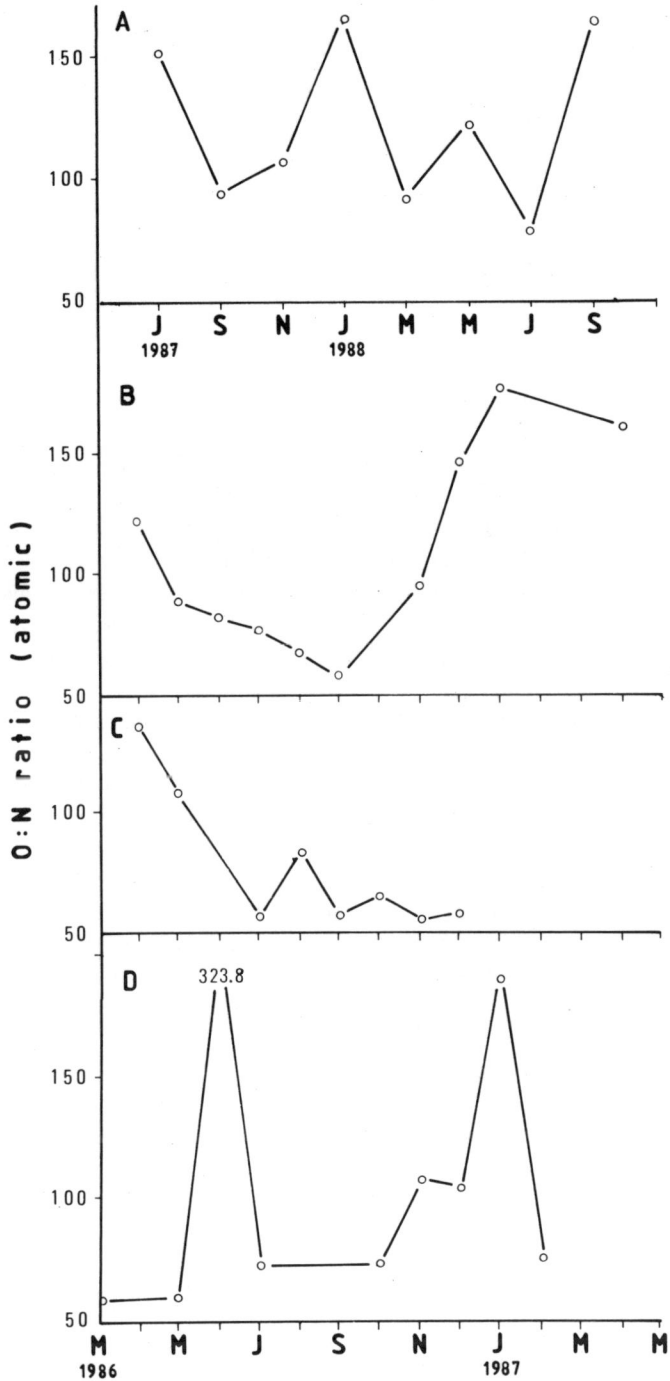

Fig. 4. *Perna viridis*. Temporal variation in O:N ratio of a standard 0.5 g dry weight individual at four sites. A, Tolo Harbour; B, Kat O; C, Tai Tam; D, Tai Lam Chung.

with an increasing proportion of protein material metabolized. The ratio was, however, not correlated with any environmental factors, i.e., neither temperature, salinity nor TPM, except from KOF where a negative correlation was obtained with temperature and a positive correlation with salinity. As temperature is negatively correlated with salinity, a low O:N ratio therefore occurred at a time of high temperatures and low salinities i.e., summer, at KOF.

DISCUSSION

Respiration

The dependence of oxygen uptake upon size, age, food, temperature and salinity in *Mytilus edulis* have been studied and reviewed by Bayne *et al.* (1976a). Of these various factors, temperature is recognised as one of the major environmental determinants of metabolic rate and the level of activity. That metabolic rate is temperature dependent has been demonstrated for *M. edulis* (Newell 1973). In contrast, independence of oxygen uptake upon temperature, with low values recorded in summer and high values in winter has also been reported upon for *M. edulis* by Bayne (1973) and Widdows (1978a). Bayne (1973) correlated this with gametogenesis. In summer, when the gametogenic cycle is in a 'resting stage', high reserves of glycogen and a high proportion of metabolically inert material results in a low rate of oxygen consumption per unit weight. During winter, when gametogenesis is active, glycogen stores are utilized and metabolic demand increases. In spring, a large mass of developing gametes continues to impose a high demand for oxygen which is only reduced after spawning.

In comparison with the work undertaken on respiration in *Mytilus edulis*, studies of *Perna* are extremely scarce (Shafee 1976; Davenport 1983; Mathew and Menon 1983; Baby and Menon 1986; Hawkins *et al.* 1987). In the present study, a positive correlation was obtained between temperature and oxygen uptake rates in Tolo Harbour and TLC. Though no correlation was obtained from TT and KOF, high respiration rates were still generally obtained in the summer months. The lack of winter data and the great variation in respiration rate in summer at TT resulted in an obscured seasonal pattern. Nevertheless, temperature is one of the factors determining respiration rate in *P. viridis* in Hong Kong waters.

The effects of salinity on mussel respiration and activity have been examined most extensively for *Mytilus edulis*. Full acclimation to changes in salinity with no change in respiration was recorded by Remane and Schlieper (1971). The response to salinity by *Perna viridis* was varied. A higher respiration rate at a salinity of 35‰ than at 17.5‰ was obtained by Shafee (1976) after acclimation for three weeks. A contrasting result was recorded by Hawkins *et al.* (1987) who showed that the normoxic oxygen consumption maintain by *P. viridis* at 15‰ was consistently, but not statistically ($P > 0.05$), greater than comparable rates at 32‰ and different oxygen tensions. This increased oxygen uptake in response to reduced salinity is common among invertebrates (Newell 1979) and presumably reflects elevated costs incurred within a range of salinity 'tolerance'. Though no correlation was found between respiration rate and salinity at any of the sites in the present study, a higher respiration rate was recorded in summer at TLC, as compared with other sites. As the animals at all sites experienced a similar temperature regime and followed the same reproductive cycle (Cheung 1990) and, moreover, were transplanted from the same population which reduced possible genetic variability with regard to physiological responses, this discrepancy can probably be related to inherent site characteristics. Environmentally induced physiological changes have also been demonstrated for *Scrobicularia plana* by Worrall and Widdows (1983) following transplantation between three experimental sites. Low salinity and low food quality, throughout the summer at TLC, thus possibly contributed to a higher measured respiration rate. Whether one or two of the above factors are responsible for this, however, requires further investigation.

Seasonal variations in respiration rate have been found to be related to the gametogenic cycle and body reserves in *Mytilus edulis* (Bayne 1973). Whether or not reproductive activities contribute to the recorded seasonal variations in respiration rate in *Perna viridis* is unknown. A seasonal variation in body biochemical components in relation to the reproductive cycle have been reported upon for *P. viridis* by Nagabhushanam and Mane (1978), but no concomitant physiological activities were measured. It is possible that *P. viridis* spawns all year round in Hong Kong (Lee 1986; Cheung 1990), but with two major peaks in May/June and January/March. During the period from June to January, i.e., summer to autumn, active gametogenesis is expected and stimulated by the high temperatures prevailing during that period. Ammonia excretion was found to be positively correlated with respiration rate and negatively correlated with O:N ratio at all sites. An increase in metabolism, though not necessarily correlated with temperature, was associated with an increase in ammonia excretion and hence to a change in the type of body reserve utilised as shown by a lower O:N ratio. This decrease in O:N ratio was probably related to gametogenesis and body reserves utilization when body reserves are lower. The relationship between metabolism, reproductive cycle and body reserves in *P. viridis*, however, requires further investigation.

Ammonia excretion

Ammonia forms the major excretory end-product of protein and amino-acid catabolism in *Mytilus edulis* (Bayne et al. 1976b). The rate of ammonia-nitrogen excretion may, therefore, be regarded as reflecting the rate of protein catabolism. The seasonal cycle in the rate of ammonia excretion by *M. edulis* appears to be related to physiological and reproductive condition. Unlike the rate of oxygen consumption, *M. edulis* has no acclimated excretion rate (Thompson and Newell 1985); the latter simply increases with temperature. In the present study, the excretion rate of *Perna viridis* was found to be positively correlated with temperature in Tolo Harbour and at KOF, and also with high values in summer and autumn at TT and TLC. Apart from the temperature effect, ammonia excretion rate was found to be positively correlated with respiration rate and negatively correlated with O:N ratio at all sites. An increase in ammonia excretion was clearly a result of an increase in protein catabolism which may, in turn, be related to the reproductive cycle.

The rate of ammonia excretion by *Mytilus edulis* was increased at reduced salinities (Bayne et al. 1976b). Similarly, an increase in ammonia excretion was also reported upon by Hawkins et al. (1987) for *Perna viridis*, i.e., from 185 µg NH_4-$N \cdot hr^{-1}$ to 228 µg NH_4-$N \cdot hr^{-1}$, when transferred from a salinity of 32‰ to that of 20‰. A higher ammonia excretion rate was recorded in summer at TLC as compared with TT and KOF which recorded higher salinities in this study. This correlation between ammonia excretion and salinity is possibly associated with osmotic adjustment in *Mytilus* (Tedengren and Kautsky 1986). It is generally accepted that marine invertebrates utilize free amino acids as solutes for cell volume regulation during salinity stress (Henry *et al*. 1980). The proposed mechanism behind this, is that the activity of glutamate dehydrogenase is modified by the external ion concentration. A decrease in environmental salinity causes a decrease in glutamate dehydrogenase activity and a subsequent decrease in the intracellular content of free amino acids by catabolism of them to keto-acids and ammonia. *P. viridis* at TLC had higher respiration and ammonia excretion rates in summer, indicating that a higher energy demand was necessary during salinity stress. This may partly account for the lower growth rate obtained at TLC.

The ammonia excretion rates at the four sites were of similar ranges. These values were, however, much lower than those recorded for *Perna viridis* by Hawkins *et al*. (1987), i.e., 185 µg NH_4–N·hr^{-1} at a salinity of 32‰ and 228 µg NH_4–N·hr^{-1} at 15‰. They are, however, comparable to those obtained for *Perna indica* in the same study with values of 27.3 and 38.7 µg NH_4–N·hr^{-1} at salinities of 32‰ and 20‰ respectively and a temperature of 28°C. As the respiration rates measured in the present study are comparable to those obtained by Hawkins *et al*. (1987), the extremely high excretion rate measured by these authors resulted in low O:N ratios of 8.0 at a salinity of 32‰ and 7.0 at 15‰, signifying almost complete catabolic reliance upon proteinaceous reserves. According to Bayne *et al*. (1985) and Hawkins *et al*. (1985), mussels with O:N ratios < 30 show a higher protein than carbohydrate catabolism, representing a stressed condition. Together with the fact that glycogen is a major storage material in *P. viridis* (Nagabhushanam and Mane 1978), the extremely low O:N ratio obtained by Hawkins *et al*. (1987) for this species may indicate that the animals were under stress in the experimental situation and may not, therefore, necessarily suggest that this animal normally relies on proteins for metabolism.

O:N ratio

High O:N ratios (> 50) were generally obtained in the present study at all sites and time periods, indicating that the animals were healthy. Values < 30 signify a considerable rate of protein catabolism, generally associated with stress (Widdows 1978b). Values > 50 suggest a high rate of lipid and carbohydrate metabolism. The mean value obtained from Tolo Harbour (122.0) was highest, followed by KOF (107.7) and TLC (91.8). The lowest value was recorded from TT (77.2). No winter data were obtained from TT. As high O:N ratios were, however, generally obtained from the other sites during this period, a higher annual mean value might be expected if the winter data were available. Notwithstanding, the data obtained for *Perna viridis* in the present study are comparable to those obtained for *Mytilus edulis* (Bayne 1973) where O:N ratios are stable around a value of 100 for most of the year. This indicates that 90% or more of the energy metabolism of *Perna viridis* is derived from carbohydrates and lipids.

Though mean values of about 100 were obtained from most of the sites, seasonal variations were still evident, with low values recorded in summer and high values in winter showing that the proportion of different reserves used in metabolism changed seasonally, and probably with the proportions of the body reserves themselves available and the gametogenic cycle.

One interesting point obtained from the present study is the values recorded from Tolo Harbour. A high O:N ratio with values > 100 in 6 out of 8 samplings from July 1987 to September 1988 indicated that the animals were, here, healthy. The values obtained were higher than from all the other experimental sites, which are considered clean. In a transplantation experiment using *Mytilus edulis* along a pollution gradient in Narragansett Bay, Widdows *et al.* (1981) reported a decline in scope for growth and O:N ratio with increasing pollution levels. The O:N ratio declined from 75.0 to 29.6. Narragansett Bay, however, receives pollutants mainly in the form of hydrocarbons from sewage effluents, oil spills and normal ship and tanker operations and also receives trace metals from domestic and general industrial wastes. In contrast, Tolo Harbour is considered to be a eutrophic embayment with pollution mainly arising from human sewage and pig and chicken wastes (Wu 1988). The low levels of trace metals measured in tissues from *Perna viridis* in Tolo Harbour were comparable to those obtained at TLC but lower than those obtained from Victoria Harbour (Chan 1988). It seems that pollution stress does not affect the condition of *P. viridis* for most of the year and that the mussels may actually benefit from a higher organic loading in the harbour. Pollution affected the animals indirectly through oxygen depletions, especially in summer when the animals were directly exposed to the air during the low tide that occurred in daylight hours. This is supported by the fact that mortality occurred mainly in summer and an exceptionally low O:N ratio was obtained in July 1988 when one mass mortality occurred. The poor water quality prevailing in summer may increase the energy expenditure of the animal thereby depleting the body reserves and resulting in the recorded low O:N ratio of 63.1. The poor condition of the mussels may eventually lead to heavy mortality, the extent of which depends on the length of time the poor water quality is maintained.

Bayne and Scullard (1977) examined the interaction between body size and ration, as they affect the O:N ratio, in *Mytilus edulis*. When the ration was in excess of the maintenance requirement, the ratio was higher in smaller than in large individuals. During starvation, however, individuals of all sizes showed a reduction in O:N. This reduction was particular marked in smaller individuals, which probably have less glycogen reserves to call upon during nutritive stress than do larger animals. In the present study, the relationship varied. No relationship was found between O:N ratio and body size in winter samples from TT and spring and autumn samples from TLC. A negative relationship existed in spring and autumn at TT. A positive relationship with higher ratios in large individuals during all seasons was obtained for KOF, winter and summer samples at TLC and summer samples at TT. In view of the weak correlations in these significant relationships, with r^2 values of < 0.2 being obtained for 7 out of 9 samples, and with no seasonal pattern identified, the relationship between O:N ratio and body size and season clearly requires further study.

ACKNOWLEDGEMENTS

This work forms part of a thesis submitted for a Ph.D. degree at The University of Hong Kong. I thank my supervisor Prof. Brian Morton for his advice and encouragement.

REFERENCES

Baby, K.V. and Menon, N.R. 1986. Oxygen uptake in the brown mussel, *Perna indica* (Kuriakose and Nair) under sublethal stress of Hg, Cd and Zn. *Indian Journal of Marine Sciences* 15:127–8.
Bayne, B.L. 1973. Physiological changes in *Mytilus edulis* L. induced by temperature and nutritive stress. *Journal of the Marine Biological Association of the United Kingdom* 53:39–58.
Bayne, B.L. 1975. Reproduction in bivalve molluscs under environmental stress. In *Physiological Ecology of Estuarine Organisms* (ed. F.J. Vernberg), 259–77. Columbia: University of South Carolina Press.
Bayne, B.L., Brown, D.A., Burns, K. Dixon, D.R., Ivanovici, A. Livingitone, D.R., Lowe, D.M., Moore, M.N., Stebbing, A.R.D. and Widdows, J. 1985. *The effects of stress and pollution on marine animals*, CBS educational and professional publishing, Praeger Publisher.
Bayne, B.L. and Scullard, C. 1977. Rates of nitrogen excretion by species of *Mytilus* (Bivalvia : Mollusca). *Journal of the Marine Biological Association of the United Kingdom* 57:355–69.
Bayne, B.L., Thompson, R.J. and Widdows, J. 1976a. Physiology I. In *Marine Mussels : Their Ecology and Physiology* (ed. B.L. Bayne), 121–206. Cambridge: Cambridge University Press.
Bayne, B.L., Widdows, J. and Thompson, R.J. 1976b. Physiology II. In *Marine Mussels : Their Ecology and Physiology* (ed. B.L. Bayne), 207–60. Cambridge: Cambridge University Press.
Chan, H.M. 1988. A survey of trace metals in *Perna viridis* (L.)(Bivalvia: Mytilacea) from the coastal waters of Hong Kong. *Asian Marine Biology* 5:89–102.
Cheung, S.G. 1990. An energy budget for *Perna viridis* (Linnaeus) (Bivalvia: Mytilidae) in Hong Kong. Ph.D. Thesis. The University of Hong Kong.
Davenport, J. 1983. A comparison of some aspects of the behaviour and physiology of the Indian mussel *Perna (=Mytilus) viridis* and the common mussel *Mytilus edulis* L. *Journal of Molluscan Studies* 49:21–6.
Environmental Protection Department. 1988. *Marine Water Quality in Hong Kong*. Environmental Protection Department, Hong Kong Government.
Hawkins, A.J.S., Menon, N.R., Damodaran, R. and Bayne, B.L. 1987. Metabolic responses of the mussels *Perna viridis* and *Perna indica* to declining oxygen tension at different salinities. *Comparative Biochemistry and Physiology*. 88A. No.4:691–94.
Henry, P.R., Magnum, C.P. and Webb, K.L. 1980. Salt and water balance in the oligohaline clam, *Rangia cuneata*. II. Accumulation of intracellular free amino acids during high salinity adaptation. *Journal of Experimental Zoology* 211:11–24.
Lam, V.M.M. 1987. *The Tap Shek Kok Power Plant, Hong Kong. A Marine Environmental Impact Assessment*. Ph.D Thesis, University of Hong Kong.
Lee, S.Y. 1986. Growth and reproduction of the green mussel *Perna viridis* (L.) (Bivalvia : Mytilacea) in contrasting environments in Hong Kong. *Asian Marine Biology* 3:111–27.
Mak, P.M.S. 1982. *Biofouling of Mariculture Cages*. Ph.D. Thesis, University of Hong Kong.
Mathew, R. and Menon, N.R. 1983. Oxygen consumption in tropical bivalves *Perna viridis* (Linn.) and *Meretrix casta* (Chem.) exposed to heavy metals. *Indian Journal of Marine Sciences* 12:57–9.
Morton, B. 1982. An introduction to Hong Kong's marine environment with special reference to the north-eastern New Territories. In *Proceedings of the First International Marine Biological Workshop: The Marine Flora and Fauna of Hong Kong and Southern China, Hong Kong, 1980* (ed. B. Morton and C.K. Tseng), 25–35. Hong Kong: Hong Kong University Press.
Morton, B. and Wu, R.S.S. 1975. The hydrology of the coastal waters of Hong Kong. *Environmental Research* 10:319–47.
Nagabhushanam, R. and Mane, U.H. 1978. Seasonal variation in the biochemical composition of *Mytilus viridis* at Ratnagiri on the west coast of India. *Hydrobiologia* 57:69–72.
Newell, R.C. 1973. Environmental factors affecting the acclimatory responses of ectotherms. In *Effect of Temperature on Ectothermic Organisms* (ed. W. Wieser), 151–64. Berlin: Springer-Verlag.
Newell, R.C. 1979. *Biology of Intertidal Organisms*. Faversham: Marine Ecological Surveys Ltd.
Packard, G.C. and Boardman, T.S. 1987. The misuse of ratios to scale physiological data that vary allometrically with body size. In *New Directions in Ecological Physiology*. (ed. M.E.

Feder, A.F. Bennett, W.W. Burggren and R.B. Huey), 216–39. Cambridge: Cambridge University Press.

Parsons, T.R., Maita, Y. and Lalli, C.M. 1984. *A Manual of Chemical and Biological Methods for Sea Water Analysis*. Oxford: Pergamon Press.

Prosser, C.J. 1955. Physiological variation in animals. *Biological Reviews* 30:229–62.

Remane, A. and Schlieper, C. 1971. *Biology of Brackish Water*. New York: Wiley-Interscience.

Shafee, M.S. 1976. Effect of salinity and time of exposure to air on the metabolism of the green mussel, *Mytilus viridis*. *Indian Journal of Marine Sciences* 5:130–2.

Tedengren, M. and Kautsky, N. 1986. Comparative study of the physiology and its probable effect on size in blue mussels (*Mytilus edulis* L.) from the North Sea and the Northern Baltic Proper. *Ophelia* 25:147–55.

Thompson, R.J. and Newell, R.I.E. 1985. Physiological responses to temperature in two latitudinally separated populations of the mussel, *Mytilus edulis*. In *Proceedings of the Nineteen European Marine Biology Symposium*, 481–95

Vernberg, F.J., Schlieper, C. and Schneider, D.E. 1963. The influence of temperature and salinity on ciliary activity of excised gill tissue of molluscs from North Carolina. *Comparative Biochemistry and Physiology* 8:271–85.

Widdows, J. 1978a. Combined effects of body size, food concentration and seston on the physiology of *Mytilus edulis*. *Journal of the Marine Biological Association of the United Kingdom* 58:109–24.

Widdows, J. 1978b. Physiological indices of stress in *Mytilus edulis*. *Journal of the Marine Biological Association of the United Kingdom* 58:125–42.

Widdows, J. and Bayne, B.L. 1971. Temperature acclimation of *Mytilus edulis* with reference to its energy budget. *Journal of the Marine Biological Association of the United Kingdom* 51:827–43.

Widdows, J., Phelps, D.K. and Galloway, W. 1981. Measurement of physiological conditon of mussels transplanted along a pollution gradient in Narragansett Bay. *Marine Environmental Research* 4:181–94.

Worrall, C.M. and Widdows, J. 1983. Physiological changes following transplantation of the bivalve *Scrobicularia plana* between three populations. *Marine Ecology Progress Series* 12:281–7.

Worrall, C.M., Widdows, J. and Lowe, D.M. 1983. Physiological ecology of three populations of the bivalve *Scrobicularia plana*. *Marine Ecology Progress Series* 12:267–79.

Wu, R.S.S. 1988. Marine pollution in Hong Kong: a review. *Asian Marine Biology* 5:1–23.

EFFECTS OF REDUCED SALINITIES ON *HOLOTHURIA LEUCOSPILOTA* BRANDT AND *POLYCHEIRA RUFESCENS* BRANDT (ECHINODERMATA: HOLOTHUROIDEA) IN HONG KONG

Rosita G. Ong Che

Department of Zoology, The University of Hong Kong, Hong Kong

ABSTRACT

The effects of reduced salinities on *Holothuria leucospilota* Brandt and *Polycheira rufescens* Brandt (Echinodermata: Holothuroidea) co-occurring on many Hong Kong beaches were studied. The tolerance range for *H. leucospilota* extended to 25‰ over a 28-day exposure period in contrast to 15‰ for *P. rufescens*. The critical salinities in which 100% mortality was recorded after eight to twelve days of exposure was 15‰ for *H. leucospilota* and 5‰ for *P. rufescens*. The 50% lethal time (LT_{50}) at these critical salinities was estimated to be six and nine days for *H. leucospilota* and *P. rufescens*, respectively. At 20‰, gravid individuals of *H. leucospilota* succumbed by day 9 suggesting that at this salinity, this species is not reproductively viable.

Activity, measured in terms of righting time, for overturned *Holothuria leucospilota*, was not significantly affected by a salinity reduction to 25‰ after 28 days. At 20‰, activity deterioration was observed after fourteen days. Activity, measured as distance moved·unit time^{-1}, for *Polycheira rufescens* was normal over salinities as low as 15‰. Activity was, however, significantly reduced at 10‰ after exposure for one day. Activity of *P. rufescens* deteriorated with increasing exposure time at all salinities tested.

Coelomic fluid osmolality of *Holothuria leucospilota* followed that of seawater in the tested range of 15–35‰. *Polycheira rufescens* is an osmoconformer at salinities between 5–35‰. Coelomic fluid volume was regulated by *H. leucospilota* and *P. rufescens* at 25 and 15‰, respectively. At their respective critical salinities, both holothurians regulated coelomic fluid volume by body wall dampening for one day only, succumbing thereafter.

INTRODUCTION

Echinoderms have been regarded as an exclusively marine stenohaline group which can tolerate little change in ambient salinity. The reasons given for this are the lack of an excretory organ (Binyon 1972) and poor osmo- and ion regulatory ability (Binyon 1972; Prosser 1973a, b). Negative effects of reduced salinities on field and laboratory populations (Kinne 1971; Stickle and Diehl 1987) include the slower developmental rates of echinoid and asteroid larvae (Greenwood and Bennett 1981; Roller and Stickle 1985), lower survival, activity, feeding, growth, absorption efficiency (Shirley and Stickle 1982a, b) and dwarfism as was observed for a population of *Ophiothrix angulata* population from the estuarine Cedar Key, Florida, as compared with a population from the oceanic North Inlet, South Carolina (Stancyk and Shaffer 1977).

Records of natural populations in habitats with low or fluctuating salinities are challenging the concept of the stenohaline echinoderm. Binyon (1966, 1972) listed 22 species of asteroids, ophiuroids, echinoids and holothuroids which occur in brackish waters. Most of these records are from the Baltic and Black Seas, where seawater dilution has taken place over several geological epochs, thus allowing for a long process of acclimatization. Euryhaline asteroids have been reported from habitats subject to short-term salinity fluctuations during seasonal periods of maximum freshwater discharge (Pearse 1967; Lawrence 1973; Ellington and Lawrence 1974; Stickle and Denoux 1976; Drouin *et al.* 1985; Watts and Lawrence 1986). Ophiuroids have penetrated successfully the brackish waters of Scottish sea lochs (Pagett 1980, 1981, 1982).

Few studies have been undertaken on the effects of reduced salinities on holothurians. Organismal responses to low salinity have been reported upon for *Eupentacta quinquesemita* and *Opheodesoma spectabilis* (Freeman 1966; Sabourin and Stickle 1981). Cleland and Ong Che (1990) investigated the freshwater tolerance of *Polycheira rufescens* as an adaptation to intertidal life. Studies on five other holothurian species provide data on ionic, osmotic and volume regulation (Stickle and Ahokas 1974; Zanders and Herrera 1974; Madrid *et al.* 1976; Stickle and Denoux 1976; Robertson 1980; Herrera and Plaza 1981; Herrera and Lopez 1983; Jurisic *et al.* 1983). Whether or not holothurians and echinoderms in general are capable of regulating coelomic fluid volume is an unsettled question.

Holothuria leucospilota Brandt and *Polycheira rufescens* Brandt are two holothurian species common on Hong Kong shores. Both co-occur at the beaches of Cape d'Aguilar, Tai Tam, Chung Hum Kok and Stanley on Hong Kong Island and at Sheung Sze Wan, Clearwater Bay, Pak Sha Wan and Hoi Sing Wan on the Sai King and Clearwater Bay Peninsulas. *P. rufescens* is restricted to the intertidal zone, with maximum abundance occurring at 1.5 m above chart datum (Ong Che 1988). *H. leucospilota* is a subtidal species, extending from chart datum to depths of 15 m (Clark 1982).

As an intertidal species, *Polycheira rufescens* is often subject to reduced salinities from freshwater runoff and summer rains. Such hyposmotic stress would be modulated by tidal mixing for the subtidal *Holothuria leucospilota*. This investigation deals with the responses of these two holothurians to reduced salinity as one factor affecting their different distribution. It is hoped that the information obtained in this study can also add to the present pool of data regarding the degree to which some echinoderm species are euryhaline.

MATERIALS AND METHODS

Specimens of *Holothuria leucospilota* and *Polycheira rufescens* were collected from Cape d'Aguilar and Sheung Sze Wan. All animals were maintained in running seawater aquaria ($23 \pm 1°C$, $34 \pm 1‰$) and were used in experiments one week after capture.

Survival

The survival by *Holothuria leucospilota* and *Polycheira rufescens* experiencing extended exposure (28 days) to decreased salinities was studied. Salinity was reduced, with distilled water, by 5‰·day^{-1} until final salinities were reached. Test salinities were 30, 25, 20 and 15‰ for *H. leucospilota* and 30, 25, 15, 10 and 5 ‰for *P. rufescens*. Two replicates were run using 5 and 10 animals·test salinity^{-1}·replicate^{-1} for *H. leucospilota* and *P. rufescens*, respectively. Temperature during the experiments was 23 ± 1°C. Experiments were started after one day acclimation in the test solutions. Mortalities determined by evisceration were recorded daily. Test solutions were changed every three days or each time a mortality was recorded. The 50% lethal time at each test salinity was estimated by the straight-line graphical interpolation method (American Public Health Association 1989).

Whole animal activity

An activity coefficient was used to indicate the functional well-being of the animals acclimated to different salinities. The activity coefficient for *Holothuria leucospilota* was expressed in terms of righting time. Righting is a basic reflex of echinoderms which involves considerable neuromuscular coordination (Reese 1966) and is calculated as the ratio of 1000 divided by the time (in seconds) taken to right itself (Ellington and Lawrence 1974). Since the apodous *Polycheira rufescens* lacks a ventral sole, the activity coefficient was measured as crawling capacity, i.e., the distance (in mm) travelled·unit time^{-1}. *P. rufescens* is negatively phototactic (Cleland and Ong Che 1990) so that when it is exposed on a tray, it immediately starts to move, seeking shade.

The activities of five individuals·test solution^{-1}·species^{-1} were recorded after 1, 7, 14 and 21 days' exposure to each of the test salinities. Experiments were run at 21 ± 1°C. Animals were not fed during the period of exposure. Data were analysed using a two-way Analysis of Variance and an *a posteriori* Student Newman Keuls multiple comparison test.

Coelomic fluid volume regulation

Coelomic fluid volume regulation was studied by following the course of body weight changes of 15 *Holothuria leucospilota* and 15 *Polycheira rufescens* directly transferred to and kept at low salinities for nine days. Weight changes were expressed as a percentage of the initial weight. Two salinities were used, one within the tolerance range i.e., wherein 100% survival was observed after 28 days, and another in the critical range, i.e., wherein 50% mortality was recorded after seven days. These salinities corresponded to 15 and 5‰ for *P. rufescens* and 25 and 15‰ for *H. leucospilota*, respectively. Differences in weight were tested by Analysis of Variance and an *a posteriori* multiple comparison test using body weights at the start of the experiment (time 0) as the control.

Osmotic regulation

Following stepwise dilution of salinity (5‰·day^{-1}) and acclimation at 21 ± 2°C for two days in the final salinities, holothurians were blotted dry and the coelomic fluid collected from a dorsal incision on the body wall. Coelomic fluid and seawater samples were analysed using a Fiske osmometer. Coelomic fluid osmolalities of five *Holothuria leucospilota* and five *Polycheira rufescens* at each test salinity were measured.

RESULTS

Survival

Results of the survival experiments on *Holothuria leucospilota* and *Polycheira rufescens* during extended exposure to decreased salinities and the estimated 50% lethal time (LT_{50}) at each salinity are presented in Table 1. No mortalities were recorded for *P. rufescens* at 35, 30, 25 and 15‰ over the 28 day period of exposure. At 10‰, *P. rufescens* survived without apparent damage for 21 days. Longer exposure resulted in 80% mortality. At 5‰, all test individuals succumbed by day 12.

In contrast, *Holothuria leucospilota* could only tolerate salinities as low as 25‰ for 28 days. At 20‰, 80% of the animals had succumbed by the end of the experiment in one replicate while only 20% mortality was recorded in the other replicate. Interestingly, these mortalities were all of gravid individuals, suggesting that they are more susceptible to the lethal effects of low salinity and that *H. leucospilota*, in this salinity, is not reproductively viable. At 15‰, mortality reached 100% by day 12.

The 50% lethal time at the critical salinities was estimated to be between 5 to 7 days for *H. leucospilota* at 15‰ and 9 to 10 days for *P. rufescens* at 5‰.

Whole animal activity

No activity was recorded for *Holothuria leucospilota* and *Polycheira rufescens* at 15 and 5‰, respectively. Individuals in these salinities were too swollen for movement. When transferred to their respective critical salinities, individuals of both species contracted body walls and constricted anal and oral openings to form a protective barrier and to reduce surface area for osmosis. The podia of *H. leucospilota* were also retracted. This physical resistance to hyposmotic stress was not, however, able to contain osmosis so that individuals in these salinities eventually became bloated, floating lightly at the bottom of the tank, instead of attaching to the substratum as under normal conditions.

Figure 1A shows the activity coefficients (mean ± 1 SEM) of *Holothuria leucospilota* exposed to different salinities for 28 days. Table 2 presents the two-way Analysis of Variance and the Student Newman Keuls multiple comparison test on the data. Both salinity and exposure time affected activity patterns of *H. leucospilota* significantly. Salinity-time combinations also differed significantly. Righting time of *H. leucospilota* exposed to a salinity of 20‰ was significantly different from that of individuals exposed to 25, 30 and 35‰. At 20‰, animals took more than 15 minutes to right themselves, in contrast, to the average time of 1–2 minutes taken by individuals maintained at higher salinities. Prolonged exposure to 20‰ (>14 days), resulted in a further decline in activity.

In contrast, activity coefficients (mean ± 1 SEM) for *Polycheira rufescens* exposed to different salinities show a severe impairment at 10‰ from the first day of exposure. The crawling capacity of *P. rufescens* at 30, 25 and 10‰ showed a decreasing trend,

Table 1
Cumulative percentage mortality of *Polycheira rufescens* and *Holothuria leucospilota* exposed to low salinities for 28 days and the estimated 50% lethal time (LT_{50}).

Salinity ‰ Replicate	1	2	3	4	5	6	7	8	9	10	11	12	13	14	15	16	17	18	19	20	21	22	23	24	25	26	27	28	LT_{50}
P. rufescens																													
A																													
B																													
A																													
B																													
A																													
B																													
A																													
B																													
A																							30	40			80	25.0
B																					10				60	80			24.5
A							10			20	80	90	100																9.5
B											60	80	100																9.3
H. leucospilota																													
A																													
B																													
A																													
B																													
A																													
B																													
A							20																						21.5
B			20							60	80																		7.2
A	20				40					100																			5.8
B				20			60		80		100																		6.5

indicating deteriorating physiological fitness with increasing exposure time. Salinity and exposure time affected activity of *P. rufescens* significantly but the interaction between salinity and time was not significant because a similar pattern of lowered activity with prolonged exposure was observed at most salinities. Results of the Student Newman Keuls test indicate that the responses of *P. rufescens* at salinities of 10, 15, and 25‰ were significantly below the normal activity level observed at 30 and 35‰ (Fig. 1B, Table 3).

Coelomic fluid volume regulation

Figure 2A shows the time course of weight changes demonstrated by *Polycheira rufescens* exposed to salinities of 15 and 5‰ for 9 days. Within the tolerated range (15‰), body weights showed an overall increasing trend, ranging from 104% to 140% of initial weights, but with loss of weight at intervals. In the critical salinity (5‰), body weights increased steadily from day 1 to day 4 reaching a peak of 149%. Thereafter,

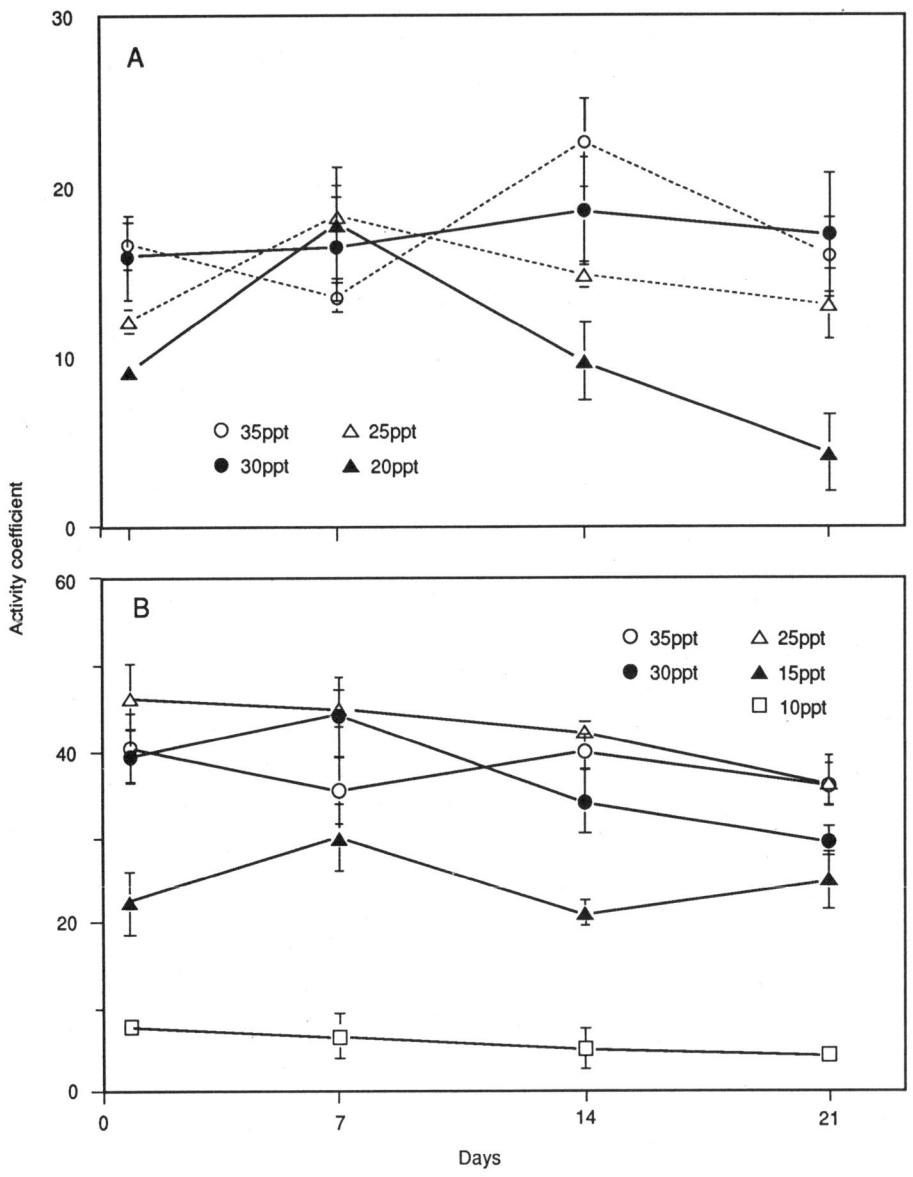

Fig. 1. Time course of changes in activity coefficients of holothurians maintained at different salinities. Points represent means ± 1 SEM. A. *Holothuria leucospilota*. Activity was expressed as the ratio of 1000 divided by righting time in seconds. B. *Polycheira rufescens*. Activity was measured as distance in mm travelled·unit time^{-1}.

weights declined until the end of the experimental period. Differences in weight recorded during the experimental period were not significant at the two tested salinities (Table 4).

Table 2
Analysis of Variance and Student Newman Keuls multiple comparison test on righting time of *Holothuria leucospilota* exposed to different salinities.

A. Analysis of Variance

Source of Variation	SS	DF	MS	F
Main Effects	722.59	6	128.76	5.30 ***
Time	206.92	3	68.98	2.84 *
Salinity	546.02	3	182.01	7.49 ***
Two-way Interactions	522.82	9	58.09	2.39 *
Time Salinity	522.82	9	58.09	2.39 *
Explained	1295.40	15	86.36	3.55 *
Residual	1458.34	60	24.31	
Total	2753.74	75	36.72	

B. Student Newman Keuls Test

Mean	Group	20‰	25‰	30‰	35‰
10.20	20‰				
14.59	25‰	*			
17.02	30‰	*			
17.18	35‰	*			

Table 3
Analysis of Variance and Student Newman Keuls multiple comparison test on crawling capacity of *Polycheira rufescens* exposed to different salinities.

A. Analysis of Variance

Source of Variation	SS	DF	MS	F
Main Effects	17956.84	7	2565.26	58.68 ***
Salinity	17305.11	4	4326.28	98.97 ***
Time	651.72	3	217.24	4.97 **
Two-way Interactions	709.30	12	59.11	1.35 n.s.
Salinity Time	709.30	12	59.11	1.35 n.s.
Explained	18666.14	19	982.43	22.47 ***
Residual	3497.13	80	43.71	
Total	22163.26	99	223.87	

B. Student Newman Keuls Test

Mean	Group	10‰	15‰	30‰	35‰	25‰
5.97	10‰					
24.47	15‰	*				
36.59	30‰	*	*			
37.88	35‰	*	*			
42.38	25‰	*	*	*		

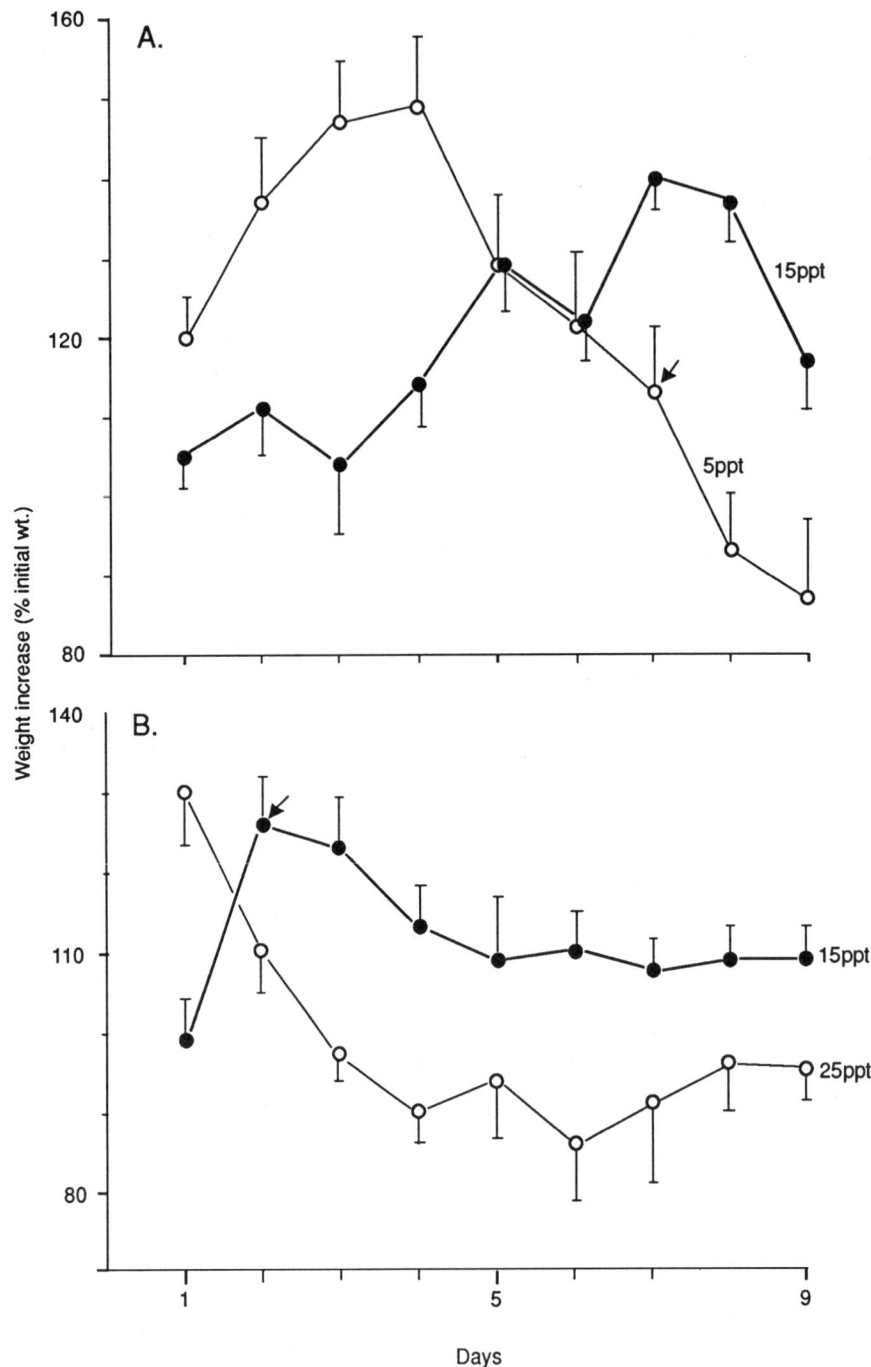

Fig. 2. Time course of body weight changes (expressed as percentage of the initial whole animal weights) of holothurians transferred from full strength sea water to lower salinities. Points represent means ± 1 SEM. Arrows indicate the first observed mortality. A. *Polycheira rufescens*; B. *Holothuria leucospilota*.

Table 4
Analysis of Variance on weight changes over time of *Polycheira rufescens* exposed to salinities within the tolerance (15‰) and critical (5‰) ranges.

A. 15‰

Source of Variation	DF	SS	MS	F
Between Groups	8	29.64	3.70	0.46 n.s.
Within Groups	126	1023.23	8.12	
Total	134	1052.87		

B. 5‰

Source of Variation	DF	SS	MS	F
Between Groups	8	119.71	14.96	1.33 n.s.
Within Groups	126	1416.95	11.24	
Total	134	1536.66		

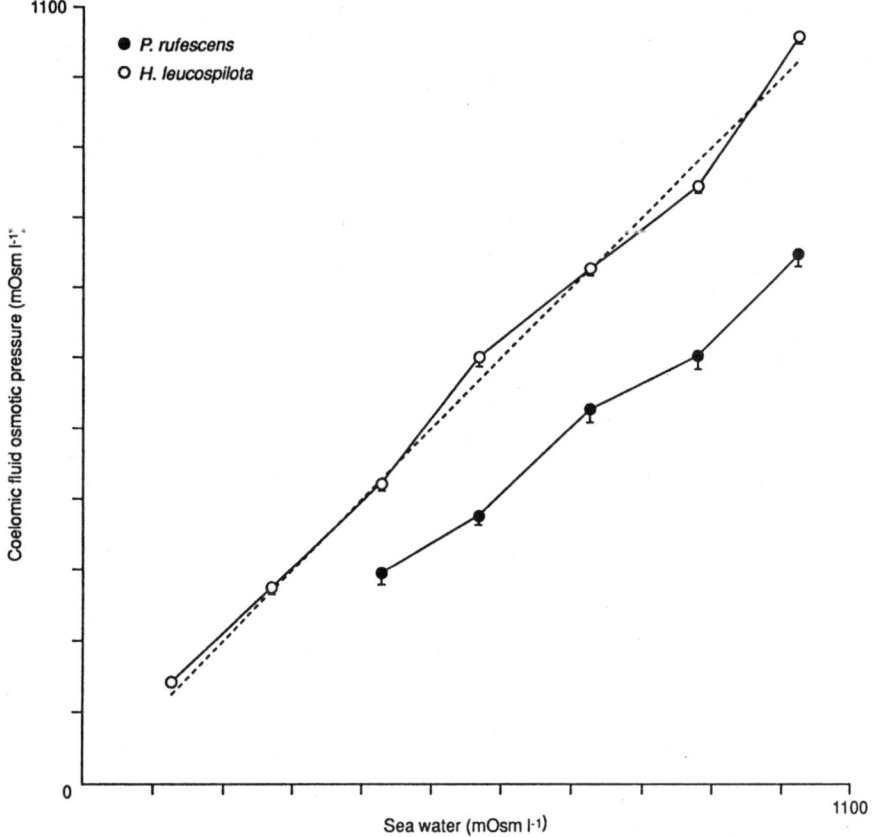

Fig. 3. Coelomic fluid milliosmolality (means ± 1 SEM) of *Holothuria leucospilota* and *Polycheira rufescens* at different salinities. Isosmoticity is represented by the broken line.

Body weight changes of *Holothuria leucospilota* are presented in Figure 2B. In the tolerated range (25‰), *H. leucospilota* did not show signs of hyposmotic stress. The podia and tentacles were extended and the animals attached firmly to the substratum. At this salinity, *H. leucospilota* body weights increased up to 130% after one day due to passive diffusion of water across the body wall. After day one, weights decreased until an equilibrium was reached by day four whereupon wet weights fluctuated between 86% and 96 % of initial weights. Analysis of Variance and *a posteriori* multiple range tests show that weight differences were largely insignificant and only weights at time one were significantly different from the control (time 0) (Table 5A).

At the critical salinity (15‰), body weights of *Holothuria leucospilota* did not increase after one day. The behavioural response to this dilution was to protect internal tissues from osmotic shock by closing all openings, thereby, minimizing surface exchange. This physical resistance to hyposmotic stress contained water influx for only one day. By day two, body weights increased to 126%. Thereafter, a decrease in body weight was recorded but initial levels were still not reached at the end of nine days. Analysis of Variance shows that weight changes were not significant (Table 5B).

Table 5

Analysis of Variance and *a posteriori* Student Newman Keuls multiple range test of weight changes over time of *Holothuria leucospilota* exposed to salinities within the tolerance (25‰) and critical (15‰) ranges.

A. 25‰

Analysis of Variance

Source of Variation	DF	SS	MS	F	
Between groups	8	85054.27	10631.78	2.37	*
Within groups	96	430694.81	4486.40		
Total	104	515749.08			

Student Newman Keuls Test

Mean	Time	0	1	2	3	4	5	6	7	8	9
134	0										
180	1	*									
150	2										
130	3										
121	4										
126	5										
115	6										
122	7										
129	8										
127	9										

B. 15‰

Analysis of Variance

Source of Variation	DF	SS	MS	F	
Between Groups	7	25228.04	3604.01	0.561	n.s.
Within Groups	69	442939.34	6419.41		
Total	76	468167.38			

Osmotic regulation

Milliosmolality of the coelomic fluid of *Holothuria leucospilota* was lower than that of seawater, but followed changes in the external salinity over the tested range of 15–35‰. Coelomic fluid osmolality of *Polycheira rufescens* similarly conformed to ambient salinities in the range of 5–35‰ (Fig. 3).

DISCUSSION

Holothuria leucospilota and *Polycheira rufescens* occupy Hong Kong shores at different tidal levels and have widely different responses to changes in their osmotic environment. *H. leucospilota* tolerates a narrow range of salinities (25–35‰) while *P. rufescens* can withstand salinities down to 15‰ for 28 days. Negative effects of low salinity for *H. leucospilota* were observed at 20‰ in which righting time, and thus physiological fitness, deteriorated after 14 days' exposure. Mortality of gravid individuals at 20‰ further indicate that *H. leucospilota* is not reproductively viable in this salinity. In contrast, adverse effects of reduced salinity were recorded for *P. rufescens* at 10‰ wherein activity was impaired from day one onwards, with death ensuing after 21 days' exposure. The LT_{50} values for *H. leucospilota* and *P. rufescens* at their respective critical salinities (15 and 5‰) were day 6 and day 9, respectively.

Many studies have shown that the vertical distribution of a species on the shore is affected by the range of salinity it can tolerate (Newell 1979). On proceeding from high to low water marks, there is an increase in the range, rate and duration of salinity fluctuation so that, lower down the shore, animals are exposed to higher salinities for longer periods. The present results showing greater euryhalinity for the higher-zoned *Polycheira rufescens*, as compared with the subtidal *Holothuria leucospilota*, are consistent with these observations.

Shumway (1977a, b) noted that the lower lethal limit of asteroids and bivalve molluscs could be reduced if the animals were exposed to fluctuating rather than constantly low salinities. Similar conclusions may be deduced from reports of euryhaline species occurring in areas subject to seasonal or tidal fluctuations in salinity such as estuarine systems, shallow coastal waters and habitats affected by glacial meltwater (Freeman 1966; Pearse 1967; Stickle and Denoux 1976; Stancyk and Shaffer 1977; Pagett 1980; Diehl and Lawrence 1984; Himmelman *et al.* 1984). The intertidal *Polycheira rufescens* experiencing freshwater exposure from rains during the ebb tide similarly shows a reduced lower lethal limit, as compared with the subtidal *Holothuria leucospilota* which is immersed constantly in higher salinity seawater.

Of the 26 studies on echinoderm salinity tolerance listed in the review of this subject by Stickle and Diehl (1987), only one was of a holothurian. The lowest limit thus far recorded for echinoderms were those of the holothuroid *Eupentacta quinquesemita* (12–13‰) (Stickle, unpublished data), the ophiuroid *Ophiophragmus filograneus* (10‰) (Turner and Meyer 1980), the asteroid *Leptasterias hexactis* (13‰) (Shirley and Stickle 1982a) and the echinoid *Strongylocentrotus droebachiensis* (13‰) (Sabourin and Stickle 1981). The salinity tolerance of *Polycheira rufescens* is comparable with these euryhaline echinoderms.

In their critical salinities, both *Polycheira rufescens* and *Holothuria leucospilota* resist changes in salinity by the 'dampening effect of the body wall,' i.e., by contracting the body wall, closing tightly the oral and anal openings and, in the case of *H. leucospilota*, retracting the podia. By these behavioural responses, holothurians reduce the area and permeability of the exchange surface, thus retarding the diffusive gain of water and loss of ions, and protecting the internal tissues from osmotic shock. Such a dampening effect has also been observed in the polychaete *Nereis diversicolor* (Wells and Ledingham 1940) and is similar to the shell closing mechanism of some molluscs when placed in diluted media (Davenport 1985). Both the body wall dampening of holothurians and the shell closing mechanism of molluscs can help the animals for short periods only. By body wall dampening, *H. leucospilota* and *P. rufescens* resisted salinity changes and maintained coelomic fluid volume at 100% and 120%, respectively, for one day. In the normal, local ecological context of semi-diurnal or diurnal tidal regimes, such resistance would be more than sufficient, during low salinity stress at ebb tide, to resist osmotic change. It may be energetically more economical than active compensatory absorption of ions from the medium and may further be more effective when extreme conditions call for an immediate defensive response. Further, the present observations indicate the inability of *H. leucospilota* and *P. rufescens* to penetrate and colonize brackish waters at their respective critical salinities. Low salinities would trigger the body wall dampening stress reaction. This, on a prolonged basis, would lead to death, since feeding, gaseous exchange and other vital functions associated with cloacal pumping and renewal of the coelomic fluid, would be impaired.

Early studies reported a volume regulatory ability for *Asterias rubens* when placed in diluted seawater (Bethe 1934; Malouf 1938 — both cited in Binyon 1972). Binyon (1961), however, obtained contrary results. Binyon (1972) suggested that earlier reports of volume regulation in *A. rubens* could have been affected by coelomic fluid loss from mechanical damage during weighing. Careful handling of the asteroid *Luidia clathrata*, however, demonstrated some degree of coelomic fluid volume regulation (Ellington and Lawrence 1974). Lange (1964) reported coelomic fluid volume regulation in the echinoid *Strongylocentrotus droebachiensis* but this was not observed in *S. purpuratus* by Giese and Farmanfarmaian (1963).

The present study shows that within the tolerated range (25‰), *Holothuria leucospilota* does not regulate coelomic fluid volume until a critical volume (about 130% of initial weight) is reached. The difference in weight between time 0 (control) and time 1 when the critical volume was attained was significant. The normal behaviour, activity and 100% survival of *H. leucospilota* upon initial exposure to 25‰ are clear indications that this dilution falls within an acceptable range. Prolonged exposure or the approach of a critical volume (with the consequent critical dilution to coelomic fluid osmolality) appeared to trigger the osmoregulatory mechanism, so that body weights gradually returned to initial levels. Regulation also occurs in *P. rufescens* during exposure to the tolerated salinity (15‰), as shown by the alternating pattern of weight gain and loss, indicating that water initially gained on exposure to a dilute medium was being expelled from the body by some regulatory process. The increasing trend of weight changes, however, may indicate that regulation was either at a growing cost to the organism or that the range of volume tolerated was wide.

Pearse (1967) reported seasonal fluctuations in body weight of the Antarctic asteroid *Odontaster validus*. Individuals of *O. validus* exposed to 50% seawater regulated coelomic water volume with a striking periodicity of ten days. The fluctuations in wet weight of *Holothuria leucospilota* and *Polycheira rufescens* recorded during this study, when the animals were exposed to reduced salinities within their tolerated ranges, may be the result of natural oscillations. Volume decrease is probably associated with ion loss to the medium, to control osmotic gain of water, and volume increase with active ion absorption from the medium to replenish ion stores.

At critical salinities, no coelomic fluid volume regulation occurred and body weights increased to a peak and thereafter declined. The mortalities recorded in these salinities during the first week of exposure indicate breakdown of the regulatory mechanism. Body weight losses observed at these salinities probably result from the loss of body wall integrity due to cell disruption. The onset of weight decrease approximated the time of first mortality recorded in the survival experiments. Imminence of death could also be noted from the loss of pigmentation and of turgescence.

Both *Holothuria leucospilota* and *Polycheira rufescens* are osmoconformers within the tested salinities of 15–35 and 5–35‰, respectively. Decreasing osmolality of the coelomic fluid when in dilute seawater, however, subjects the tissues to hyposmotic stress. This suggests that the internal tissues of these holothurians must have either a precise mechanism for volume regulation over these ranges or a strong degree of tolerance to changes in coelomic fluid concentration, or both. Cells of respiratory tree tissues of *Holothuria glaberrima* exposed to seawater in which sodium was isosmotically reduced showed increasing loss of sodium, potassium and chloride in a solution isosmotic to the external medium (Herrera and Lopez 1983). Water and ion fluxes in *H. leucospilota* and *P. rufescens* subjected to depressed salinities need to be further studied. Which inorganic ions and/or organic molecules serve as osmotic effectors and how exactly intracellullar regulation, if such exists in these two holothurians, functions are further questions that require clarification.

The different salinity tolerances, as measured by survival and activity, explain in part how *Holothuria leucospilota* and *Polycheira rufescens* occupy different components of the same habitat.

ACKNOWLEDGEMENT

I acknowledge with thanks the comments and suggestions by an anonymous referee of this paper.

REFERENCES

American Public Health Association, 1989. *Standard Methods for the Examination of Water and Waste Water*. Washington, D.C.: American Public Health Association.
Binyon, J. 1961. Salinity tolerance and permeability to water of the starfish *Asterias rubens L. Journal of the Marine Biological Association of the United Kingdom* 41:161–74.
Binyon, J. 1966. Salinity tolerance and ionic regulation. In *Physiology of Echinodermata* (ed. R.A. Boolootian), 359–77. New York: Interscience.
Binyon, J. 1972. *Physiology of Echinoderms*. London: Pergamon Press.
Clark, A.M. 1982. Echinoderms of Hong Kong. In *Proceedings of the First International Marine Biological Workshop: The Marine Flora and Fauna of Hong Kong and Southern China, Hong Kong, 1980* (ed. B. Morton and C.K. Tseng), 485–501. Hong Kong: Hong Kong University Press.

Cleland, J.D. and Ong Che, R.G. 1990. The physiological ecology of the intertidal holothurian *Polycheira rufescens*. In *Proceedings of the Second International Marine Biological Workshop: The Flora and Fauna of Hong Kong and Southern China, Hong Kong, 1986* (ed. B. Morton), 1191–1200. Hong Kong: Hong Kong University Press.

Davenport, J. 1985. *Environmental Stress and Behavioural Adaptation*. London and Sydney: Croom Helm.

Diehl, W.J. and Lawrence, J.M. 1984. The effect of salinity on coelomic fluid osmolyte concentration and intracellullar water content in *Luidia clathrata* (Say) (Echinodermata: Asteroidea). *Comparative Biochemistry and Physiology* 79A:119–26.

Drouin, G., Himmelman, J.H. and Beland, P. 1985. Impact of tidal salinity fluctuations on echinoderm and mollusc populations. *Canadian Journal of Zoology* 63:1377–87.

Ellington, W.R. and Lawrence, J.M. 1974. Coelomic fluid volume regulation and isosmotic intracellullar regulation by *Luidia clathrata* (Echinodermata: Asteroidea) in response to hyposmotic stress. *Biological Bulletin* 146:20–31.

Freeman, P.J. 1966. Observations on osmotic relationships in the holothurian *Opheodesoma spectabilis*. *Pacific Science* 22:60–9.

Giese, A.C. and Farmanfarmaian, A. 1963. Resistance of the purple sea urchin to osmotic stress. *Biological Bulletin* 124:182–92.

Greenwood, P.J. and Bennett, T. 1981. Some effects of temperature-salinity combinations on the early development of the sea urchin *Parechinus angulosus* (Leske). I. Fertilization. *Journal of Experimental Marine Biology and Ecology* 51:119–31.

Herrera, F.C. and Plaza, M. 1981. The role of extracellullar sodium on isosmotic intracellullar regulation in the respiratory tree of *Holothuria glaberrima*. *Comparative Biochemistry and Physiology* 68A:373–82.

Herrera, F.C. and Lopez, I. 1983. Relationship between external sodium concentration and intracellullar osmotic effectors in respiratory tree of *Holothuria glaberrima*. *Comparative Biochemistry and Physiology* 68A:373–82.

Himmelman, J.H., Guderley, H., Vigneault, G., Drouin, G. and Wells, P.G. 1984. Response of the sea urchin *Strongylocentrotus droebachiensis* to reduced salinities: importance of size, acclimation and interpopulation differences. *Canadian Journal of Zoology* 62:1015–21.

Jurisic, M., Roque, S., Lopez, I. and Herrera, F.C. 1983. Role of chloride in isosmotic intracellullar regulation in *Holothuria glaberrima*. *Comparative Biochemistry and Physiology* 76A:831–7.

Kinne, O. 1971. Salinity: animals: invertebrates. In *Marine Ecology. Environmental Factors*. Part 2, Vol. 1. (ed. O. Kinne), 821–995. New York: Wiley.

Lange, R. 1964. The osmotic adjustment in the echinoderm, *Strongylocentrotus droebachiensis*. *Comparative Biochemistry and Physiology* 13:205–16.

Lawrence, J.M. 1973. Level, content and caloric equivalent of the lipid, carbohydrate and protein in the body components of *Luidia clathrata* (Echinodermata: Asteroidea) in Tampa Bay. *Journal of Experimental Marine Biology and Ecology* 11:263–74.

Madrid, E., Zanders, I.P. and Herrera, F.C. 1976. Changes in the coelomic fluid and intracellullar ionic composition in holothurians exposed to diverse seawater concentrations. *Comparative Biochemistry and Physiology* 54A:167–74.

Newell, R.C. 1979. *Biology of Intertidal Animals*. Kent: Marine Ecology Surveys.

Ong Che, R.G. 1988. The energy budget of *Holothuria leucospilota* Brandt and a respiratory strategy comparison with *Polycheira rufescens* Brandt. University of Hong Kong, Ph.D. thesis.

Pagett, R.M. 1980. Tolerance to brackish water by ophiuroids with special reference to a Scottish sea loch, Loch Etive. In *Echinoderms: Past and Present* (ed. M. Jangoux), 223–9. Rotterdam: A.A. Balkema.

Pagett, R.M. 1981. The penetration of brackish water by the Echinodermata. In *Feeding and Survival Strategies of Estuarine Organisms*, 135–51. New York: Plenum Press.

Pagett, R.M. 1982. Further observations on the penetration of brackish waters by *Ophiura albida* (Forbes). In *International Echinoderms Conference, Tampa Bay* (ed. J.M. Lawrence), 359–64. Rotterdam: A.A. Balkema.

Pearse, J.S. 1967. Coelomic water volume control in the Antarctic sea star *Odontaster validus*. *Nature* 216:1118–9.

Prosser, C.L. 1973a. Water: osmotic balance: hormonal regulation. In *Comparative Animal Physiology* (ed. C.L. Prosser), 51–78. Philadelphia: Saunders.

Prosser, C.L. 1973b. Inorganic ions. In *Comparative Animal Physiology* (ed. C.L. Prosser), 15–22. Philadelphia: Saunders.

Reese, E.S. 1966. The complex behaviour of echinoderms. In *Physiology of Echinodermata* (ed. R.A. Boolootian), 157–218. New York: Interscience.

Robertson, J.D. 1980. Osmotic constituents of some echinoderm muscles. *Comparative Biochemistry and Physiology* 67A:535–43.

Roller, R.A. and Stickle, W.B. 1985. Effects of salinity on larval tolerance and early development rates of 4 species of echinoderms. *Canadian Journal of Zoology* 63:1531–8.

Sabourin, T.D. and Stickle, W.B. 1981. Effects of salinity on respiration and nitrogen excretion in two species of echinoderms. *Marine Biology* 65:91–9.

Shirley, T.C. and Stickle, W.B. 1982a. Responses of *Leptasterias hexactis* (Echinodermata: Asteroidea) to low salinity. I. Survival, activity, feeding, growth and absorption efficiency. *Marine Biology* 69:147–54.

The Marine Biology of the South China Sea
(ed. B. Morton). Proceedings of the First
International Conference on the Marine
Biology of Hong Kong and the South China Sea,
Hong Kong, 28 October – 3 November 1990.
Hong Kong: Hong Kong University Press, 1993.

LEAF CHOICE OF SESARMINE CRABS, *CHIROMANTHES BIDENS* AND *C. MAIPOENSIS*, IN A HONG KONG MANGAL

S.Y. Lee

Department of Zoology and The Swire Marine Laboratory,
The University of Hong Kong, Hong Kong

ABSTRACT

Senescent leaves from the three local mangroves *Avicennia marina* (Forsk.) Vierh., *Aegiceras corniculatum* Blanco and *Kandelia candel* (L.) Druce were offered to individuals of the sesarmine crabs *Chiromanthes bidens* and *C. maipoensis* in a leaf choice experiment. Both crab species showed the same preference order: *Avicennia marina* > *Kandelia candel* > *Aegiceras corniculatum*. *Aegiceras corniculatum* leaves were untouched by the crabs in > 50% of the cases. Measurement of % moisture, % organic carbon, % organic nitrogen and % soluble tannins suggests that the C:N ratio correlates best with leaf preference. Crabs preferred leaves with lower C:N ratios, which are indicative of the nutritive value of the leaves. The various implications of the results for organic matter turnover and crab fitness are discussed.

INTRODUCTION

Sesarmine crabs are important components of Indo-Pacific and south Asian mangals. Both species richness and abundance are high, reaching a total of > 50 species and densities typically between 2 and 10 individuals·m^{-2} throughout the region (Macnae 1968; Jones 1984; Macintosh 1984; Lee 1989). In addition to this species richness and numerical abundance, the ecological importance of these crabs is further amplified by their habit of feeding on mangrove propagules, leaves and litter at various stages of decomposition (Malley 1978; Leh and Sasekumar 1985; Giddens *et al.* 1986; Robertson 1986; Smith 1987a, b; Hatcher *et al.* 1989; Lee 1989; Robertson and Daniel 1989). Robertson (1986) and Robertson and Daniel (1989) compared rates of crab-mediated and microbe-mediated decomposition and suggested that crabs are capable of effecting turnover up to > 75 times faster than microbes. Data are therefore accumulating to indicate that these sesarmine crabs are important functional components in the Indo-Pacific mangals in terms of effecting organic detritus turnover and regulating mangrove community structure, aspects which have been largely neglected in the Odum and Heald model proposed for New World mangals (Robertson 1986; Robertson 1987; Hatcher *et al.* 1989).

Lee (1898) estimated that during the active season, the sesarmine crabs *Chiromanthes bidens* and *C. maipoensis* together consumed > 50% of the daily litter production in infrequently inundated, landward, mangroves at the Mai Po Marshes, northwestern Hong Kong. Preference was, however, for decaying as opposed to fresh mangrove litter. In contrast, Robertson (1986) and Robertson and Daniel (1989) recorded that *Sesarma* spp. readily conserved and consumed fresh litter in tidal mangroves in tropical Australia. This difference in leaf preference was attributed to variations in foraging time and the limited availability of the more desirable decaying litter in the tidal situation by Lee (1989). It is thus of interest to know which properties of the leaves influenced leaf choice of the sesarmines and the implications of leaf choice for mangrove function and crab fitness. The present study aims at investigating the leaf choice of *Chiromanthes* spp. when offered fresh leaf litter of various mangrove species, and possible reasons behind such choices.

MATERIALS AND METHODS

Leaf choice experiments

Individuals of the sesarmine crabs *Chiromanthes bidens* and *C. maipoensis* were collected from the intertidal mangrove forests floor at the Mai Po Marshes, Deep Bay, northwest Hong Kong. The mangrove community at Mai Po is dominated by three mangrove species: *Avicennia marina* (Forsk.) Vierh., *Kandelia candel* (L.) Druce and *Aegiceras corniculatum* Blanco. The first two species are roughly co-dominant and grow to abut 4 to 6 m tall, whereas *A. corniculatum* is shruby and is restricted to the banks of creeks and drainage channels. Senescent leaves were collected from the canopy of the trees and only leaves which were ready to absciss were used in the experiments.

The sex and carapace width of the crabs were recorded before they were kept in separate containers. Each container was filled up to about 1 cm deep with 50% seawater to avoid desiccation of the crabs. In order to recognise leaf identity after crab consumption, the senescent leaves of the three species were cut into different geometric shapes of the same area (4 cm^2): circles for *A. marina* (AM), squares for *A. corniculatum* (AC) and trapezia for *K. candel* (KC). The same leaf area for all three species equilibrated the encounter rate.

The leaf pieces were offered to the crabs and the consumption on the three leaf types compared after 24 hours. The amount of leaf biomass offered for each leaf type was smaller than the consumption expected of the crabs in 24 hours, thus encouraging the crabs to feed on progressively less desirable leaf types after exhausting the more desirable species. Since the objective of this experiment was to define leaf preference, consumption by the two crab species of the three leaf types was ranked for each crab trial. Actual consumption was measured only for cases with very similar consumption for different leaf species. A total of 78 crab trials were performed, with the use of 20 individuals each of the two crab species. Leaf preference was compared by applying the Friedmann test to the rank data (Conover 1980).

Physical and chemical characteristics of the leaves

The physical and chemical properties of the senescent leaves of the three mangrove

Table 1
List of physical and chemical properties measured for the three leaf types and methods of analysis. Methods follow Allen et al. (1989).

Property	Method
% moisture	Drying at 80°C for 48 hrs
% organic matter	Loss-on-ignition at 500°C for 3 hrs
% organic carbon (based on dry wt.)	Wet oxidation by acid-dichromate, back titration using ammonium ferrous sulphate
% organic nitrogen (based on dry wt.)	Sulphuric acid-hydrogen peroxide digestion, semi-micro distillation
% soluble tannins (based on dry wt.)	Hot water extraction, colour development by Folin-Denis reagent, absorbance at 760 nm measured

species measured and the methods employed are summarised in Table 1. Leaf preference pattern obtained from the experiments was then correlated with the various properties of the leaves.

RESULTS

Leaf preference

There was a strong tendency for both species of *Chiromanthes* to preferentially consume senescent leaves of *Avicennia marina*. The mean ranks for the three leaf types follow the order AM < KC < AC, indicating a consistent and significant preference pattern in the order AM, KC, AC for both species and sexes (Table 2). The same pattern was reflected by the frequency of cases with 100% consumption of *A. marina* (32.1%) or 0% consumption of *A. corniculatum* (55.1%).

Table 2
Friedman test on preference of *Chiromanthes bidens* and *C. maipoensis* for fresh leaf litter of *Aegiceras corniculatum*, *Avicennia marina* and *Kandelia candel*. Multiple comparisons show that preference for *Avicennia marina* leaves > *Kandelia candel* leaves > *Aegiceras corniculatum* leaves at $P < 0.001$ for the pooled data. AM, *Avicennia marina*; KC, *Kandelia candel*; AC, *Aegiceras corniculatum*.

Crab	Sex	Mean ranks			X^2	P
		AM	KC	AC		
C. bidens						
	Male	1.50	1.60	2.90	30.5	<0.0001
	Female	1.29	1.71	3.00	19.0	<0.0001
C. maipoensis						
	Male	1.14	2.14	2.73	14.2	0.0008
	Female	1.16	2.08	2.76	39.8	<0.0001
Pooled data		1.30	1.89	2.80	86.8	<0.0001

Leaf characteristics

The three mangrove species have rather different physical and chemical characteristics (Table 3). Whereas the amount of moisture and total organic matter were similar for all leaf types, the leaves differed significantly in terms of their carbon, nitrogen and soluble tannin contents. The surprisingly high organic carbon content of *A. corniculatum* resulted in a high C:N ratio of 69.1, despite that the organic nitrogen content of this species was rather similar to that of *K. candel*. *A. marina* has the lowest C:N ratio and % soluble tannins amongst all three mangrove species.

Table 3
Physical and chemical characteristics of the leaves of the three mangroves offered to *C. maipoensis* and *C. bidens*. All figures are based on dry weights (mean ± 1S.D.).

Species	% moisture	% organic matter	% organic carbon	% organic nitrogen	C:N	% soluble tannins
Aegiceras corniculatum	56.9 ± 5.0	94.8 ± 0.2	54.6 ± 4.4	0.79 ± 0.02	69.1	1.95 ± 0.19
Avicennia marina	67.9 ± 6.0	91.0 ± 0.6	34.5 ± 1.9	1.26 ± 0.05	27.4	0.86 ± 0.03
Kandelia candel	57.2 ± 7.2	89.2 ± 0.2	36.7 ± 1.0	0.75	49.1	2.35 ± 0.29

DISCUSSION

This study shows that *Chiromanthes* spp. consume fresh litter from the three common local mangroves, albeit at distinctly different rates. Strong preference was for *Avicennia marina* leaves, whereas leaves of *Kandelia candel* and *Aegiceras corniculatum* were grazed only to significantly lesser extents. The ability of detritivorous invertebrates to select food according to their physical and chemical properties has been recorded in past studies (Poovachiranon *et al.* 1986; Lee 1989; Poovachiranon 1990). Lee (1989) and Poovachiranon (1990) both documented the preference of *Chiromanthes* spp. for decaying leaf litter as opposed to fresh litter. Similar findings have been reported upon for *Neosarmatium smithi* (Giddens *et al.* 1986).

Preference of the sesarmine crabs for decaying mangrove leaves is expected, since only food materials of C:N ratios lower than 17 are considered nutritious to marine invertebrates (Russell-Hunter 1970). The fact that senescent mangrove leaves generally have high initial C:N ratios (up to 100) which decrease rapidly with decay (Fell and Master 1980; Lee 1989) probably explains the preference for decaying leaves. Giddens *et al.* (1986) discovered that assimilation efficiency of *Neosarmatium smithi* for carbon, nitrogen and organic matter increased rapidly with the age of the decaying leaf litter they consumed. It then becomes apparent why *Chiromanthes* spp. tend to select decaying leaves when offered leaf litter at various ages for one species (Lee 1989; Poovachiranon 1990) and, in the present study, that species of mangrove leaf which have the most favourable nutritive status (low C:N ratio) when offered fresh litter of various species.

Nevertheless, other physical and chemical properties of the leaves may also be important in the selection. For example, toughness of the leaves may have played an important part in the selection, as different toughness may imply differences in the energy expenditure associated with foraging and increase handling time. Recently, Lucas and Pereira (1990) devised a simple apparatus to measure toughness of leaves and this may provide more information to explain the choice pattern. The very low soluble tannin content of *Avicennia marina* may also explain the crabs' preference for this species. Alongi (1987) investigated the effects of tannins on detritivore utilization of various mangrove litter and concluded that detritivorous nematode growth was strongly inhibited by high tannin contents. He recorded a soluble tannin content of 0.8% dry weight for leaves of *A. marina*, which is very close to the value of 0.86% recorded in the present study.

The large size and abundance of crabs make them important detritivores in effecting litter turnover. Lee (1989) found a positive correlation between crab density and leaf litter turnover rate. O'Dowd and Lake (1989) also documented spatial heterogeneity in litter distribution on tropical rain forest floors due to feeding activities of the terrestrial red crab *Gecarcoidea natalis* (Pocock). The distinct preference of the crabs for fresh litter from the three mangrove species implies that leaf litter may be processed at different rates in different patches of the forest. In locations where more frequent tidal inundation is present, microbial decomposition is probably responsible for initial leaf litter breakdown. *A. marina* seems to be a species which allows rapid decomposition. Decomposition studies by Van der Valk and Attiwill (1984), Steinke and Ward (1987), Robertson (1988) and Angsupanich et al. (1989) all recorded that *A. marina* had the shortest half-life among various mangroves species. The same fast turnover rate probably also applies to *A. marina* litter in the landward part of the mangal. In less frequently inundated mangroves, sesarmine crabs act as dominant agents effecting leaf litter turnover (Lee 1989). The present study therefore also suggests that *A. marina* leaf litter is probably recycled at the fastest rate among the three local species.

In contrast to microbial decomposition, comparative data on rates of crab-mediated decomposition are scarce. Macintosh (1984) reported upon the distribution and abundance of ten species of ocypodid and grapsid crabs in a Malaysian mangal, but generally there are few data on differences in abundances of crabs in various parts of the mangal dominated by different mangrove species. A correlation between mangrove species (and thus the quality of its litter as food) and crab production may exist when feeding on different litter type implies different fitness for the crabs. Feeding on a more desirable litter type, e.g., of a much high C:N ratio or less easily handled type, may mean slower growth or reduced reproductive output in the long term. The diet then has to be subsidised by other nitrogen sources such as crustaceans and insects (Leh and Sesakumar 1985; Giddens et al. 1986), which are comparatively more difficult to obtain. While the importance of crabs as agents controlling mangrove species structure is stressed (Smith 1987a, b), crab production as an important component of mangal secondary productivity is probably influenced reciprocally by the identity of the mangrove species present.

REFERENCES

Allen, S.E. 1989. *Chemical Analysis of Ecological Materials.* Oxford: Blackwell Scientific Publications.

Alongi, D.M. 1987. The influence of mangrove-derived tannins on intertidal meiobenthos in tropical estuaries. *Oecologia (Berlin)* 71:537-40.

Angsupanich, S., Miyoshi, H. and Hata, Y. 1989. Degradation of mangrove leaves immersed in the estuary of Nakama River, Okinawa. *Nippon Suisan Gakkaishi* 55:147-51.

Conover, W.J. 1980. *Practical Nonparametric Statistics.* New York: John Wiley & Sons.

Fell, J.W. and Master, I.M. 1980. The association and potential role of fungi in mangrove detrital systems. *Botanica Marina* 23:257-63.

Giddens, R.L., Lucas, J.S., Neilson, M.J. and Richards, G.N. 1986. Feeding ecology of the mangrove crab *Neosarmatium smithi* (Crustacea: Decapoda: Sesarmidae). *Marine Ecology Progress Series* 33:147-55.

Hatcher, B.G., Johannes, R.E. and Robertson, A.I. 1989. Review of research relevant to the conservation of shallow tropical marine ecosystems. *Oceanography and Marine Biology Annual Review* 27:337-414.

Jones, D.A. 1984. Crabs of the mangal ecosystem. In *Hydrobiology of the mangal* (ed. F.D. Por and I. Dor), 89-109. The Hague: Dr. W. Junk Publishers.

Lee, S.Y. 1989. The importance of sesarmine crabs *Chiromanthes* spp. and inundation frequency on the decomposition of mangrove (*Kandelia candel* (L.) Druce (Rhizophoraceae)) leaf litter in a Hong Kong tidal shrimp pond. *Journal of Experimental Marine Biology and Ecology* 130:23-43.

Lee, S.Y. 1990. The intensity of consequences of herbivory on *Kandelia candel* (L.) Druce leaves at the Mai Po Marshes, Hong Kong. In *Proceedings of the Second International Marine Biological Workshop: The Marine Flora and Fauna of Hong Kong and Southern China, Hong Kong, 1986* (ed. B. Morton), 717-25. Hong Kong: Hong Kong University Press.

Leh, C.M.U. and Sasekumar, A. 1985. The food of sesarmine crabs in Malaysian mangrove forests. *Malaysian Nature Journal* 39:135-45.

Lucas, P.W. and Pereira, A. 1990. Estimation of the fracture toughness of leaves. *Functional Ecology* 4:819-22.

Macintosh, D.J. 1984. Ecology and productivity of Malaysian mangrove crab populations (Decapoda: Brachyura). In *Proceedings of the Asian Symposium on Mangrove Environment, Research and Development* (ed. E. Soepadmo, A.N. Rao and D.J. Macintosh), 354-77. Kuala Lumpur: University of Malaya and Unesco.

Macnae, W. 1968. A general account of the fauna and flora of mangrove swamps and forests in the Indo-West Pacific region. *Advances in Marine Biology* 6:73-270.

Malley, D.F. 1978. Degradation of mangrove leaf litter by the tropical crab *Chiromanthes onychophorum*. *Marine Biology* 49:377-86.

O'Dowd, D.J. and Lake, P.S. 1989. Red crabs in rain forest, Christmas Island: removal and relocation of leaf-fall. *Journal of Tropical Ecology* 5:337-48.

Poovachiranon, S. 1990. The food of two sesarminae crabs *Chiromanthes bidens* and *C. maipoensis* in Hong Kong mangrove stands. In *Proceedings of the Second International Marine Biological Workshop: The Marine Flora and Fauna of Hong Kong and Southern China, Hong Kong, 1986* (ed. B. Morton), 727-35. Hong Kong: Hong Kong University Press.

Poovachiranon, S., Boto, K. and Duke, N. 1986. Food preference studies and ingestion rate measurements of the mangrove amphipod *Parhyale hawaiensis* (Dana). *Journal of Experimental Marine Biology and Ecology* 98:129-40.

Price, A.R.G., Medley, P.A.H., McDowall, R.J., Dawson-Sheperd, A.R., Hogarth, P.J. and Ormond, R.F.G. 1987. Aspects of mangal ecology along the Red Sea coast of Saudi Arabia. *Journal of Natural History* 21:449-64.

Robertson, A.I. 1986. Leaf-burying crabs: their influence on energy flow and export from mixed mangrove forests (*Rhizophora* spp.) in northern Australia. *Journal of Experimental Marine Biology and Ecology* 102:237-48.

Robertson, A.I. 1987. The determination of trophic relationships in mangrove dominated systems: areas of darkness. In *Mangrove ecosystems of Asia and the Pacific: status, exploitation and management* (ed. C.D. Field and A.J. Dartnall), 292-304. Townesville: Australian Institute of Marine Science.

Robertson, A.I. 1988. Decomposition of mangrove leaf litter in tropical Australia. *Journal of Experimental Marine Biology and Ecology* 116:235-47.

Robertson, A.I. and Daniel, P.A. 1989. The influence of crabs on litter processing in high intertidal mangrove forests in tropical Australia. *Oecologia (Berlin)* 78:191-8.

Russell-Hunter, R. 1970. *Aquatic Productivity: an introduction to some basic aspects of biological oceanography and limnology.* London: Collier-Macmillan.

Smith III, T.J. 1987a. Effects of seed predators and light level on the distribution of *Avicennia marina* (Forsk.) Vierh. in tropical, tidal forests. *Estuarine, Coastal and Shelf Science* 25:43-51.

Smith III, T.J. 1987b. Seed predation in relation to tree dominance and distribution in mangrove forests. *Ecology* 68:266-73.

Steinke, T.D. and Ward, C.J. 1987. Degradation of mangrove leaf litter in the St Lucia Estuary as influenced by season and exposure. *South African Journal of Botany* 53:323-8.

Van der Valk, A.G. and Attiwill, P.M. 1984. Decomposition of leaf and root litter of *Avicennia marina* at Westernport Bay, Victoria, Australia. *Aquatic Botany* 18:205-21.

ENIGMONIA AENIGMATICA: AN ENIGMATIC MOLLUSCAN CHAMELEON

Shaun M. Moss

Department of Zoology, University of Hawaii at Manoa, Honolulu, Hawaii 96822 USA

ABSTRACT

Evidence for shell colour plasticity in molluscs is not well documented, and rare in bivalves. The anomiid bivalve, *Enigmonia aenigmatica*, found in Southeast Asian mangrove communities, typically exhibits two discrete shell colours, cream and purple-brown, within a single population. Until recently, researchers considered the two shell colours to represent two distinct species or conspecific colour morphs. This study was conducted to determine if shell colour in *E. aenigmatica* is associated with a particular substrate type, and if *E. aenigmatica* can change shell colour when transplanted from one substrate type to another. Field observations indicate that shell colour is not independent of substrate type. Cream individuals were only found on green *Avicennia* leaves, whereas 94% of the purple-brown individuals were attached to dark brown *Avicennia* trunks, stems, and roots. In a laboratory transplant study, 71% of cream *E. aenigmatica* exhibited discrete purple-brown pigmentation bands along their newly formed left valve margins after six weeks, when transplanted from *Avicennia* leaves to pieces of *Avicennia* trunk. A control group, consisting of cream *E. aenigmatica* attached to leaves of *Avicennia* saplings, exhibited no colour change after six weeks. These results corroborate earlier work regarding shell colour plasticity in *E. aenigmatica*.

INTRODUCTION

Conspecific organisms inhabiting either spatially or temporally heterogeneous environments often exhibit different phenotypes in response to environmental variation. The extent to which an organism's phenotype is modified by the environment is termed 'phenotypic plasticity' (Via and Lande 1985), and the phenotypic change that occurs is the 'response' (Bradshaw 1965). Although a response by an organism to a heterogeneous environment does not necessarily confer an adaptive advantage, morphological, physiological, or behavioural responses often increase individual fitness (Bradshaw 1965).

Studies of molluscan shell morphologies are particularly informative when investigating phenotypic plasticity because time-integrated responses to environmental heterogeneity are permanently recorded in deposited shell layers. Examples in the literature illustrate the plasticity of shell shape in a variety of molluscs (Moore 1934; Seed 1968; Evans 1968; Largen 1971; Britton and Morton 1979; McMahon and Whitehead 1987; Appleton and Palmer 1988; Balla and Walker 1991), and the plasticity of shell colour in gastropods (Moore 1936; Ino 1949; Leighton 1961; Creese and Underwood 1976; Underwood and Creese 1976). However, evidence for shell colour plasticity in bivalves is rare. In the corbiculid clam, *Corbicula fluminea*, hydrological parameters such as pH, dissolved oxygen, and potassium concentrations appear to be important in initiating and sustaining its variable shell colour (Britton and Morton 1986; Morton 1987). Recently, Sigurdsson and Sundari (1990) documented a substrate-dependent colour change in the shell of the anomiid bivalve, *Enigmonia aenigmatica*.

Enigmonia aenigmatica is a characteristic member of Southeast Asian mangrove communities and typically exhibits two discrete shell colours, cream and purple-brown, within a single population. Previously, researchers considered the two shell colours to represent either two distinct species (Berry 1975) or conspecific colour morphs associated with particular substrates within the mangal (Morton 1976; Yonge 1977). Cream individuals were observed mostly on the undersurface of green mangrove leaves, while purple-brown individuals were reported to occur on dark brown trunks, stems, and roots of mangrove trees.

The objectives of this study were to statistically determine if shell colour in *Enigmonia aenigmatica* is associated with a particular substrate type to which it attaches, and to determine if *E. aenigmatica* can change shell colour when transplanted from one substrate type to another.

MATERIALS AND METHODS

Field transect study

Field data were collected in March of 1986 from a mangal fringing the Straits of Johore in northwest Singapore, near the Kranji Reservoir (1°25'N, 103°43'E). As with most coastal areas in Singapore, anthropogenic disturbances were apparent. The dominant mangrove trees were of the genus *Avicennia*, with occasional *Sonneratia*, *Bruguiera*, and *Rhizophora* trees interspersed. Two 20 m transects were established from the landward fringe of the mangal to the seaward edge. All *Enigmonia aenigmatica* within one metre of either transect were counted and categorized according to shell colour; shell lengths were measured with calipers, and the substrate type upon which each individual set was noted. All observations were made at low tide.

A chi-square test of independence was used to determine if shell colour was independent of substrate type (Sokal and Rohlf 1981). A 2 x 2 contingency table was constructed, with cream and purple-brown representing shell colour and mangrove leaf and mangrove trunk representing substrate type. Individuals observed on mangrove stems and roots were included in the latter group. Mean shell lengths of cream versus purple-brown individuals were compared using the t-test at a significance level of $P < 0.05$. Shell length data were initially tested for normality using the Kolmogorov statistic and for homogeneity of variance using the F-test.

Laboratory transplant study

A laboratory experiment was conducted in April of 1986 to determine if *Enigmonia aenigmatica* can change shell colour when transplanted from one substrate type to another. Twenty-five cream individuals (mean shell length = 1.67 cm ± 0.25) were collected from the undersurface of *Avicennia* leaves in the field and were transplanted onto pieces of dead *Avicennia* trunk contained in a plastic aquarium in the lab. A control treatment was run concurrently, in which 25 cream individuals (mean shell length = 1.67 cm + 0.23), collected from *Avicennia* leaves in the field, were transferred to leaves of *Avicennia* saplings contained in a separate plastic aquarium. Both treatments received daily additions of the dinoflagellate, *Isochrysis galbana* (Parke), at concentrations of 50,000–150,000 cells·mL^{-1}. Feeding occurred during a three hour period each day when individuals were submerged in seawater with a mean temperature of 25.5°C and a mean salinity of 28.3‰. Both treatments were exposed to a 12 hour light/dark cycle throughout the six week experiment. A number (1–25) was written in indelible ink on the left valve of all *E. aenigmatica* to aid in individual identification. If an individual exhibited a discrete purple-brown pigmentation band along its newly formed left valve margin, the date when the colour change occurred and the valve number were recorded. Mortalities were monitored daily and individual shell lengths were recorded once each week. Periodically, movements of individuals in the aquaria were noted after observing changes in an individual's location over time. These movements were not quantified.

RESULTS

Field transect study

Observations made along both transects were pooled, resulting in data on 151 individuals. Seventy-eight were cream and 73 were purple-brown. (An additional seven individuals observed in the field exhibited dichromy. Three were purple-brown with discrete cream bands along their left valve margins, and four were cream with purple-brown bands. These individuals were not included in the chi-square analysis.) All individuals were attached to *Avicennia* trees, as no other suitable substrata were present along either transect. Results from the chi-square test of independence indicate that shell colour is not independent of substrate type (x^2 = 135.8, $P < 0.001$). All 78 cream individuals were attached to *Avicennia* leaves (Fig. 1). Ninety-four percent were on the undersurface of the leaves, while six percent were on the upper surface. Sixty-nine purple-brown individuals were attached to *Avicennia* trunks, stems, and roots, while four were on the undersurface of *Avicennia* leaves (Fig. 1). Purple-brown individuals had a mean shell length of 3.19 cm (SD = 0.58), and were significantly larger ($P < 0.001$) than cream individuals with a mean shell length of 2.15 cm (SD = 0.88, Fig. 2).

Laboratory transplant study

After six weeks, 71% of the transplanted cream individuals exhibited discrete purple-brown pigmentation bands along the newly formed margin of the upper left valve (Plate IA). Several individuals exhibited these pigmentation bands less than nine days after being transplanted from the leaves to the trunk. None of the individuals in the control

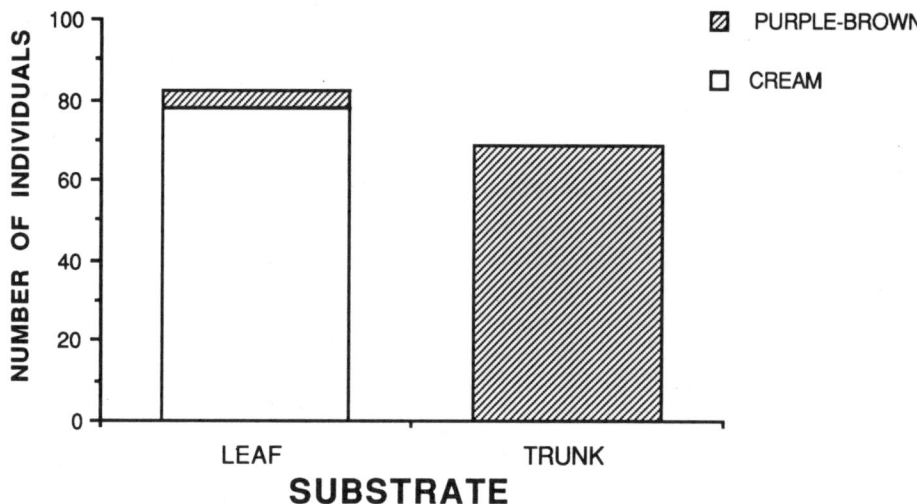

Fig. 1. Number of cream and purple-brown *Enigmonia aenigmatica* attached to *Avicennia* leaves and trunks along two transects in a Singapore mangal.

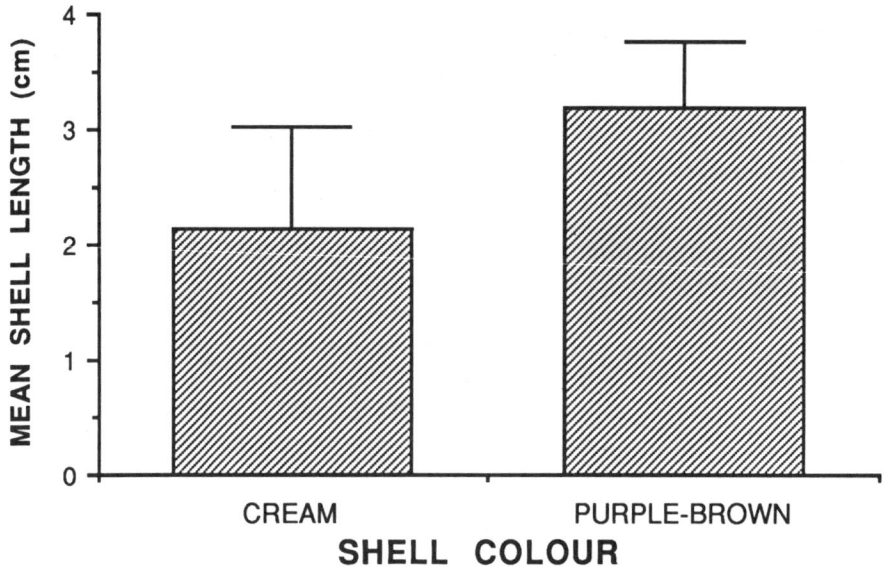

Fig. 2. Mean shell lengths (cm, +SD) of cream and purple-brown *Enigmonia aenigmatica* recorded along two transects in a Singapore mangal. Purple-brown individuals had a significantly greater mean shell length than cream individuals (t-test, $P < 0.001$).

treatment showed any colour change after six weeks. Shell colour along the newly formed margin of these individuals was the same cream colour as the old growth (Plate IB). Survival was 96% in the transplanted treatment and 60% in the control treatment. None of the mortalities exhibited a colour change at the time of death. Mean shell length in-

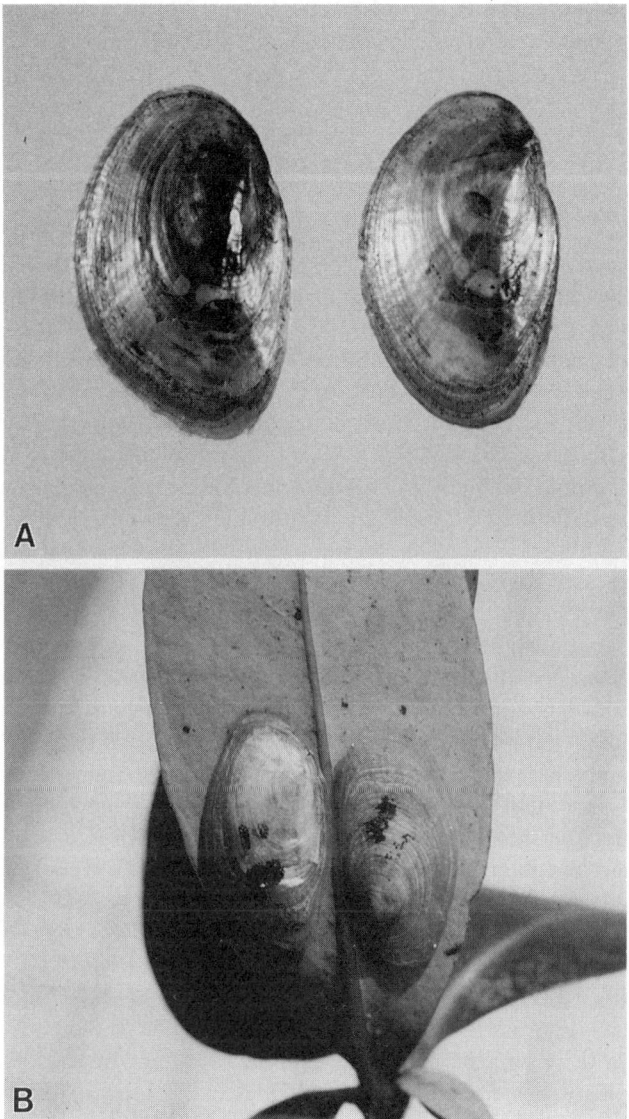

Plate IA. Cream *Enigmonia aenigmatica* exhibiting discrete purple-brown pigmentation bands along the newly formed margin of their upper left valves. This photograph was taken six weeks after the individuals were transplanted from *Avicennia* leaves in the field to pieces of *Avicennia* trunk contained in an aquarium. The dark markings in the centre of the shells are numbers written in ink to aid in individual identification. Individuals are approximately 1.8 cm in shell length.

Plate IB. Cream *Enigmonia aenigmatica* attached to *Avicennia* saplings contained in an aquarium. Shell colour along the newly formed margin of the upper left valve is the same cream colour as the old growth. This photograph was taken six weeks after the individuals were transferred from mangrove leaves in the field to leaves of mangrove saplings in the laboratory. Individuals are approximately 2.0 cm in shell length.

creased from 1.67 cm (SD = 0.25) to 1.80 cm (SD = 0.23) after six weeks for individuals in the transplanted treatment, and from 1.67 cm (SD = 0.23) to 1.99 cm (SD = 0.23) for individuals in the control treatment.

DISCUSSION

Numerous molluscan species exhibit discontinuous shell colour variation within a population, including terrestrial pulmonates (Hedrick et al. 1976; Jones et al. 1977; Cain 1983), littorines (Raffaelli 1982; Hughes and Mather 1986; Reid 1987) and other shallow-water mesogastropods (Hoagland 1977; Byers 1989). This type of variation is defined as a polymorphism and is presumed to be genetically mediated (Ford 1945). For many molluscs, shell colour is considered, 'a genetic character basically unchanged by the environment, and constant throughout the lifetime of any individual' (Hoagland 1977, p. 367). However, examples in the literature provide evidence for shell colour plasticity in gastropods, whereby an individual inhabiting a heterogeneous environment exhibits changes in its shell colour within its lifetime (Moore 1936; Ino 1949; Leighton 1961; Creese and Underwood 1976). In these examples, diet has been implicated as the likely agent affecting shell colour.

Although the proximate cause of the shell colour change in *Enigmonia aenigmatica* is not known, laboratory results from this study and those of Sigurdsson and Sundari (1990) indicate that the change is substratum dependent. A direct dietary influence of the substrate on shell colour is unlikely because *E. aenigmatica* is a filter-feeder (Morton 1976), ingesting bacterioplankton, phytoplankton, detritus, and inorganic particles suspended in the ambient water column. However, although *E. aenigmatica* does not feed directly on the substrate it occupies, it may incorporate compounds released by the substratum that affect its shell colour.

When occupying their characteristic substrata, both cream and purple-brown *E. aenigmatica* appear cryptically coloured. Predatory crabs, fish, and birds are known to possess colour vision (Pettitt 1975; Hyatt 1975; Bursey 1984) and have been implicated in regulating the distribution of molluscan colour morphs (Pettitt 1973, 1975; Heller 1975; Reimchen 1979; Hughes and Mather 1986). Predators such as mudskippers (*Periophthalmus*), grapsid crabs (*Metapograpsus*), and portunid crabs (*Scylla*), inhabit the mangal near the Kranji Reservoir (Ang et al. 1985) and might preferentially prey on less cryptic *E. aenigmatica* attached to mismatched substrata. Although visual predation may be an important agent in regulating *E. aenigmatica* shell colour frequency, confirmation from field observations and experimental evidence is lacking.

Colouration not only affects the visual properties of a molluscan shell, but also its thermal properties. Dark morphs are presumed to absorb more heat from solar radiation than light morphs, and should be found in more shaded habitat patches if mortality from heat stress is common (Mitton 1977). *E. aenigmatica* inhabiting mangrove leaves may be more exposed to solar radiation than individuals residing under the mangrove canopy, and would thus benefit from a lighter shell colour. Evidence for selective heat death is, however, lacking for this species.

Mangrove ecosystems represent a mosaic of light and dark substrates upon which *E. aenigmatica* can attach. An individual can potentially experience a variety of these substrates within its lifetime, either by being physically dislodged from an attachment site or because of its motility (Yonge 1957; Sigurdsson and Sundari 1990). The adaptive value of shell colour plasticity in *E. aenigmatica* may be significant if movement between substrata is common and if there is a potential for differential mortality from such agents as visual predation or heat stress. However, the extent to which *E. aenigmatica* move between substrata in the field has not been well documented and laboratory observations from this study indicate that individuals in aquaria exhibit limited motility.

The importance of shell colour plasticity in *E. aenigmatica* may also be realized immediately after larval settlement. *E. aenigmatica* are broadcast spawners and exhibit typical planktonic, larval development for bivalves, at least through four days post-fertilization (personal observation). It is likely that the substratum upon which *E. aenigmatica* initially set dictates initial shell colour (Morton 1976). If larvae randomly settle on mangrove leaves or trunks, the mangal represents a fine-grained environment for newly-set *E. aenigmatica* (Levins 1968), where phenotypic plasticity is favoured over polymorphism as an adaptive strategy (Hoagland 1977).

In summary, results from this study corroborate those of Sigurdsson and Sundari (1990) regarding shell colour plasticity in the anomiid bivalve, *Enigmonia aenigmatica*. Bivalve shell colour is not necessarily genetically determined but can change in response to environmental heterogeneity. Clearly, more research needs to be conducted in order to elucidate the proximate cause of the colour change and the adaptive significance of such a change.

ACKNOWLEDGEMENTS

I would like to thank Dr Jon Sigurdsson for his ideas, input, and support; Ms Marinee Chuah Lay Khim and Mr Ow Ping Yu for their technical assistance; Mr H.K. Yip for his photographic assistance; Dr Julie Brock, Mr Jeff Burgett, Dr Alison Kay, and Dr Steven Palumbi for improving earlier drafts of the manuscript; Ms Sue Monden for preparing the photographic plates; and Prof. Brian Morton for his support and for putting together a most informative conference. The author was supported by a Rotary Foundation Scholarship during this study.

REFERENCES

Ang, B.K., Lam, W.M., Lee, E., Lim, W.T., Si, H.C.K., Tan, T.P and Wong, E. 1985. *A Closer Look at Kranji*. Singapore: Singapore Science Center and the Science Teachers Association of Singapore.

Appleton, R.D. and Palmer, A.R. 1988. Water-borne stimuli released by predatory crabs and damaged prey induce more predator resistant shells in a marine gastropod. *Proceedings of the National Academy of Sciences of the United States of America* 85:4387–91.

Balla, S.A. and Walker, K.F. 1991. Shape variation in the Australian freshwater mussel *Alathyria jacksoni* Iredale (Bivalvia, Hyriidae). *Hydrobiologia* 220:89–98.

Berry, A.J. 1975. Molluscs colonizing mangrove trees with observations on *Enigmonia rosea* (Anomiidae). *Proceedings of the Malacological Society of London* 41:589–600.

Bradshaw, A.D. 1965. Evolutionary significance of phenotypic plasticity in plants. In *Advances in Genetics* (eds. E.W. Caspari and J.M. Thoday), vol. 13, 115–55. New York: Academic Press.

Britton, J.C. and Morton, B. 1979. *Corbicula* in North America: the evidence reviewed and evaluated. In *Proceedings of the First International Corbicula Symposium* (ed. J.C. Britton), 249–87. Fort Worth: Texas Christian University Research Foundation.

Britton, J.C. and Morton, B. 1986. Polymorphism in *Corbicula fluminea* (Bivalvia: Corbiculoidea) from North America. *Malacological Review* 19:1–43.

Bursey, C.R. 1984. Color recognition in the blue crab, *Callinectes sapidus* Rathburn (Decapoda, Brachyura). *Crustaceana* 47:278–84.

Byers, B.A. 1989. Habitat-choice polymorphism associated with cryptic shell-color polymorphism in the limpet *Lottia digitalis*. *The Veliger* 32:394–402.

Cain, A.J. 1983. Ecology and ecogenetics of terrestrial molluscan populations. In *The Mollusca* (ed. W.D. Russell-Hunter), vol. 6, 597–647. London: Academic Press.

Creese, R.G. and Underwood, A.J. 1976. Observations on the biology of the trochid gastropod *Austrocochlea constricta* (Lamarck) (Prosobranchia). I. Factors affecting shell-banding pattern. *Journal of Experimental Marine Biology and Ecology* 23:211–28.

Evans, J.W. 1968. Factors modifying the morphology of the rock-boring clam, *Penitella penita* (Conrad, 1837). *Proceedings of the Malacological Society of London* 38:111–9.

Ford, E.B. 1945. Polymorphism. *Biological Reviews* 20:72–88.

Hedrick, P.W., Ginevan, M.E. and Ewig, E.P. 1976. Genetic polymorphisms in heterogeneous environments. *Annual Review of Ecology and Systematics* 7:1–32.

Heller, J. 1975. Visual selection of shell colour in two littoral prosobranchs. *Zoological Journal of the Linnean Society* 56:153–70.

Hoagland, K.E. 1977. A gastropod color polymorphism: one adaptive strategy of phenotypic variation. *Biological Bulletin* 152:360–72.

Hughes, J.M. and Mather, P.B. 1986. Evidence for predation as a factor in determining shell color frequencies in a mangrove snail *Littorina* sp. (Prosobranchia: Littorinidae). *Evolution* 40:68–77.

Hyatt, G. 1975. Physiological and behavioral evidence for color discrimination by fiddler crabs (Brachyura, Ocypodidae, genus *Uca*). In *Physiological Ecology of Estuarine Organisms* (ed. F.J. Vernberg), 333–65. Columbia: University of South Carolina Press.

Ino, T. 1949. The effect of food on growth and coloration of the top shell (*Turbo cornutus* Solander). *Journal of Marine Research* 8:1–5.

Jones, J.S., Leith, B.H. and Rawlings, R. 1977. Polymorphism in *Cepaea*: a problem with too many solutions? *Annual Review of Ecology and Systematics* 8:109–43.

Largen, M.J. 1971. Genetic and environmental influences upon the expression of shell sculpture in the dog whelk (*Nucella lapillus*). *Proceedings of the Malacological Society of London* 39:383–8.

Leighton, D.L. 1961. Observations of the effect of diet on shell colouration in the red abalone, *Haliotus rufescens* Swainson. *The Veliger* 4:29–32.

Levins, R. 1968. *Evolution in changing environments: some theoretical explanations*. Princeton: Princeton University Press.

McMahon, R.F. and Whitehead, B.E. 1987. Environmental induction of shell morphometric variation in the European stream limpet, *Ancylus fluviatilis* (Müller) (Pulmonata: Basommatophora). *American Malacological Bulletin* 5:105–24.

Mitton, J.B. 1977. Shell color and pattern variation in *Mytilus edulis* and its adaptive significance. *Chesapeake Science* 18:387–90.

Moore, H.B. 1934. The relation of shell growth to environment in *Patella vulgata*. *Proceedings of the Malacological Society of London* 21:217–22.

Moore, H.B. 1936. The biology of *Purpura lapillus*. 1. Shell variation in relation to environment. *Journal of the Marine Biological Association of the United Kingdom* 21:61–89.

Morton, B. 1976. The biology, ecology and functional aspects of the organs of feeding and digestion of the S.E. Asian mangrove bivalve, *Enigmonia aenigmatica* (Mollusca: Anomiacea). *Journal of Zoology, London* 179:436–66.

Morton, B. 1987. Polymorphism in *Corbicula fluminea* (Bivalvia: Corbiculoidea) from Hong Kong. *Malacological Review* 20:105–27.

Pettitt, C.W. 1973. An examination of variation in shell colour and pattern in *Littorina saxatilis* (Olivi) with particular regard to the possibility of visual selection in this species. *Malacologia* 14:339–43.

Pettitt, C.W. 1975. A review of the predators of *Littorina*, especially those of *L. saxatilis* (Olivi) (Gastropoda: Prosobranchia). *Journal of Conchology* 28:343–57.

Raffaelli, D.G. 1982. Recent ecological research on some European species of *Littorina*. *Journal of Molluscan Studies* 48:342–54.

Reid, D.G. 1987. Natural selection for apostasy and crypsis acting on the shell colour polymorphism of a mangrove snail, *Littoraria filosa* (Sowerby) (Gastropoda: Littorinidae). *Biological Journal of the Linnean Society* 30:1–24.

Reimchen, T.E. 1979. Substrate heterogeneity, crypsis, and colour polymorphism in an intertidal snail (*Littorina mariae*). *Canadian Journal of Zoology* 57:1070–85.

Seed, R. 1968. Factors influencing shell shape in the mussel *Mytilus edulis*. *Journal of the Marine Biological Association of the United Kingdom* 48:561–84.

Sigurdsson, J.B. and Sundari, G. 1990. Colour changes in the shell of the tree-climbing bivalve *Enigmonia aenigmatica* (Holten, 1802) (Anomiidae). *Raffles Bulletin of Zoology* 38:213–8.

Sokal, R.R and Rohlf, F.J. 1981. *Biometry. The principles and practice of statistics in biological research.* New York: W.H. Freeman and Co.

Underwood, A.J. and Creese, R.G. 1976. Observation on the biology of the trochid gastropod *Austrocochlea constricta* (Lamarck) (Prosobranchia). II. The effects of available food on shell-banding pattern. *Journal of Experimental Marine Biology and Ecology* 23:229–40.

Via, S. and Lande, R. 1985. Genotype-environment interaction and the evolution of phenotypic plasticity. *Evolution* 39:505–22.

Yonge, C.M. 1957. *Enigmonia aenigmatica* (Sowerby), a motile anomiid (saddle oyster). *Nature* 180:765–6.

Yonge, C.M. 1977. Form and evolution in the Anomiacea (Mollusca: Bivalvia) — *Pododesmus, Anomia, Patro, Enigmonia* (Anomiidae): *Placunaomia, Placuna* (Placunidae Fam. Nov.). *Philosophical Transactions of the Royal Society of London* 276:453–527.

A COMPARATIVE STUDY OF THE EFFECTS OF SALINITY UPON GROWTH AND RESPIRATION IN TWO SPECIES OF MANGROVE

C.D. Field

City Polytechnic of Hong Kong, 83 Tat Chee Avenue, Kowloon, Hong Kong

ABSTRACT

Salinity levels in mangrove forests vary markedly in space and time. The extent to which a species can flourish in an environment of changing salinity will be an significant factor in the distribution and relative importance of that species along salinity gradients. The experiments to be described examine the relationship between growth parameters and respiration under various conditions of salinity in seedlings of *Avicennia marina* and *Aegiceras corniculatum*. The results show that the overall growth rates of the plants and the respiration rate of the roots were maximum when the external medium was at a salinity of 25% seawater. However, there was a marked difference between the two species in the response of leaf respiration to salinity. These results are discussed in terms of salt tolerance.

INTRODUCTION

Mangroves are the only trees amongst a relatively small group of halophytic plants that live in the intertidal zone at the interface between land and sea. Marked zonation patterns usually occur that are correlated with the frequency and duration of tidal immersion. Such correlations between vegetation patterns and tidal characteristics are often site specific as the two factors are not directly related (Field and Dartnall 1985). Growth of the mangroves is influenced by factors such as degree of saturation of the soil, form and availability of nutrients and the salinity of surface and soil water (Hutchings and Saenger 1987). The growth of mangroves is stimulated by saline conditions but there is a broad spectrum of responses between different species (Clough 1984). The aim of the present studies was to compare the responses to changes in salinity of growth, and root and leaf respiration of *Avicennia marina* (Forsk.) Vierh and *Aegiceras corniculatum* (L) Blanco. *Avicennia*, sometimes known as the grey mangrove, is considered to be a salt resistant species with salt glands on the leaves and well developed aerial roots. It is found in habitats over a wide range of latitudes and with varying salinity levels.

Aegiceras, sometimes known as the river mangrove, also has salt glands on the leaves but it is considered to be a much less salt tolerant mangrove species that is often found in rather brackish conditions.

MATERIALS AND METHODS

Growth of seedlings

Propagules of *Avicennia* and *Aegiceras* were collected from the same estuary near Sydney, Australia, and planted in plastic pots containing a soil mixture. The pots were placed in tanks containing 1–2 cm of seawater collected from Sydney Harbour as follows: 100% seawater, 25% seawater, and tap water. The measured sodium chloride concentrations were 32 g·l^{-1}, 8 g·l^{-1}, and 0 g·l^{-1}, respectively. The solutions in the tanks were replenished twice a week. Pots were fertilised every six weeks with a liquid fertiliser. The plants were harvested six months after germination.

Growth and respiration measurements

With both species, six plants per treatment were harvested. After washing, the plants were divided into roots, stems and leaves. Samples of leaves and roots were used for respiration measurements and the rest of the material was dried at 70°C for dry weight determination. Oxygen uptake of tissue samples was determined in the dark at 25°C using a Clark oxygen electrode. The bathing solution in the chamber was 5 mL of the solution used for growth.

RESULTS

Avicennia

Value at harvest of mean dry weight for leaves, stems and roots at 25% seawater was: 266 ± SE16, 224 ± SE20 and 248 ± SE19 mg·plant^{-1}, respectively. Figure 1 shows for the different plant tissues the variation with salinity of the dry weight·plant^{-1} normalised to the dry weight·plant^{-1} at 25% seawater. Dry weights for plant tissues examined were all maximal in 25% seawater. It can be seen that the dry weight, and hence the growth, is depressed at 0% and 100% seawater treatments as compared to the 25% seawater treatment.

Oxygen uptake, as micromoles of oxygen·g dry weight^{-1}·hour^{-1} for leaves and roots at 25% seawater was 27.0 and 31.0, respectively. Figure 2 shows for the different plant tissues the variation with salinity of the respiration normalised to the respiration at 25% seawater. It can be seen that the respiration rate for root tissue is depressed at high and low values of salinity but that the respiration rate for leaf tissue is slightly depressed at 0% salinity but elevated at high values of salinity.

Aegiceras

Value at harvest of mean dry weight for leaves, stems and roots at 25% seawater was:

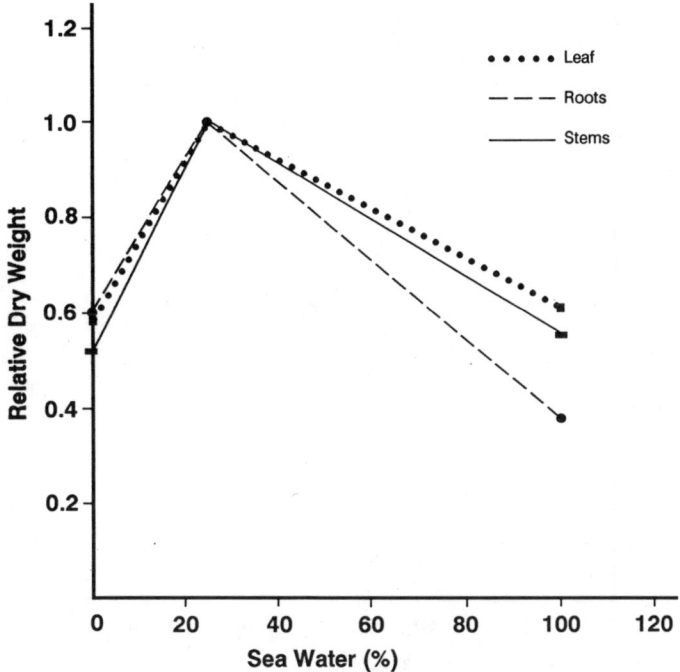

Fig. 1. Relative distribution of dry weights of leaf, roots and stem of *Avicennia* in 0, 25 and 100% seawater.

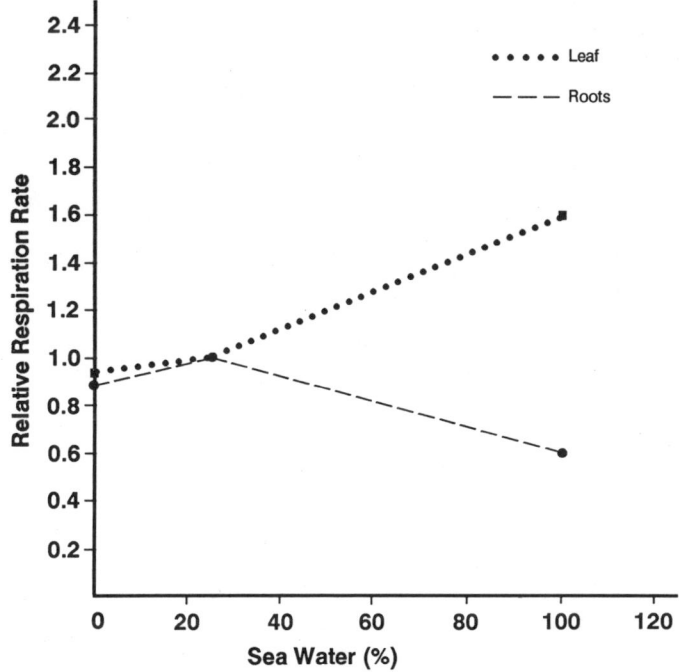

Fig. 2. Relative respiration rates for leaf and roots of *Avicennia* in 0, 25 and 100% seawater.

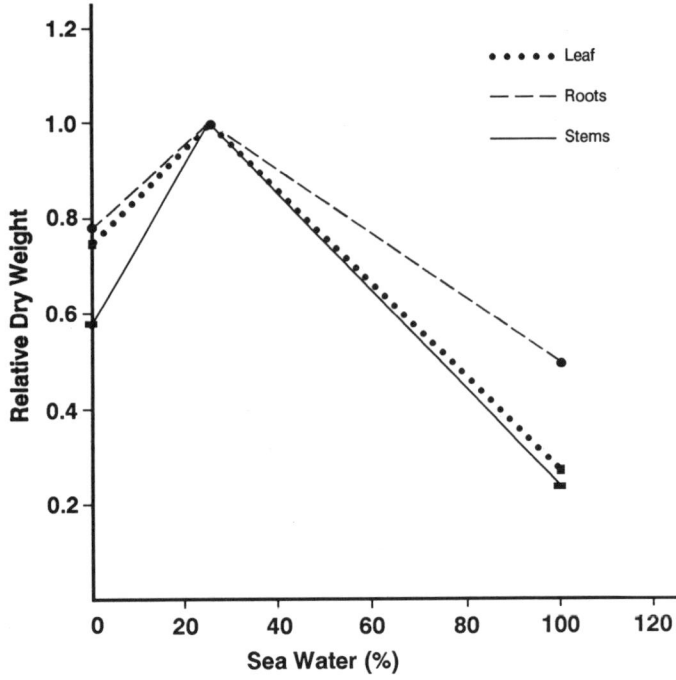

Fig. 3. Relative distribution of dry weights of leaf, roots and stem of *Aegiceras* in 0, 25 and 100% seawater.

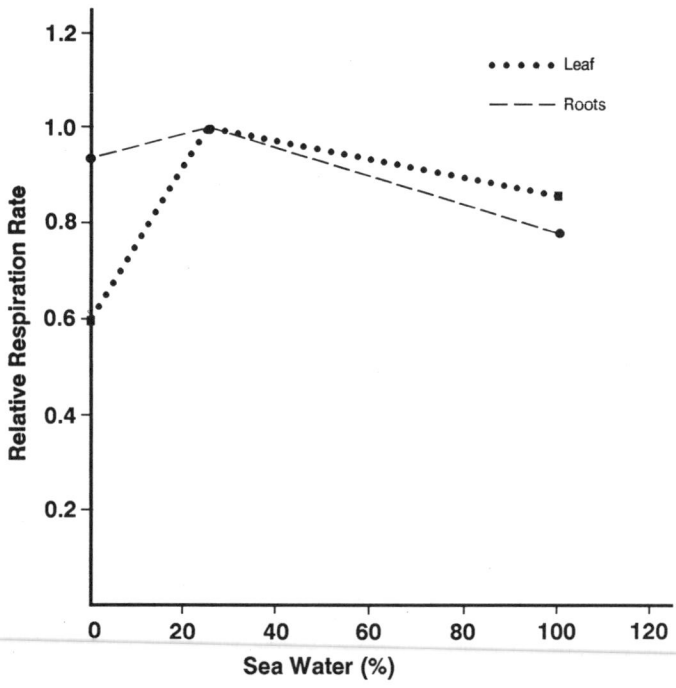

Fig. 4. Relative respiration rates for leaf and roots of *Aegiceras* in 0, 25 and 100% seawater

$120 \pm SE15$, $40 \pm SE4$, $60 \pm SE7$ mg·plant^{-1}, respectively. Figure 3 shows, for the different plant tissues, the variation with salinity of the dry weight·plant^{-2} normalised to the dry weight·plant^{-2} at 25% seawater. The results are similar to those obtained for *Avicennia*.

Oxygen uptake, as micromoles of oxygen·g dry weight^{-1}·hour^{-1} for leaves and roots at 25% seawater was 47 and 43, respectively. Figure 4 shows the results in the same manner as used for *Avicennia*. In this case the respiration rates for leaves and roots are all depressed at low and high salinities. It is interesting to note that the respiration rates of *Aegiceras* were always higher than those of *Avicennia*, regardless of the plant tissue used.

DISCUSSION

Salt stimulation of growth is a common feature of halophytes, although the precise mechanism has yet to be defined (Greenway and Munns 1980; Yeo and Flowers 1980). The present results show that the overall growth rate and the growth rate of the individual plant parts are relatively enhanced with 25% seawater as the bathing medium, for both *Avicennia* and *Aegiceras*. Root respiration in the two species showed similar responses to changes of salinity, with a slight decrease in respiration at 0% seawater and a more marked decrease at 100% seawater. However, leaf respiration responded differently in the two species. In *Avicennia* there was only a slight decline in respiration rate at 0% seawater but in *Aegiceras* there was a marked decline in the respiration rate. In 100% seawater the respiration rate in the leaves of *Avicennia* continued to rise, whereas in *Aegiceras* the respiration rate of the leaves began to decline, relative to that observed at 25% seawater.

Yeo and Flowers (1980) suggested that turgor-controlled growth response could account for the increase in growth with increasing salt concentration in some halophytes and that the decrease in growth at high salinities might be due to toxic effects of the salt. The present results are consistent with these suggestions. In *Avicennia*, photosynthetic rates decrease with increasing salinity (Ball 1988). The effect is believed to be the result of high internal ion concentration. The present study shows that the respiration rates in the leaves and roots of both species rise with an initial increase in salinity while, at the same time, the capacity for assimilation in the leaves is declining. The respiratory demands of the leaves of both mangrove species may be such that there is little in the way of assimilates to supply the roots. This situation could account for the low root weights and low root respiration in both species at high salinities. Eventually, the leaf respiration would also be decreased and it is interesting to note that in this study the eventual decline in leaf respiration was found in the less salt-tolerant species.

There are possible ecological implications of these results as the structure of mangrove forests, with respect to changes of salinity, probably depends on the salt tolerance of the species and competitive advantages reflecting differences in such physiological parameters as assimilation rates and water use efficiency. It is interesting to note that the leaf respiration in the less salt tolerant species declined quicker than in the more salt tolerant species and that this effect may give the salt tolerant species a competitive edge in regions of high salinity. Further investigation is needed to derive and compare total carbon budgets for both species and to show how such budgets are altered by changes in salinity.

REFERENCES

Ball, M.C. 1988. Ecophysiology of mangroves. *Trees* 2:129–42
Clough, B.F. 1984. Growth and salt balance of the mangroves, *Avicennia marina* (Forsk.) Vierh and *Rhizophora stylosa* Griff. in relation to salinity. *Australian Journal of Plant Physiology* 11:419–30.
Field, C.D. and Dartnall, A.J. eds. 1985. *Mangrove Ecosystems of Asia and the Pacific: Status, Exploitation and Management.* Townsville: Australian Institute of Marine Science.
Greenway, H. and Munns, R. 1980. Mechanisms of salt tolerance in non halophytes. *Annual Review of Plant Physiology* 31:149–90.
Hutchings, P. and Saenger, P. 1987. *Ecology of Mangroves.* Australia: University of Queensland Press.
Yeo, A.R. and Flowers, T.J. 1986. Ion transport in *Suadea maritima*: its relationship to growth and implications for the pathway of radial transport of ions and water across the root. *Journal of Experimental Botany* 37:143–59.

THE HEART OF *HYOTISSA IMBRICATA* (BIVALVIA: GRYPHAEIDAE)

Li Xiaoxu and Chen Tiejie

Institute of Oceanology, Academia Sinica, Qingdao, China

and

George A. Evseev and Yuri M. Yakovlev

Institute of Marine Biology, Far East Branch, Russian Academy of Sciences, Vladivostok, Russia

ABSTRACT

Unlike other bivalve molluscs, the right auricle of *Hyotissa imbricata* is subdivided into two parts, with connections to two blood vessels. That is, in addition to the large general vein which delivers blood from the right ctenidium and anterior part of the right mantle lobe to the lower right auricles, there is a small posterior vein mainly transporting blood from the posterior parts of the mantle lobes and the anal regions to the upper right auricle. Both auricles share their posterior walls with the kidneys. Two funnel-shaped reno-pericardial ducts also open into the large kidneys.

INTRODUCTION

Hyotissa imbricats (Lamarck, 1819) is representative of the Ostreoidea, for which detailed descriptions of the circulatory and excretory systems have been given by Leenhardt (in Stenzel 1971) for *Crassostrea angulata* (Lamarck), Awati and Rai (1931) for *Saccostrea cucullata* (Born), White (1942) for *Ostrea edulis* L. and *Ostrea madrasensis* Preston and by Galtsoff (1964) for *Crassostrea virginica* (Gmelin). Each has a blood-filled thin-walled pericardium enclosing the elongate heart, which has a pair of thin-walled contractile auricles leading into a single larger ventricle sheathed with muscles. The auricles connect with two general veins directly, while the ventricle connects with two aortae. The kidneys, or the organs of Bojanus, are two highly contorted tubules encased in a blood-filled sinus, located at the dorsal flank of the adductor muscle (Stenzel, 1971). These two systems are nearly the same as those in other bivalve molluscs (White 1942; Russell-Hunter 1979). Harry (1985) has described briefly these systems in oysters at the subfamily level and described the irregularly outpocketed auricles of *Hyotissa hyotis* (Linnaeus), but failed to locate the renopericardial passage. Although *H. imbricata* is classified in this genus also, some aspects of the anatomy remain unclarified.

MATERIALS AND METHODS

Nine individuals of *Hyotissa imbricata* were collected from the intertidal zones of Linchang, Hainan Province, China, in 1990, and fixed in 5% formalin. Anatomical observations were made under the binocular dissecting microscope. The orientation used in this paper was suggested by Harry (1985).

RESULTS

The heart is surrounded by the thin pericardial walls and antero-ventrally shares them with the large kidneys (Figs. 1 and 2). Inside the pericardium, there is one ventricle which is pierced by the intestine and two auricles which are extensively fused to the ventral wall of the pericardium and irregularly outpocketed (Fig. 3). The right auricle is subdivided into two parts, the upper right auricle, which connects with the posterior vein, and the lower right auricle, which connects with the right general vein (Fig. 3A, B and D). The left auricle is sometimes also subdivided (Fig. 3A and C), but only links up with one blood vessel, the left general vein (Fig. 3D). The ventricle connects with the anterior and the posterior aortae directly. Between the auricles and the ventricles, and the ventricle and the anterior aorta, are valves (Fig. 2). The veins, including the posterior, the general, the efferent branchial and the mantle veins, run inside the thin kidney walls towards the auricles (Fig. 2).

The pericardium is elongate antero-ventrally, forming a funnel-shaped reno-pericardial tube on either side of the pyloric pouch, which is the ventrally extended part of the visceral mass, and opens into the kidneys directly. The kidneys, located at the anterior and ventral flanks of the heart, comprise a large, thin-walled, sac and three highly contorted tubular extensions which run antero-laterally towards the labial palps on either side and posteriorly towards the anus (Fig. 1).

The kidneys discharge by way of a pair of small pores near the genital openings in the short slit-like uro-genital clefts, which lie on the pyloric pouch between the inner and the outer plates of the inner demibranchs of the ctenidia (Fig. 2).

DISCUSSION

A comparison of the heart region of *Hyotissa imbricata* with that of other oysters shows that it is closely similar to that of the Pycnodonteinae, but different from the remainder. As in the Pycnodonteinae described by Harry (1985), the auricles, which are fused to each other, are also extensively fused to the ventral wall of the pericardium, over the adductor muscle, and are irregularly outpocketed, appearing lobate. In *H. imbricata*,

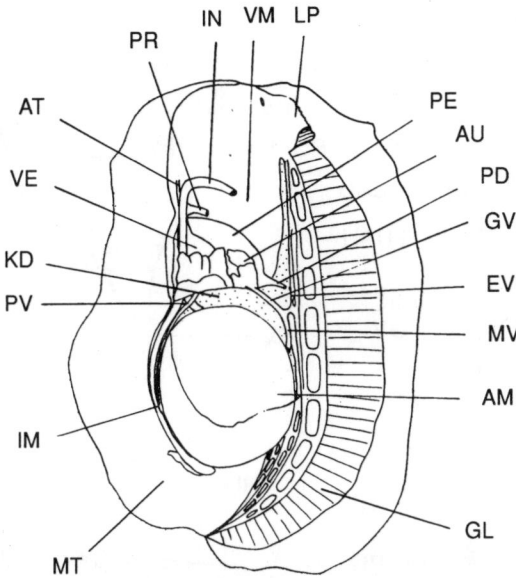

Fig. 1. *Hyotissa imbricata*. Right lateral view after removal of the right mantle and the right pericardial wall; the anterior arteries are shown partly.

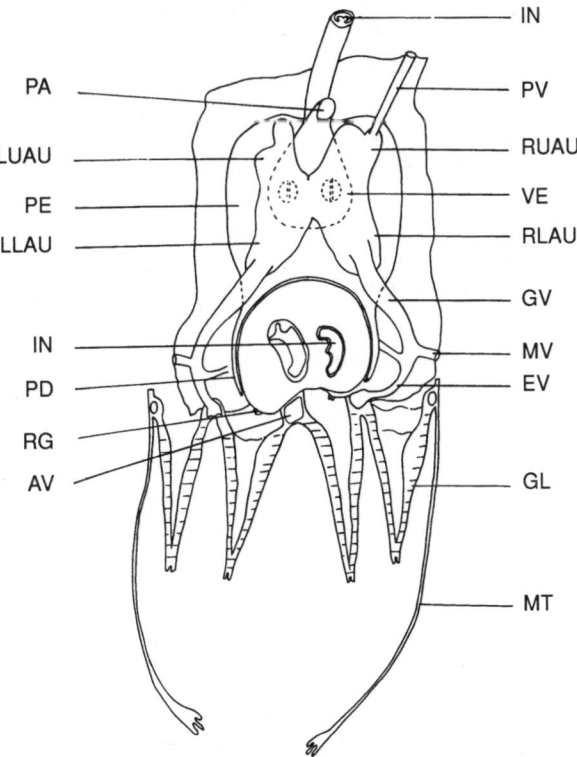

Fig. 2. *Hyotissa imbricata*. Transverse section through the kidney. The dorsal mantle lobes have been removed.

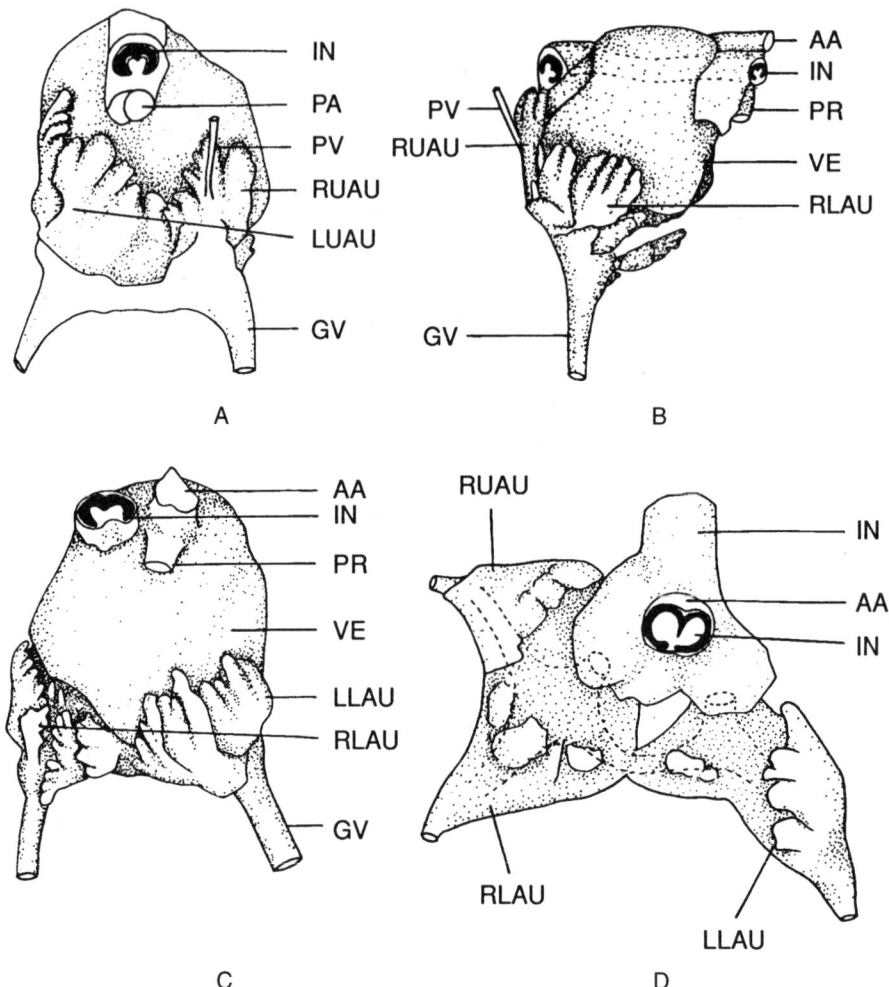

Fig. 3. The heart of *Hoytissa imbricata*. A, dorsal view; B, right lateral view; C, ventral view and D, ventral view. (AA, anterior aorta; AM, adductor muscle; AT, anterior artery; AU, auricle; AV, afferent branchial vein; EV, efferent branchial vein; GL, gills; GV, general vein; IN, intestine; KD, kidney; LLAU, left lower auricle; LP, labial palp; LUAU, left upper auricle; MT, mantle; MV, mantle vein; PA, posterior aorta; PD, the funnel-shaped reno-perticardial duct; PV, posterior vein; RG, uro-genital cleft; RLAU, right lower auricle; RUAU, right upper auricle; VE, ventricle; VM, visceral mass).

however, the right auricle is subdivided into two parts and connects with two veins directly, that is, in addition to the large general vein which delivers blood from the efferent branchial veins and from the mantle veins to the lower right auricle, there is special small posterior vein mainly transporting blood from the posterior parts of the mantle lobes and the anal regions to the upper right auricle. This small posterior vein is unique to *H. imbricata*.

Harry (1985) did not locate the reno-pericardial passage in the Pycnodonteinae; in

Hyotissa imbricata, this passage, being similar to that of *Crassostrea gigas*, is a funnel-shaped duct extending from the pericardium.

The kidneys are well developed in the Pycnodonteinae. Each consists of a large, flattened, thin-walled, sac with several extensions (Harry 1985). In other oysters, the narrow central part of the excretory system extends across the body from one side to the other and contains a narrow and twisted inter-nephridial passage which connects the two limbs (Galtsoff 1964).

The urogenital cleft lies between the inner and the outer plates of the inner demibranch in *Hyotissa imbricata*, while in *Crassostrea gigas*, it lies on the visceral mass laterally.

ACKNOWLEDGEMENT

Sincere thanks are expressed to Professor Qi Zhongyan for a critical reading of the manuscript of this paper.

REFERENCES

Awati, P.R. and Rai, H.S. 1931. *Ostrea cucullata* (the Bombay oyster). *Indian Zoological Memoir on Indian Animal Types* 3:1–107.
Galtsoff, P.S. 1964. The American oyster *Crassostrea virginica* Gmelin. *United States Bureau of Commercial Fisheries, Fishery Bulletin* 64:1–480.
Harry, H.W. 1985. Synopsis of the supraspecific classification of living oysters (Bivalvia: Gryphaeidae and Ostreidae). *The Veliger* 28:121–58.
Russell-Hunter, W.D. 1979. *A Life of Invertebrates*. New York: MacMillan Publishing Co.
Stenzel, H.B. 1971. Oysters. In *Treatise on Invertebrate Paleontology* (ed. R.C. Moore), Part N, 3(6), N953–N1224. Kansas: The Geological Society of America and University of Kansas Press.
White, K.M. 1942, The pericardial cavity and the pericardial gland of the Lamellibranchia. *Proceedings of the Malacological Society of London* 25:37–88.

THE INTERTIDAL ECOLOGY OF A ROCKY SHORE AT YANGKOU, QINGDAO, CHINA

Qi Zhongyan, Lin Guangyu, Yang Zongdai, Ren Xianqiu and Li Fenglan

Institute of Oceanology, Academia Sinica, 7 Nan Hai Road, Qingdao, China

ABSTRACT

One-hundred and twenty-three species were obtained from rocky shores at Yangkou, Qingdao, China: Mollusca (36; 38.14%), Crustacea (10; 10.31%), Polychaeta (9; 9.27%). The remainder included representatives of the Platyhelminthes, Nemertea, Coelenterata, Echinodermata and Ascidiacea. There are no estuarine species. Twenty-six species of algae were obtained: Phaeophyta (10), Rhodophyta (9), and Chlorophyta (7).

The total biomass was 594.09 $g \cdot m^{-2}$: Mollusca (277.14 $g \cdot m^{-2}$; 38.28%), Algae (207.09 $g \cdot m^{-2}$; 44.06%), Crustacea (77.53 $g \cdot m^{-2}$; 13.06%), Polychaeta (0.6 $g \cdot m^{-2}$; 0.11%) and the others (21.33 $g \cdot m^{-2}$; 3.59%).

Five typical communities were identified as follows: (1) Supra-intertidal zone, dominated by *Littorina brevicula* and *Nodilittorina radiata*; (2) Upper mid-littoral zone, dominated by *Chthamalus challengeri*, *Xenotrobus atrata* and *L. brevicula*; (3) Lower mid-littoral zone (facing the sun), dominated by *Saccostrea cucullata*, *Rissoa* sp. and *Ulva pertusa*; (4) Lower mid-littorinal zone (in the shade) dominated by *Caulacanthus okamurai*; (5) Sub-littoral fringe zone, dominated by *Sargassum thunbergii*, *S.argassum pallidium* and *Temnopleurus hardwickii*.

Seasonal variations in community structure were evident although the animals showed less prominent community variations than the algae. Warm water species appeared in summer and autumn; cold water species in winter and spring.

INTRODUCTION

Intertidal ecology plays an important role in marine production, environmental preservation and in developing and using marine resources. Much work has been done on the rocky intertidal, and its division into zones. Although scientists have researched the ecology of the intertidal zone of China, very little research has been undertaken upon northern, open, rocky shores. This paper concerns itself with a seasonal (March, July, October and December) investigation of an open rocky shore at Yangkou, Qingdao, from 1981–82 by the Institute of Oceanology, Academia Sinica. This work will supply basic scientific data for further study of the intertidal zone and for rationally developing potential resources.

MATERIALS AND METHODS

Sampling stations for transects were selected according to biological divisions identified by Stephensen and Stephensen (1949) and the vertical distribution of organisms down the transects investigated. Analyses of species composition, biomass and seasonal variations in community structure have been undertaken (Fig. 1).

RESULTS

Yangkou (120°43'E, 36°15'N) is located at the base of Laoshan Mountain on the coast of the Yellow Sea with steep rocks and clear water. The intertidal zone at Yangkou is open, exchanges frequently with the outer sea and is affected greatly by wave action. The intertidal zone is narrow (35 m) and the lower mid-littoral zone can be divided into two ecological categories, i.e., facing the sun and in the shade.

At Yangkou, the tide is semidiurnal with a range of 4.12 m. In summer and autumn, the tidal range is greater during the night than during the day, but the reverse is true in spring and winter.

Water temperature and salinity are also important factors influencing the distribution of organisms. The average of 15 years water temperature records show a range from 2.1°C (January) to 25.1°C (August) with no ice throughout the year. The salinity ranges from 29.62 to 31.24‰. There is no freshwater input.

Species composition

The intertidal zone investigated is located in the warm temperate zone so that the majority of species are eurytopic. No typically tropical, cold water or estuarine species occur.

Totally, 97 species of benthos were obtained and included representatives of the Mollusca (36 species; 38.10%), Crustacea (10; 10.31%), Polychaeta (9; 0.27%), Echinodermata (5; 5.1%), with the remaining nine species comprising representatives of the Coelenterata, Nemertea, Platyhelminthes and Ascidia. Algae comprised 26 species as follows: Phaeophyta (10), Rhodophyta (9) and Chlorophyta (7) (Fig. 2).

The dominant species of the intertidal zone are *Littorina brevicula*, *Nodilittorina radiata*, *Saccostrea cucullata*, *Xenostrobus atrata*, *Chthamalus challengeri*, *Temnopleurus hardwickii*, *Sargassum thunbergii*, *Ulva pertusa* and *Caulacanthus okamurai*.

Station 1 (above EHWST), is sprayed only during highest high water springs tides; the organisms which occur here are *Littorina brevicula* and *Nodilittorina radiata* which gregariously dwell in cavities and crevices. *Ligia exotica* occurs occasionally.

Station 2 (near HHWST). More species (12 species) appear and include the Mollusca (10), Crustacea (1) and Polychaeta (1). The dominant species are *Chthamalus challengeri*, *Xenostrobus atrata* and *Littorina brevicula*. Algae occur at this level seasonally.

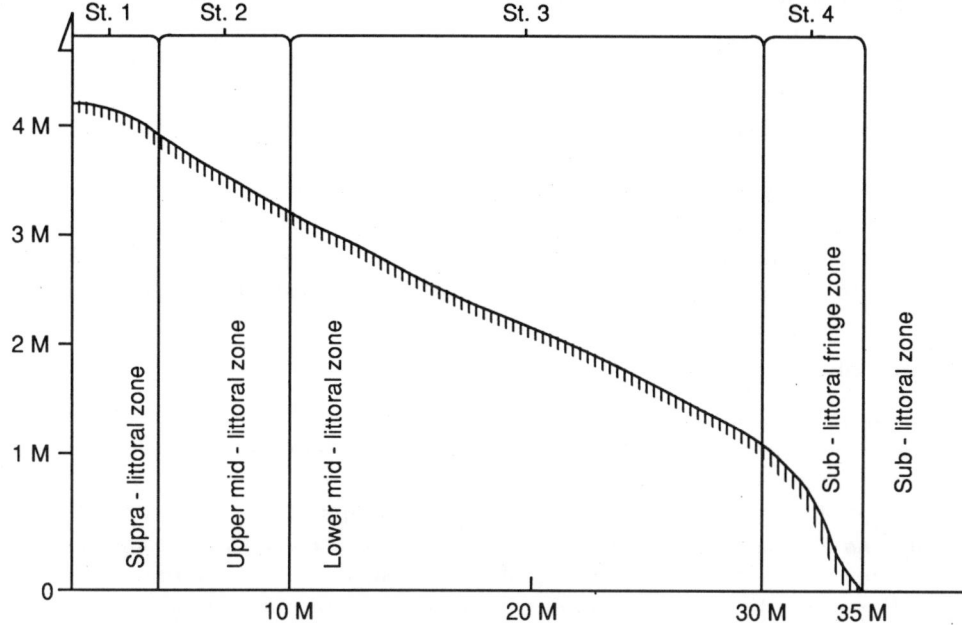

Fig. 1. The transect at Yangkou showing the stations.

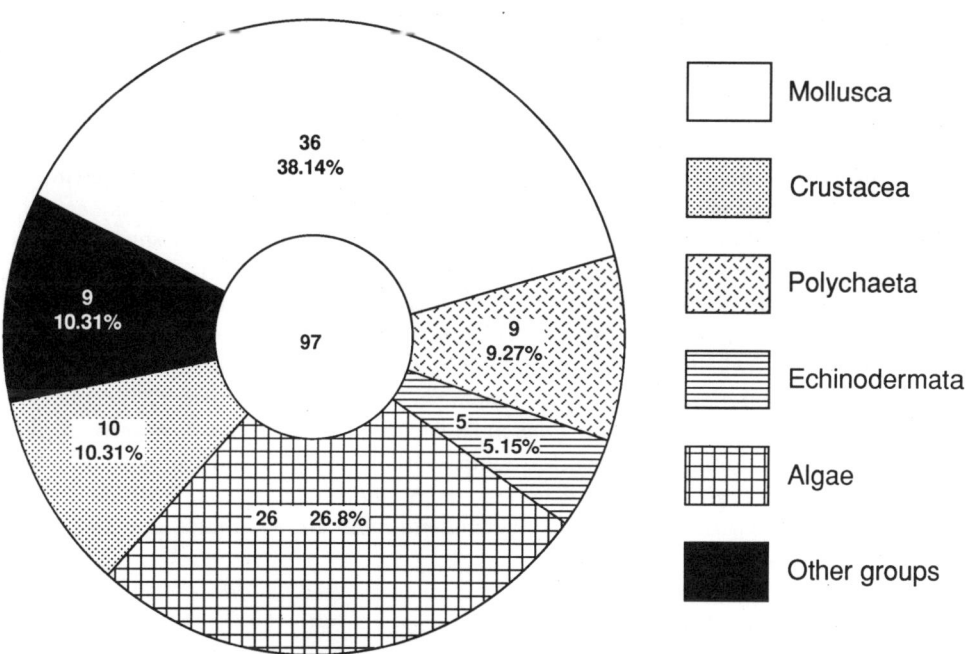

Fig. 2. The average percentage importance of organism groups in the transect investigated.

Station 3 (below HHWNT). Twenty-five species were recorded from this level with the Mollusca dominant. Representatives of the Coelenterata, Nemertea and Ascidia began to occur at this station. There are two subcommunities: (1) (facing the sun): *Saccostrea cucullata*, *Rissoa* sp., *Xenostrobus atrata* and *Ulva pertusa*; (2) (in the shade): Algae dominate here and few animals occur. *Xenostrobus atrata* was occasionally recorded, but the dominant species is *Caulacanthus okamurai*.

Station 4 (MLWNT). Fifty-six species were recorded and a great many algae grow luxuriantly. Representative of the Echinodermata and Platyhelminthes were recorded. Dominant species included *Sargassum thunbergii*, *S. pallidum* and *Temnopleurus hardwickii*. The species representative of this zone extend into the sub-littoral zone.

Community structure

The frequency of occurrence of each species in the seasonal quantitative samples and additional quantitative sampling along the main and auxiliary transects have been used to analyse and classify the different communities.

Supra-littoral zone (Station 1). Dominated by only two species of Mollusca (*Littorina brevicula* and *Nodilittorina radiata*). *L. brevicula* is distributed downwards to the upper mid-littoral zone, lower mid-littoral zone and sub-littoral fringe.

Upper mid-littoral zone (Station 2). Dominated by *Chthamalus challengeri*, *Xenostrobus atrata* and *L. brevicula*. More species of animals appear and commonly include *Patelloida pygmaea*, *Acanthochiton rubrolineatus*, *Thais clavigera*, *Notoacmea schrencki* and *Lasaea undulata*. *L. brevicula* connects this region with the supra-littoral zone and *L. brevicula*, *X. atrata* and *Patelloida pygmaea* extend downwards to connect up with the lower mid-littoral zone.

Lower mid-littoral zone (Station 3, facing the sun). Dominated by *Saccostrea cucullata*, *Rissoa* sp. and *Ulva pertusa*. More species occur here and commonly include *L. brevicula*, *Cellana toreuma*, *Patelloida pygmaea*, *Lunella coronata coreensis*, *Siphonaria japonica*, *Perinereis fleridama* and *Caulacanthus okamurai*. *L. brevicula*, *X. atrata* and *C. okamurai* connect this region with the lower mid-littoral zone (in the shade). *Saccostrea cucullata*, *Lunella coronata coreensis* and *Ulva pertusa* connect this zone with the sub-littoral fringe. Lower mid-littoral zone (Station 3, in the shade). Dominated by *Caulacanthus okamurai*.

Sub-littoral fringe zone (Station 4). Dominated by *Sargassum thunbergii*, *S. pallidum* and *Temnopleurus hardwickii*. Other common species include *Siphonaria japonica*, *Patelloida pygmaea*, *Ulva pertusa*, *Lunella coronata coreensis*, *Haliotis discus hannai*, *Hemigrapsus penicillatus*, *Stichopus japonicus*, *Gracilaria textorii*, *G. verrucosa*, *Desmarestia viridis*, *Scytosiphon Lomentarius*, *Colpomenia sinuosa*, *Enteromorpha intestinalis* and *Chorda filum*. Species composition is complex and varies seasonally. *Sargassum thunbergii*, *Gracilaria verrucosa*, *Stichopus japonicus*, *Haliotis discus hannai*, *Temnopleurus hardwickii* and *Monodonta labio* are distributed downwards to the sub-littoral zone.

Biomass

The total average biomass of the transect investigated was 594.09 g·m^{-2} which included Mollusca (227.14 g·m^{-2}; 38.28%), Algae (267.09 g·m^{-2}; 44.09%), Crustacea (77.53

g·m^{-2}; 13.06%), Polychaeta (0.67 g·m^{-2}; 0.11%) and others (21.31 g·m^{-2}; 3.59%) (Fig. 3; Table 1). At Yangkou, the density of species such as *Saccostrea cucullata* and *Littorina brevicula* are much lower than on sheltered, estuarine, shores, but they appear in relatively greater quantities and cause the Mollusca to have a greater biomass than the other groups. Although *Chthamalus challengeri* is smaller than *Saccostrea cucullata*, its density is much greater, creating a clear zone of relatively high biomass. The large kelp, *Sargassum thunbergii*, is characteristic of the lower levels of the transect investigated. Although the economic species *Haliotis discus hannai* and *Stichopus japonicus* did not appear in the quantitative samples, they are important components of the shore fauna.

The average biomass of Station 1 was 120.98 g·m^{-2} and was reached by spray only during high spring tides and the community here comprises only two species of Mollusca: *L. brevicula* and *Nodilittorina radiata* which gregariously dwell in cavities and crevices in high densities.

The average biomass of Station 2 was 93.74 g·m^{-2} with the Crustacea dominant. The density of *Chthamalus challengeri* (685 g·m^{-2}) was greater than that of the other species in spring and autumn. The Mollusca biomass was second because only three species occur here in low densities.

The average biomass of Station 3 (facing the sun) was 3257.02 g·m^{-2} with high species numbers also. There were eight species of Mollusca with an average biomass of 3214.02 g·m^{-2}. *Saccostrea cucullata* had the greatest density and biomass which reached a maximum of 3030.9 g·m^{-2} in winter (December). Only two species of algae appear, but their biomass was second highest, because they are large kelp. The biomass of Station 3 (in the shade) was low (42.4 g·m^{-2}) and dominated by *Caulacanthus okamurai*. Only *Xenostrobus atrata* occurred with *Caulacanthus*.

The average biomass of Station 4 was 3577.23 g m^{-2} with a great species diversity. Dominated by four species of kelp, their biomass was high (256 g·m^{-2}, in September). Seven species of Mollusca were recorded and their biomass was second (91.62 g·m^{-2}). The biomass of Coelenterata was also important (12.8 g·m^{-2}).

Seasonal variation

The shore at Yangkou is located in the warm temperate zone so that water temperature fluctuates greatly from 2.7°C (February) to 26.5°C (August). Water temperature increases from March to July and decreases from September to January. Water temperature is the main factor influencing the geographic distribution and quantitative fluctuations in organism occurrence. Most of the animals at Yangkou are eurythernic, euryhaline and eurytopic and show only a slight seasonal variation. Of the 25 species of Mollusca recorded, 19 occurred in summer, 17 in autumn, 11 in winter and 15 in spring. Of the ten species of Crustacea, nine occurred in winter with somewhat stable numbers recorded during the other three seasons (6–8 species). Of the 9 species of Polychaeta, 4 occurred in winter, 3 in spring and autumn and 2 in summer (Figs. 4 and 5).

Benthic biomass was greater in spring and autumn than in winter and summer. Density reached a maximum in spring and was stable during the other three seasons.

The seasonal sequence (from high to low) in biomass of the supra-littoral zone was spring > autumn > summer > winter; that of density was summer > spring > autumn > winter. Mollusca accounted for 100% of the samples.

Table 1
Seasonal vertical distribution of biomass and density of important groups of organism on the shore at Yangkou.

Zone	Season	Term	Mollusca	Crustacea	Polychaeta	Algae	other	Total
Supra-littoral zone	Spring	g·m⁻²	6700					6700
		no's·m⁻²	49					49
	Summer	g·m⁻²	2140					2140
		no's·m⁻²	61.8					61.8
	Autumn	g·m⁻²	2650					2650
		no's·m⁻²	9.5					9.5
	Winter	g·m⁻²	140					140
		no's·m⁻²	0.6					0.6
Mid-littoral zone	Spring	g·m⁻²	2140	34000				36140
		no's·m⁻²	71.8	336.5		13		421.3
	Summer	g·m⁻²	1340	10800	80			12220
		no's·m⁻²	284.6	80	0.6	10.2		375.4
	Autumn	g·m⁻²	13000	14800	300			28100
		no's·m⁻²	1825	349	7.5			2181.5
	Winter	g·m⁻²	6720	11880				18600
		no's·m⁻²	342.42	161.4		19.2		523.02
Sub-littoral fringe zone	Spring	g·m⁻²	2950	150				3100
		no's·m⁻²	8	1.5		1665.5		1675
	Summer	g·m⁻²	380	180				560
		no's·m⁻²	1.11	2		21.2		24.31
	Autumn	g·m⁻²	2200					2200
		no's·m⁻²	5.3			1256		1261.3
	Winter	g·m⁻²	5580	40			20	6640
		no's·m⁻²	66.42	4		220	256	546.42

Transect: Yangkou, Qingdao

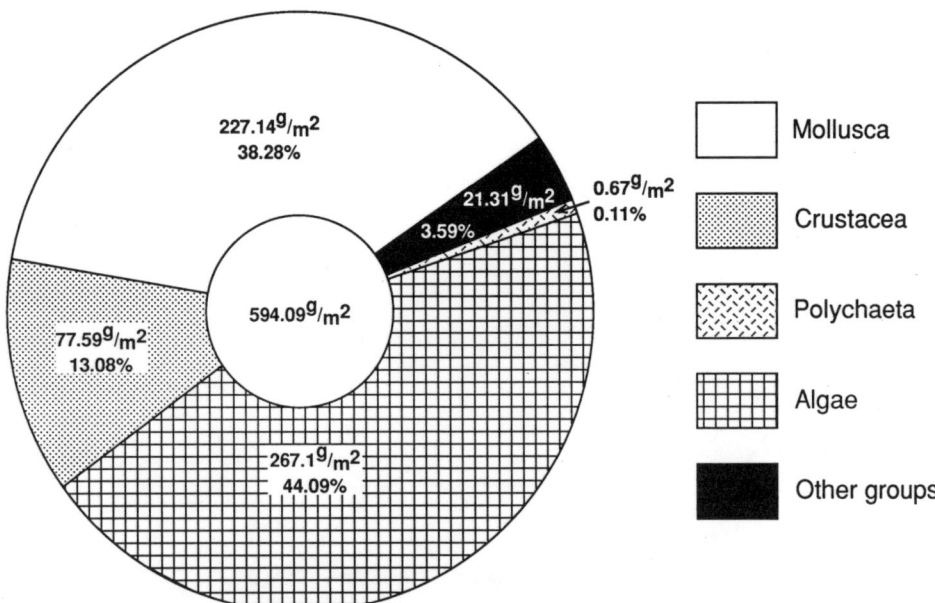

Fig. 3. Average percentage importance of organisms in the biomass of the transect investigated.

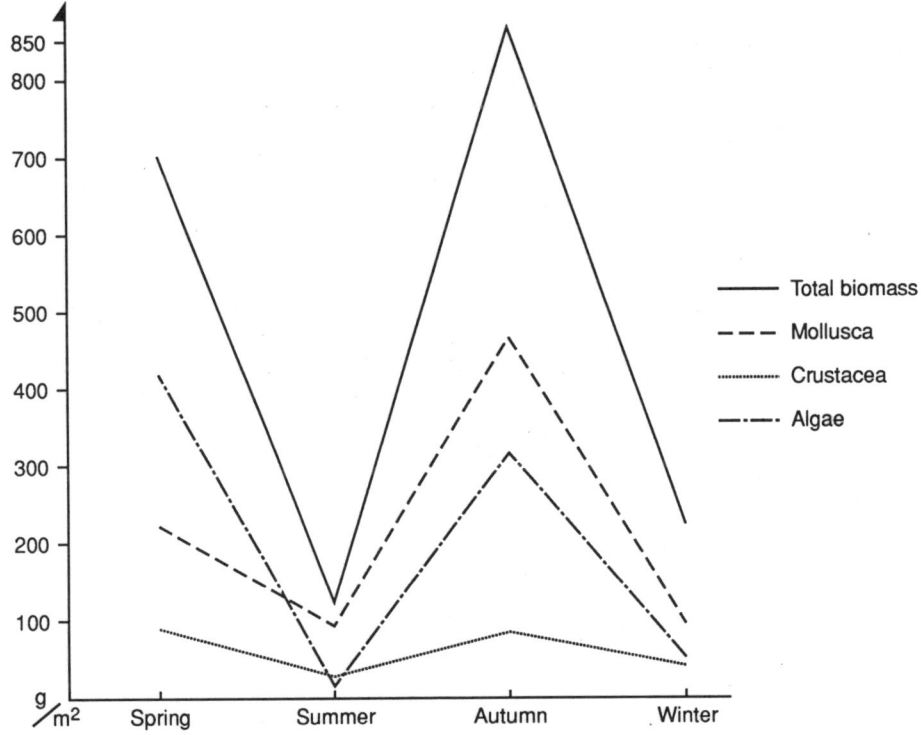

Fig. 4. The average biomass of important groups of organisms along the transect investigated.

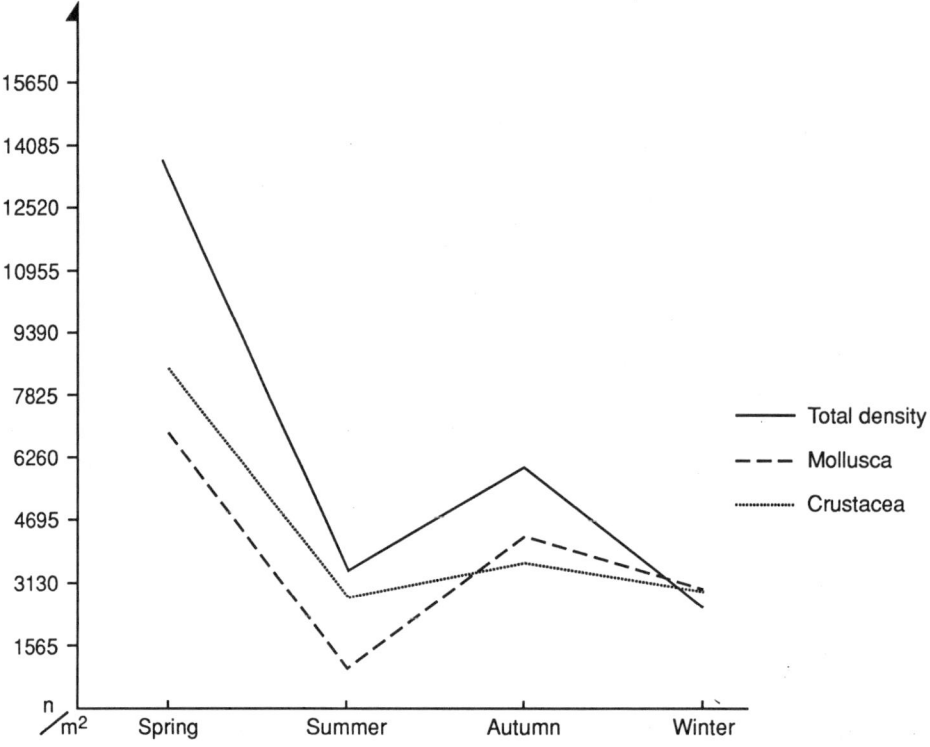

Fig. 5. The average density of important groups of organisms along the transect investigated.

The seasonal sequence in biomass of the mid-littoral zone was autumn > winter > spring > summer; that of density was winter > spring > autumn > summer. Mollusca accounted for 87%, Crustacea 12.7% and Polychaeta 0.3% of the samples.

The seasonal sequence in biomass of the sub-littoral fringe zone was winter > spring > autumn > summer; that of density was spring > autumn > winter > summer. Mollusca and Crustacea accounted for 82.3% and 17%, respectively.

The algae showed prominent seasonal variations in biomass. The number of Phaeophyta species fluctuated from 9 to 6 with only *Sargassum thunbergii* and *Ulva pertusa* occurring throughout the year. The warm water species *Dictyota indica* and *Padina crassa* appeared only in summer and autumn. The cold water species *Scytosiphon lomentarius* appeared in winter and spring when the water temperature nearly equalled that of the sub-cold zone. Although most of species of algae are distributed below the mid-littoral zone, *Gloiopeltis furcata* occurred on the upper mid-littoral zone in spring and in the sub-littoral fringe in summer.

DISCUSSION

The species occurring in the transects investigated at Yangkou are mostly eurythermal, euryhaline and eurytopic, and the fauna is typical of the temperate zone. This is similar to the conclusion of Morton (1990). At Qingdao, seawater temperature is higher than 20°C in summer and autumn (close to the water temperature of the subtropics). Some warm water species occurring in summer, for example, *Dictyota indica* and *Padina crassa* (Morton 1990) also occur in autumn. In spring and winter, the seawater temperature at Qingdao is lower than 2°C, (close to the water temperature of the subarctic) and some cold water species occurring in winter, for example, *Scytosiphon lomentarius* (Morton 1990) also occur in spring. Information on the seasonal species composition and distribution and variation in the intertidal zone can be learned only through seasonal investigations.

The biomass of the rocky intertidal at Yangkou is as high as 594.09 g·m^{-2}, and is greater than that of the intertidal of the Yellow Sea, which usually ranges between 150–200 g·m^{-2}, with the highest value of 600 g·m^{-2} being recorded by Gurjanova *et al.* (1958). This is because Yangkou is far from the city and is disturbed by people to little extent. Another reason for this is that macroalgae such as *Sargassum thunbergii* have a large biomass. The biomass of Yangkou intertidal is lower than the sheltered or semi-sheltered intertidal zone of Jiaozhou Bay. For example, at Daheilan, Qingdao, where there is no human interference, the biomass is as high as 1769.29 g·m^{-2} (Gurjanova *et al.* 1958). From the above discussion, it is clear that human activity plays an very important role in the distribution of organisms. Yangkou intertidal is open and influenced by currents and waves. Here, vertical cross distribution of organisms is affected by the tide and is different from that of Jiaozhou Bay. One or more species connect the different communities of the Yangkou intertidal. Some species, such as *Saccostrea cucullata*, are distributed down to the sub-littoral fringe at Yangkou. But at Zhonggang, Qingdao, thus species is only distributed down to the mid-littoral zone and adults dwell at higher levels than smaller individuals. *Littorina brevicula* can be distributed down to the sub-littoral fringe at Yangkou. However, at Zhonggang, Qingdao, it is distributed down no more than the upper mid-littoral zone because of tides and currents.

The structure and fluctuations in intertidal communities are influenced by not only environmental factors, such as tides and waves, but also by competition between species for space and food (Chapman 1974). There are two apparently different communities in the Yangkou lower mid-littoral zone, i.e., facing the sun and in the shade. The surface of rocks in the shade is nearly wholly occupied by *Caulacanthus okamurai*. On the other side, facing the sun, *Saccostrea cucullata* and *Ulva pertusa* do not occur because there is no space for their settlement. This indicates that the competition between species directly affects the formation of biological zonation.

ACKNOWLEDGEMENT

We are indebted to Prof. B. Morton for providing grants for us participate in the International Conference on the Marine Biology of Hong Kong and South China Sea, 1990, and for his criticisms of the first draft of the manuscript of this paper.

REFERENCES

Chapman, A.R.O., 1974. The ecology of macroscopic marine algae. *Annals of Ecology and Systematics* 5:65–80.

Gurjanova, E.F., Liu, J.Y., Scarlato, Q.A., Uschkov, P.V., Wu, B.L. and Tsi, C.Y. 1958. A short report on the intertidal zone of the Shantong peninsula (Yellow Sea). *Bulletin of the Institute of Marine Biology, Academia Sinica* 1:1–113. (In Chinese and Russian)

Morton, B. 1990. The rocky shore ecology of Qingdao, Shandong Province, People's Republic of China. *Asian Marine Biology* 7:167–87.

Stephenson, T.A. and Stephenson, A. 1949. The universal features of zonation between tide-marks on rocky coasts. *Journal of Ecology* 37:259–305.

PELAGIC POLYCHAETES FROM THE SOUTH CHINA SEA

B.L. Wu and Lu Hua

First Institute of Oceanography, State Oceanic Administration, Qingdao, China

ABSTRACT

Forty-one species of pelagic polychaetes have been identified from the South China Sea. Among them, there are 15 cosmopolitan species and 26 warm water ones. The evolutionary relationships of the pelagic Polychaeta have been examined using cluster analysis of twelve morphological characters. The pelagic polychaetes are included in six families, i.e., Lopadorrhynchidae, Iospilidae, Pontodoridae, Alciopidae, Tomopteridae and Typhloscolecidae. The Lopadorrhynchidae may either be the ancestral group or have a close relationship with the ancestors of all other five families.

INTRODUCTION

There are more than 100 species of pelagic polychaetes in the world which belong to 23 genera in six families. They are considered to be holopelagic, spending their entire life cycle in the water column. The six pelagic polychaete families are: Lopadorrhynchidae, Iospilidae, Pontodoridae, Alciopidae, Tomopteridae and Typhloscolecidae.

Each of the holopelagic polychaete families shows special adaptations to life in the water column (Rice 1987). Most of them have transparent bodies for protection. The Alciopidae have complicated telescopic eyes which can change the direction of the eye axis, thus enabling them to survey the surroundings (Ushakov 1972). The cephalic lobe of the Typhloscolecidae ends in an elongate, finger-like appendage, the palpod, and the dorsal and ventral cirri of Typhloscolecidae are in the form of broad plates which promote the maintenance of a vertical position in the water. The parapodia of the Tomopteridae possess special fins.

The phylogenetic relationships among the pelagic polychaete families are not clear. Some workers (Fauvel 1923; Tebble 1962; Ushakov 1972) defined the Phyllodocidae as containing three subfamilies: Lopadorrhynchinae, Iospilinae and Pontodorinae. Bergstrom (1914) removed the Iospilidae and Pontodorinae from the Phyllodocidae, and Hartman (1959) established the family Lopadorrhynchidae. These separations have been accepted by Dales and Peter (1972). The Alciopidae and Lopadorrhynchidae are rather closely related to the benthic Phyllodocidae (Dales 1955). The Typhloscolecidae are considered to be neotenic, adapted to an ecoparasitic life and developed from an ancestor of the free-swimming pelagic Phyllodocidae (Dales 1955b). The Iospilidae, Tomopteridae and Typhloscolecidae differ from the phyllodocid pelagic families in many respects. The systematic position of the Pontodoridae is not clear (Ushakov 1972).

This paper lists all the pelagic polychaetes identified from the South China Sea during the past two decades. The evolutionary relationships among the six families of pelagic Polychaeta are examined using cluster analysis.

MATERIALS AND METHODS

It must be emphasized that this paper is a presentation of preliminary results based upon information from the literature. A total of twelve morphological characters of the pelagic Polychaeta are employed and which have been used in standard taxonomies by previous authors. Table 1 lists 12 characters, and Table 2 shows the character scoring.

Table 1
Morphological characteristics of pelagic Polychaeta.

A. Parapodia: 1-Uniramous; 2-Biramous
B. Eyes: 1-Present; 2-Absent
C. Eye lens: 1-Present; 2-Absent
D. The direction of the axis of eye can change: 1-Yes; 2-No
E. Sete: 1-Well developed; 2-Reduced; 3-Absent
F. Compound sete: 1-All sete are compound; 2-All have compound sete except for a few which also possess special simple sete; 3-Some genera have compound sete, but others have only simple sete; 4-Sete absent
G. Antenna number: 1–1; 2–2; 3–3; 4–4; 5–5
H. Palps: 1-Present; 2-Absent
I. Proboscis: 1-Long; 2-Short; 3-Adapted to ecoparasitic life
J. The jaws on proboscis: 1-Present 2-One genus present; 3-Absent
K. The number of segments with tentacular cirri: 1–1; 2–'1 to 2" 3–2 4–3
L. The number of tentacular cirri: 1–2 pairs 2–'2 to 3 pairs 3–'3 to 5 pairs'

A dendrogram of affinities has been constructed using the Minkowiski Distance on an IBM computer according to the data matrix contained in Table 2.

Table 2
Character scoring of the six pelagic families. See Table 1.

	A	B	C	D	E	F	G	H	I	J	K	L
Lopadorrhynchidae	1	1	1	2	1	2	4	2	1	2	2	2
Pontodoridae	1	1	1	2	1	1	1	2	1	3	1	1
Iospilidae	1	1	1	2	1	1	3	1	1	2	3	1
Alciopidae	1	1	1	1	1	3	5	2	1	3	4	3
Tomopteridae	2	1	2	2	3	4	1	1	2	1	3	1
Typhloscolecidae	2	2	2	2	2	4	2	2	3	3	4	2

RESULTS AND DISCUSSION

Pelagic polychaetes collected from the South China Sea

In the past two decades, many investigations have been made in the South China Sea by the Institute of Oceanology and the South China Sea Institute of Oceanology, Academia Sinica. The collections were made with a plankton net. Altogether, 41 species of pelagic polychaetes have been identified from the South China Sea belonging to 18 genera in 6 families (Wu and Sun 1978; Shen and Wu 1978; Sun and Wu 1979; Chen and Wu 1983).

Following, is a list of pelagic polychaetes recorded from the South China Sea and their distributions:

	ABCD
LOPADORRHYNCHIDAE	
1. *Lopadorrhynchus*	
Lopadorrhynchus brevis Grube	**** 2
Lopadorrhynchus unicinatus Fauvel	*_*_ 2
Lopadorrhynchus krohnii Claparede	_*_ 2
Lopadorrhynchus nationalis Reibisch	_** 2
2. *Pelagobia*	
Pelagobia longicirrata Greeff	**** 1
3. *Maupasia*	
Maupasia coeca Viguier	*_*_ 1
4. *Pedinosoma*	
Pedinosoma curtum Reibisch	_*_ 2
IOSPILIDAE	
5. *Phalacrophorus*	
Phalacrophorus pictus Greeff	_*_ 1
Phalacrophorus uniformis Reibisch	_*_ 2
PONTODORIDAE	
6. *Pontodora*	
Pontodora pelagica Greeff	_*_ 2
TYPHLOSCOLECIDAE	
7. *Sagitella*	
Sagitella kowalevskii Wagner	**** 1
8. *Travisiopsis*	
Travisiopsis lobifera Levinsen	**** 2
Travisiopsis levinseni Southern	**_ 1
Travisiopsis dubia Stop-Bowitz	*_* 2
9. *Typhloscolex*	
Typhloscolex muelleri Busch	**** 1
Typhloscolex phyllodes Reibisch	*_ 2

TOMOPTERIDAE
   10. *Tomopteris*
      Tomopteris nationalis Apstein   *_* 2
      Tomopteris pacifica Izuka   *_* 2
      Tomopteris planktonis Apstein   *_*_ 1
      Tomopteris duccii Rosa   *_*_ 2
      Tomopteris ligulata Rosa   *_*_ 2
      Tomopteris cavalii Rosa   *_** 1
      Tomopteris elegans Chun   *_** 1
      Tomopteris rolasii Greeff   **_* 2
      Tomopteris septentrionalis Quatrefages   _*_ 1
      Tomopteris carpenteri Quatrefages   *_ 1
      Tomopteris helgolandica Greeff   *_ 2
      Tomopteris krampi Wesenberg-Land   *_ 2

ALCIOPIDAE
   11. *Rhynchonereella*
      Rhynchonereella gracilis Costa   **_* 2
      Rhynchonereela xishaensis Shen   *_*_ 2
      Rhynchonereela petersii (Langerhans)   _*_ 1
   12. *Naiades*
      Naiades cantraini Delle Chiaje   **** 1
   13. *Torrea*
      Torrea candida (Delle Chiaje)   *_ 1
   14. *Vanadis*
      Vanadis fuscapunctata Treadwell   *_*_ 2
      Vanadis minuta Treadwell   *_** 2
      Vanadis crystallis Greeff   ***_ 2
      Vanadis longissima Levinsen   *_ 2
   15. *Alciopina*
      Alciopina parasitica Claparede and Panceri   **** 2
   16. *Krohnia*
      Krohnia lepidota (Krohn)   _*_ 1
   17. *Plotohelmis*
      Plotohelmis capitata Greeff   *_*_ 2
      Plotohelmis alata Chamberlin   *_ 2
   18. *Watelio*
      Watelio sp.   _*_

1, Cosmopolitan species; 2, Warm-water species.
A, Nansha Islands; B, Zhongsha Islands; C, Xisha Islands; D, Taiwan Bank.
'*', Present; '–', Absent

    In the above species list, we have identified 17 species from the Taiwan Bank, 28 species from the Xisha Islands, 11 species from the Zhongsha Islands and 32 species from the Nansha Islands. Of these, 7 species are most abundant, i.e., *Lopadorrhynchus brevies*, *Vanadis fuscapunctata*, *Tomopteris rolasii*, *Tomopteris nationalis*, *Sagitilla*

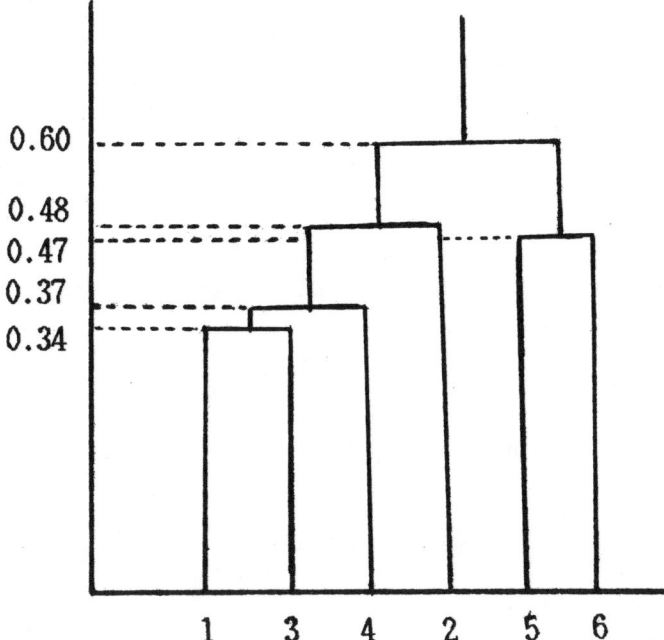

Fig. 1. A dendrogram showing the evolutionary relationships among six pelagic polychaete families using the Nearest-neighbour method.
1, Lopadorrhynchidae; 2, Pontodoridae; 3, Iospilidae;
4, Alciopidae; 5, Tomopteridae; 6, Typhloscolecidae.

kowalevskii, *Travisiopsis lobifera* and *Vanadis crystallia*. An analysis of the species composition of these pelagic polychaetes indicate that the fauna is similar to that of its neighbouring regions, such as southern Japan, Malaysia, Indonesia, Philippines and India.

Table 3
The nearest distance among the six pelagic families of Polychaeta using the Nearest-Neighbour method.

Step		Distance
1	Lopadorrhynchidae & Iospilidae	0.34
2	Lopadorrhynchidae & Alciopidae	0.37
3	Tomopteridae & Typhloscolecidae	0.47
4	Lopadorrhynchidae & Pontodoridae	0.48
5	Lopadorrhynchidae & Tomopteridae	0.60

Figure 1 indicates that the Lopadorrhynchidae, Iospilidae and Pontodoridae cannot be put in one family, so we agree with Bergstrom (1914) and Hartman (1959) to keep all the pelagic polychaetes in six families.

According to Table 3, the Iospilidae, Pontodoridae and Alciopidae all have a nearest relationship with the Lopadorrhynchidae. The Lopadorrhynchidae is also the second nearest group to the Tomopteridae (the Typhloscolecidae is its nearest group). It has been accepted that the Lopadorrhynchidae can be derived from a phyllodocid stock. We can therefore hypothesize that the Lopadorrhynchidae have an important status in the evolutionary history of the pelagic Polychaeta. Representatives retain many characters similar to those of the ancestors of other pelagic families. In other words, other families of pelagic Polychaeta have either possibly evolved from the Lopadorrhynchidae or from ancestors which have a close relationship with the Lopadorrhynchidae.

ACKNOWLEDGMENTS

We are particularly indebted to Prof. S.P. Shen of the South China Sea Institute of Oceanology, Academia Sinica, for providing us with the data on the pelagic Polychaeta of the Nansha Islands. This research was supported by a grant from the National Natural Science Foundation of China, number 3870080.

REFERENCES

Bergstrom, E. 1914. *Zur Systematik des polychaeten Familie der Phyllodociden.* Zoologische Beiträge. Uppsala.

Chen, M. and Wu, B.L. 1983. Pelagic polychaetes from the Taiwan Bank. *Marine Science Bulletin* 2:42–50.

Dales, R.P. 1955. The evolution of the pelagic phyllodocid and alciopid polychaetes. *Proceedings of the Zoological Society of London* 125:411–20.

Dales, R.P. and Peter, G. 1972. A synopsis of the pelagic Polychaeta. *Journal of Natural History* 6: 55–92.

Fauvel, P. 1923. Polychetes Errantes. *Faune de France* 5:1–488.

Hartman, 0. 1959. *Catalogue of the Polychaetous Annelids of the World.* Allan Hancock Foundation Publication.

Rice, S.A. 1987. Reproductive biology, systematics, and evolution in the polychaete family Alciopidae. *Bulletin of the Biological Society of Washington* 7:114–27.

Shen, S.P. and Wu, B.L. 1978. Preliminary report on the pelagic polychaetes from Zhongsha Islands. *Oceanologia et Limnologia Sinica* 9:99–107.

Sun, R.P. and Wu, B.L. 1979. Preliminary report on the pelagic polychaetes from Xisha Islands, Guangdong Province, China. *Studia Marina Sinica* 15:59–70.

Tebble, N. 1962. The distribution of pelagic polychaetes across the North Pacific Ocean. *Bulletin of the British Museum of Natural History* 7:373–492.

Ushakov, P.V. 1972. *Polychaetes, Vol 1. Fauna of the USSR.* Akademia Nauk, Zoological Institute, Series No. 102.

Wu, B.L. and Sun, R.P. 1978. Preliminary studies on geographical distribution and evolution of pelagic polychaetes from South China Sea Islands. *Oceanologia et Limnologia Sinica* 9:215–33.

The Marine Biology of the South China Sea
(ed. B. Morton). Proceedings of the First
International Conference on the Marine
Biology of Hong Kong and South China Sea,
Hong Kong, 28 October – 3 November 1990.
Hong Kong: Hong Kong University Press, 1993.

THE DISTRIBUTION OF INTERTIDAL FUNGI ON *RHIZOPHORA APICULATA*

Kevin D. Hyde

Department of Botany, The University of Hong Kong, Hong Kong

and

Aniwat Chalermpongse and Thirawat Boonthavikoon

Central Forest Research Laboratory and Training Centre, Royal Forest Department, Bangkok 10900, Thailand

ABSTRACT

Root, bark and wood samples of *Rhizophora apiculata* were collected from the intertidal zone of Ranong mangrove, Thailand and examined for higher marine fungi. Sixty-one fungi were identified including ascomycetes (47), basidiomycetes (3) and fungi imperfecti (11). These results and literature pertaining to the intertidal fungi of *Rhizophora apiculata* illustrate features of vertical distribution, succession and preferences for either bark, wood, trunks, branches or twigs. A diagrammatic scheme of fungal distribution is given.

INTRODUCTION

Recent investigations into intertidal mangrove fungi have provided information on frequency of occurrence, host distribution, succession, distribution with depth and substrate distribution (Hyde 1988, 1989a, 1990a, b; Hyde and Jones 1988; Leong *et al.* 1991). Much of this information is derived from studies on several mangrove trees, but in particular *Rhizophora apiculata* Blume. We have also recently carried out a study of the distribution of intertidal fungi on *R. apiculata* at Ranong mangrove, Thailand. The results from this study are discussed and compared with those of previous studies. Information is used to illustrate the distribution of fungi on this host.

MATERIALS AND METHODS

Root, bark, wood (355) and seedlings (21) of *Rhizophora apiculata* were collected from the intertidal region of Ranong mangrove, Thailand. Decayed samples, i.e., those easily broken from the mangrove tree, were collected from various tidal levels (Level 4:100; Level 3:125; Level 2:114; Level 1:16) and returned to the laboratory in sealed plastic bags. They were examined (within 7 days) for fruiting bodies of higher fungi. Details of the samples collected were noted together with the fungi present, so that any correlation between fungi and sample type could be determined. Sample details included diameter, whether twigs (branches) or roots, whether with or lacking bark, and their vertical position in the intertidal region. Voucher slides of the taxa reported are held in the herbarium of K.D. Hyde and may be loaned on request.

RESULTS

In the course of this study, 355 samples of *Rhizophora apiculata* were collected from established stands at four areas in Ranong mangrove. Sixty-one fungi including 47 ascomycetes were identified. The fungi identified are listed in Table 1. The most commonly recorded species was *Savoryella longispora* (on 14% of samples), while *Hydronectria tethys* (7.6%), *Leptosphaeria australiensis* (7.1%), *Lulworthia grandispora* (8.5%), *Halocyphina villosa* (7.1%) and *Phialophorophoma* cf. *litoralis* (8.2%) were also common. The topographic distribution of the fungi recorded (3 or more records) can be seen in Table 2. The most common species above mean tide were *Savoryella longispora*, *Phialophorophoma* cf. *litoralis*, *Hydronectria tethys* and *Massarina ramunculicola*. Below mean tide *Lulworthia grandispora*, *Verruculina enalia* and *Phomopsis mangrovei* were common. Twenty-two taxa were confined to above mean tide, 13 occurred across the tidal range, while 3 were found below mean tide only.

Bark was an important factor in determining the mycota present on *Rhizophora* samples. Above mean tide, young roots with bark were invariably colonised by *Rhizophila marina*, *Saccardoella mangrovei* and *Massarina ramunculicola*. Below mean tide *Lulworthia grandispora* and *Phomopsis mangrovei* were the dominant species. Larger samples with bark were colonised by *Hypophloeda rhizospora* (unique to bark), *Halosarpheia abonnis*, *Ascocratera* cf. *manglicola*, *Aigialus grandis* and *Phialophorophoma* cf. *litoralis*. Young roots lacking bark were colonised by a different group of fungi, i.e., above mean tide: *Dactylospora haliotrepha*, *Halocyphina villosa*, *Hydronectria tethys*, *Marinosphaera mangrovei*, *Phialophorophoma* cf. *litoralis*, *Savoryella lignicola* var. *longispora*; below mean tide: *Verruculina enalia*, *Leptosphaeria australiensis*, *Xylomyces* sp., while *Ascocratera* cf. *manglicola*, *Aigialus striatispora*, *Carysporella rhizophorae*, *Halocyphina* sp. and *Ophiodeira monosemeia* were common to large barkless samples.

There were little difference between fungi colonising samples of small diameter (less than 2.5 cm) when compared to samples of large diameter (exceptions being influenced by bark). Large trunks (30–50 cm in diameter) were also sampled. A distinctive group of fungi developed within the marine borer tunnels, i.e., *Acrocordiopsis patilii*, *Aniptodera longispora*, *Caryosporella rhizophorae*, *Verruculina enalia*, *Halocyphina* sp., *Ophiodeira monosemeia*.

Seedlings of *Rhizophora apiculata* were planted in tin mining areas as part of a

Table 1
Intertidal fungi identified from roots, bark and wood (not seedling) samples of *Rhizophora apiculata*, collected at Ranong mangrove.

Fungus	Percentage occurrence
Ascomycotina	
Acrocordiopsis patilii Borse and Hyde	2.3
Aigialus grandis Kohlm. and Schatz	9.6
Aigialus striatispora Hyde	2.8
Aniptodera chesapeakensis Shearer and Miller	0.3
A. longispora Hyde	1.7
A. mangrovei Hyde and Jones (in Hyde, Farrant and Jones)	0.6
Antennospora quadricornuta (Cribb and Cribb) T.W. Johnson	0.6
Ascocratera manglicola Kohlm.	0.3
Ascocratera cf. *manglicola* Kohlm.	3.9
Bathyascus grandisporus Hyde and Jones	1.2
Bathyascus sp.	0.6
Belizeana tuberculata Kohlm. and Volkm.-Kohlm.	0.3
Caryosporella rhizophorae Kohlm.	3.7
Cryptosphaeria mangrovei Hyde (as *Ascomycete* sp.)	0.9
Cucullosporella mangrovei Hyde and Jones	1.1
Dactylospora haliotrepha (Kohlm. and Kohlm.) Hafellner	6.8
Halosarpheia abonnis Kohlm.	2.8
H. marina (Cribb and Cribb) Kohlm.	0.3
H. ratnagiriensis Patil and Borse	0.9
H. viscosa (I. Schmidt) Shearer and Crane ex Kohlm. and Volkm.-Kohlm.	0.9
Hydronectria tethys Kohlm. and Kohlm.	7.6
Hypophloeda rhizospora Hyde and Jones	2.0
Hypoxylon oceanicum Schatz	0.6
Leptosphaeria australiensis (Cribb and Cribb) G.C. Hughes	7.1
Lignincola laevis Höhnk	0.6
Lignincola longirostris (Cribb and Cribb) Kohlm.	1.4
Lineolata rhizophorae (Kohlm. and Kohlm.) Kohlm. and Volkm.-Kohlm.	0.3
Lophiostoma mangrovei Kohlm. and Vittal	1.1
Lulworthia grandispora Meyers	8.5
Lulworthia spp.	3.4
Marinosphaera mangrovei Hyde	6.2
Massarina ramunculicola Hyde	5.6
Massarina thalassiae Kohlm. and Volkm.-Kohlm.	0.6
Massarina velatospora Hyde and Borse	1.4
Mycosphaerella cf. *salicorniae* (Auerswald) Petrak	1.1
Nais glitra Crane and Shearer	0.3
Hypoxylon hypomiltum Montagne (as Xylariaceous sp.)	4.3
Ophiodeira monosemeia Kohlm. and Volkm.-Kohlm.	2.0
Passeriniella savoryellopsis Hyde and Mouzouras	0.3
Quintaria lignatilis (Kohlm.) Kohlm. and Volkm.-Kohlm.	2.9
Rhizophila marina Hyde and Jones	2.9
Saccardoella mangrovei Hyde	3.9
Savoryella longispora Jones and Hyde	14.0
Swampomyces triseptatus Hyde and Nakagiri (as *Sphaerulinea oraemaris* Linder)	5.1
Swampomyces cf. *armeniacus* Kohlm. and Volkm.-Kohlm.	0.9
Thalassogena sphaerica Kohlm. and Volkm.-Kohlm.	0.6
Verruculina enalia (Kohlm.) Kohlm. and Volkm.-Kohlm.	7.6

Table 1 (continued).

Fungus	Percentage occurrence
Basidiomycetes	
Halocyphina villosa Kohlm. and Kohlm.	7.1
Halocyphina sp.	3.1
Calathella sp.	1.1
Deuteromycetes	
Bactrodesmium sp.	0.3
Cirrenalia pseudomacrocephala Kohlm.	0.3
C. tropicalis Kohlm.	1.4
Helicoon sp.	0.3
Humicola alopallonella Meyers and Moore	0.9
Mycelia sterilia	0.6
Periconia prolifica Anastasiou	0.6
Phialophorophoma cf. *litoralis* Linder in Barghoorn and Linder	8.2
Phoma spp.	3.9
Phomopsis mangrovei Hyde (as *Phomopsis* sp.)	5.1
Xylomyces sp.	2.9

regeneration program. However, many died due to the unfavourable clay soil. The dead seedlings were collected and examined for higher marine fungi and were found to be colonised by a characteristic group of fungi (Fig. 1). The cause of death was not established but may be due to physiological stress. The common fungi on the dead seedlings were *Cryptosphaeria* sp., *Halosarpheia ratnagiriensis*, *Saccardoella mangrovei*, *Leptosphaeria australiensis*, *Lulworthia grandispora*, *Pedumispora rhizophorae*, *Massarina ramunculicola* and *Rhizophila marina*.

DISCUSSION

Frequency of occurrence of mangrove fungi

In recent years, considerable effort has been spent investigating the ecology of mangrove fungi, particularly with respect to frequency of occurrence. Hyde and Jones (1988) have tried to evaluate various results, attempting to rationalize understanding of this aspect. Unfortunately, we are still far from a complete understanding since so many factors are involved.

Several studies on the fungi of *R. apiculata* have now been undertaken and we have a better understanding of the intertidal fungi occurring on this host. Some fungi were found to be common in all studies, e.g., *Leptosphaeria australiensis*, *Savoryella longispora* (Hyde 1988, 1990a, 1991; Leong *et al.* 1991), while in others the common fungi varied, e.g., *Trichocladium* cf. *opacum* was only common at Kampong Kapok mangrove (Hyde 1990a). Notable common fungi were *Caryosporella rhizophorae*,

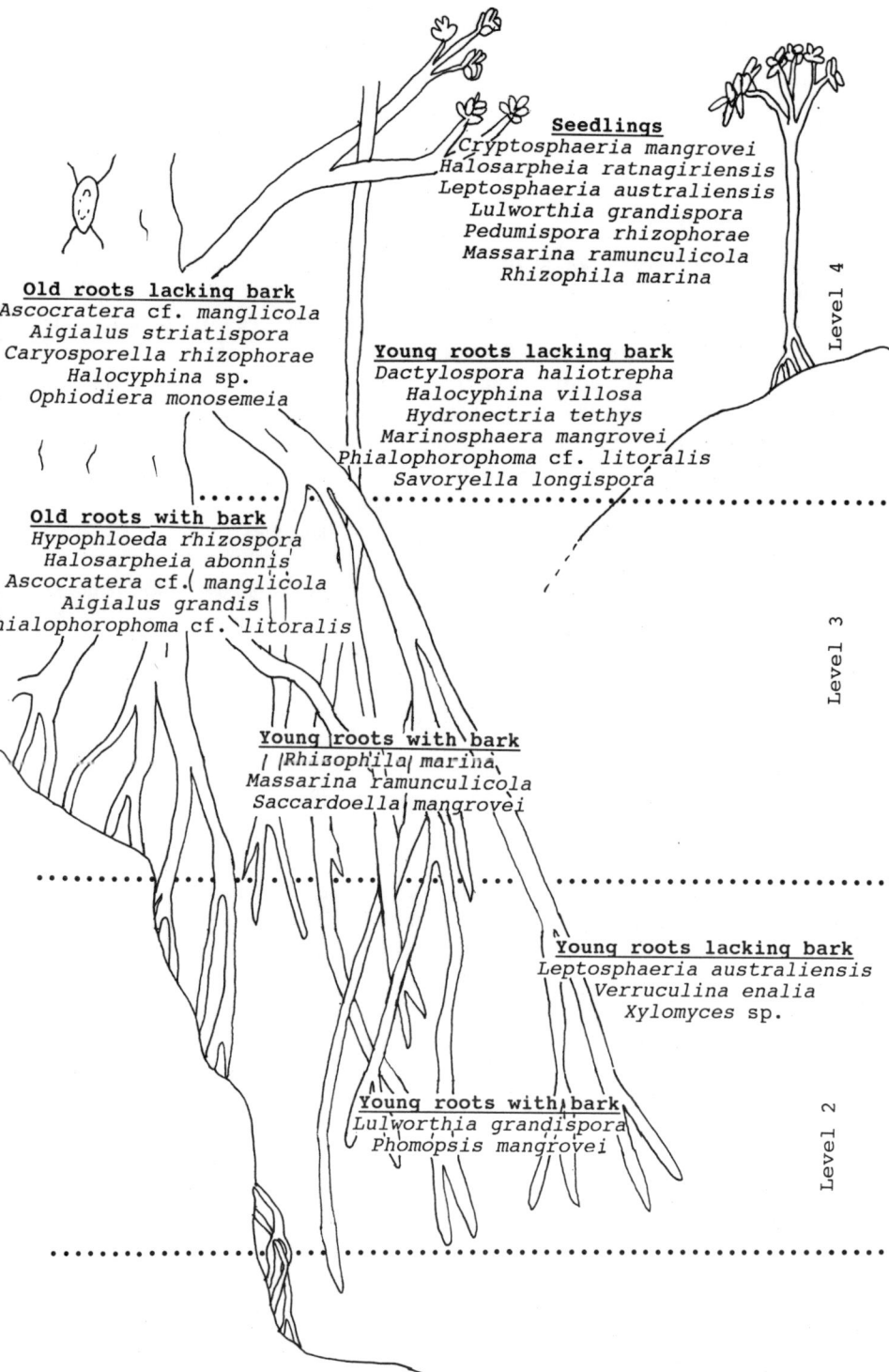

Fig. 1. Distribution of some common fungi on *Rhizophora apiculata*

Cirrenalia pygmea, Halocyphina villosa, Halosarpheia marina, Leptosphaeria australiensis, Lulworthia sp. and *Savoryella longispora* (Hyde 1988, 1990a). The frequency of occurrence, however, is still dependant on several factors, e.g., vertical distribution, sea temperature, salinity, succession, type of substrate, and some of these are addressed below.

Vertical distribution

Hyde (1988, 1990a) investigated the vertical distribution of intertidal fungi on *Rhizophora apiculata*. His results indicate that intertidal fungi are vertically distributed, with most fungi confined to a relatively small vertical zone. Few fungi were widely distributed and only two were found throughout the tidal range. The greatest diversity of fungi (41 species) occurs above mean tide. Since results are based on the presence of red fruiting bodies, critics may suggest that the mycelial state of the fungus is more widely distributed. However, in most cases the area occupied by a particular fungus is small (5–10 cm) and can be observed on the sample by an associated coloured zone or wood texture. For example, the wood beneath *Massarina thalassiae* is usually soft and bleached white, with *Leptosphaeria australiensis* soft and grey, while in *Hypoxylon oceanicum* Schatz the surface of the wood is blackened.

In this study fungi were also shown to be vertically distributed (Table 2) and confirm the results of Hyde (1988, 1990a). Many similarities between Brunei and Thailand are evident. In Brunei, *Ascomycete* sp. (a *Cryptosphaeria*-like species), *Dactylospora haliotrepha, Hypophloeda rhizospora, Hypoxylon oceanicum, Marinosphaera mangrovei, Phialophorophoma* cf. *litoralis, Savoryella longispora* and *Quintaria lignatilis* were common above mean tide, while *Antennospora quadricornuta* and *Xylomyces* sp., were collected frequently below. Similar results (exceptions *H. oceanicum* and *A. quadricornuta*) are found in Ranong mangroves (Table 2).

Hyde (1989b) also showed that fungal fructifications appeared to be adapted to the level at which the fungus developed. A distribution pattern was found in spore colour, ascoma wall texture and ascospore release mechanisms, e.g., fungi with active spore release were only located in the upper intertidal region, while those with passive release, were found throughout the tidal range. Although vertical distribution has been conclusively shown by Hyde (1988, 1990a), the situation is complicated by the nature of the substrate. Hyde *et al.* (1990) has shown that lower intertidal dead young roots of *Rhizophora* (with bark) are invariably colonised by *Phomopsis mangrovei* and *Lulworthia grandispora*, while roots lacking bark are colonised by *Verruculina enalia, Leptosphaeria australiensis* and *Xylomyces* sp.

Succession

Studies on the succession of fungi occurring on *R. apiculata* were undertaken by Leong *et al.* (1991). They showed that some fungi were early colonisers, e.g., *Lignincola laevis, Verruculina enalia*, while other fungi appeared later, e.g., *Dactylospora haliotrepha, Hypoxylon oceanicum*. Their results, however, did not express vertical distribution which would affect the fungi colonising their baited samples. Whether this succession is an expression of the rate at which the fungus can sporulate or actual succession is yet to be established. In nature, the speed with which a fungus can grow and sporulate may

Table 2
Vertical distribution within the tidal range of some of the more common intertidal fungi (3 or more records) on *Rhizophora apiculata*. The figures show the percentage occurrence in the samples at each tidal level.

Fungus	Intertidal level		
	4	3	2
Quintaria lignatilis	10		
Cryptosphaeria mangrovei	3		
Aigialus striatispora	8	2	
Ascocratera cf. *manglicola*	13	1	
Lophiostoma mangrovei	3	1	
Hypoxylon hypomiltum	11	4	
Lignincola longirostris	4	1	
Savoryella longispora	36	13	
Halosarpheia viscosa	2	1	
Massarina velatospora	3	2	
Phialophorophoma cf. *litoralis*	19	10	
Hydronectria tethys	15	10	
Marinosphaera mangrovei	12	8	
Dactylospora haliotrepha	13	11	
Massarina cf. *salicorniae*	2	2	
Saccardoella mangrovei	5	9	
Massarina ramunculicola	12	8	
Swampomyces cf. *armeniacus*	1	2	
Aniptodera longispora	1	5	
Hypophloeda rhizospora	1	6	
Halosarpheia abonnis	1	9	
Halocyphina sp.	1	10	
Aigialus grandis	7	25	2
Phoma spp.	6	6	1
Rhizophila marina	2	7	1
Swampomyces triseptatus	5	7	1
Caryosporella rhizophorae	1	8	1
Acrocordiopsis patilii	2	5	1
Leptosphaeria australiensis	9	7	9
Ophiodeira monosemeia		7	
Bathyascus grandisporus	1		3
Halocyphina villosa	3	13	5
Verruculina enalia	1	3	18
Lulworthia spp.		2	5
Lulworthia grandispora		3	19
Humicola alopallonella			3
Xylomyces sp.			9
Phomopsis mangrovei			14

Level 4	3.2 – 4.0 m	Highest tide during October and November 1988 = 4.3 metres
Level 3	2.4 – 3.2 m	Lowest tide = 0.7 metres
Level 2	1.6 – 2.4 m	Mean tide = 2.4 metres

Only 16 samples were collected below level 2 as no material was available here. The fungi found on these samples are not included in this table.

be an important factor in competition, as they may be under pressure to sporulate quickly. Alternatively, the situation may involve one fungus which by its activity, could create ideal conditions for development of a second fungus, although both being present from the outset.

Hyde (1991) also investigated 'succession' and found a group of rarely identified fungi colonised *Rhizophora apiculata* during the first year. These fungi were also dependent on vertical distribution. The fungi, however, developed in the bark and little or no decay of the wood beneath had occurred in the first year. These early colonisers, e.g., *Capillataspora corticola* Hyde and *Halosarpheia minuta* Leong, differed from those found by Leong *et al.* (1991). In Leong *et al.* (1991) the core wood was exposed as samples were split in two. The fungi recorded were therefore colonisers of wood rather than colonisers of bark. This indicates that in nature prop roots may first be colonised by a group of bark inhabiting fungi (Hyde 1991). Once the bark is detached, a second group of wood colonising fungi may cause decay of the wood (Leong *et al.* 1991). However, severely damage roots may be simultaneously decayed by both groups.

The final stage of decay is difficult to establish as in both studies wood was submerged for 60 weeks or less. Borer and fungal damage cause the wood to break up into smaller detritus. We know that the C and N from this detritus is eventually utilised by higher consumers (Hutchings and Saenger 1987), however, little is known of the agents of this pathway. These studies serve to illustrate succession, but since baits were used, may not reflect the true situation in nature. Random sampling reveals a much larger group of fungi that cause decay, than was found in either of these studies, but this will be influenced by many other factors.

Fungi unique to *Rhizophora apiculata* and *Rhizophora* spp.

Several fungi have now been shown to be unique to *Rhizophora* spp. or having a greater preference for this host genus. These include *Capillataspora corticola*, *Caryosporella rhizophorae*, *Hypophloeda rhizospora*, *Rhizophila marina* and *Etheirophora blepharospora* (Kohlm. and Kohlm.) Kohlm. and Volkm.-Kohlm. The nature of the bark and cortex of *R. apiculata* is unusual as the bark is hard, thin and strongly cuticularised, while the cortex is soft, thick, highly lacunate, and rich in tannins (Chapman 1975; Tomlinson 1986). Both *Capillataspora corticola* and *Etheirophora blepharospora* are confined to the crust-like bark. *Hypophloeda rhizospora* and *Rhizophila marina* develop in the cortex, while *Caryosporella rhizophorae* develops on the wood. The fungi may be adapted for development in material high in tannins or in some other way. These fungi appear to be less competitive on other hosts where they have yet to be recorded.

Preference for bark/wood/twigs and seedlings

Hyde *et al.* (1990) investigated the distribution of fungi on *Sonneratia griffithii* and showed that some fungi were more common on pneumatophores, e.g., *Aigialus grandis* and *Massarina velatospora*, while others were common on twigs, e.g., *Saccardoella mangrovei* and *Savoryella lignicola* var. *longispora*. A similar model is used in this paper to show the distribution of fungi on *R. apiculata* (Fig. 1).

The model illustrates that certain fungi are adapted to growing in certain ecological niches. Some fungi are only found in bark, e.g., below mean tide: *Phomopsis mangrovei*; above mean tide: *Hypophloeda rhizospora, Rhizophila marina*, while others are confined to woody tissues, e.g., above mean tide: *Caryosporella rhizophorae*. Observations similar to these have been noted by previous authors (Kohlmeyer and Kohlmeyer 1979; Hyde and Jones 1988; Hyde *et al.* 1990). Sample diameter was found to have little correlation to the fungi identified.

The fungi identified from dead seedlings (exception: *L. grandispora*) are those shown to be distributed on prop roots at the upper end of the tidal region (Hyde 1990a), rather than specifically adapted for development on seedlings. Newell (1976) reported fungi from seedlings of *Rhizophora mangle* including an *Anthostomella* sp., a *Leptosphaeria* sp. and *Lulworthia grandispora*, but generally showed a different group of fungi, e.g., *Hyphomycetes* and *Coelomycetes*, to be present. However, Newell (1976) used media to isolate most of the fungi from discs taken from the seedlings in Florida, and this may account for the large number of hyphomycetes that he recorded.

Unstudied parameters

Studies have now been undertaken to examine several of the parameters important in the ecology of fungi on *R. apiculata*. However, many parameters have still to be considered and future studies should try to elucidate the effects of salinity, wood borers, pH, and temperature on the mycoflora. *Rhizophora apiculata* will often develop in areas of low salinity, but little is known about the fungi developing on *Rhizophora* in these areas. This paper has attempted to bring together the available data on the intertidal fungi on *Rhizophora apiculata* with a view to illustrate the ecology of fungi on this common mangrove host. Although several factors still need examining, we can at least begin to see the effect of natural parameters on the distribution of intertidal fungi.

ACKNOWLEDGEMENTS

Dr K.D. Hyde wishes to acknowledge the Royal Society, London, for a grant to visit Thailand and Xenova Ltd, UK for financial assistance. His gratitude is also extended to Mr Sopon Havanond, Miss Prapasri Thanasukarn, Miss Sriprai Jaturongkal and many other people who made his stay in a Thailand so productive and enjoyable. We would like to thank UNDP/UNESCO and the NRC (Thailand) for help with organisation, coordination and financial help to allow these studies to take place. Thanks are also extended to the Royal Forest Department, Thailand, for accommodation and use of facilities at the Mangrove Research Centre, Ranong.

REFERENCES

Chapman, V.J. 1975. *Mangrove vegetation*. Vaduz: J. Cramer.
Hutchings, P. and Saenger, P. 1987. *Ecology of mangroves*. St. Lucia: University of Queensland Press.
Hyde, K.D. 1988. Observations on the vertical distribution of marine fungi on *Rhizophora* spp., at Kampong Danau mangrove, Brunei. *Asian Marine Biology* 5:77–81.
Hyde, K.D. 1989a. Ecology of tropical marine fungi. *Hydrobiologia* 178:199–208.

Hyde, K.D. 1989b. Vertical zonation of intertidal mangrove fungi. In *Recent Advances in Microbial Ecology* (ed. T. Hattori, Y. Ishida, Y. Maruyama, R. Morita and A. Uchida), 302-6. Tokyo: Japan Scientific Societies Press.

Hyde, K.D. 1990a. A study of the vertical zonation of intertidal fungi on *Rhizophora apiculata* at Kampong Kapok mangrove, Brunei. *Aquatic Botany* 36:255-62.

Hyde, K.D. 1990b. A comparison of the intertidal mycota of five mangrove tree species. *Asian Marine Biology* 7:93-107.

Hyde, K.D. 1991. Fungal colonization of *Rhizophora apiculata* and *Xylocarpus granatum* poles in Kampong Kapok mangrove, Brunei. *Sydowia* 43:31-8.

Hyde, K.D. and Jones, E.B.G. 1988. Marine mangrove fungi. *Marine Ecology* 9:15-33.

Hyde, K.D., Chalermpongse, A. and Boonthavikoon, T. 1990. Ecology of intertidal fungi at Ranong mangrove, Thailand. *Transactions of the Mycological Society of Japan* 31:17-27.

Kohlmeyer, J. and Kohlmeyer, E. 1979. *Marine Mycology. The higher fungi.* New York: Academic Press.

Leong, W.F., Tan, T.K. and Jones, E.B.G. 1991. Fungal colonisation of submerged *Bruguiera cylindrica* and *Rhizophora apiculata* wood. *Botanica Marina* 34:69-76.

Newell, S.Y. 1976. Mangrove fungi. The succession in the mycoflora of red mangrove (*Rhizophora mangle* L.) seedlings. In *Recent Advances in Microbial Ecology* (ed. E.B.G. Jones), 49-91. London: Elek Science.

Tomlinson, P.B. 1986. *The Botany of Mangroves.* London: Cambridge University Press.

The Marine Biology of the South China Sea
(ed. B. Morton). Proceedings of the First
International Conference on the Marine
Biology of Hong Kong and the South China,
Hong Kong, 28 October – 3 November 1990.
Hong Kong: Hong Kong University Press, 1993.

THE EFFECT OF PHOTOPERIOD AND TEMPERATURE ON THE RELEASE OF MONOSPORES BY *PORPHYRA SUBORBICULATA* KJELLMAN

K.Y. Lee, H.C. Leung, I.J. Hodgkiss

Department of Botany, The University of Hong Kong, Hong Kong

and

K.W. Cheung

Hong Kong Herbarium, Agriculture and Fisheries Department,
The Hong Kong Government, Hong Kong

ABSTRACT

Porphyra species show heteromorphic life histories with the leafy *Porphyra* phase alternating with the shell encrusting *Conchocelis* phase. Photoperiod and temperature are two important factors affecting the types of spores released and hence affect the alternation of the two phases. Leafy thalli of *Porphyra suborbiculata* Kjellman were cultured at 23°C with photoperiods of 12L/12D, 10L/14D and 8L/16D. Liberation of monospores was recorded in all cases. Carpospores were also produced under these conditions but in much smaller numbers.

INTRODUCTION

Members of the Bangiophyceae, especially species of *Porphyra* and *Bangia*, exhibit morphological alternation of generations. The leafy *Porphyra* or *Bangia* phase alternates with the shell boring *Conchocelis* phase. Each phase can produce different types of spores which may develop into either phase (Richardson 1972). Photoperiod and temperature are two factors which can affect growth and spore liberation (Richardson 1970). Formation of sporangia was found to be mediated by light in *Porphyra tenera* Kjellman (Dring 1967; Rentschler 1967) and *Bangia atro-purpurea* (Roth.) Ag. (formerly *B. fuscopurpurea* [Dillw.] Lyngbye) (Richardson and Dixon 1968). The type of spores produced by the *Bangia* phase in *B. atro-purpurea* was found to be influenced by photoperiod and temperature (Sommerfeld and Nichols 1973). Carpospores were produced at low temperatures with a light period of more than 11 hours while monospores were produced at higher temperatures. Kurogi (1959) found that short day length was favourable for the release of monospores in *P. tenera*. Short day length also favoured the formation of monosporangia in *P. psuedolinearis* Ueda although spore release was not recorded. Tseng and Chang (1955) reported that *P. tenera* produced monospores at temperatures > 15°C but carpospores were produced at temperatures lower than this. It is thus of interest to investigate the effects of daylength and temperature on *P. suborbiculata*, which is commonly found along the coasts of the South China Sea.

MATERIALS AND METHODS

Young thalli of *P. suborbiculata* (approximately 2 cm in diameter) were collected from Shek O, a headland on the east coast of Hong Kong Island, in December when the alga flourishes locally. The thalli were rinsed and subsequently grown in natural filtered seawater continually circulated through 20 cm high and 9 cm in diameter glass tubes. The thalli were grown under four different regimes to simulate field conditions: three batches were kept at 23°C with photoperiods of 12, 14 or 16 hours darkness, respectively, on a 24 hour cycle, the fourth batch were kept at 16°C with a photoperiod of 16 hours darkness. A 76 x 25 mm glass slide placed at the bottom of the vessel was examined daily for released spores.

RESULTS

Monospores and carpospores were observed after 10 days in all four treatments (Table 1). Carpospores represented less than 5% of the total numbers of spores observed. The predominating monospores appeared as small red dots on the walls of the culture vessels and on the glass slides. The highest spore density on the slides was 70 spores·mm^{-2}. Microscopic examination of the thalli at this time revealed the presence of both carpogonia and spermatangia. Within 10 days, the spores had developed into small thalli approximately 2 mm in length and, at the same time, the mother thalli rapidly disinte-

Table 1
Influence of photoperiod and temperature on sporulation by *Porphyra suborbiculata*.

Photo-period L/D	Temperature °C	Sporulation 5 days	10 days	15 days	20 days	Spore type mono-spores	carpo-
12/12	23	–	++	++	+	√	√
10/14	23	–	++	++	+	√	√
8/16	23	–	++	++	+	√	√
8/16	16	–	+	+	++	√	√

grated. Young thalli differentiated into hundreds of cells and grew to about 1 cm in diameter in less than 1 month. Leafy thalli had a life span of approximately 8 weeks under laboratory conditions.

DISCUSSION

The results indicate that *Porphyra suborbiculata* could form and liberate monospores under various photoperiods and temperatures. This correlates well with field observations. Leafy thalli flourish on the wave-beaten rocky shores of Hong Kong from October to April (Hodgkiss 1984). The photoperiod during this time varies from 12 hours light and 12 hours darkness to 8 hours light and 16 hours darkness and average water temperatures vary from 30°C to 15°C (Morton and Wu 1975; Hodgkiss 1984). Since the life span of *P. suborbiculata* is about 8 weeks, the continuous appearance of leafy thalli must result from rapid reproduction, most probably by means of monospores. Leafy thalli could be grown continuously in the laboratory, even at times of year when they would have disappeared from the field (that is, May to September). This implies that it is short day length and temperatures < 23°C which act synergistically to favour the formation of monospores by *Porphyra*.

Lowering the temperature to 16°C did not result in a shift from the production of monospores to entirely carpospores, it only slowed down the production of monospores and hence delayed the disintegration of the mother thalli. This might be due to a slowdown in the algal metabolism at low temperatures. The phenomenon is different from *P. tenera* which switched to the production of carpospores below 15°C (Tseng and Chang 1955). Average winter water temperatures in Hong Kong, however, seldom fall below 15°C and, therefore, the production of carpospores by *P. suborbiculata* does not appear to be mediated by low temperatures.

The co-occurrence of carpospores with monospores shows that short day length and low temperatures do not wholly suppress the production of carpospores by *Porphyra suborbiculata*. This is different from the situation seen in *Bangia atro-purpurea* (Sommerfeld and Nichols 1973), but is similar to that reported for *P. tenera* (Kurogi 1959). Temperature effects on the types of spores released by *P. suborbiculata* were also different from those seen in *P. tenera*, as discussed above. This implies that different species have different requirements for completion of their life cycles. Different geographic isolates of the same species may have different requirements allowing them to live successfully in specific habitats, as in the case of *B. atro-purpurea* (Sommerfeld and Nichols 1973).

The disappearance of leafy thalli from local shores after April suggests a switch to development of the *Conchocelis* phase. Long day length and high temperatures might be key conditions for phase alternation, causing carpospore production to replace that of monospores. This, however, requires further field and culture studies.

ACKNOWLEDGEMENT

We would like to thank Mr S.T. Chan for his assistance in the collection of specimens.

REFERENCES

Dring, M.J. 1967. Effect of daylength on growth and reproduction of the *Conchocelis*-phase of *Porphyra tenera*. *Journal of the Marine Biological Association of the United Kingdom* 47:501–10.

Hodgkiss, I.J. 1984. Seasonal patterns of intertidal algal distribution in Hong Kong. *Asian Marine Biology* 1:49–57.

Kurogi, M. 1959. Influence of light on the growth and maturation of *Conchocelis*-thallus of *Porphyra*. I. Effect of photoperiod on the formation of monosporangia and liberation of monospores. *Bulletin of the Tohoku Regional Fisheries Research Laboratory* 15:33–42.

Morton, B. and Wu, S.S. 1975. The hydrology of the coastal waters of Hong Kong. *Environmental Research* 10:319–47.

Rentschler, H.G. 1967. Photoperiodische induktion der monosporenbildung bei *Porphyra tenera* Kjellm. (Rhodophyta - Bangiophyceae). *Planta* 76:65–74.

Richardson, N. 1970. Studies of the photobiology of *Bangia fuscopurpurea*. *Journal of Phycology* 6:215–9.

Richardson, N. 1972. Spore classification in the genera *Bangia* and *Porphyra*. *British Phycological Journal* 15:49–51.

Richardson, N. and Dixon, P.S. 1968. Life history of *Bangia fuscopurpurea* (Dillw.) Lynbg. in culture. *Nature* 218:496–7.

Sommerfeld, M.R. and Nichols, H.W. 1973. The life cycle of *Bangia fuscopurpurea* in culture. I. The effects of temperature and photoperiod on the morphology and reproduction of the *Bangia* phase. *Journal of Phycology* 9:205–10.

Tseng, C.K. and Chang, T.J. 1955. Studies on the life history of *Porphyra tenera* Kjellm. *Scientia Sinica* 4:375–98.

The Marine Biology of the South China Sea
(ed. B. Morton). Proceedings of the First
International Conference on the Marine
Biology of Hong Kong and the South China Sea,
Hong Kong, 28 October – 3 November 1990.
Hong Kong: Hong Kong University Press, 1993.

THE MACROBENTHIC INFAUNA OF HOI HA WAN AND TOLO CHANNEL, HONG KONG

Andrew S.Y. Mackie, P. Graham Oliver

Department of Zoology, National Museum of Wales, Cathays Park, Cardiff CF1 3NP, Wales, UK

and

Paul F. Kingston

Institute of Offshore Engineering, Heriot-Watt University, Riccarton, Edinburgh EH14 4AS, Scotland, UK

ABSTRACT

In April 1989 the benthic macrofaunal communities at ten stations in Hoi Ha Wan and Tolo Channel were investigated. Analysis of duplicate 0.1 m^2 van Veen grab samples showed that a dramatic increase in numerical abundance and a marked decline in diversity (H') had occurred in the channel since 1986. The dominant species (*Minuspio* sp.) at the stations concerned had been identified in previous surveys (1980 and 1986) as an indicator of organic pollution in Tolo Harbour. This species was also among the dominants in Hoi Ha Wan suggesting the proposed marine reserve there was already under threat. The decline in the infaunal communities was further highlighted by indications that species were now being excluded from both Tolo Harbour and Tolo Channel. Paradoxically, the shallowest station in Hoi Ha Wan was the richest ever found in the area, comparing favourably with the higher species richness and diversity values evident in temperate waters.

INTRODUCTION

The macrobenthic infauna of the Tolo Channel region (22° 27'N, 114° 16'E) in the northeastern part of the New Territories, Hong Kong, has been investigated quantitatively on three previous occasions; 1976–77 (Shin and Thompson 1982), 1980 (Shin 1982) and 1986 (Shin 1990). Hoi Ha Wan, near the mouth of the channel, has received little attention with only two stations sampled in 1986. The proposal to make Hoi Ha Wan a nature reserve highlights the need for detailed biological investigations of its fauna and flora. The rapid and extensive urbanization around Tolo Harbour, with the associated increase in sewage pollution very evident (Wu 1988; Morton 1990), makes such studies a vital and urgent necessity. In April 1989 the senior author carried out a quantitative survey of the Hoi Ha Wan benthos. For comparative purposes additional samples were also taken in Tolo Channel proper. The results of our investigations are considered in relation to previous studies and possible faunal trends discussed.

MATERIALS AND METHODS

Ten stations were studied quantitatively using duplicate 0.1 m^2 van Veen grab samples. This sampling regime was so restricted owing to practical limitations. It was, however, considered adequate for a study involving diversity indices and classification analysis (see Kingston and Riddle 1989). Additionally, the area sampled per station was close to that of previous studies in the Tolo region. Five stations were located within Hoi Ha Wan itself, with two stations at the entrance and three stations in a transect along Tolo Channel (Fig. 1). The sediment of Station 40, the shallowest station, was muddy sand with considerable amounts of terrestrial detritus. Sediments of the remaining stations were predominantly mud, usually with some broken shell and small amounts of detritus retained on the 0.5 mm sieve used. The sediments of the Tolo area have been studied in more detail by Shin (1982; 1990). Sieved samples were fixed in 10–15% formaldehyde in seawater, stained with Rose Bengal and washed in freshwater prior to being sorted into 80% ethanol.

Data from both replicates were pooled for each station prior to further analyses. Several diversity and evenness measures were calculated (Moore 1983) to allow comparison with other studies, past and future. The indices of Margalef (d), Simpson (D), Fisher (α), Shannon-Wiener (H') and Pielou's Evenness (J) are commonly employed in ecological studies. Brillouin's index (H) and Heip's Evenness (E) were also calculated. The former is considered the appropriate index for most ecological studies (Kaesler *et al.* 1978), while the latter is regarded as theoretically superior to other evenness indices (Heip 1974). The Shannon-Wiener, Pielou and Heip indices are calculated using $\log_2$ values. Diversity was additionally displayed as rarefaction curves generated by the Hurlbert method (see Moore 1983).

The relationships between stations were investigated using the Jaccard coefficient (co-occurrences/total occurrences) for binary and the Bray-Curtis measure for quantitative data (see Clifford and Stephenson 1975). The latter analysis was carried out employing the programme PATN (Belbin 1988) with $\log_{10}$ (x+1) transformed values and group average fusion.

The distributions of several polychaete species were examined relative to the 1986 grab survey of the Tolo area (Shin 1990). The 1986 samples analysed were collected by the senior author as an adjunct to the Shin survey from locations (Fig. 5) in Tolo Harbour (stations 38, 39, 49–57), Tolo Channel (stations 26, 27, 40–48, 58) and Mirs Bay (stations 18–25). Additional material was obtained from a number of other 1986 stations (see Table 5) courtesy of Akira Hirayama. Samples were not quantitative, consisting only of animals collected (0.5 mm sieve) after several decantations of the fluidised sediments from one or two 0.05 m^2 van Veen grabs.

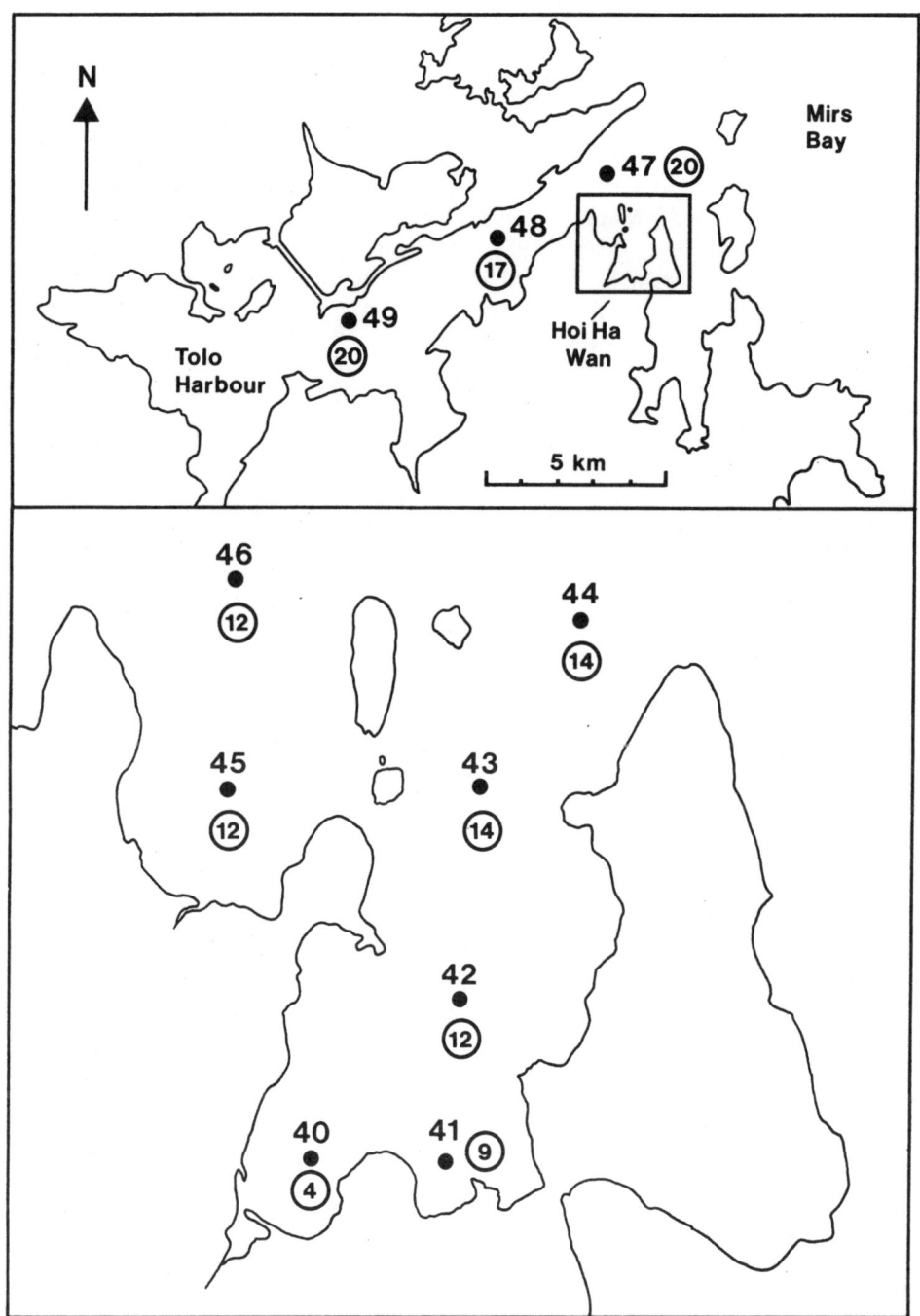

Fig. 1. Sampling stations in Hoi Ha Wan and Tolo Channel, April 1989. (Circled values represent depths in metres).

RESULTS

Species

Considerable taxonomic problems were encountered in this study (see also Oliver 1993). Species were separated as far as possible according to their morphological features, but no attempt was made to name them unless they agreed well with published descriptions. Most taxa were identified using a variety of taxonomic works, e.g., Fauchald (1977), Gallardo (1968), Mackie (1990), Mackie and Hartley (1990) and Uschakov (1982) for the Polychaeta, Erséus (1984, 1990) for the Oligochaeta and Sakai (1965) for the Brachyura. In the case of the Polychaeta it appears likely that a fair number will prove, on detailed examination, to be new to science. Evidence for this is amply demonstrated by the discovery in Hoi Ha Wan of three genera (*Diaphorosoma* Wolf, 1986; *Aberranta* Hartman, 1965; *Octocapitella* Brown, 1987) previously known only from the east coast of the USA. A total of 153 taxa were recorded (Appendix), though for the numerical analyses *Linopherus* and *Paramphinome* were combined due to the difficulty in separating the two among the large number of juveniles at Station 40.

Abundance

In total, 11,608 individuals were enumerated from the 10 stations. The infauna were dominated overall by the Polychaeta (96 species; 8531 individuals) accounting for 63% of the species and 73% of the individuals encountered. Although the Mollusca (2239 individuals) only accounted for 19% of the survey total, *Theora* cf. *lata* was the dominant species at four stations in Hoi Ha Wan. With the exception of Station 47, all other stations had *Minuspio* sp. as the dominant species (Table 1). The three most common species (*Minuspio* sp., *Theora* cf. *lata* and *Sigambra* sp.A) collectively represented 71% of the total survey abundance. These same species accounted for 86% of the total for stations 42–49.

Diversity and Evenness

The high level of dominance evident with respect to relatively few species (Table 1) was reflected in the generally low diversity values obtained for stations 41–49 (Table 2). In contrast, Station 40 had both the least degree of dominance among the top ranked species and a considerably greater number of species (118 vs. 13–33). Diversity values for Station 40 were higher than any reported from previous surveys of the Tolo area (Shin 1982, 1990).

Displayed graphically, diversity (stations 41–49) increased greatly toward the mouth of Tolo Channel and decreased slightly within Hoi Ha Wan (Fig. 2). The differences were least marked using Fisher's α as this, like Margalef's index, is essentially a species richness measure. The other indices are influenced to a greater extent by the relative abundances of the species present. Hence, for stations 41–49, the values of H' and D had comparatively wider ranges. Evenness (the extent to which individuals are equally apportioned among species) was greatest in the outer Tolo Channel (Station 47) and outer Hoi Ha stations (stations 44–46). The lowest values were recorded from those stations (stations 49, 48 and 41) where the top-ranked species were most dominant.

The rarefaction methodology allows diversity to be visualised graphically in terms

Table 1
Abundances of dominant species at each station, April 1989.

	Station 40	Number	Cum. %
1	*Minuspio* sp.	467	14.35
2	*Theora* cf. *lata*	373	25.81
3	AMPHINOMIDAE	330	35.96
4	TANAIDACEA sp. A	247	43.55
5	*Paradoneis* sp.	206	49.88
6	SIPUNCULA	177	55.32
7	*Paralacydonia* sp.	167	60.45
8	*Sigambra* sp. A	148	65.00
9	*Lumbrineris* sp. A	120	68.68
10	CUMACEA sp. C	91	71.48

	Station 41	Number	Cum. %
1	*Theora* cf. *lata*	827	58.08
2	*Minuspio* sp.	254	75.91
3	*Sigambra* sp. A	185	88.90
4	*Nephtys* sp. B	33	91.22
5	NEMERTEA	17	92.42
	AMPHINOMIDAE	17	93.61

	Station 42	Number	Cum. %
1	*Theora* cf. *lata*	238	47.89
2	*Minuspio* sp.	94	66.80
3	*Sigambra* sp. A	70	80.89
4	RETUSIDAE sp. A	20	84.91
5	*Nephtys* sp. B	19	88.73

	Station 43	Number	Cum. %
1	*Theora* cf. *lata*	260	56.28
2	*Minuspio* sp.	82	74.03
3	*Sigambra* sp. A	42	83.12
4	*Nephtys* sp. B	21	87.66
5	NEMERTEA	11	90.04

	Station 44	Number	Cum. %
1	*Minuspio* sp.	153	29.31
2	*Theora* cf. *lata*	128	53.83
3	*Sigambra* sp. A	82	69.54
4	*Nephtys* sp. B	31	75.48
5	*Aglaophamus* sp. C	17	78.74
	Mediomastus sp.	17	81.99

	Station 45	Number	Cum. %
1	*Theora* cf. *lata*	95	46.34
2	*Nephtys* sp. B	30	60.98
3	*Minuspio* sp.	19	70.24
4	*Aglaophamus* sp. C	17	78.54
5	*Sigambra* sp. A	16	86.34

	Station 46	Number	Cum. %
1	*Minuspio* sp.	141	28.26
2	*Theora* cf. *lata*	79	44.09
3	*Sigambra* sp. A	72	58.52
4	*Nephtys* sp. B	38	66.13
5	*Aglaophamus* sp. C	32	72.55
6	*Prionospio* sp. D	27	77.96

	Station 47	Number	Cum. %
1	*Nephtys* sp. B	49	28.00
2	*Aglaophamus* sp. C	35	48.00
3	*Prionospio* sp. D	26	62.86
4	*Theora* cf. *lata*	22	75.43
5	*Sigambra* sp. A	11	81.71

	Station 48	Number	Cum. %
1	*Minuspio* sp.	828	70.08
2	*Sigambra* sp. A	82	86.92
3	*Nephtys* sp. B	64	93.03
4	*Aglaophamus* sp. C	19	94.84
5	NEMERTEA	12	95.99

	Station 49	Number	Cum. %
1	*Minuspio* sp.	3246	91.14
2	*Sigambra* sp. A	182	97.30
3	*Theora* cf. *lata*	24	97.98
4	*Nephtys* sp. B	21	98.58
5	*Anelassorhynchus* sp.	11	98.89

	Combined stations	Number	Cum. %
1	*Minuspio* sp.	5292	45.59
2	*Theora* cf. *lata*	2053	63.28
3	*Sigambra* sp. A	890	70.94
4	AMPHINOMIDAE	365	74.09
5	*Nephtys* sp. B	320	76.84

	Stations 42-49 only	Number	Cum. %
1	*Minuspio* sp.	4571	65.96
2	*Theora* cf. *lata*	853	78.27
3	*Sigambra* sp. A	557	86.31
4	*Nephtys* sp. B	273	90.25
5	*Aglaophamus* sp. C	135	92.19

of the relationship between species and individuals at each station. It can also be of considerable use in the comparison of investigations involving different sample sizes. The Hurlbert rarefaction curves (Fig. 3) revealed three groups of stations: 'High' diversity (Station 40), 'Medium' diversity (stations 41–47) and 'Low' diversity (stations 48 and 49). The positions of the individual curves suggest the same trends as indicated in Figure 2.

Table 2
Numerical, diversity and evenness values for each station, April 1989.

Station	40	41	42	43	44	45	46	47	48	49
Species:										
Annelida	83	23	13	15	24	8	21	10	13	13
Mollusca	11	5	7	5	1	2	2	4	4	2
Crustacea	16	2	-	-	1	1	-	1	-	-
Others	8	3	2	3	4	2	5	3	3	4
Total:	118	33	22	23	30	13	28	18	20	19
Individuals:										
Annelida	2152	541	217	177	377	92	396	142	1008	3482
Mollusca	483	847	270	272	128	96	81	26	11	25
Crustacea	371	16	-	-	1	1	-	1	-	-
Others	248	20	10	13	16	16	22	6	28	16
Total:	3254	1424	497	462	522	205	499	175	1047	3523
Diversity:										
α	24.00	6.04	4.71	5.09	6.92	3.09	6.41	5.03	3.51	2.64
d	14.47	4.41	3.38	3.59	4.63	2.25	4.35	3.29	2.73	2.20
D	0.93	0.61	0.71	0.64	0.82	0.74	0.86	0.84	0.36	0.15
H'	4.66	2.06	2.46	2.25	3.14	2.52	3.44	3.05	1.30	0.56
H	3.17	1.39	1.64	1.49	2.09	1.65	2.29	1.97	0.87	0.38
Evenness:										
J	0.68	0.41	0.55	0.50	0.64	0.68	0.72	0.73	0.30	0.13
E	0.21	0.10	0.21	0.17	0.27	0.39	0.37	0.43	0.08	0.03

Similarity between stations

The Jaccard similarity coefficient values for presence–absence data (Table 3) showed that stations 44 and 46 had the highest degree (53%) of shared species. With this exception, the interstation species similarity for stations 42–49 ranged from 28 to 42%. Station 41 had a slightly lower affinity with these stations, while Station 40 differed most. Given the high numerical dominance exhibited by the top three or four ranked species at each station, the Jaccard similarity values between stations 42–49 must be considered high. These findings were confirmed by the relationships between station groups as determined by the quantitative Bray-Curtis classification analysis (Fig. 4). Hence the benthic fauna of Tolo Channel and Hoi Ha Wan can be considered as essentially belonging to the same community; a finding consistent with previous studies of the area (Shin 1990).

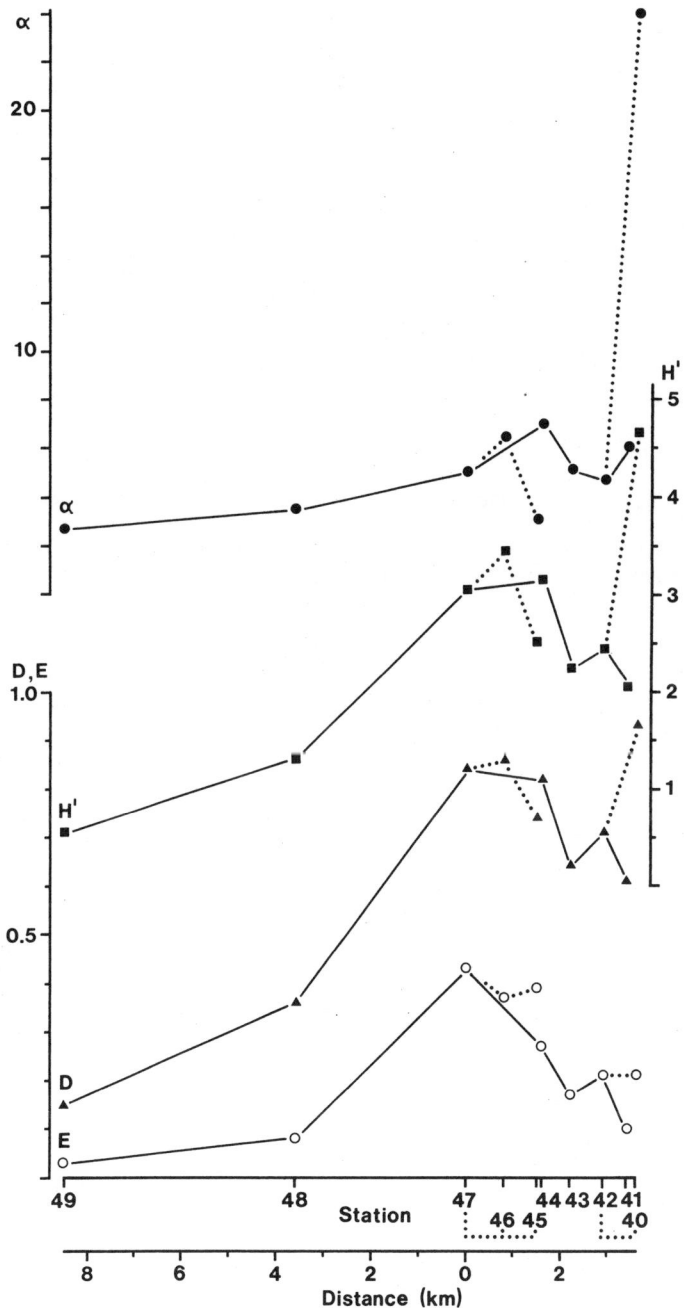

Fig. 2. A comparison of diversity and evenness values relative to sampling station position (April 1989). Positions expressed as distance from Station 47.

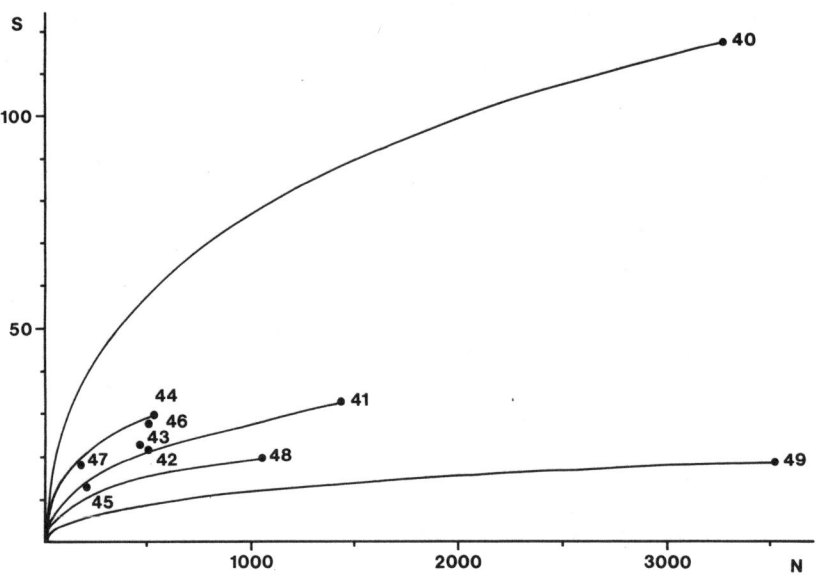

Fig. 3. Hurlbert rarefaction curves for 1989 survey. (For clarity only 5 curves are drawn; remaining curves are represented by end points).

Table 3
Interstation similarity values (Jaccard coefficient).

Station	40	41	42	43	44	45	46	47	48
41	0.21								
42	0.15	0.28							
43	0.12	0.33	0.41						
44	0.14	0.29	0.30	0.39					
45	0.07	0.24	0.30	0.29	0.30				
46	0.15	0.33	0.35	0.42	0.53	0.32			
47	0.06	0.19	0.29	0.32	0.33	0.41	0.31		
48	0.10	0.18	0.31	0.39	0.32	0.32	0.41	0.36	
49	0.09	0.30	0.28	0.35	0.29	0.39	0.38	0.28	0.39

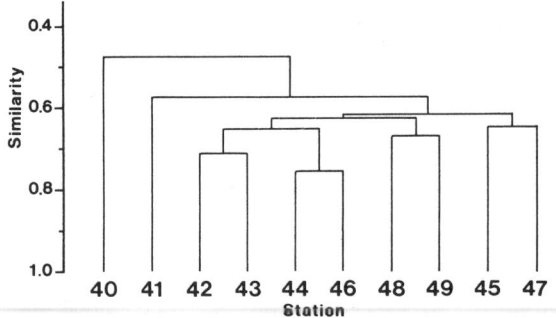

Fig. 4. Classification analysis of Hoi Ha Wan and Tolo Channel stations, April 1989. (Bray-Curtis measure: transformed data).

Table 4

Summary of quantitative soft-bottom macrobenthic investigations in Hong Kong waters, and a comparison with a temperate study. (Numerical, diversity and evenness attributes are mean values).

Survey	Locality	S	N	H'	J	Area sampled (m^2)	Sieve size (mm)	Reference
	Hong Kong							
1980	Tolo Harbour	9.9	161.2	2.15	0.70	0.15	0.5	Shin 1982
	Tolo Channel	10.0	34.0	2.70	0.87	"	"	"
1986	Tolo Harbour	8.1	102.0	1.27	?	"	"	Shin 1990
	Tolo Channel	12.1	62.6	2.15	?	"	"	"
	Mirs Bay	11.2	41.1	1.95	?	"	"	"
1989	Tolo Channel (Stns. 48 & 49)	19.5	2285.0	0.93	0.22	0.2	"	this paper
	Tolo Channel/Hoi Ha (Stns. 42-47)	22.3	393.3	2.81	0.64	"	"	"
	Hoi Ha (Stn. 40)	118	3254	4.66	0.68	"	"	"
1976-77	Mirs Bay	13.3	105.5	2.07	?	0.5	0.4	Shin 1990
	East Hong Kong	19.2	44.1	3.84	0.91	"	"	Shin and Thompson 1982
	West Hong Kong	17.2	53.6	3.55	0.88	"	"	"
	West-central Hong Kong	18.8	48.0	3.70	0.88	"	"	"
	South Hong Kong	16.2	27.4	3.51	0.89	"	"	"
1979	Victoria Harbour (VH2)	8.7	26.7	2.26	0.86	0.2	"	Thompson and Shin 1983
1985	South-East Hong Kong	30.0	81.3	3.03	0.87	0.3	0.5	Shin 1989
1987	South-East Hong Kong	39.0	192.0	3.16	0.87	0.4	"	"
	Scotland							
1979	Loch Creran (mud)	60.8	1066.8	3.75	0.64	0.2	"	Mackie (unpublished)
	Loch Creran (sandy mud)	82.2	1142.5	4.51	0.72	"	"	"
	Loch Creran (muddy sand)	169.0	2226.0	5.47	0.74	"	"	"
	Loch Creran (mud/sand/gravel)	112.0	2289.3	4.57	0.67	"	"	"

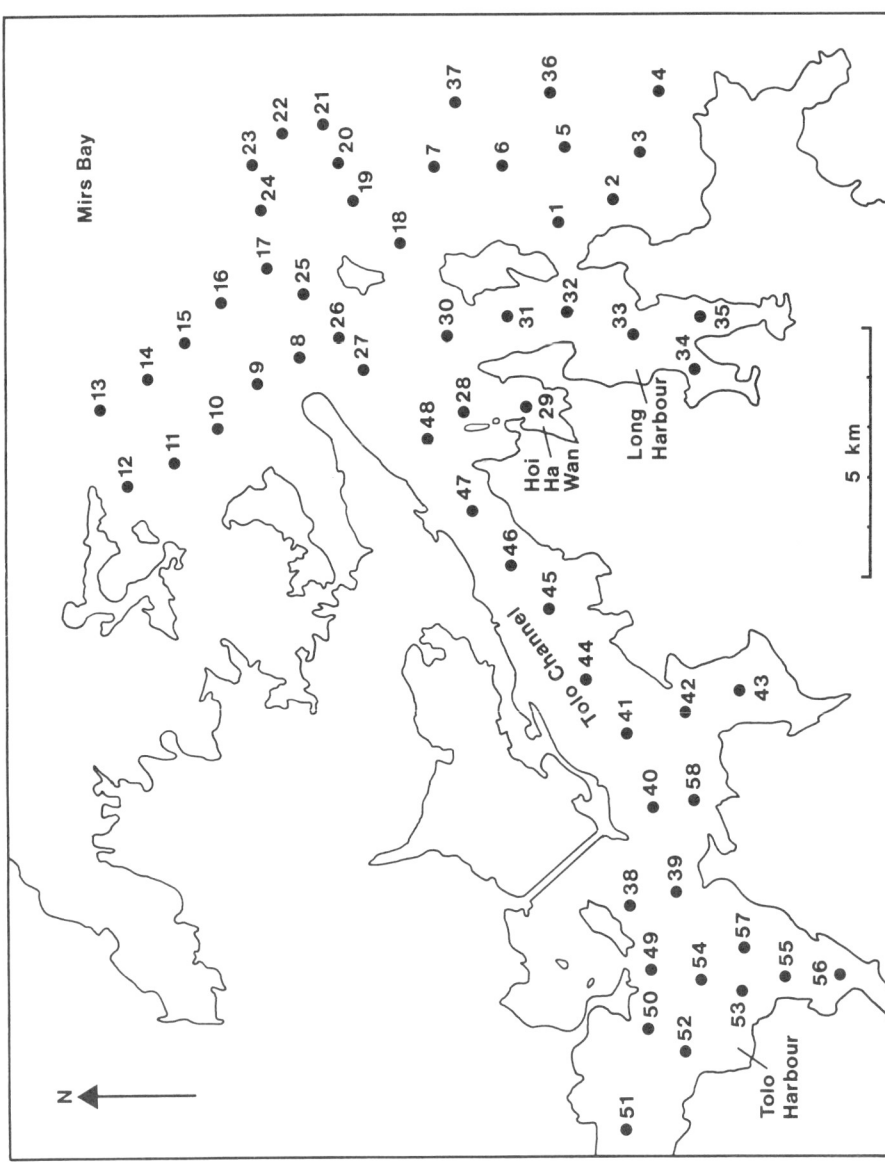

Fig. 5. Sampling stations in the Tolo region, April 1986.

Table 5.
Distribution of *Prionospio saccifera* and five nephtyid species in the Tolo region in 1986 and 1989. (Note: abundances for 1986 survey not quantitative).

1986 stations	1989 stations	Aglaophamus A	B	C	Nephtys A	B	Prionospio saccifera
Tolo Harbour							
56		-	-	-	-	1	-
52		-	-	-	1	-	-
39		-	-	-	2	-	-
38		-	-	-	1	-	-
Tolo Channel							
58		-	-	-	-	6	-
40		-	-	3	2	1	3
	49	-	-	4	-	21	-
41		-	-	1	2	1	8
42		-	-	-	-	1	-
43		-	-	-	-	3	-
44		-	-	1	-	5	8
45		2	-	-	1	1	5
	48	-	-	19	-	64	-
46		1	-	-	-	1	3
47		2	-	4	-	1	9
	47	-	-	35	-	49	-
48		2	2	3	-	-	9
27		5	-	1	-	-	10
26		7	-	3	-	-	4
30		-	-	-	-	1	3
Hoi Ha Wan							
28		-	-	-	-	-	1
29		1	-	1	1	-	12
	40-46	0-1	-	0-32	-	13-38	-
Long Harbour							
31		-	1	-	-	-	3
32		-	1	-	-	-	5
33		-	-	-	-	-	5
34		-	-	-	11	1	3
35		-	-	-	4	-	3
Mirs Bay							
4		-	-	1	-	-	3
3		2	-	1	-	-	4
2		1	-	1	-	-	2
1		-	1	1	-	1	-
5		1	-	3	-	-	-
7		-	1	-	-	-	-
18		-	2	5	-	-	1
19		3	1	8	-	-	-
20		6	-	10	-	-	-
21		2	1	-	-	-	-
22		3	1	3	-	-	1
23		5	1	2	-	-	-
24		2	2	2	-	-	-
17		-	-	6	-	-	-
25		3	4	11	-	-	-
8		1	-	-	-	-	1

Table 5 (Continued).

1986 stations	1989 stations	Aglaophamus			Nephtys		Prionospio saccifera
		A	B	C	A	B	
9		3	-	-	-	-	-
10		4	2	-	-	-	2
11		-	-	1	-	-	4
12		1	1	-	-	-	1
13		-	-	4	-	-	-
14		2	-	3	-	-	-
15		-	3	8	-	-	-
16		-	1	2	-	-	1

DISCUSSION

The sublittoral infaunal communities of Hong Kong have been subject to considerable investigation (Shin 1982, 1989, 1990; Shin and Thompson 1983; Thompson and Shin 1982). A collation of data from these studies (Table 4) indicates that in 'undisturbed' localities, species richness and numerical abundance are generally low, diversity low to moderately high and evenness high. Shin and Thompson (1982) compared the Hong Kong benthos with other tropical and subtropical areas. Later, Thompson and Shin (1983) and Shin (1989) commented on the marked contrast between the characteristics of Hong Kong benthic habitats and those of temperate waters. For example, typical baseline measurements for the North Sea (Europe) range from 100–177 species and 1576–3110 individuals·0.5 m^{-2}, with diversities (H') of 4.4–5.8 and evenness (J) values of 0.64–0.78 (Kingston 1987). Temperate inshore sediments can also be faunistically rich. Only the shallowest Hoi Ha Wan station (Station 40) compares favourably with like sediments from Loch Creran, Scotland (Table 4) and, interestingly, both sediments had a considerable terrestrial detritus component.

The reasons why the structure of the subtropical Hong Kong benthos differs from that of temperate regions are complex and not fully understood. The influences of reduced salinity, large annual temperature fluctuations, biological interactions, high sediment silt-clay content, sediment instability and negative sediment Eh have all been considered either major or contributing factors (Shin and Thompson 1982; Shin 1989). The richness of Station 40 is unusual in comparison with previous assessments of the Hong Kong benthos and could simply be a localised anomaly. Alternatively, however, it may indicate that conditions for the development of soft-bottom infaunal communities are optimal in shallow nearshore situations. In this context, it may be significant that Erséus (1992) has noted that the number of oligochaete species was comparatively high in the shallow (0.5–3.5 m) sandier sediments of the outer parts of Hoi Ha Wan. By contrast, the number of oligochaete species recorded from the deeper muddier sediments of the Tolo region was low.

The biological health of Tolo Harbour has long been of concern (Wu 1988; Morton 1990) due to the ever increasing input of organic effluents (human sewage and livestock wastes). The detrimental effects of these on the whole Tolo region have been exacerbated by land reclamation around a harbour subject to naturally poor water exchange. Morton (1990) tabulated the progressive deleterious influence of this pollution on the marine life since the early 1970's. Evidence of effects on the benthic soft-bottom habitat include distinct alterations (1976–86) in the epifaunal predatory gastropod communities of both Tolo Harbour and Channel (Taylor and Shin 1990). Shin (1990) found no distinct changes in the infaunal communities between the 1980 and 1986 surveys, but speculated that this could also result if the benthic habitat was already stressed at the time of the first survey. In both surveys species (*Minuspio* sp. and *Sigambra* sp.A) that were considered indicators of organic enrichment were only dominant in Tolo Harbour. While organic enrichment is clearly the major threat in the Tolo area, the presence of other important pollutants, e.g., inorganic nutrients and metals, should not be forgotten. In 1989, for example, an examination of heavy metal (cadmium, chromium, copper, zinc) concentrations in Tolo Harbour barnacles showed significant increases relative to a 1986 study (Rainbow and Smith 1992).

Analysis of diversity and evenness values shows that a clear deterioration has occurred in the infaunal communities over much of Tolo Channel since 1986. The extreme dominance of *Minuspio* sp. at stations 48 and 49 would, in light of previous work (Shin 1982, 1990; Thompson and Shin 1983), indicate the presence of considerable organic pollution. These stations exhibit some of the classic features of communities (i.e. dramatic increase in total abundance; low diversity and evenness values) affected by levels of organic enrichment that, at the very least, are sufficient to classify a benthic habitat as polluted (see Pearson and Rosenberg 1978). Certainly, the community structure at these two stations can be considered to be beyond the so-called 'ecotone point', though it is not clear whether the characteristic peak abundance of opportunists (marking the decline into grossly polluted situations where no macrofauna survive) has been passed. *Minuspio* was also commonly among the dominants of the Hoi Ha Wan stations. This could be a response to the large inputs of terrestrial organic material that periodically occur due to heavy freshwater runoff, particularly at the onset of the wet (summer) season (see Morton 1990). The fact that *Minuspio* was previously only a dominant in Tolo Harbour (Shin 1990) suggests, however, that pollution is now threatening the Hoi Ha reserve.

Additional evidence for a marked change in the infauna of Tolo Channel comes from a comparison of the distributions of the Nephtyidae and *Prionospio saccifera* in 1986 and 1989 (Table 5, Fig. 5). The 1986 abundances of the six species are not quantitative but, nevertheless, the data appear to show two trends. The first suggests that the abundances of *Nephtys* sp.B and *Aglaophamus* sp.C may have increased since 1986. Of course, even if real and not a product of sampling differences, such a trend could be due as much to natural population fluctuations as to an organic enrichment response. The second is the reverse of the first, with several species having either reduced abundances or being excluded from Tolo Harbour and Channel. In 1986 *Nephtys* sp.A was encountered frequently from Tolo Harbour to Long Harbour, while *Aglaophamus* sp.A penetrated halfway down Tolo Channel. Of these two species, only *Aglaophamus* sp.A was found in 1989 (at the two outermost Hoi Ha stations). More noticeably, *Prionospio saccifera* (as *Prionospio ehlersi* in earlier studies) was not encountered in the 1989 samples. In 1980 this species was present in Tolo Harbour, but by 1986 it was excluded from there, though it was the third dominant species in the Tolo Channel area. Again, other explanations of these observations are possible, but the abundance of *Minuspio* in Tolo Channel is strongly indicative of a pollution induced change. Further evidence for a decline in the health of the Tolo Channel benthos between 1986 and 1989 is provided by a pronounced decrease in the species richness of the Gastropoda in the outer channel (Taylor 1992).

ACKNOWLEDGEMENTS

We would like to thank Professor Brian Morton for inviting two of us (ASYM, PGO) to the 1986 and 1989 International Marine Biological Workshops, and the National Museum of Wales for funding our visits. Special thanks to Christer Erséus and Per Sundberg for identifying the oligochaetes and nemerteans. Christer Erséus, John Taylor and Phil Rainbow kindly allowed us to view their manuscripts. Welcome assistance in the field was provided by Paul Shin, Vivian Lam, Chiu Sein-Tuck and Akira Hirayama in 1986, and Takashi Ohwada and Albert Leung in 1989.

REFERENCES

Belbin, L. 1988. *PATN pattern analysis package*. CSIRO Division of Wildlife and Ecology, Australia.
Brown, B. 1987. A new genus and species of Capitellidae (Polychaeta) from the Atlantic coast of the United States. *Bulletin of the Biological Society of Washington* 7:56–61.
Clifford, H.T. and Stephenson, W. 1975. *An introduction to numerical classification*. New York: Academic Press.
Erséus, C. 1984. The marine Tubificidae (Oligochaeta) of Hong Kong and southern China. *Asian Marine Biology* 1:135–75.
Erséus, C. 1990. Marine Oligochaeta of Hong Kong. In *Proceedings of the Second International Marine Biological Workshop: The Marine Flora and Fauna of Hong Kong and Southern China, Hong Kong, 1986* (ed. B. Morton), 259–335. Hong Kong: Hong Kong University Press.
Erséus, C. 1992. Oligochaeta from Hoi Ha Wan. In *Proceedings of the Fourth International Marine Biological Workshop: The Marine Flora and Fauna of Hong Kong and Southern China, Hong Kong, 1989* (ed. B. Morton), 909–17. Hong Kong: Hong Kong University Press.
Fauchald, K. 1977. *The polychaete worms. Definitions and keys to the orders, families and genera*. Los Angeles: Natural History Museum of Los Angeles County. *Science Series* 28.
Gallardo, V.A. 1968. Polychaeta from the Bay of Nha Trang, South Viet Nam. *NAGA Reports* 4(3):35–279.
Hartman, O. 1965. Deep-water benthic polychaetous annelids off New England to Bermuda and other North atlantic areas. *Allan Hancock Foundation Publications Occasional Paper* 28:1–378.
Heip, C. 1974. A new index measuring evenness. *Journal of the Marine Biological Association of the United Kingdom* 54:555–7.
Kaesler, R.L., Herricks, E.E. and Crossman, J.S. 1978. Use of indices of diversity and hierarchical diversity in stream surveys.In *Biological Data in Water Pollution Assessment: Quantitative and Statistical Analyses* (ed. K.L. Dickson, J. Cairns and R.J. Livingston), 92–112. *Special Technical Publication* 652. Philadelphia: American Society for Testing Materials.
Kingston, P.F. 1987. Field effects of platform discharges on benthic macrofauna. *Philosophical Transactions of the Royal Society of London, Series B* 316:545–65.
Kingston, P.F. and Riddle, M.J. 1989. Cost effectiveness of benthic faunal monitoring. *Marine Pollution Bulletin* 20:490–6.
Mackie, A.S.Y. 1990. The Poecilochaetidae and Trochochaetidae (Annelida: Polychaeta) of Hong Kong. In *Proceedings of the Second International Marine Biological Workshop: The Marine Flora and Fauna of Hong Kong and Southern China, Hong Kong, 1986* (ed. B. Morton), 337–62. Hong Kong: Hong Kong University Press.

Mackie, A.S.Y. and Hartley, J.P. 1990. *Prionospio saccifera* sp. nov. (Polychaeta: Spionidae) from Hong Kong and the Red Sea, with a redescription of *Prionospio ehlersi* Fauvel, 1928. In *Proceedings of the Second International Marine Biological Workshop: The Marine Flora and Fauna of Hong Kong and Southern China, Hong Kong, 1986* (ed. B. Morton), 363–75. Hong Kong: Hong Kong University Press.
Moore, C.G. 1983. A BASIC Program for the investigation of species diversity. *Water Pollution Control* 82:102–6.
Morton, B. 1990. Pollution and the sub-tropical inshore hydrographic environment of Hong Kong. In *Proceedings of the Second International Marine Biological Workshop: The Marine Flora and Fauna of Hong Kong and Southern China, Hong Kong, 1986* (ed. B. Morton), 3–30. Hong Kong: Hong Kong University Press.
Oliver, P.G. 1993. Taxonomic sufficiency and the role of systematics in marine invertebrate studies with special reference to Hong Kong. In *Proceedings of the First International Conference on the Marine Biology of Hong Kong and the South China Sea, Hong Kong, 1990* (ed. B. Morton), 3–35. Hong Kong: Hong Kong University Press.
Pearson, T. H. and Rosenberg, R. 1978. Macrobenthic succession in relation to organic enrichment and pollution of the marine environment. *Oceanography and Marine Biology Annual Review* 16:229–311.
Rainbow, P.S. and Smith, B.D. 1992. Biomonitoring of Hong Kong coastal trace metals by barnacles, 1986–1989. In *Proceedings of the Fourth International Marine Biological Workshop: The Marine Flora and Fauna of Hong Kong and Southern China, Hong Kong, 1989* (ed. B. Morton), 585–97. Hong Kong: Hong Kong University Press.
Sakai, T. 1965. *The crabs of Sagami Bay*. Honolulu: East-West Center Press.
Shin, P.K.S. 1982. The macrobenthic infauna of Tolo Harbour and Tolo Channel, Hong Kong. In *Proceedings of the First Marine Biological Workshop: The Marine Flora and Fauna of Hong Kong and Southern China, Hong Kong, 1980* (ed. B. Morton and C.K. Tseng), 721–31. Hong Kong: Hong Kong University Press.
Shin, P.K.S. 1989. Natural disturbance of benthic infauna in the offshore waters of Hong Kong. *Asian Marine Biology* 6:193–207.
Shin, P.K.S. 1990. Benthic invertebrate communities in Tolo Harbour and Mirs Bay: a review. In *Proceedings of the Second International Marine Biological Workshop: The Marine Flora and Fauna of Hong Kong and Southern China, Hong Kong, 1986* (ed. B. Morton), 883–98. Hong Kong: Hong Kong University Press.
Shin, P.K.S. and Thompson, G.B. 1982. Spatial distribution of the infaunal benthos of Hong Kong. *Marine Ecology-Progress Series* 10:37–47.
Sundberg, P., Erséus, C. and Mackie, A.S.Y. 1992. Distribution of annelids and nemerteans along three transects at Hoi Ha Beach. In *Proceedings of the Fourth International Marine Biological Workshop: The Marine Flora and Fauna of Hong Kong and Southern China, Hong Kong, 1989* (ed. B. Morton), 865–81. Hong Kong: Hong Kong University Press.
Taylor, J.D. 1992. Long-term changes in the gastropod fauna of Tolo Channel and Mirs Bay, Hong Kong: the 1989 survey. In *Proceedings of the Fourth International Marine Biological Workshop: The Marine Flora and Fauna of Hong Kong and the Southern China III, Hong Kong, 1989* (ed. B. Morton), 557–73. Hong Kong: Hong Kong University Press.
Taylor, J.D. and Shin, P.K.S. 1990. Trawl surveys of sublittoral gastropods in Tolo Channel and Mirs Bay; a record of change from 1976-1986. In *Proceedings of the Second International Marine Biological Workshop: The Marine Flora and Fauna of Hong Kong and Southern China, Hong Kong, 1986* (ed. B. Morton), 857–82. Hong Kong: Hong Kong University Press.
Thompson, G.B. and Shin, P.K.S. 1983. Sewage pollution and the infaunal benthos of Victoria Harbour, Hong Kong. *Journal of Experimental Marine Biology and Ecology* 67:279–99.
Uschakov, P.V. 1982. Polychaetes of the suborder Aphroditiformia of the Arctic Ocean and the northwestern part of the Pacific. Families Aphroditidae and Polynoidae. *Fauna of the USSR, New Series* 126:1–272.
Wolf, P.S. 1986. Four new genera of Dorvilleidae (Annelida: Polychaeta) from the Gulf of Mexico. *Proceedings of the Biological Society of Washington* 99:616–26.
Wu, R.S.S. 1988. Marine pollution in Hong Kong: a review. *Asian Marine Biology* 5:1–23.

Appendix
Numbers of animals collected at each station (No'·0.2m⁻²), April 1989.

Station number	40	41	42	43	44	45	46	47	48	49
ANNELIDA										
CHRYSOPETALIDAE sp.	1	-	-	-	-	-	-	-	-	-
Linopherus/Paramphinome*	330	17	4	1	-	-	8	-	2	3
Harmothoe sp.*	2	-	-	-	-	-	-	-	-	-
Paralepidonotus ampulliferus	2	-	-	-	1	-	-	-	-	-
POLYNOIDAE sp.	-	-	-	-	-	-	-	-	1	-
Sthenelais nami	-	-	-	2	5	2	11	1	3	6
Pholoe sp.*	51	2	-	-	-	-	2	-	-	-
Eumida sp.	6	-	-	-	-	-	-	-	-	-
Mystides sp.	2	-	-	-	-	-	-	-	-	-
Pionosyllis sp.	3	-	-	-	-	-	-	-	-	-
Eusyllis sp. A*	12	-	-	-	-	-	-	-	-	-
Eusyllis sp. B	4	-	-	-	-	-	-	-	-	-
Sphaerosyllis sp. A*	4	-	-	-	-	-	-	-	-	-
Sphaerosyllis sp. B	10	-	-	-	-	-	-	-	-	-
Exogone sp. A	12	-	-	-	-	-	-	-	-	-
Exogone sp. B	15	-	1	-	-	-	-	-	-	-
Podarke sp. A*	1	-	-	-	3	-	2	-	-	-
Podarke sp. B*	1	-	-	-	-	-	-	-	-	-
Podarkeopsis sp. A*	10	1	-	-	-	-	-	-	-	-
Podarkeopsis sp. B	1	-	1	1	1	-	1	-	-	-
Gyptis sp.	2	-	-	-	-	-	-	-	-	-
HESIONIDAE	2	-	1	-	-	-	-	-	-	-
Ancistrosyllis sp.	3	2	3	8	13	-	7	3	1	1
Ancistargis sp.	1	-	-	-	-	-	-	-	-	-
Sigambra sp. A*	148	185	70	42	82	16	72	11	82	182
Sigambra sp. B	1	-	1	-	14	2	3	-	-	1
Cabira sp.	-	1	-	1	4	-	1	-	-	-
Synelmis ? sp.	1	-	-	-	-	-	-	-	-	-
Leonnates sp.	2	-	-	-	-	-	5	-	2	-
Neanthes sp.	-	-	-	-	-	-	-	-	-	1
Aglaophamus sp. A	-	-	-	-	1	-	1	-	-	-
Aglaophamus sp. C	-	1	3	8	17	17	32	35	19	4
Nephtys sp. B	14	33	19	21	31	30	38	49	64	21
Micronephthys sp.*	2	-	-	-	-	-	-	-	-	-
Paralacydonia sp.*	167	-	-	1	-	-	-	-	1	-
Glycera sp. B	2	-	-	-	-	-	-	-	-	-
Glycinde sp.*	29	-	-	-	-	-	-	-	-	-
Marphysa sp. A	11	-	-	-	-	-	-	-	-	-
Marphysa sp. B	3	1	-	-	-	-	-	-	-	-
Eunice sp.	75	1	-	-	-	-	-	-	-	-
Diopatra sp.	1	-	-	-	-	-	-	-	-	-
Oenone sp.	1	-	-	-	-	-	-	-	-	-
Lumbrineris sp. A	120	-	-	-	-	-	-	-	-	-
Lumbrineris sp. B	1	-	-	-	-	-	-	-	-	-
Dorvillea sp. B	25	-	-	-	-	-	-	-	-	-
Diaphorosoma sp.	-	-	-	1	-	-	-	-	-	-
Leitoscoloplos sp.	3	-	-	-	-	-	-	-	-	-
Scoloplos juv.	2	-	-	-	-	-	-	-	-	-
Levinsenia sp. A	-	2	-	-	1	-	-	-	-	-
Levinsenia sp. B	8	16	1	-	-	-	-	-	-	-

Appendix (Continued).

Station number	40	41	42	43	44	45	46	47	48	49
Paradoneis sp.	206	-	-	-	-	-	-	-	-	-
Aricidea sp. B	7	-	-	-	-	-	-	-	-	-
Aricidea sp. C	3	-	-	-	-	-	-	-	-	-
Aricidea sp. D	5	-	-	-	-	-	-	-	-	-
Aricidea sp. E	-	-	-	-	2	-	-	-	-	-
Aberranta sp.	2	-	-	-	-	-	-	-	-	-
Scolelepis sp. C	1	-	-	-	-	-	-	-	-	-
Paraprionospio sp. A	-	1	-	-	-	2	1	-	2	9
Paraprionospio sp. B	-	-	-	-	-	-	-	-	-	1
Prionospio sp. D	2	4	-	5	14	4	27	26	-	6
Prionospio sp. E	3	-	-	-	-	-	-	-	-	-
Minuspio sp.*	467	254	94	82	153	19	141	8	828	3246
Polydora sp. A	1	-	-	-	-	-	-	-	-	-
Polydora sp. B	1	-	-	-	-	-	-	-	-	-
Polydora sp. C	-	-	-	-	1	-	-	-	2	-
Polydorella sp.	-	-	-	-	-	-	1	-	-	-
Poecilochaetus tricirratus	-	-	-	-	1	-	-	-	-	-
Poecilochaetus sp.	1	-	-	-	-	-	-	-	-	-
Phyllochaetopterus sp.	-	-	-	-	-	-	-	-	-	1
Magelona crenulifrons	-	1	-	-	-	-	-	-	-	-
Cirriformia sp. B*	1	-	-	-	-	-	-	-	-	-
Chaetozone flagellifera	2	1	-	-	1	-	2	-	-	-
Chaetozone maotienae	3	-	-	-	-	-	-	-	-	-
Caulleriella sp. A*	1	-	-	-	-	-	-	-	-	-
Caulleriella sp. B	10	-	-	-	-	-	-	-	-	-
Aphelechaeta sp. A	29	1	-	1	2	-	-	-	-	-
Aphelochaeta sp. B	50	10	10	2	6	-	5	-	-	-
Aphelochaeta sp. C	50	-	-	-	1	-	-	-	-	-
Cossura sp.	67	2	-	-	-	-	-	-	-	-
Ctenodrilus sp.	1	-	-	-	-	-	-	-	-	-
Octocapitella sp.	1	-	-	-	-	-	-	-	-	-
Capitella sp.*	2	-	-	-	-	-	-	-	-	-
Mediomastus sp.	45	-	1	1	17	-	20	1	1	-
Heteromastus sp.	5	-	-	-	-	-	-	-	-	-
Paraleiocapitella sp.	2	-	-	-	-	-	-	-	-	-
Notomastus sp.	1	-	-	-	-	-	-	-	-	-
Galathowenia sp.*	13	1	-	-	-	-	-	-	-	-
Lagis sp.	1	1	-	-	-	-	-	-	-	-
AMPHARETIDAE juv. A	-	-	-	-	5	-	16	7	-	-
AMPHARETIDAE juv. B	-	-	-	-	-	-	-	1	-	-
Terebellides sp.	4	-	-	-	-	-	-	-	-	-
Sabellaria sp.	2	-	-	-	-	-	-	-	-	-
Potamilla sp.	2	-	-	-	-	-	-	-	-	-
Euchone sp.	20	-	-	-	-	-	-	-	-	-
Myxicola sp.	1	-	-	-	-	-	-	-	-	-
Duridrilus piger	9	-	-	-	-	-	-	-	-	-
Tectidrilus pictoni	4	-	-	-	-	-	-	-	-	-
Limnodriloides toloensis*	12	-	-	-	-	-	-	-	-	-
Limnodriloides tenuiductus*	1	-	-	-	-	-	-	-	-	-
Smithsonidrilus tenuiculus	22	3	-	-	1	-	-	-	-	-
Tubificoides imajimai	1	-	-	-	-	-	-	-	-	-
MOLLUSCA										
Onoba sp.	-	-	-	1	-	-	-	-	-	-

Appendix (Continued).

Station number	40	41	42	43	44	45	46	47	48	49
Eulima sp.	1	-	1	-	-	-	-	-	-	-
TURRIDAE sp.	-	-	1	-	-	1	-	-	-	-
PROSOBRANCHIA sp.	1	-	-	-	-	-	-	-	1	-
PYRAMIDELLIDAE sp.	1	-	3	-	-	-	-	-	-	-
CEPHALASPIDEA sp.	19	-	-	-	-	-	-	-	-	-
RETUSIDAE sp. A	1	2	20	5	-	-	-	-	-	-
RETUSIDAE sp. B	-	-	-	1	-	-	-	-	-	-
Ringicula sp. A	-	-	-	-	-	-	-	-	2	-
Philine sp.	-	-	-	-	-	-	2	-	-	-
SCAPHOPODA sp.	-	-	-	-	-	-	-	1	-	-
Modiolus metcalfi	2	-	-	-	-	-	-	-	-	-
Arcuatula elegans	4	-	-	-	-	-	-	-	-	-
Pillucina sp.	5	-	-	-	-	-	-	-	-	-
Montacutona sp.	-	16	-	-	-	-	-	-	-	-
Fulvia hungerfordi	-	1	-	-	-	-	-	-	-	1
Tellina (Nitiditellina) sp.	74	1	-	-	-	-	-	-	-	-
Tellina (Laciolina) sp.	-	-	5	5	-	-	-	-	-	-
Theora cf. *lata*	373	827	238	260	128	95	79	22	7	24
Veremolpa micra	-	-	2	-	-	-	-	2	-	-
Circe juv.	2	-	-	-	-	-	-	-	-	-
VENERIDAE juv.	-	-	-	-	-	-	-	1	1	-
CRUSTACEA										
STOMATOPODA sp.	1	-	-	-	-	-	-	-	-	-
CUMACEA sp. A	3	-	-	-	-	-	-	-	-	-
CUMACEA sp. B	1	-	-	-	-	-	-	-	-	-
CUMACEA sp. C	91	-	-	-	-	-	-	-	-	-
CUMACEA sp. D	3	-	-	-	-	-	-	-	-	-
TANAIDACEA sp. A	247	-	-	-	-	-	-	-	-	-
TANAIDACEA sp. B	9	-	-	-	-	-	-	-	-	-
AORIDAE sp.	7	3	-	-	-	1	-	-	-	-
MELITIDAE sp.	1	-	-	-	-	-	-	-	-	-
Corophium sp.	1	13	-	-	-	-	-	-	-	-
ALPHEIDAE sp. A	1	-	-	-	-	-	-	-	-	-
ALPHEIDAE sp. B	1	-	-	-	-	-	-	-	-	-
CARIDEA sp.	1	-	-	-	-	-	-	-	-	-
Dorippe granulata	-	-	-	-	-	-	-	1	-	-
Thalamita sima	1	-	-	-	-	-	-	-	-	-
Charybdis truncata ?	1	-	-	-	-	-	-	-	-	-
BRACHYURA sp.	2	-	-	-	-	-	-	-	-	-
Asthenognathus sp.?	-	-	-	-	1	-	-	-	-	-
OTHER PHYLA										
ANTHOZOA spp.	14	2	-	1	-	-	-	-	-	1
Cancrosocia expansa	-	-	-	-	-	-	-	1	-	-
PALEONEMERTEA	1	-	-	-	-	-	-	-	-	2
HETERONEMERTEA	9	1	2	-	2	-	5	-	5	2
NEMERTEA	38	17	8	11	12	15	7	3	12	–
SIPUNCULA	177	-	-	-	-	-	6	-	-	-
Anelassorhynchus sp.	-	-	-	1	1	-	2	-	11	11
Phoronis sp.	-	-	-	-	1	1	-	2	-	-
OPHIUROIDEA	7	-	-	-	-	-	2	-	-	-
HOLOTHUROIDEA	1	-	-	-	-	-	-	-	-	-
ENTEROPNEUSTA	1	-	-	-	-	-	-	-	-	-

* denotes species also listed in Sundberg *et al.* (1992)

The Marine Biology of the South China Sea
(ed. B. Morton). Proceedings of the First
International Conference on the Marine
Biology of Hong Kong and the South China Sea,
Hong Kong, 28 October – 3 November 1990.
Hong Kong: Hong Kong University Press, 1993.

THE CALAPPIDAE (CRUSTACEA:BRACHYURA) OF CHINESE WATERS

H.L. Chen

Institute of Oceanology, Academia Sinica, Qingdao 266071, China

ABSTRACT

The taxonomy and geographical distribution of the Calappidae in Chinese waters are examined. Of twenty species identified belonging to six genera and three subfamilies, two species, *C. calappa* and *C. capellonis,* are recorded for the first time from Chinese waters, and one species, *Calappa undulata,* is new. *C. undulata* is characterized by front border thin, with four small teeth; hepatic region slightly depressed; carapace covered with coarse tubercles; posteriorly with reddish wave-like mottles. Keys to subfamilies and species of most genera are given.

INTRODUCTION

The present study is based upon a large collection made by the Institute of Oceanology, Academia Sinica, between 1953 and 1990 in Chinese waters. The Calappidae Dana 1852, includes thirty three species from the Indo-West Pacific. Twenty species are found in Chinese waters (about 2/3 that of the Indo-West Pacific region). With the exception of *Paracylois milneedwardsii* and *Mursia curtispina* which were obtained from deeper water. All the other species are from shallow waters.

Calappid fauna and distribution

The Chinese calappids have a tropical and subtropical distribution. Of the twenty species recorded from the South China Sea, thirteen species are found in the East China Sea; only two species occur in the Yellow Sea and Bohai Sea; and eighteen species are widely distributed in the Indo-West Pacific. Of these, sixteen species are common to Chinese and Japanese waters. Thus, it is obvious that the Chinese calappid fauna is related to that of Japan. Only one species, *Orithyia sinica* is known from Chinese and Korean waters. *Calappa terraereginae* also is not known to occur in Japanese waters. *Paracylois milneedwardsii, Mursia armata, M. trispinosa, M. curtispina* and *Matuta curtispina* are found in the western Pacific but are not present in the Indian Ocean. The only circumtropical species is *Calappa gallus*.

SYSTEMATIC ACCOUNT

Calappidae Dana, 1852

Calappidae and Matutidae Dana 1852: 393–394. —Miers 1886: 282. Calappidae Alcock 1896: 137. —Ihle 1918: 161–179. —Sakai 1937: 83, 1976:127. —Chen 1975: 158. —Dai and Yang 1991:100.

Key to the subfamilies of Calappidae

1. Exopodite of third maxillipeds with flagellum 2
   —Exopodite of third maxillipeds without flagellum .... Orithyinae

2. Posterolateral borders of carapace with clypeiform expansion. Ambulatory legs not natatorial .... Calappinae
   —Posterolateral borders of carapace without any clypeiform expansion. Ambulatory legs natatorial .... Matutinae

Calappinae Alcock, 1896

Calappinae Alcock 1896: 138. —Ihle 1918: 161–179. —Rathbun 1937: 197. —Sakai 1937:83; 1965:50; 1976: 127. —Dai and Yang 1991:101.

Key to the genera of Calappinae

1. Carapace relatively broad; clypeiform expansion well-developed .... *Calappa*
   —Carapace subcircular; clypeiform expansion small or absent 2

2. Clypeiform expansion with 3 or 4 teeth, basal joint of antenna swollen ....
   .... *Paracyclois*
   —Clypeiform expansion absent, basal joint of antenna slender 3

3. Carapace transversely oval, with strong spine at junction of anterolateral and posterolateral borders .... *Mursia*
   —Carapace subcircular, with small denticle at junction of anterolateral and posterolateral borders .... *Cycloes*

Calappa Weber, 1795

Calappa Weber, 1795: 92 (not seen). —Miers 1886: 283. —Alcock 1896:139. —Ihle 1918: 181. —Rathbun 1937: 179. —Barnard 1950:346. —Sakai 1937: 83; 1976:127. —Chen 1975: 158. —Dai and Yang 1991:101.

Key to the species of *Calappa*

1. Carapace with typically well-developed clypeiform expansion 2
   —Carapace with weakly developed clypeiform expansion. Carapace subcircular ..
   .... *C. pustulosa*

2. Carapace very broad 3
   —Carapace moderately broad 4

3. Carapace distinctly tuberculate. Clypeiform expansions with broad teeth ....
   .... *C. hepatica*
   —Carapace with some indistinct tubercles. Clypeiform expansion entire and smooth
   .... *C. calappa*

4. Posterior border of carapace distinctly produced .... *C. terraereginae*
   —Posterior border of carapace not produced 5

5. Posterior border of carapace with 3 strong teeth, an incomplete reddish loop on each orbital region .... *C. philargius*
   —Posterior border of carapace with 3 broad lobes 6

6. Transverse reddish mottles between teeth of clypeiform expansion .... *C. lophos*
   —Without transverse reddish mottles between teeth of clypeiform expansion 7

7. Frontal border thick; hepatic region strongly depressed .... *C. gallus*
   —Frontal border thin; hepatic region slightly depressed 8

8. Carapace covered with large wart-like tubercles .... *C. capellonis*
   —Carapace covered with coarse tubercles; posteriorly with reddish wave-like mottles .... *C. undulata* sp. nov.

Calappa hepatica (Linnaeus, 1758)

Cancer hepatica Linnaeus, 1758: 1048 (not seen).
Calappa hepatica: De Haan 1837:70. —Miers 1884:257, 550; 1886:285. —Haswell 1882: 136. —Ortmann 1892: 568. —Henderson: 1893:395. —Nobili 1906: 148. —Alcock 1896: 142. —De Man 1902: 687. —Borradaile 1903: 436, plate 22, figs. 6–6a. —Rathbun 1906:887. —Parisi 1914: 285. —Ihle 1918: 183. —Balss 1922: 123. —Sakai 1934: 284; 1937: 89, 101, 12 fig. 2. —Buitendijk 1939: 230. —Stephensen 1945: 65. —Barnard 1950: 348, 350, figs. 66a–d. —Tyndale-Biscoe and George 1962: 69–70, fig. 2(6). —Shen and Dai 1964: 10. —Chen 1975: 158, plate I(1). —Sakai 1976: 128, plate 38, figs. 1–3. —Dai and Yang 1991:102, plate 11(3), fig. 49(1).

Cancer tuberculata: Herbst 1785: 204, plate 3, fig. 78.

Material. Dongdao, Xisha Islands, 1 carapace (60.0 x 84.0 mm), 12. VI. 1975. —Yongxingdao, Xisha Islands, 1 ♂, 1♀, 15. IV. 1957. —Yongxingdao, Xisha Islands, 1 ♂17.II. 1977. —Shidao, Xisha Islands, 3♀, 10. V. 1975. —Xincun, Hainan Island, 1♂ (47.0 x 67.0 mm), 1 ♂ (36.0 x 64.0 mm), 13. VII. 1975. —Sanya, Hainan Island, 1 ♂ 13.VII. 1957. —Hainan Island, 1♂ (43.0 x 62.0 mm), 8.IV.1955. —Yulin, Hainan Island, 1♀, 3.IV. 1957. —Xincun, Hainan Island, 1♀, 21. IV. 1955.

Habitat. Found on coral reefs; broken shells and rock bottoms; littoral to 59 m depths.

Type locality. Unknown.

Distribution. China (Xisha Islands, Hainan Island and Taiwan), Japan, Hawaii, Tonga, East Australia, New Zealand, Indonesia, India, Maldives, Laccadives, Sri Lanka, Seychelles, Mozambique, Mali, South Africa, Persian Gulf and Red Sea. Very common.

Calappa calappa (Linnaeus, 1758). Fig. 1.

Cancer calappa Linnaeus 1758: 1048 (not seen). —Herbst 1758: 196, plate 12, figs. 73–74.

Calappa calappa Rathbun 1906: 887; 1911: 197. —Parisi 1914: 286. —Ihle 1918: 184. —Balss 1922: 123. —Sakai, 1934: 90, plate 17, fig. 1. —Tyndale-Biscoe and George 1962: 69, fig. 2(5). —Sakai 1976: 129, plate 39, figs. 1, 3.

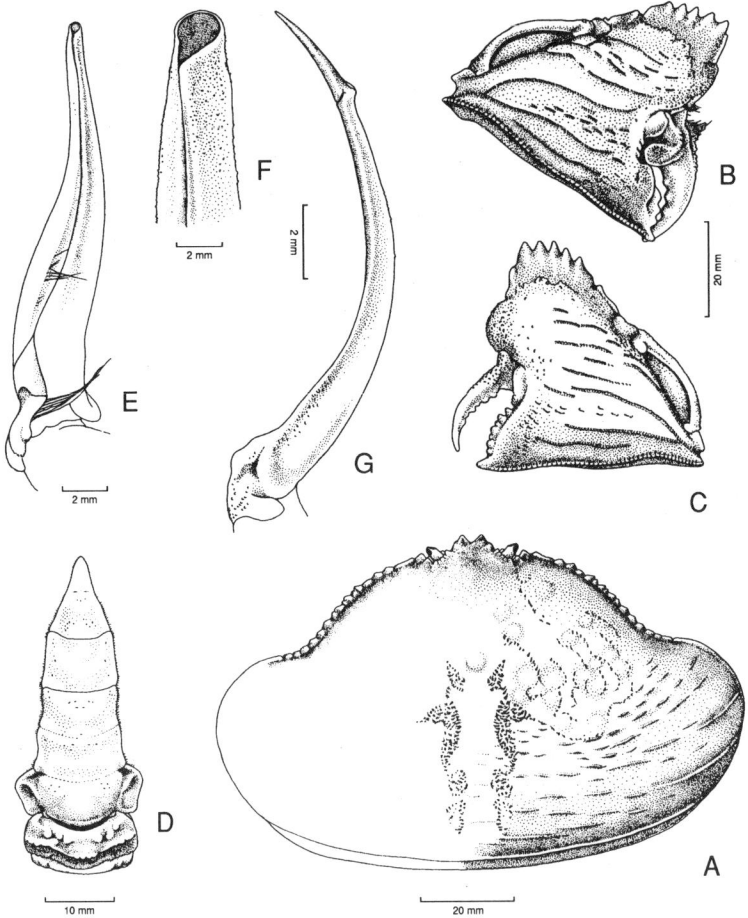

Fig. 1. *Calappa calappa* (Linnaeus, 1758). A, Carapace; B, major chela; C, minor chela; D, male abdomen; E–F, first male pleopod and enlarged tip; G, second male pleopod.

Calappa fornicata Herklots 1861: 25 (not seen). —Ortmann 1892: 569. —Alcock 1896: 142.

Material. Sanya, Hainan Island, 1 ♂ (74.0 x 125.0 mm), coll. by Chen Canzhong.

Habitat. Found on broken shell bottoms, 9–46 m depth.

Type locality. Unknown.

Remarks. Body shiny. Anterior carapace with some indistinct, smooth tubercles; posteriorly with smooth transversely wavy beaded lines of various length. Clypeiform expansion very large and entire, without teeth. Only one male collected. This species is recorded or the first time from Chinese waters.

Distribution. China, Japan, Hawaii, New Caledonia, Australia, Indonesia, India, Mauritius and Zanzibar.

Calappa philargius (Linnaeus, 1758). Fig. 2.

Cancer philargius Linnaeus 1758: 1042 (not seen).

Calappa philargius De Haan 1837: 71, plate 19, fig. 1. —Alcock 1896: 145. —Balss 1922: 122. —Shen 1931: 104, plate 8, text-figs. 10–11. —Sakai 1937: 93, plate 12, fig. 3. —Shen and Dai 1964: 11. —Tyndale-Biscoe and George 1962: 69. —Sakai 1965: 56, plate 22, fig. 1; 1976: 130–131, plate 37, fig. 2. —Dai and Yang 1991:104, plate 11(6), fig.50(2)

Calappa cristata Whitelegge 1899: 231 (not seen). —Stimpson 1907: 165.

Material. Yingehai, Hainan Island, 1 ♂ (42.4 x 61.2 mm), 5. VII. 1955. —Xinying, Hainan Island, 1 ♂ (56.4 x 86.0 mm), 1 juv. ♀, 25.V. 1955. —Sanya, Hainan Island, 1 ♀ (64.5 x 100.0 mm), 14.IV.1955. —Haimen, Guangdong, 1 ♂, 18.III. 1954; 1 ♂, 1 ♀, 14.III. 1956; 1 ♀, 7.V.1957. —Baoan, Guangdong, 1 ♂ (57.0 x 95.0 mm), 1957. —Xuwen, Guangdong, 1 ♂ (22.1 x 29.5 mm), 1955. —Weizhoudao, Guangxi, 2 ♂, 28.XI. 1954. —Xiongdiadao, Fujian, 1 ♀, 18.IV.1957. —Dongshan, Fujian, 1 ♀, 27.V.1975. —Zhangpu, Fujian, 1 ♂, 31.V.1975. —Shenhu, Fujian, 3 ♂, 24.VI.1975. —Weitou, Fujian, 4 ♂, 27.VI.1975. —East China Sea, 1 ♂, 2 ♀, depth: 64 m, Bottom: muddy sand, 11.VII. 1959. —East China Sea. 1 ♀, depth: 57 m, bottom, silt, 23. X. 1959. —South China Sea, 12 ♂, 9 ♀, depth: 13–50 m, bottom: sandy mud, and muddy sand, IV–X.1959. —Beibu Gulf, 7 ♂, 3 ♀, depth: 24–51 m, bottom: fine sand, ooze and muddy sand, I–VII.1960,

Habitat. Found on muddy sand, sandy mud or broken shell, sand bottoms, 24–100 m depths.

Type locality. Unknown.

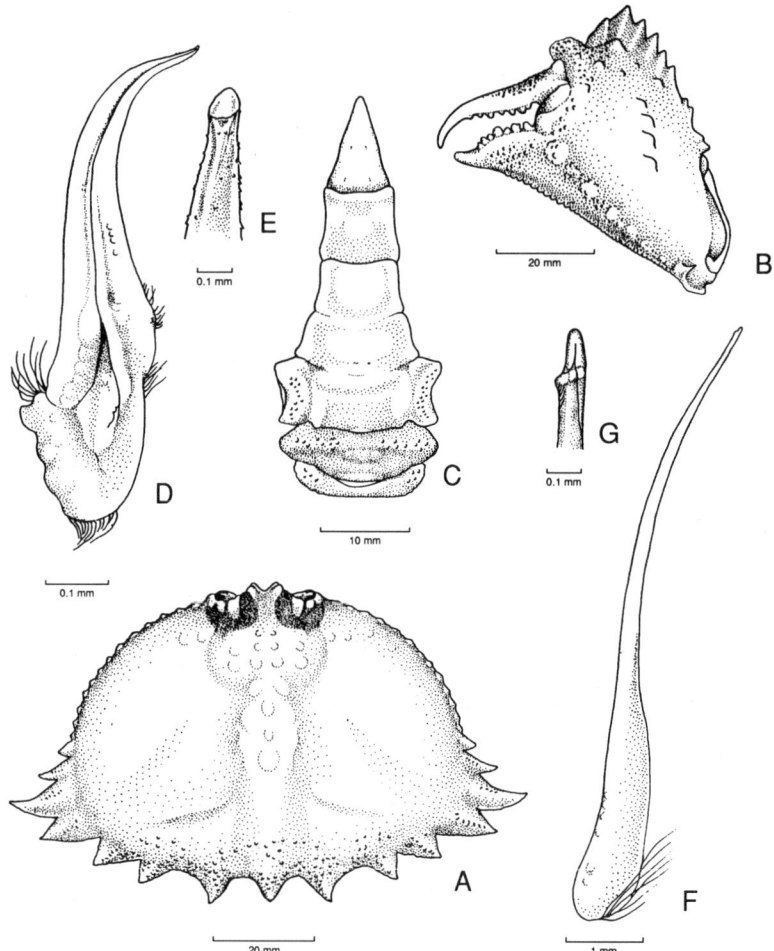

Fig. 2. *Calappa philargius* (Linnaeus, 1758). A, Carapace; B, minor chela; C, male abdomen, D–E, first male pleopod and enlarged tip; F–G. second male pleopod and enlarged tip.

Remarks. This present species is easily distinguished by having 3 triangular teeth at its posterior border and an incomplete reddish loop on each orbital region; carpus and palm of cheliped each have a large spot of the same colour.

Distribution. South China Sea and East China Sea, Japan, Korea, Vietnam, Indonesia, Singapore, Burma, India, Persian Gulf and Red Sea.

***Calappa lophos* (Herbst, 1782). Fig. 3.**

Cancer lophos Herbst 1782: 201, plate 13, fig. 17.

Calappa lophos De Haan 1837: 72, plate 20, fig. 1. —De Man 1887: 389. —Henderson 1893: 395. —Alcock 1896: 144. —Parisi 1914: 283. —Ihle 1918: 182. —Balss

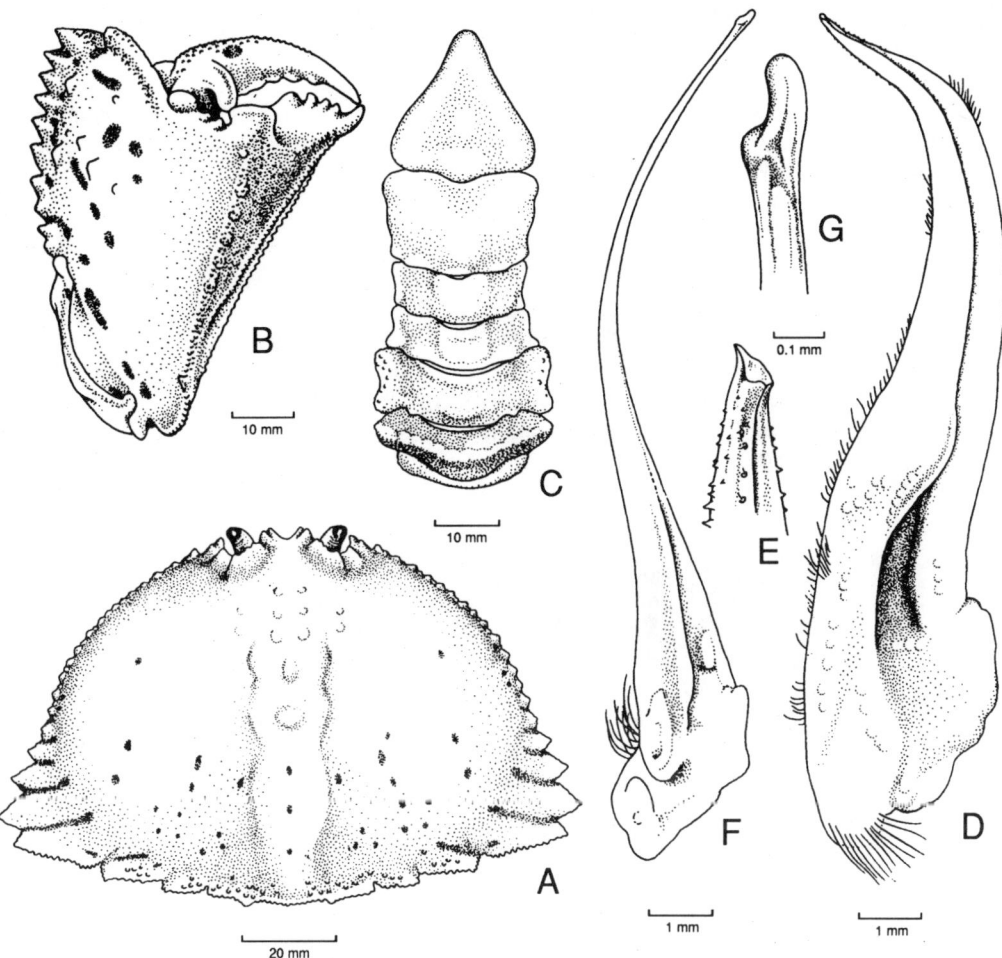

Fig. 3. *Calappa lophos* (Herbst, 1782). A, Carapace; B, major chela; C, female; D–E, first male pleopod and enlarged tip; F–G, second male pleopod and enlarged tip.

1922:123. —Rathbun 1923: 137. —Shen 1936: 64. —Sakai 1937: 90–91, plate 12, fig. 1. —Stephensen 1945: 65, figs. 5a–b. —Barnard 1950: 351, figs. 66 j–m. —Tyndale-Biscoe and George 1962: 70. —Shen and Dai 1964: 11. —Sakai 1976: 129–130, plate 37, fig. 1, plate 38, fig. 2. —Dai and Yang 1991: 103, plate 11(4), fig. 49(2).

Material. Shanwei, Guangdong, 2 ♀ (33.0 x 44.5; 44.5 x 67.0 mm), 15.I.1955. —1 ♂, 2 ♀, 10.I.1955. —1 ♀ (32.5 x 44.4 mm.), IV.1953. —Zhapo, Guangdong, 2 ♀ (88.5 x 129.0; 32.0 x 45.0 mm), 1956. —East China Sea: 1 ♂ (79.0 x 120.2 mm), depth: 98 m, bottom, broken shells, 23.X.1959. —1 ♂, depth: 44 m, bottom, ooze, 10.X.1959. —South China Sea: 9 ♂, 7 ♀, depth: 38–122 m, bottoms, muddy sand or fine sand, I–XII.1959. —5 ♂, 1 ♀, depth: 30–124 m, bottoms muddy sand or fine sand, II–IV.1960.

Habitat. Found on muddy sand, fine sand and broken shell bottoms, 30–150 m depth. *Type locality.* Unknown.

Remarks. Juvenile specimens agree with Sakai's description and figure. The carapace has reddish brown stripes and a pair of large ocelli, one on each epibranchial region but these disappear in adults.

Distribution. South China and East China Sea, Japan, Indonesia, Thailand, Sri Lanka, India, Dar-es-Salaam and Persian Gulf.

Calappa terraereginae Ward, 1936. Fig. 4A.

Calappa terraereginae Ward 1936: 11, plate 3, figs. 9–11. —Sakai 1937: 92, plate 18, fig. 1, text-figs. 6b, 7. —Tyndale-Biscoe and George 1962: 70, plate 1, fig. 2, plate 2, fig. 2. —Sakai 1976: 130, text-figs. 72a–b. —Dai and Yang 1991: 103, plate 11(5), fig. 50(1).

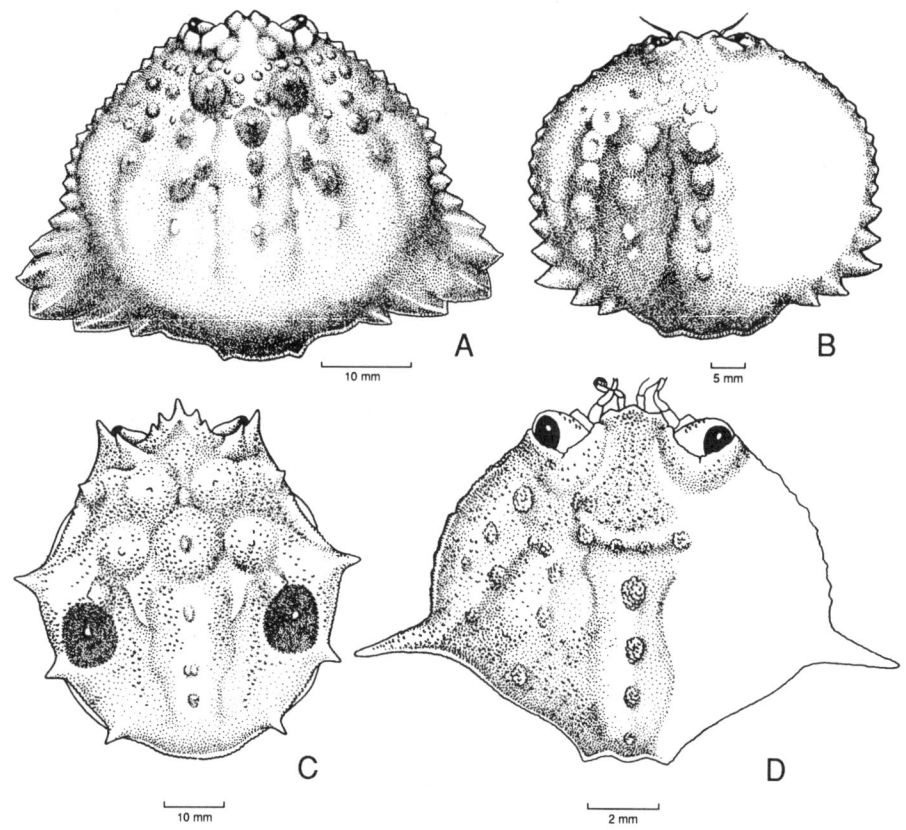

Fig. 4. A. *Calappa terraereginae* Ward, 1936.
B. *Calappa pustulosa* Alcock, 1896.
C. *Orithyia sinica* (Linnaeus, 1771).
D. *Mursia curtispina* Miers, 1886.

Material. Wezhoudao, Guangdong, 1 ♂ (33.0 x 46.5 mm), 26.XII.1954. —Zhuxi, Guangdong, 1 ♀ (35.0 x 47.0 mm), 31.III.1956. —Beihai, Guangxi, 1 ♂ (35.5 x 56.0 mm), 10.IV.1956. —South China Sea: 18 ♂, 13 ♀, depth: 30–67 m, bottom, muddy sand or sandy mud, I–XII,1959;– 8 ♂, 5 ♀, depth: 30–104 m, bottom, muddy sand or sandy mud, I–V.1960. —Beibu Gulf: 26 ♂, 19 ♀, depth: 30–122 m, bottom, muddy sand or sand, XII.1959: 96 ♂, 90 ♀, depth: 18–79 m, bottom, muddy sand or sandy mud. II–XI.1961; 16 ♂, 12 ♀, 9 juv., depth: 15–68 m, bottom, muddy or sandy mud.

Habitat. Found on muddy sand or sandy mud bottoms, 15–122 m depths.

Type locality. Lindeman Island, Queensland.

Remarks. The posterior border of the carapace is produced backwards. This feature is constant from the juvenile to the full-grown specimens.

Distribution. China, Vietnam, Australia and Korean Channel.

Calappa gallus (Herbst, 1803). Fig. 5.

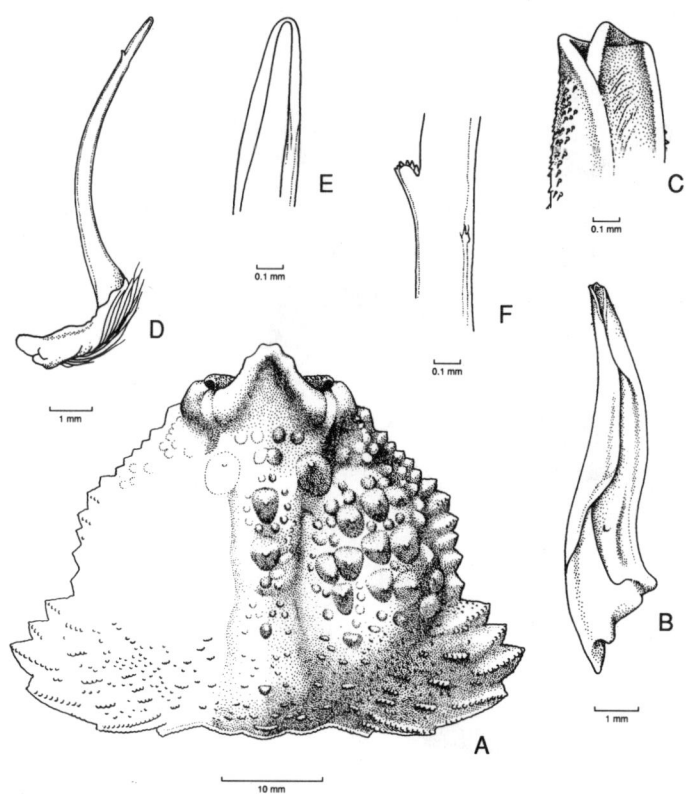

Fig. 5. *Calappa gallus* (Herbst, 1803). A, Carapace; B–C, first male pleopod and enlarged tip; D–F, second male pleopod and enlarged parts.

Cancer gallus Herbst 1803:46, plate 58, fig. 1.

Calappa gallus H. Milne-Edwards 1837: 105. —De Haan 1837: 70. —Klunzinger 1906: 61, plate 2, fig. 14. —Henderson 1893: 395. —Rathbun 1937: 214, plate 65, figs. 2–3. —Sakai 1937: 94, plate 17, fig. 2. —Barnard 1950: 350, figs. 66, e–i. —Monod 1956: 100, figs. 115–116. —Shen and Dai 1964: 10. —Sakai 1976: 131, plate 39, fig. 2. —Dai and Yang 1991: 105, fig. 51.

Material. Xizhoudao, Hainan Island, 1 ♂ (36.5 x 46.2 mm), 1 ♀ (36.0 x 48.0 mm), 8.IV.1955.

Habitat. Found on coral reefs, muddy sand and broken shell bottoms, littoral to 220 m depth.

Type locality. Unknown.

Distribution. This is a circumtropical species. China (Nansha Islands, Xisha Islands and Taiwan), Japan, Hawaii, Philippines, Indonesia, India, Burma, Sri Lanka, Mascarene Islands, Suvadiva Atoll, East and South Africa, Persian Gulf, Red Sea and tropical Atlantic coasts.

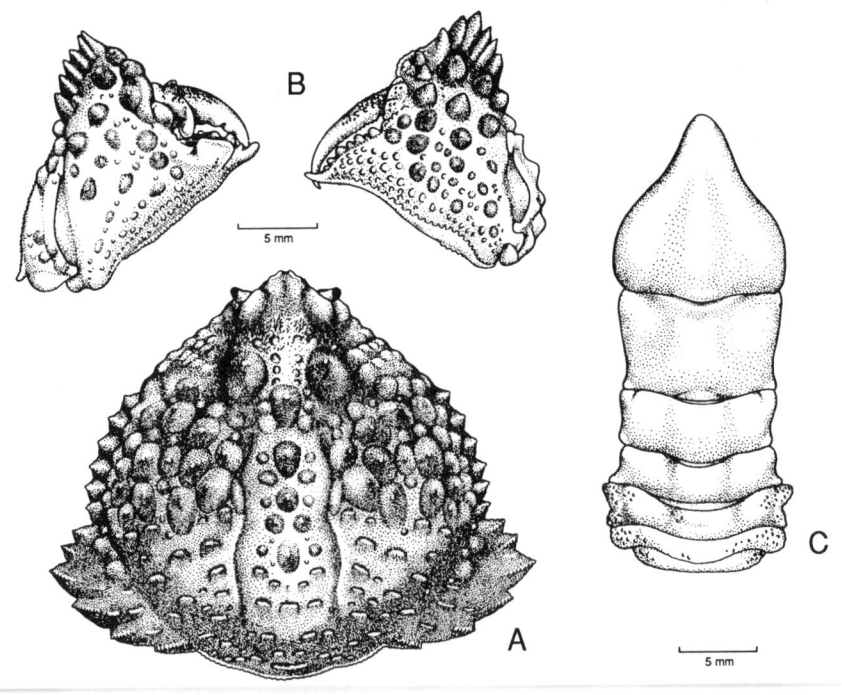

Fig. 6. *Calappa capellonis* Laurie, 1906. A, Carapace; B, chelae; C, female abdomen.

Calappa capellonis Laurie, 1906. Fig. 6.

Calappa gallus var. *capellonis* Laurie 1906: 355, —Sakai 1934:284: 1937: 95, plate 17, fig. 3; 1976:131, text-fig. 73. —Rathbun 1937:214.

Material. Xincun, Hainan Island, 1 ♀ (47.8 x 71.0 mm), 2.IV.1960. —South China Sea, 1 juv. ♀ (19.0 x 23.0 mm), depth: 23 m, bottom, coarse sand, 14.V.1960.

Habitat. Found on coarse sand, pebbles or rock bottoms, 15–30m. depths,

Type locality. Sri Lanka.

Distribution. South China Sea, Japan and Sri Lanka.

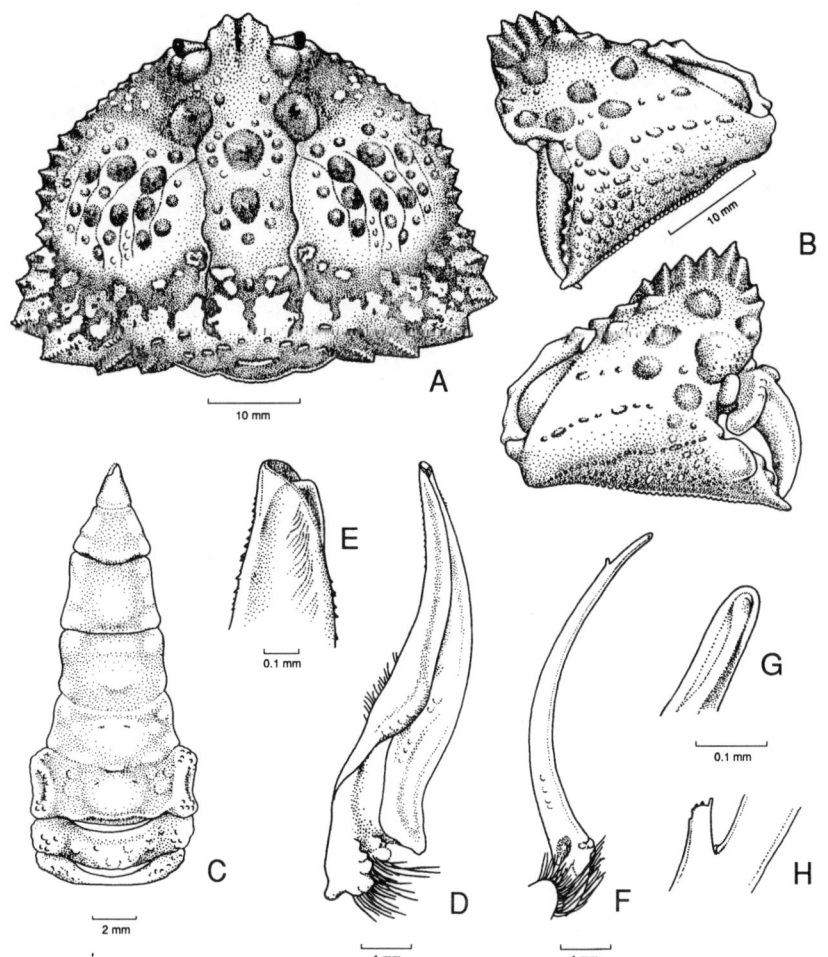

Fig. 7. *Calappa undulata* sp. nov. A, Carapace; B, chelae; C, male abdomen; D–E, first male pleopod and enlarged tip; F–H, second male pleopod and parts.

Calappa undulata sp. nov. Fig. 7.

Material. Holotype ♀ (38.6 x 48.5 mm), K16B–7, South China Sea (21°30'N, 113°30'E), muddy sand bottom, 39 m depth, 10.IV.1960. Allotype ♂ (38.0 x 52.0 mm), SSDI12–8, Nansha Islands, depth: 66 m, 10.IV.1990.

The holotype is deposited in the Institute of Oceanology, Academia Sinica, the allotype is kept in the South China Sea Institute of Oceanology, Academia Sinica.

Description. Carapace broader than long, covered with low, smooth tubercles. Frontal border thin, divided into 4 small teeth, the medial pair more distinct than the lateral pair. A pair of broad, shallow, longitudinal grooves situated between gastric-cardiac-intestinal region and the branchial region. Hepatic region slightly depressed. Anterior 1/2 of anterolateral border with indistinct teeth and posterior 1/2 with 6 small teeth. Posterolateral border cut into 6 lobes. Posterior border with 3 lobes, each edge of which has beady granules.

Chelipeds asymmetrical. Merus widening distally; with transverse hairy ridge cut into 4 broad lobes. Carpus small; outer surface with a few small tubercles. The larger palm high and thick, upper portion of outer surface covered with some wart-like tubercles of varying sizes; anterior border crested, divided into 7 triangular teeth; middle portion of palm with three rows of granules of varying sizes; posterior border of palm with 3 rows of fine, close-set granules. Proximal 1/2 of dorsal border of movable finger with a median tooth and some indistinct teeth; basal part of its outer surface with a finger-like tooth. Basal portion of immovable finger with a molar and 3 blunt teeth. First two ambulatory legs longer than posterior two. Surface of ambulatory legs smooth.

Male. Abdomen consists of five segments (3rd to 6th fused): first segment shortest, second longer than the first, its middle part produced, 6th segment square. Telson triangular. First male pleopod stout, distal part curved outwards, distal end thin, denticulate. Second male pleopod slender, its distal part with a small tooth.

Etymology. The name is from the Latin 'undulata' wavy, alluding to the wavy reddish mottles of the posterior part of the carapace.

Remarks. Carapace (in spirit) yellowish, and with reddish tubercles. Posterior 1/3 of carapace with reddish wavy mottles. This new species closely resembles *Calappa gallus* and *Calappa capellonis* but differences between the three species are summarized in Table 1.

Calappa pustulosa Alcock, 1896. Fig. 4B.

Calappa pustulosa Alcock 1896: 147, plate 6, fig. 1. —Borradaile 1903: 436. —Ihle 1918: 306, —Chopra 1933: 29. —Sakai 1937: 97, plate 18, figs. 2–3. —Shen and Dai 1964: 12. —Sakai 1965: 57, plate 23; 1976: 134, plate 41, fig. 1. —Dai and Yang 1991: 106, plate 12(1), fig. 12.

Material. Zhapo, Guangdong, 1 ♀ (44.5 x 50.0 mm), 1956. —South China Sea, 1 ♀ (48.0 x 52.0 mm), depth: 125 m, muddy sand bottom, 20.XI.1959.

Table 1
Characters separating *Calappa undulata* sp. nov. from its nearest relatives.

Character	*Calappa gallus*	*Calappa capellonis*	*Calappa undulata* sp. nov.
Frontal border	thick and obtusely triangular in adult; with 4 blunt teeth in juvenile	thin and with 4 distinct teeth	thin and with 4 indistinct teeth
Surface of carapace	rough; without hairs	smooth; with short hairs on gastric region	smooth; without hairs
Size of tubercles on anterior 2/3 of carapace	medium	large	medium
Size and number of squamiform tubercles of posterior 1/3 of carapace	small and numerous	small and few	large and few
Depth of longitudinal grooves of carapace	deep	shallow	shallow
Depth of hepatic region	deep	shallow	shallow
Distribution	Indian, Pacific and Atlantic	South China Sea, Japan and Sri Lanka	South China Sea

Habitat. Found on sand, broken shells and muddy sand bottoms, 50–150 m depth.

Type locality. India.

Remarks. The subcircular carapace and the weakly developed clypeiform expansion easily distinguish this species from its congeners.

Paracyclois **Miers, 1886**

Paracyclois Miers 1886: 288. —Sakai 1976: 134.

Paracyclois milneedwardsii Miers, 1886. Fig. 8.

Paracyclois milneedwardsii Miers 1886: 289, plate 24, fig. 1. —Sakai 1976: 134, plate 41, fig. 2.

Material. South China Sea, 1 ♂ (26.4 x 27.0 mm), depth: 300 m, bottom, coarse sand, 23.X.1959.

Habitat. Found on soft sand, coarse sand, and sandy mud bottoms, 80–300 m depths.

Remarks. Anterior 2/3 of carapace subcircular, posterior 1/3 narrow. The middle portion of posterolateral border with some small teeth. Posterior border produced backwards; with 3 strong teeth. Male abdomen of 5 segments with 3rd to 5th fused, and first segment short and small; second segment with three tubercles; 6th segment square. Telson elongate, triangular. First male pleopod long and stout; second male pleopod long, slender, and inwardly curved.

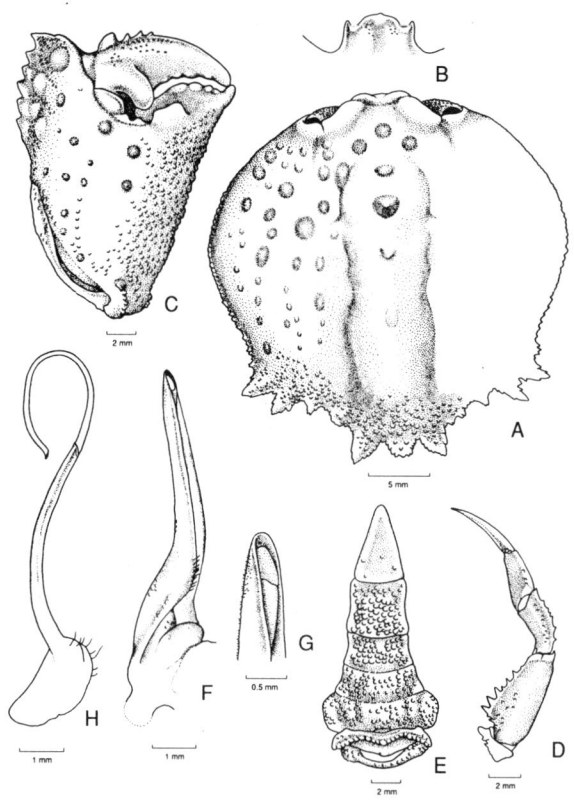

Fig. 8. *Paracyclois milneedwardsii* Miers, 1886. A, Carapace; B, front; C, major chela; D, 4th ambulatory leg; E, male abdomen; F–G, first male pleopod and enlarged tip; H, second male pleopod.

Mursia Leach, 1823

Mursia Leach 1823 in Desmarest: 231 (not seen). —Alcock 1896:148. —Doflein 1904:36. —Ihle 1918: 300, 307. —Rathbun 1937: 215. —Barnard 1950: 353. —Sakai 1937: 85: 1976: 134. —Dai and Yang 1991: 106.

Key to the Chinese species of *Mursia*

1. Lateral processes of carapace long 2
   —Lateral processes of carapace short .... *Mursia curtispina*

2. Palm of chelipeds with three strong teeth along the outer inferior border; lateral processes of carapace bent .... *M. trispinosa*
   —Palm of chelipeds with flat tubercles of nearly equal size; lateral processes of carapace straight .... *M. armata*

Mursia armata De Haan, 1837. Fig. 9.

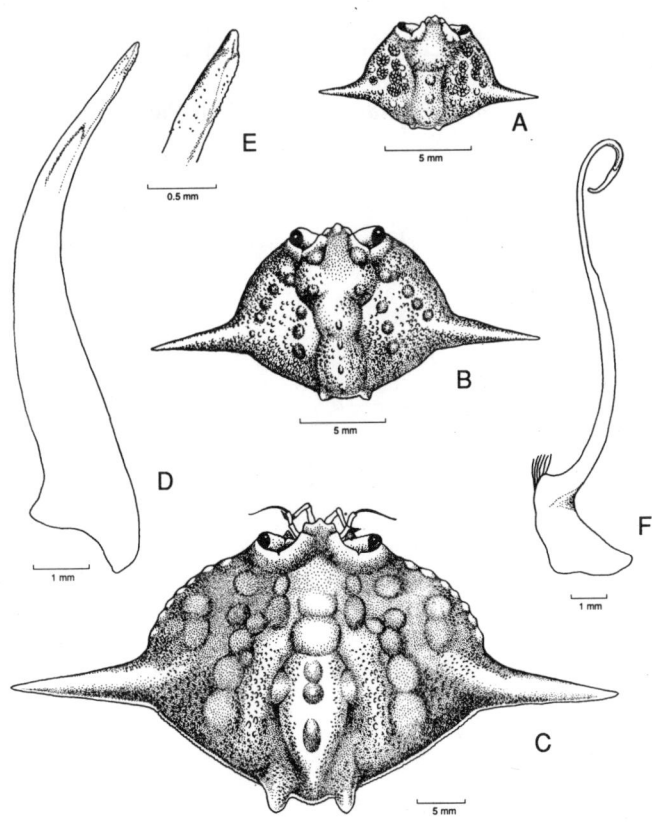

Fig. 9. *Mursia armata* De Haan, 1837. A–C, Carapaces; D–E, first male pleopod and enlarged tip; F, second male pleopod.

Mursia armata De Haan 1837: 73, plate 19, fig. 2. —Ortmann 1892: 564. —Doflein 1902: 653. —Parisi 1914: 290. —Ihle 1918: 179. —Balss 1922: 124. —Yokoya 1933: 114. —Sakai 1937: 85, plate 11, fig. 3. —Shen 1940a: 214. —Shen and Dai 1964: 12. —Sakai 1965: 51, plate 20, fig. 4; 1976: 135–136, plate 43, fig. 2. —Dai and Yang 1991: 107, plate 12(2), fig. 53.

Material. Shanwei, Guangdong, 1 ♀ (24.7 x 30.0 mm), IX.1953. —Jieshi, Guangdong, 1 ♂ (20.0 x 20.5 mm), 28.IV.1954. —Shangchuandao, Guangdong, 1 ♂ (26.5 x 33.0 mm), 1 ♀ (37.0 x 40.0 mm), 8.VII.1959. —Zhapo, Guangdong, 2 ♀ (27.0 x 36.0; 25.0 x 32.5 mm), 9.IV.1956; —1 ♂, 6 ♀, 16.XI.1956. —Beibu Gulf, 1 ♂ (24.0 x 37.0 mm), 8.IV.1956. —South China Sea, 62 ♂, 64 ♀, depth: 47–195 m, bottom, muddy sand, ooze, and sand mud. II–XII.1959. —East China Sea, 1 ♂, depth: 126 m, bottom, fine sand, 21.IX.1976.

Habitat. Found on muddy sand, ooze, sandy mud and sand botoms, 47–195 m depth.

Remarks. The lateral process is very long (about 18 mm), probably longer than any of its congeners; thick, and straight. The posterior border of the cheliped palm has 3 blunt teeth.

Distribution. South China Sea, East China Sea and Japan.

Mursia trispinosa Parisi, 1914. Fig. 10.

Mursia trispinosa Parisi 1914: 290, plate 12.

Mursia armata curtispina: Balss 1922: 124 (part). —Sakai 1937: 87, plate 11, fig. 4.

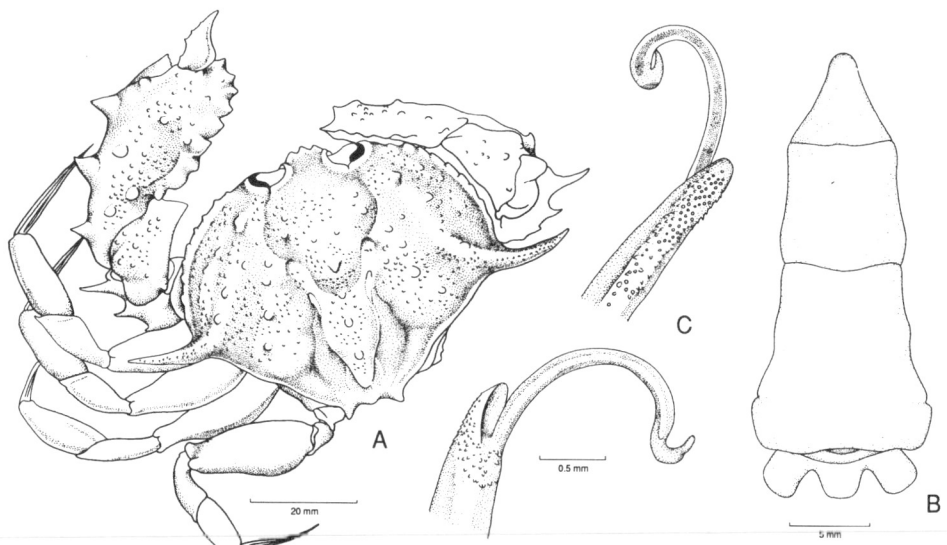

Fig. 10. *Mursia trispinosa* Parisi, 1914. A, Carapace and legs; B, male abdomen; C, tips of first and second male pleopods.

Mursia curtispina trispinosa: Sakai 1965. 53, plate 21, fig. 1, text fig. 8 b–b'.

Mursia trispinosa Campbell 1971:35. —Sakai 1976: 137, plate 43, fig. 4, text-figs. 74 b–b'.

Material. East China Sea, 1 ♂ (50.0 x 64.2 mm).

Habitat. Found on muddy sand, fine sand bottoms, 65–184 m depths.

Type locality. Japan.

Remarks. The lateral process is long and curved at base. Posterior border of cheliped palm has 3 triangular teeth. First male pleopod stout and has small spines at tip; second male pleopod very long and slender but tip differs from that shown in text-fig. 74 of Sakai (1976, p. 138).

Distribution. Nansha Islands, East China Sea and Japan.

Mursia curtispina Miers, 1886. Fig. 4D.

Mursia curtispina Miers 1886: 291–292, plate 24, fig. 2. —Sakai 1965: 52, plate 21, fig. 2, text-figs. 8 a–a': 1976: 136, plate 43, fig. 1, text-figs. 74 a–a'.

Mursia armata curtispina: Doflein 1902: 40; 1904: plate 17, fig. 2. plate 18, fig. 3. — Ihle 1918: 179 (part). —Balss 1922: 124 (part). —Yokoya 1933: 115 (part).

(Nec *Mursia curtispina*: Sakai 1937:87, plate 11, fig. 4 (= *M. trispinosa* Parisi, 1914)

Material. South China Sea, 1 ovig. ♀ (15.0 x 17.2 mm), depth: 260 m, bottom, sand, 19.IV.1959; 6♂, 2♀ (7.5 x 9.0–15.5 x 19.0 mm), depth: 194–195 m, bottom, fine sand, muddy sand, IV–VII.1959. —East China Sea, 4♂, 1♀, depth: 107–162 m, bottom, fine sand, 10.X.1975; 2♂, 2♀, depth: 107–126 m, bottom, fine and coarse sand, VI–VII. 1976.

Habitat. Found on muddy sand and sand bottoms, 40–576 m depths.

Type locality. Fiji Islands.

Remarks. Lateral processes of carapace shorter than those of the former two species.

Distribution. South China Sea, East China Sea, Japan Indonesia and Fiji Islands.

Cycloes De Haan, 1837

Cycloes De Haan 1837: 67–68. Rathbun 1937: 225. —Chace 1968: 610. —Sakai, 1976: 139. —Dai and Yang 1991: 108.

Cryptosoma Brulle 1840 (not seen). —H. Milne-Edwards 1837: 110. —Miers 1886:292. —Alcock 1896: 151. —Sakai 1937: 84; 1965: 50.

Cycloes granulosa De Haan, 1837. Fig. 11.

Cycloes granulosa De Haan 1837: 71, plate 19, fig. 3. —Rathbun 1906: 888; 1937: 225. —Chace 1968: 610.
Cryptosoma granulosum Miers 1886: 293. —Alcock 1896: 152, —Laurie 1906: 356. Ihle 1918: 179. —Sakai 1937: 84, plate 13, fig. 1; 1965: 50, plate 20, fig. 3; 1976: 139, plate 43, fig. 3. —Dai and Yang 1991: 108, plate12(3), fig. 54.

Material. South China Sea, 4 ♂, 13 ♀ (8.5 x 8.1–18.3 x 18.0 mm), depth: 29–43 m, bottom, fine sand or silt, IV.1959;4 ♂, 3 ♀ (6.0 x 5.7–8.4 x 7.9 mm), depth: 32–44 m, bottom, fine sand, coarse sand and muddy sand; III–IV.1960. —Beibu Gulf, 4 ♂, 1 ♀, depth: 25–49 m, bottom, fine sand, muddy sand, IV–VII.1960.

Habitat. Found on sand, muddy sand and silt bottoms, 25–100 m depths.

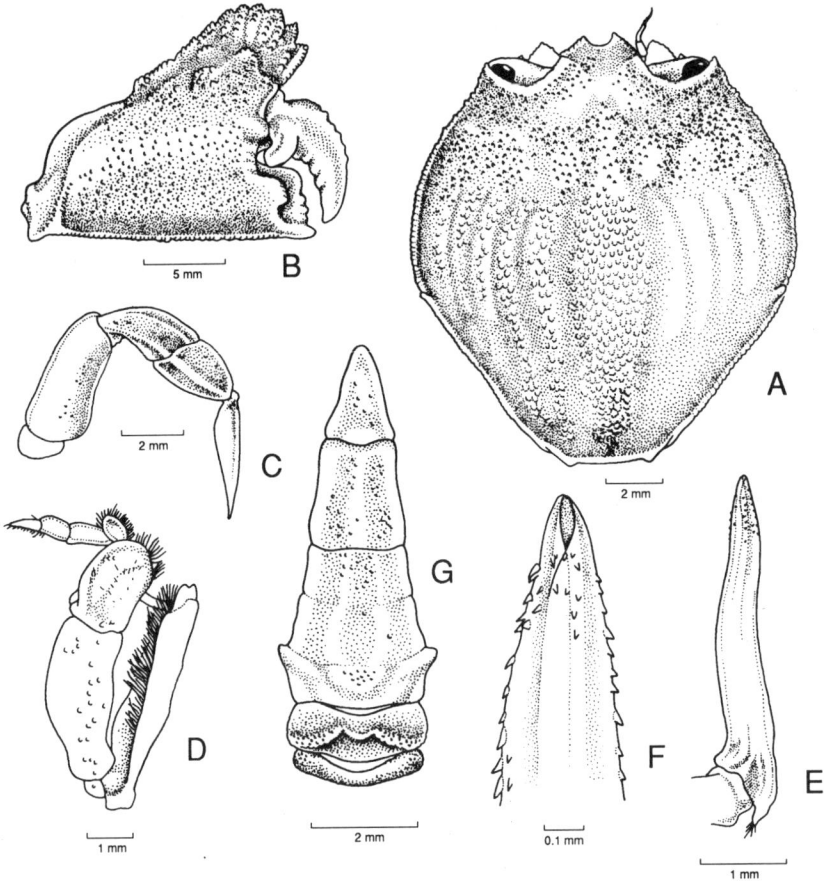

Fig. 11. *Cycloes granulosa* De Haan, 1837. A, Carapace; B, major chela; C, 4th ambulatory leg; D, third maxilliped; E–F, first male pleopod and enlarged tip. G, male abdomen.

Type locality. Japan.

Remarks. This is a relatively small species. The carapace is slightly longer than broad and has its surface covered with granules of various sizes. Between the anterolateral and posterolateral borders there is a small tooth. The posterior border has two small tubercles on each side. The chelipeds are of a similar shape to those of *Calappa*.

Matutinae Alcock, 1896

Matutinae Alcock 1896: 139. —Ihle 1918: 178. —Rathbun 1937: 234. —Sakai 1937: 84, 98; 1965: 59; 1976: 139. —Dai and Yang 1991: 109

Matuta Weber, 1795

Matuta Weber 1795: 92 (not seen). —H. Milne-Edwards 1837: 113. —Miers 1877: 178; 1886: 294. —Alcock 1896: 153. —Klunzinger 1906: 230. —Stebbing 1910: 335. —Chopra 1933: 31. —Barnard 1950: 357. —Tyndale-Biscoe and George 1962: 70. —Sakai 1937: 98; 1976: 139. —Dai and Yang 1991: 109

Key to the Chinese species of *Matuta*

1. Lateral processes long 2
   —Lateral processes short, body small .... *M. curtispina*

2. Carapace with 6 distinct tubercles and posterolateral border with a small tubercle
   .... *M. banksii*
   —Carapace with 6 indistinct tubercles and posterolateral border with or without an indistinct tubercle 3

3. Carapace smooth 4
   —Carapace covered with coarse granules and 6 relatively distinct tubercles..........
   .... *M. granulosa*

4. Carapace after spirit preservation with closely set red dots .... *M. lunaris*
   —Carapace after spirit preservation with red dots forming rings and loops............
   .... *M. planipes*

Matuta planipes Fabricius, 1798. Fig. 12.

Matuta planipes Fabricius 1798: 369 (not seen). —Laurie 1906: 356. —Ihle 1918: 308. —Balss 1922: 125. —Shen 1932: 35, text-figs. 20–21, plate 3, fig. 2. —Sakai 1937: 101, plate 13, fig. 4; 1965:60, plate 24, fig. 3; 1976: 141, plate 44, fig. 2. —Buitendijk 1939: 232. —Stephensen 1945: 67, figs. 5c–d. —Barnard 1950: 357. —Tyndale- Biscoe and George 1962: 71. —Shen and Dai 1964: 13. —Romimohtarto 1972: 11–13, figs. 6–9; 21–26, plates Ib–b', IIIb–b'. Dai and Yang 1991: 109, plate 12(4), fig. 55(1).
Matuta lunaris Herbst 1799: 43, plate 48, fig. 6. —Alcock 1896: 161. —Stimpson 1907: 166.

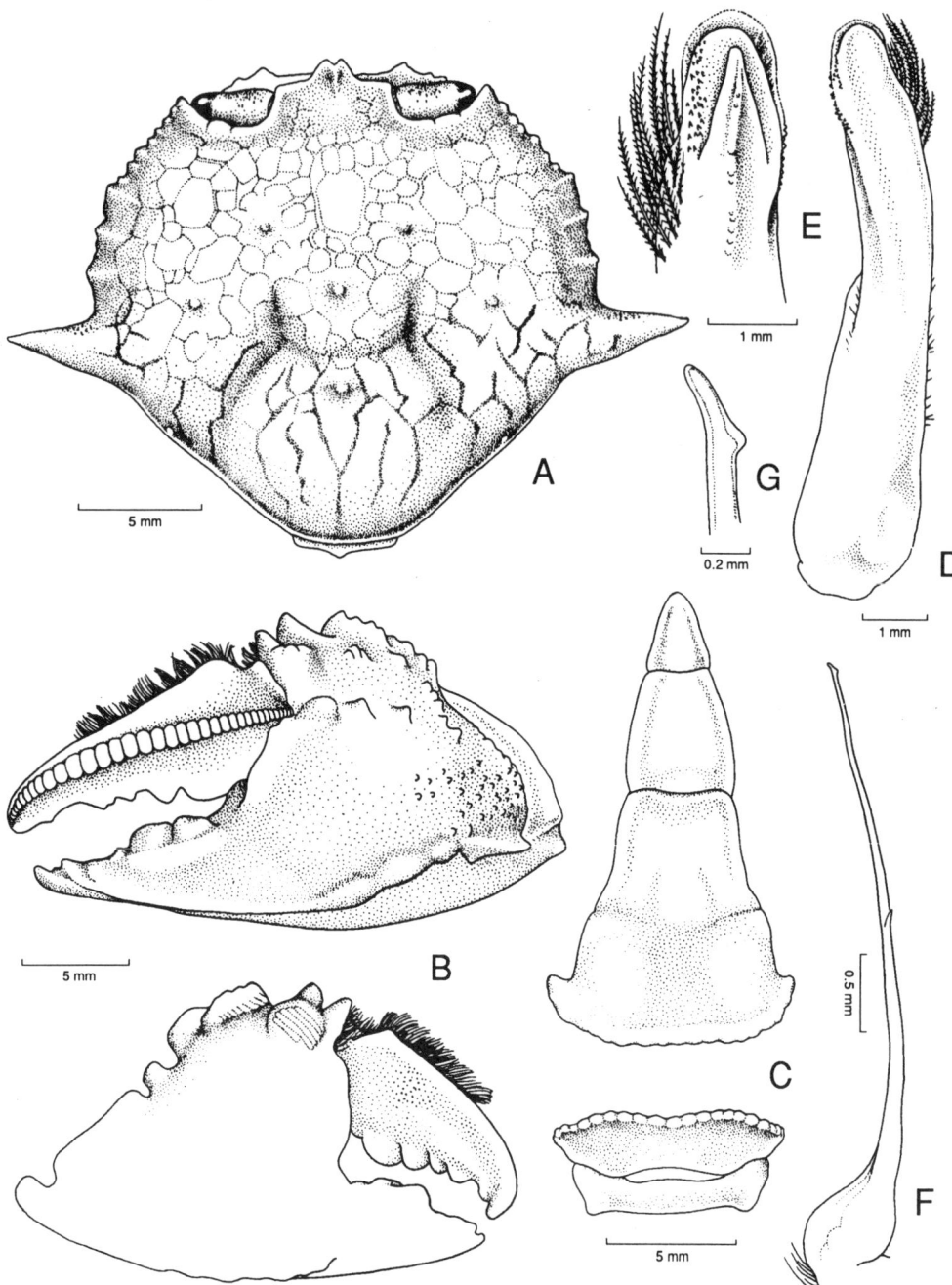

Fig. 12. *Matuta planipes* Fabricius, 1798. A, Carapace; B, chelae; C, male abdomen; D–E, first male pleopod and enlarged tip; F–G, second male pleopod and enlarged tip.

Matuta flagra Shen 1936: 64–66, text-fig. 1.

Material. Huangdao, Qingdao, 7 ♂ (29.2 x 30.2–39.5 x 40.5 mm), 9.IX.1957. —Qingdao, 6 ♂ (17.5 x 18.0– 25.0 x 26.0 mm), 4 ♀ (19.3 x 19.8–24.0 x 25.0 mm), 3.VI.1956. — Rudong, Jiangsu, 4 ♀ (25.4 x 26.0–30.5 x 30.7 mm), 3.VI.1956. —Changle, Fujian, 1 ♂, 1♀, 22.V.1963. —Dongshan, Fujian, 3♂, 24.V.1975. —Xuwen, Guangdong, 2 ♂, 13 ♀ (11 ovig.), 18.VI.1955. —Weizhoudao, Guangxi, 1 ♂, 20.XI.1954. —Beibu Gulf 1♀, 8.VI.1956. —Qinglan, Hainan Island, 1 ♂, 24.III.1955. —Sanya, Hainan Island, 1 ♢, 4.XII.1955. —Haitangtou, Hainan Island, 1♀, 30.VI.1957. —Yinggehai, Hainan Island, 1 ♂, 7.V.1955. —Bohai and Yellow Sea, 26 ♂, 7 ♀ (3 ovig), depth: 21–40 m, IV–XII.1959, bottom, fine, coarse sand, and muddy sand, IV–XII.1959. —South China Sea, 1♂, 1♀, depth: 22–64 m, bottom, sand or broken shells. East China Sea, 1♂, depth: 31 m, bottom, fine sand and broken shells —17.IX.1976. —Beibu Gulf, 1♀, 4.VI.1956.

Habitat. Found on sand, broken shell or muddy sand bottoms, depth littoral to 15 m.

Type locality. 'Oceano Indico'.

Remarks. The carapace is yellowish in spirit and has dotted red lines and loops. These characters are, however, variable.

Distribution. The entire China coast, Korea, Japan, Australia, Indonesia, Singapore, Vietnam, Thailand, India, Persian Gulf and South Africa.

Matuta lunaris (Forskål, 1775). Fig. 13.

Cancer lunaris Forskål 1775: 91 (not seen).

Matuta lunaris Rathbun 1902: 30; 1910: 315. —Laurie 1906: 356. —Balss 1922: 124. —Sakai 1937: 100, plate 13. —Buitendijk 1939: 231. —Shen 1940b: 77;1940a: 214. —Shen and Dai 1964: 14. —Barnard 1950: 358, fig. 67L. —Tyndale-Biscoe and George 1962: 71. —Romimohtarto 1972: 11–13, figs. 1–3, 5, 8, 15–20, plates Ia, a', .IIIa–a'. —Sakai 1967: 140, plate 44, fig. 1. —Dai and Yang 1991: 110, plate 12(5), fig. 55(2)

Material. Xiongdidai, Fujian, 1 ♂ (45.2 x 47.0 mm), 18.IV.1957. —Changle, Fujian, 2 ♂ (41.0 x 43.0; 39.0 x 40.3 mm), 21.V.1963. —Pingtan, Fujian, 1 ♂ (45.0 x 49.0 mm), 14.III.1957. —Jinjiang, Fujian, 2♂ (16.0 x 16.0–20.0 x 20.0 mm). —Qiongtou, Tongan, Fujian, 6 ♂, 5.IV.1957. —Baoan, Guangdong, 1 ♂ (44.5 x 47.1 mm). —Zhapo, Guangdong, 2 ♂, 2 ♀ 18.XI.1954. —Naozhoudao, Guangdong, 1 ♂, 20.XI.1954. — Weizhoudao, Guangxi, 2♂, 20.XI.1954. —Yinggehai, Hainan Island, 1♂, 28. VII.1957. —Haikou, Hainan Island, 1♂, 18.XI.1954. —Sanya, Hainan Island, 2♂, 1♀, 14.IV.1954. —Xingying, Hainan Island, 1 ♂, 7.V.1955.

Habitat. Found on muddy sand, sand or broken shells bottoms, littoral to 15 m depth.

Type locality. Red Sea.

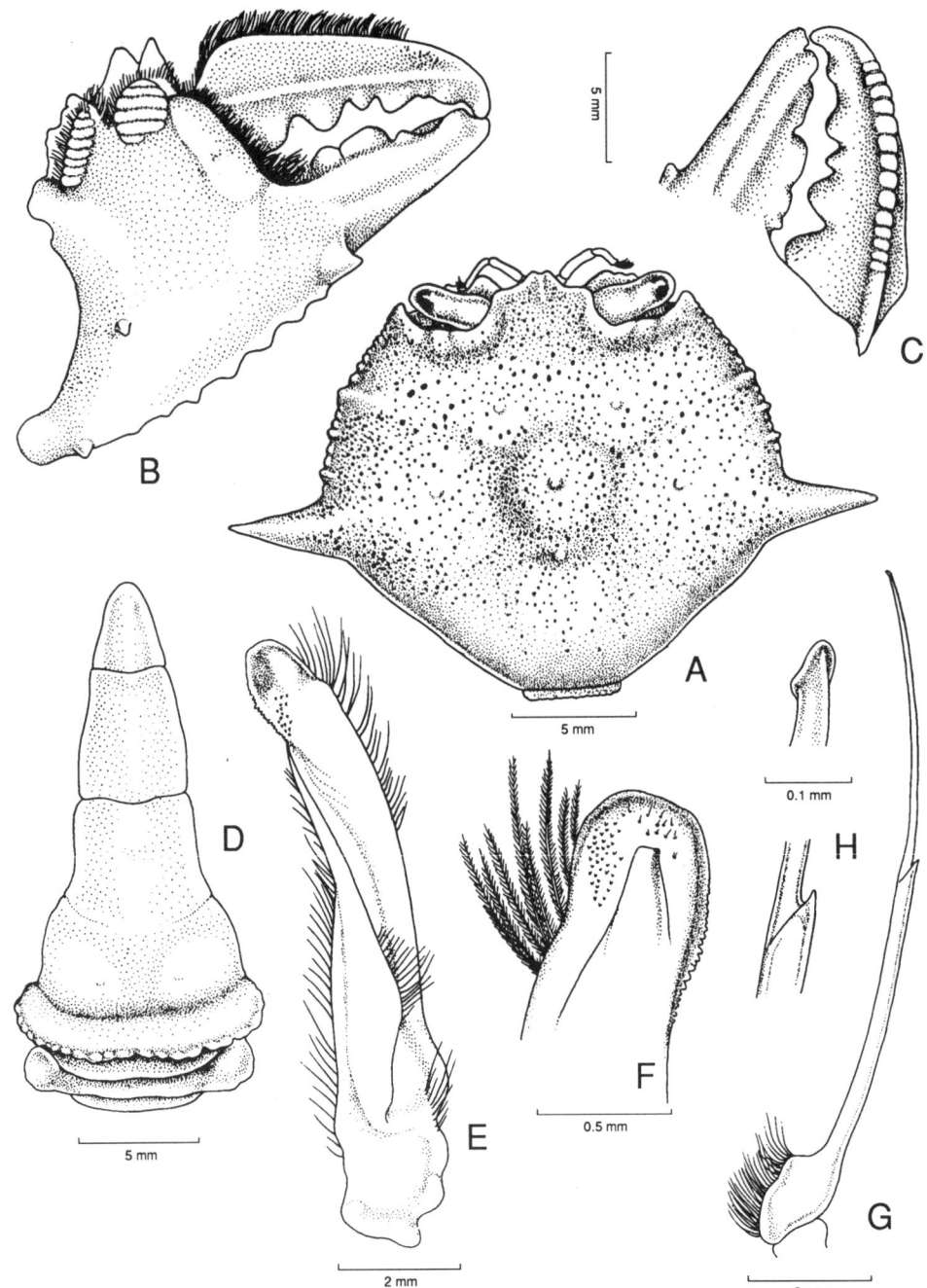

Fig. 13. *Matuta lunaris* (Forskål, 1775). A, Carapace; B, chela; C, fingers; D, male abdomen; E–F, first male pleopod and enlarged tip; G–H, second male pleopod and enlarged parts.

Remarks. The carapace is yellow in spirit and has many reddish dots.

Distribution. China (Hainan Island, Guangdong, Guangxi, Fujian and Taiwan), Korea, Japan, Australia, Indonesia, Thailand, India and Red Sea.

Matuta banksii Leach, 1817. Fig. 14.

Matuta banksii Leach 1817: 14 (not seen). —Alcock 1896: 158. —Nobili 1906: 149. —Ihle 1918: 185. —Balss 1922: 125. —Sakai 1937: 98–100, plate 3, fig. 2. —Buitendijk 1939: 231. —Barnard 1950: 359. —Tyndale-Biscoe and George, 1962: 71. —Shen and Dai 1964: 14. —Romimohtarto 1972: 13–16, figs. 7, 10, 27–32, plates Ic, IIIc, c'. —Dai and Yang 1991: 110, plate 12(6), fig. 56(1)

Material. Xinying, Hainan Island, 2♂, 4 ♀ (20.5 x 22.3–39.0 x 39.5 mm), 28.VII.1957. —Xincun, Hainan Island, 1♂, 2 ♀, 21.IV.1955. —Xinying, Hainan Island, 1 ♀ (30.5 x 30.5 mm), 22.V.1955. —Weizhoudao, Guangxi, 1 ♂ (32.3 x 34.0 mm), 26.XII.1954.

Habitat. Found on shallow sand beach below low tidal mark.

Type locality. Unknown.

Remarks. This species is easily distinguished from the former two species in having six distinct tubercles on the carapace, one tubercle at the middle of the posterolateral border and an obsolete stridulating ridge on the outer surface of the movable finger, which consists of very fine or indistinct striae.

Distribution. China (Guangdong, Guangxi, Hainan Island, and Taiwan), Japan, Polynesia, Australia, Indonesia, India, South Africa, Persian Gulf and Red Sea.

Matuta granulosa Miers, 1877

Matuta granulosa Miers 1877: 245, plate 59, figs. 8–9. —De Man 1881: 114. —Haswell 1882: 134. —Ortmann 1892: 572–573. —Tyndale-Biocoe and George 1962: 71–72. —Dai and Yang 1991: 113, plate 12(8), fig. 57.

Habitat. Dredged at 30 fathoms.

Type locality. Eastern Seas.

Remarks. This species was recorded by Dai and Yang (1991) from Hainan Island but as yet I have not collected this species.

Distribution. China, Australia and Indian Ocean.

Matuta curtispina Sakai, 1961. Fig. 15.

Matuta curtispina Sakai 1961: 139, plate 3, fig. 7; 1965: 60, 61, plate 24, fig. 2; 1976: 14, plate 45, fig. 2.

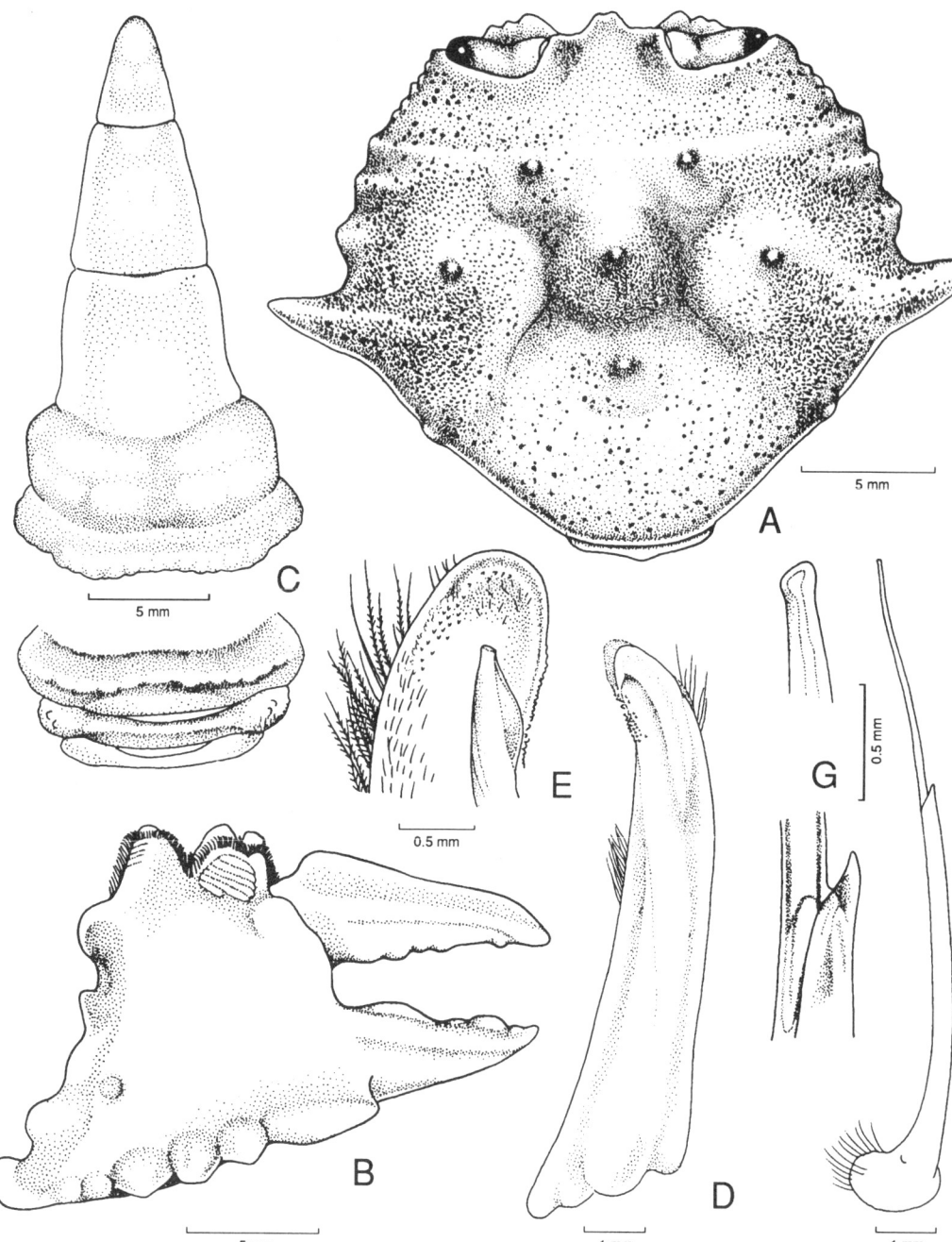

Fig. 14. *Matuta banksii* Leach, 1817. A, Carapace; B, chela; C, male abdomen; D–E, first male pleopod and enlarged tip; F–G, second male pleopod and enlarged parts.

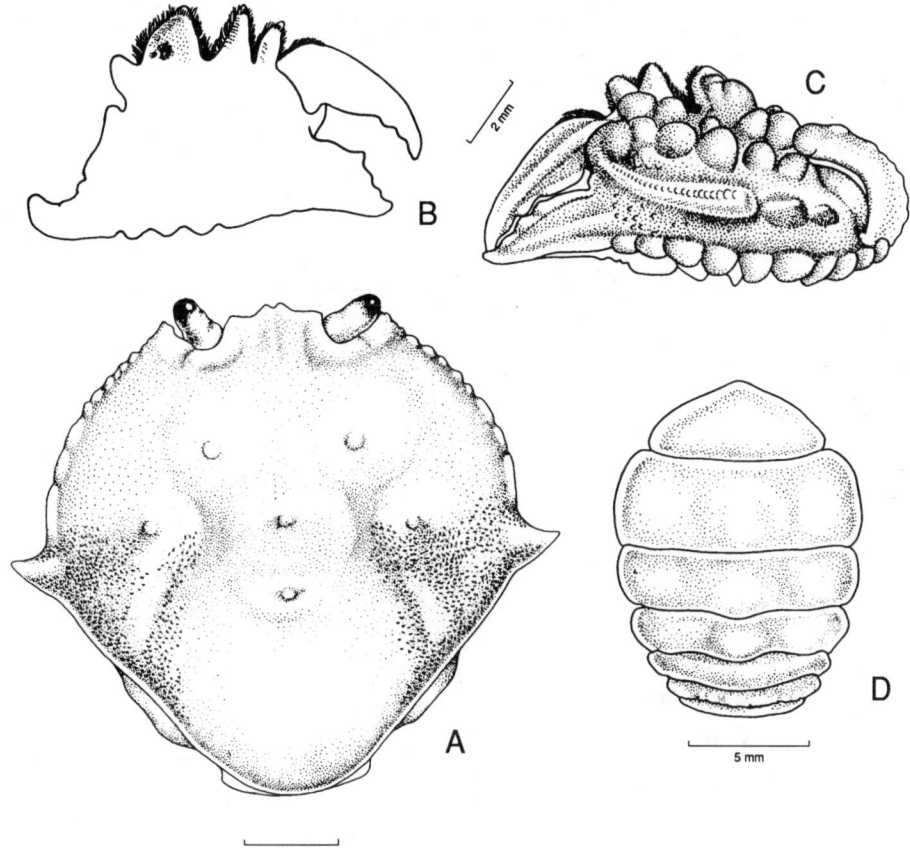

Fig. 15. *Matuta curtispina* Saiki, 1961. A, Carapace; B–C, chelae; D, female abdomen.

Material. South China Sea, 1 ♀ (16.5 x 16.7 mm), depth: 217 m, bottom, sand, 26.II.1959. —East China Sea, 1 ♀ (18.0 x 18.2 mm), depth: 100 m, bottom, fine sand, 29.VIII.1976; 1 ♀ (14.0 x 14.1 mm), depth: 104 m, bottom, fine sand, 27.VIII.1976; 1 ♂ (19.0 x 19.0 mm), depth: 105 m, bottom, fine or broken shells, 11.VI.1978.

Habitat. Found on fine sand or broken shell bottoms, 35–105 m depths.

Type locality. Japan.

Distribution. South China Sea, East China Sea and Japan.

Orithyinae Dana, 1852

Orithyinae Dana 1852: 391. —Miers 1886: 283. —Ihle 1918: 178. —Sakai 1937: 84, 101; 1976: 143. Dai and Yang 1991: 113.

Orithyoida Alcock 1896

Orithyia Fabricius, 1798

Orithyia Fabricius, 1798: 363 (not seen). —Ortmann 1892; 569. —Alcock 1896: 138. —Ihle 1918: 178. —Sakai 1937:84, 101; 1976:143. Dai and Yang 1991: 113.

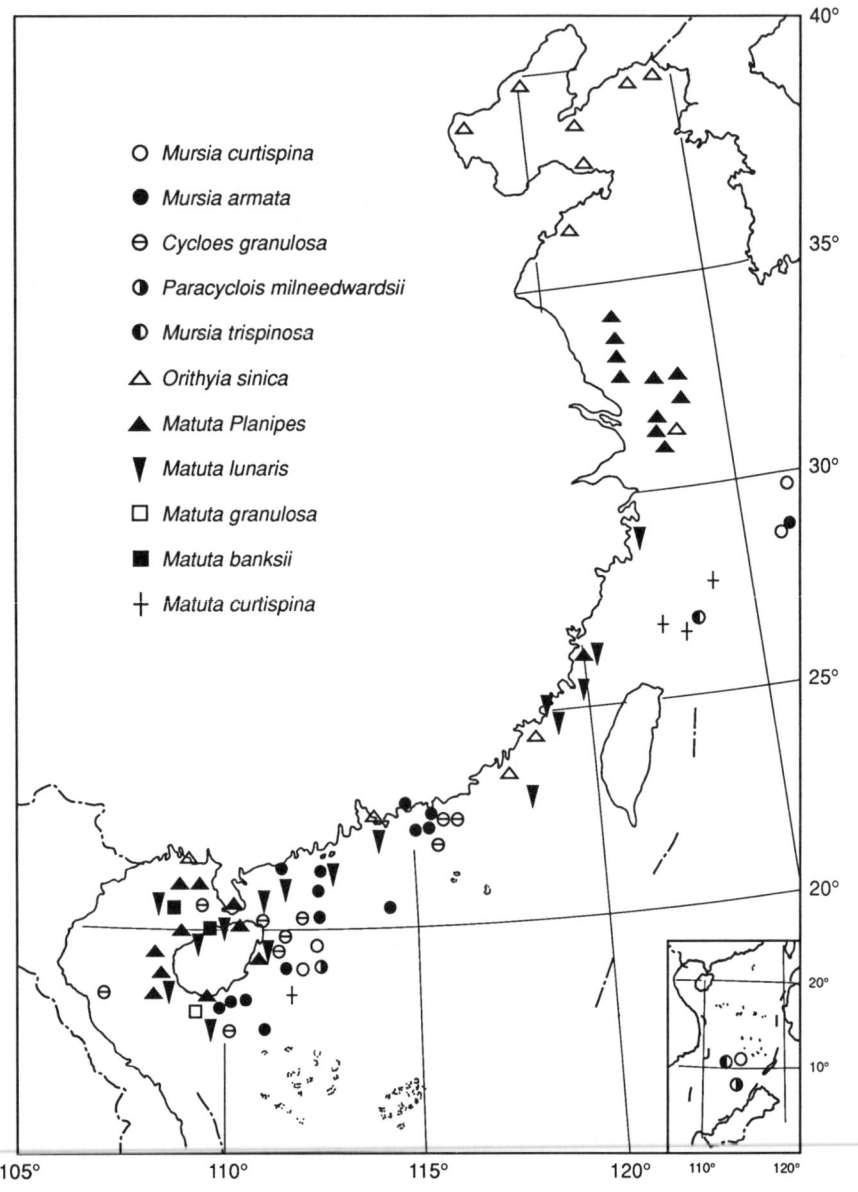

Fig. 16. The distribution of *Calappa* spp. recorded from Chinese waters.

Orithyia sinica (Linnaeus, 1771). Fig. 4C.

Cancer sinicua Linnaeus 1771: 541 (not seen).
Cancer bimaculatus Herbst 1790: 248, plate 18, fig. 101.

Orithyia mammillaris Fabricius 1798: 363 (not seen). —H. Milne-Edwards 1837: 112. —Ortmann 1892: 569. —Shen 1931: 106–107, plate 9, figs. 1–3; 1932: 30, text-figs.

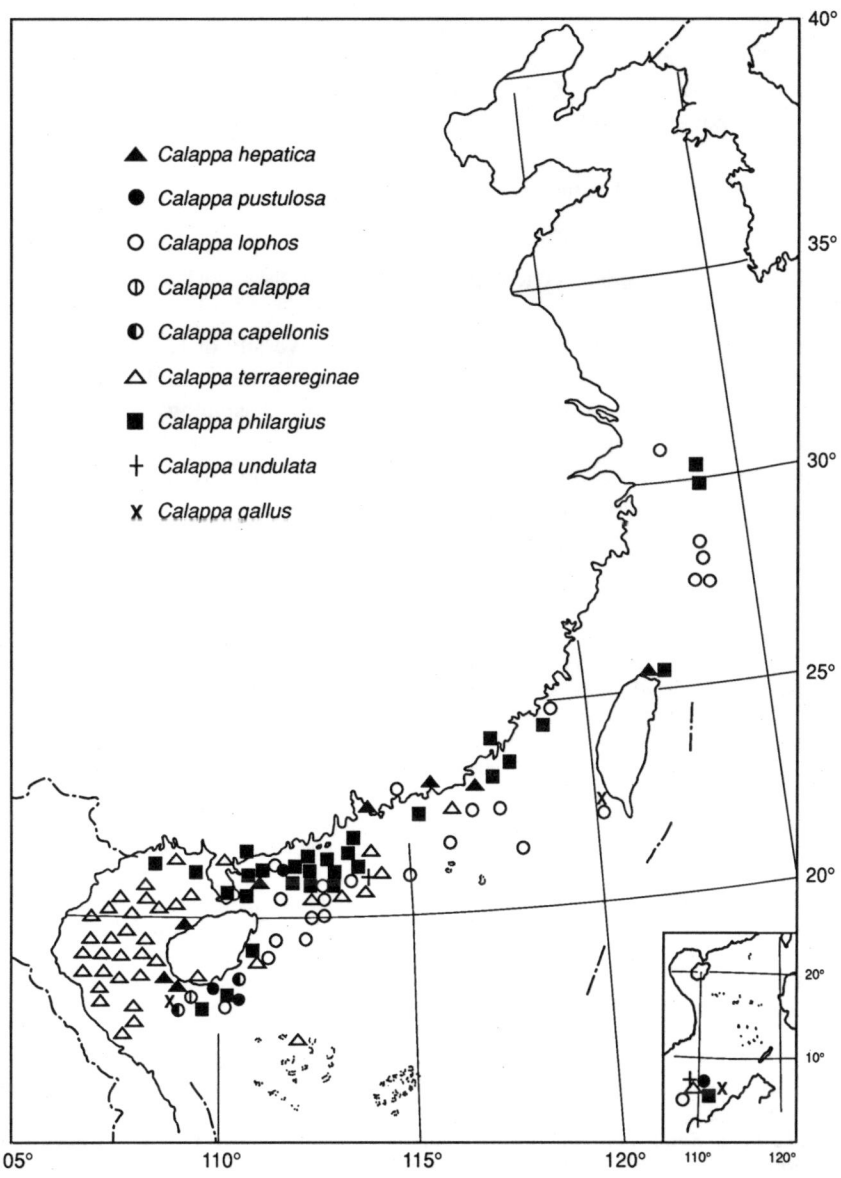

Fig. 17. The distribution of some species of Calappidae from Chinese waters.

18–19, plate 3, fig. 1. —Shen and Dai 1964: 13. —Dai and Yang 1991: 113, plate 12(8), fig. 57.

Material. Qingdao, 1 ♀ (57.5 x 50.2 mm), 19.VI.1957. —1 ♀ (67.0 x 60.0 mm), 24.X.1982. —Xiamen, 1 ♀ (58.0 x 51.0 mm), 3.III.1984.

Habitat. Found on sand or mud bottoms.

Type locality. China.

Remarks. This is the only species of the subfamily Orithyinae. It is recorded from the Bohai Sea, Yellow Sea, East China Sea, and South China Sea. It has not yet been reported from Japanese waters.

Distribution. The entire China coasts and Korea.

ACKNOWLEDGEMENTS

I am sincerely grateful to Prof. B. Morton of The University of Hong Kong, for inviting me to take part in the International Conference on the Marine Biology of Hong Kong and the South China Sea; to Prof. J.Y. Liu, Institute of Oceanology, Academia Sinica, for reading the manuscript; to Prof. Chen Cunzhong, Xiamen Fisheries College, who loaned me an excellent specimen and to Mrs Liang Yoping, Marine Product Museum, Qingdao, for drawing most of the figures of specimens.

REFERENCES

Alcock, A. 1896. Materials for a Carcinological Fauna of India. No. 2. —The Brachyura Oxystomata. *Journal of the Asiatic Society of Bengal* 65:134–296, plates 6–8.
Balss, H. 1922. Ostasiatische Decapoden III. Die Dromiaceen, Oxystomen und Parthenopiden. *Archiv für Naturgeschichte* 88:104–40.
Barnard, K.H. 1950. Descriptive catalogue of South African Decapoda Crustacea. *Annals of the South African Museum* 38:1–837.
Borradaile, L.A. 1903. *The Fauna and Geography of the Maldive and Laccadive Archipelagoes.* Marine Crustaceans. VI. —Oxystomata. London: Cambridge University Press, vol. 1, 434–39, plate 22.
Buitendijk, A.M. 1939. Biological results of the Snellius Expedition, 5. —The Dromiacea, Oxystomata and Oxyrhyncha of the Snellius Expedition. *Temminckia* 4:223–76, plates 7–11.
Campbell, B.M. 1971. New records and new species of crabs (Crustacea, Brachyura) trawled off Southern Queensland: Dromiacea, Homolidea, Gymnopleura, Corystoidea, and Oxystomata. *Memoirs of the Queensland Museum* 16:27–48, figs. 1–4, plates 1–2.
Chace, F. A. 1968. A new crab of the genus *Cycloes* (Decapoda: Brachyura Calappidae) from Saint Helena, South Atlantic Ocean. *Proceedings of the Biological Society of Washington* 81:605–12, 2 figs.
Chen, H.L. 1975. Studies on the crabs of Xisha Islands, Guangdong Province, China, I. *Studia Marina Sinica* 10:157–79, 12 text-figs., 3 plates. (in Chinese)
Chopra, B. 1933. On the Decapod Crustacea collected by the Bengal Pilot Service off the mouth

of the River Hughli. Dromiacea and Oxystomata. Further Notes on the Crustacea Decapoda in the Indian Museum, III. *Records of the Indian Museum* 35(1):25–52.

Dai, A.Y. and Yang, S.L. 1991. *Crabs of the China Seas*. Beijing: China Ocean Press, 1–682 (plates1–74, figs. 1–295).

Dana, J.D. 1852. Crustacea. United States Exploring Expedition during the years 1838, 1839, 1840, 1841, 1842, under the Command of Charles Wilkes, U.S.N. 13, 1–685. Atlas (1855), 1–27, plates 1–96. Philadelphia.

de Haan, W. 1833–1850. Crustacea. In: Ph. F. Von Siebold, Fauna Japonica, Jussus et auspiciis superiorum, qui summun in India Batave Imperium tenent, suscepto, annis 1823–1830 collegit, notis, observationibus a adumbationibus illustravit. Lugduni Batavorum, fasc. 1–8, i–xxxi+vii–xvii+ix–xvi+1–244, plates 1–5, A–q, circ., 1–2.

de Man, J.G. 1887–1888b. Bericht uber die im Indischen Archipel von Dr. J. Brock gesammelten Decapoden und Stomatopoden. *Archiv für Naturgeschichte* 53:215–288, plates 7–10(1887); 289–600, plates 11–22a (1888).

de Man, J.G. 1902. Ergebnisse einer zoologischen Forschungsreise in den Molukken und Borneo, im Auftrage der Senckenberg naturforsch. Gesellschaft ausgefuhrt von Dr. Willy Kukenthal. Teil. 2. Reiseergebn. Bd. 3 Heft. 3. *Abhandlungen der Senckenbergischen Naturforschender Geselleschaft.* 25:467–929.

Doflein, F. 1902. Ostasiatische Dekapoden. *Abhandlung der koniglichen bayerischen Akademie der Wissenschaften (Munchen)* 21:613–70, 6 plates

Doflein, F. 1904. Brachyura. Wissenschaftliche Ergebnisse der Deutschen Tiefsee-Expedition auf dem Dampfer 'Valdivia' 1898–1899, 6, xiv+314, Atlas, text-figs. 1–68, plates 1–58.

Haswell, W.A. 1882. *Catalogue of the Australian stalk- and sessile-eyed Crustacea*. Sydney:The Australian Museum. iii–xxiv, 1–324, plates 1–4.

Henderson, J.R. 1893. A contribution to Indian carcinology. *Transactions of the Linnean Society of London, Series 2, Zoology* 5:325–458, plates 36–70.

Herbst, J.F.W. 1782–1804. Versuch einer Naturgeschichte der Krabben und Krebse, nebst einer systematischen Beschreibung ihrer verschiedenen Arten. Vols. 1–3: 1–515, 62 plates, Berlin and Stralsund.

Ihle, J.E.W. 1918. Die Decapoda Brachyura der siboga- Expedition. III. Oxystomata: Calappidae, Leucosiidae, Raninidae. *Siboga Expeditie Monographie* 39b2, 159–322, figs. 78–148.

Klunzinger, C.B. 1906. Die Spitz-and Spitzmundkrabben des Roten Meeres. Stuttgart: 1–88, plates 1–2.

Laurie, R.D. 1906. Report on the Brachyura collected by Professor Herdman, at Ceylon, in 1902. In: W. A. Herdmann, Report to the Government of Ceylon on the Pearl Oyster Fisheries of the Gulf of Manaar. Part. V. Supplementrary Report 40, 349–432, plates 1–2.

Miers, E.J. 1884. Crustacea. In: Report on the Zoological Collections made in the Indo-Pacific Ocean during the Voyage of H.M.S. 'Alert' 1881-2, 178–322, plates 18–34. London: British Museum (Natural History).

Miers, E.J. 1886. Brachyura. Report on the Scientific Results of the Voyage of H.M.S. *Challenger* 1873-76. *Zoology* 17: i–1, 1–362, plates 1–29.

Milne Edwards, H. 1837. Histoire naturelle des Crustacés. Paris. II. 1837, 1–532, Atlas, (1834, 1837, 1840): 1–32, plates 1–42.

Monod, T. 1956. Hippidea et Brachyura ouest-africains. *Mémoires de l'Institut Francais d'Afrique Noire* 45:1–674.

Nobili, G. 1906. Crustacés Decapodes et Stomatopodes (Mission J. Bonnier et Ch. Perez) (Golfe Persique 1901). *Bulletin Scientifique de la France et de la Belgique* 40:13–159, plates 2–7.

Ortmann, A. 1892. Die Abtheilungen Hippidea, Dromiidea und Oxystomata. Die Decapoden-Krebse des Strassburger Museums, mit besonderer Berücksichtigung der von Herrn Dr. Doderlein bei Japan und bei den Liu-Kiu-Inseln gesammelten und z.Z. im Strassburger Museum aufbewahrten Formen V. Theil. *Zoologische Jahrbücher, Abtheilung für Systematik, Geographie und Biologie der Thiere* 6:532–88, plate 26.

Parisi, B. 1914. Oxystomata. I Decapodi giapponesi del Museo de Milano. I. *Atti della Societa Italiana di Scienze Naturali* 53:280–312.

Rathbun, M.J. 1902. Japanese stalk-eyed Crustaceans. *Proceedings of the United States National Museum* 26(1307):23–55.

Rathbun, M.J. 1906. The Brachyura and Macrura of the Hawaiian Islands. *Bulletin of the United States Fish Commission* 23(3): 827–930, plates 1–24.

Rathbun, M.J. 1923. Report on the Brachyrhyncha, Oxystomata and Dromiacea. In: Report or the crabs obtained by the F.I.S. 'Endeavour' on the Coasts of Queensland, New South Wales, Victoria, South Australia and Tasmania, Biological Results of the Fishing Experiments carried on by the F.I.S. 'Endeavour' 1909–14, Sydney. Vol. 5, part 3, 95–156, figs. 1–3, plates 16–42.

Rathbun, M.J. 1937. The Oxystomatous and allied crabs of America. *Bulletin of the United States National Museum* 166:1–278, plates 1–86.

Romimohtarto, K. 1972. Five species of *Matuta* (Calappidae, Brachyura, Decapoda) From Indonesia. *Marine Research in Indonesia* 12:3–23.

Sakai, T. 1934. Brachyura from the coast of Kyushu, Japan. *Science Reports of the Tokyo Burika Daigaku, Section B* 1(25):281–330.

Sakai, T. 1937. Studies on the crabs of Japan. II. Oxystomata. *Science Reports of the Tokyo Burika Daigaku, Section B* 3(2):67–192, plates 1–19, text-figs. 1–45.

Sakai, T. 1961. New species of JapanesecCrabs from the collection of His Majesty the Emperor of Japan. *Crustaceana* 3:131–50, 1 plate, 1–4 text-fig.

Sakai, T. 1965. The crabs of Sagami Bay, collected by His Majesty the Emperor of Japan. Edited by Biological Laboratory, Imperial Household, Tokyo. pp. 1–206, plates 1–100 (coloured), text-figs. 1–27.

Sakai, T. 1976. Crabs of Japan and the adjacent seas. Tokyo: Kodansha Ldt, 3 vol. I-XXIX, 1–773 (in English); 1–461 (in Japanese); plates 1–251.

Shen, C.J. 1931. The crabs of Hong Kong. Part I. *Hong Kong Naturalist* 2(2):92–110, plates 4–10.

Shen, C.J. 1932. The brachyuran Crustacea of North China. *Zoologica Sinica* (A) 9(1), 1–300, 171 text-figs., plates 1–10, 1 map.

Shen, C.J. 1936. On a collection of brachyuran Decapoda from Hainan Island with descriptions of three new species. *The Chinese Journal of Zoology* 2:63–80, text-figs. 1–4.

Shen, C.J. 1940a. The brachyuran fauna of Hong Kong. *Journal of the Hong Kong Fisheries Research Station* 1:211–42.

Shen, C.J. 1940b. On the collections of crabs of South China. *Bulletin of the Fan Memorial Institute (Zoology series)* 10:69–104.

Shen, C.J. and Dai A.Y. 1964. *Fauna of China. Crustacea, Part. 2*. Beijing: Science Press, 1–142, figs. 1–277. (in Chinese)

Stebbing, T.R.R. 1910. General catalogue of South African Crustacea. *Annals of the South African Museum.* 6:281–593.

Stephensen, K. 1945. The Brachyura of the Iranian Gulf, with an Appendix: the male pleopoda of the Brachyura. In: *Danish Scientific Investigations in Iran, part IV*. Copenhagen: E. Munksgaard. 57–237, figs. 1–60.

Stimpson, W. 1907. Report on the Crustancea (Brachyura and Anomura) collected by the North Pacific Exploring Expedition, 1853–1856. *Smithsonian Miscellaneous Collections* 49:1–240.

Tyndale-Biscoe, M. and R.W. George. 1962. The Oxystomata and Gymnopleura (Crustacea, Brachyura) of Western Australia with descriptions of two new species from Western Australia and one from India. *Journal of the Royal Society of Western Australia* 45:65–96, plates 1–3.

Yokoya, Y. 1933. On the distribution of decapod crustaceans inhabiting the continental shelf around Japan, chiefly based upon the materials collected by S.S. *Soyo-Maru*, during the year 1923–1930. *Journal of the College of Agriculture, Tokyo Imperial University* 12:1–226, text-figs. 1–71.

MARINE DIATOMS OF THE XISHA ISLANDS, SOUTH CHINA SEA. I. *MASTOGLOIA* THW. EX. WP. SM. SPECIES OF THE GROUP *SULCATAE*

Liu Shicheng

Department of Biology, Xiamen University, Xiamen, China

ABSTRACT

Forty species of the diatom of the genus *Mastogloia* have been recorded from the Xisha Islands, South China Sea. For selected species, external and internal valve structure have been investigated by LM, TEM and SEM. Three new species have been identified and are described. Three are new records for China.

INTRODUCTION

Observations on some *Mastogloia* species in Hustedt's (1933) group *Sulcatae* are described. Stephens and Gibson (1979, 1980) and Yohn and Gibson (1982) have previously described some species belonging to the group *Sulcatae*. The objective of the present study was to describe the ultrastructure of some species in the group *Sulcatae* from the Xisha Islands by transmitted light microscopy (LM), transmission electron microscopy (TEM) and scanning electron microscopy (SEM). These species were compared with corresponding species in the Academy of Natural Sciences of Philadelphia. A key to the *Sulcatae* group species of *Mastogloia* is also given.

MATERIALS AND METHODS

The material studied was collected from the intertidal zone of the Xisha Islands, Guangdong Province, China (PRC). All materials were cleaned using of potassium dichromate-peroxide (Van der Werff 1955). Slides were made according to standard procedures, using Hyrax as a mounting medium. Specimens were observed under a microscope using phase contrast oil immersion (LM) at 1000x magnification, a JEM-100 CX11 80kv transmission electron microscope (TEM) and a Hitachi S5 20 20kv scanning electron microscope (SEM).

RESULTS

A key to the species of group *Sulcatae*

1. Partecta (loculi) ring under six. Partecta only in the middle of each side.
2. Only two (a few six) partecta equal in form and size. With a spine affixed in the middle of the inner margin (usually loose).
3. Round at the ends, length to width 5:1 ....*M. mediterranea* (24)
3. Slightly drawn out ends, length to width 2.3:1 .*M. mediterranea* var. *elliptica* (25)
2. Three partecta; largest one in the middle of the band, others small. Without a spine affixed in the middle of the inner margin ....*M. lentiformis* (20)
1. Partecta more than six, not only in the middle of each side.
5. Partecta differ in form and size.
6. Large partecta between the middle and the ends of each band.
7. Lateral areas arcuate ....*M. mauritiana* (22)
   Rostrate ends .... *M. mauritiana* var. *capitata* (23)
   ....(aff. *M. mauritiana* var. *rostrata*)
7. Lateral area arcuate, transapically constricted in the middle ....
   ....*M. peragalli* (30)
6. Large partecta in the middle of the ring.
8. Ends only slightly constricted.
9. Transapical striae more than 25 and of 10 µ.
10. Ends only slightly constricted, Transapical striae about 26–28 and of 10 µ. ...
    ....*M. minutissima* (26)
10. Ends slightly obtuse, rarely constricted. Transapical striae about 27 and of 10
    ....*M. pseudexilis* (32)
10. Ends more pointed than above. Transapical striae about 28–33 and of 10 µ.
11. Without a spine affixed on the inner margin on each partectum. ....
    ....*M. exilis* (10)
11. With a spine affixed on the inner margin on each partectum ....
    .... *M. xishaensis* (40)
9. Transapical striae not more than 25 and of 10 µ ....*M. omissa* (29)
8. Ends not constricted
12. Partecta distant from ends; one-two large partecta in the middle of the ring.
13. 3–4 on each margin. Length to width 2. 7–2.8:1 .... *M. pseudonuiensis* (33)
13. 4–6 on each margin. Length to width about 4:1 .... *M. intrita* (15)
13. 6–8 on each margin. Length to width about 2.5:1 .... *M. pumila* (34)
    Ends round (or slightly cuneate) not rostrate .... *M. pumila* var. *papuarum* (35)
    valve elongate-oval, one end wider than another .... *M. pumila* var. *rennellensis* (36)
12. Partecta reach subends, decreasing in size gradually or equally towards the ends.
14. Lateral areas combined with the central area into a H-shape.
15. Length to width 3:1 .... *M. brauni* (2)
15. Length to width 4:1 .... *M. brauni* cf. *elongata* (3)
14. Lateral areas arcuate, completely separate from the central area.
16. Partecta decreasing in size by steps .... *M. hustedtii* (13)
16. Partecta decreasing in size from middle towards the ends .... *M. grunowi* (11)

5. Partecta nearly equal in form and size.
17. Lateral areas sub-arcuate.
18. Valves elliptical .... *M. jaoi* (16)
18. Valves naviculoid .... *M. hainanensis* (12)
18. Valves cucurbitoid .... *M. cucurbita* (7)
17. Lateral areas arcuate.
19. With an apiculus, affixed on the inner margin of the partecta. ....
   .... *M. indonesiana* (14)
19. Without an apiculus on the inner margin of the partecta.
20. Lateral areas not separated from central axial area by different punctate rows.
21. Valves broadly naviculoid. Ends constricted into rostrate or capitate shape.
22. Ends rostrate .... *M. pisciculus* (31)
22. Ends capitate .... *M. corallum* (4)
21. Valves rhombic. Ends not constricted into rostrate shape. *M. neorugosa* (27)
20. Lateral areas separated from central axial area by different punctate rows.
23. With noticeable longitudinal lines in lateral areas ...... *M. quinquecostata* (38)
23. With longitudinal rows of short 'dashes' in lateral areas.
24. Valve broad, naviculoid.. *M. obesa* (28)
24. Valve naviculoid-rhomboid
25. Without depression between middle and ends.
26. Transapical striae less than 20 in 10 µ.
27. Partecta 2. 5–4 in 10 µ, width about 1.5 µ .... *M. jelinecki* (17)
    Lateral areas limited by prolonged striae, forming four dissociated areas; chilli-shaped .... *M. jelineki* var. *extensa* (18)
27. Partecta 6–7 in 10 µ, width 1 µ............................ *M. leminiscata* (19)
26. Transapical striae more than 20 and of 10 µ .... *M. depressa* (8)
25. With depression between midde and ends.
28. Lateral areas accounting for about 1/2 of the valve width, central area not stauroid .... *M. elegantula* (9)
28. Lateral areas larger than 2/3 of the valve width.
    Central area stauroid; .....(5) more lanceolate than typical species *M. cruciata*
    Ends slightly rostrate .... *M. cruciata* var. *elliptica* (6)
23. With three-five longitudinal hyaline lines from nearly raphe to 1/2 wide to valve (lateral areas) .... *M. qionzhouensis* (37)
23. Without special striae in lateral areas.
29. Central area not sharply demarcated .... *M. baldjikiana* (1)
29. Central area stauroid, sharply demarcated .... *M. macdonaldii* (21)

17. With broad linear furrows at some distance from the raphe ... *M. sulcata* (39)

Information on each species

Information is given for each species in the following manner:
- Almost all the plates of the paper were taken from specimens using a phase contrast microscope (TLM) x1000, TEM and SEM, unless otherwise stated.
- The species are arranged alphabetically.
- Species identifications were verified by comparison with material in the ANSP (Academy of Natural Sciences of Philadelphia).

- For the species which have been recorded from China, only new photographs and references to them are given. For newly recorded species from China, a detailed description and references to them after 1979 are given.
- Diatom terminology is according to Smith (1856), Hustedt (1933), Voigt (1942), Anon. (1975) and Ross et al. (1979)
- Presence on sampling dates used the following scale (from 1000 cells):
  very rare = 1–5 observations
  rare = 6–8 observation
  frequent = 11–17 observation
  common = 18–26 observations
- Water temperatures and salinities were: 24.2-29.8°C and 33.4–34.1‰.
- In the list, an asterisk marks the species which are new records from China.

1. *M. baldjikiana* Grunow. Plate 4, Figs. 1–3. Very rare.
   Ricard 1975b 11 (1): p. 58, Plate 4, figs. 26–28; Foged 1978, p. 77, 19/ta-2b; Navarro 1982, p. 38. XXV/3.4; Paddock and Kemp 1990 5 (1), fig. 127.
   Comparative Material. None available at the ANSP.

2. *M. brauni* Grunow. Plate 4, Figs. 7–8. Very rare.
   Stephens and Gibson 1980, p. 221, figs. 1–4.
   Stephens and Gibson 1980 fig. 4 very similar to *M. pseudonuiensis*, but the former raphe sinuose, striae are parallel near the centre, 17–21/1µ; the latter raphe leniter sinuose, striae are radiate throughout 28–29/10 µ.
   Comparative Material. None available at the ANSP.

3. *M. brauni* cf. *elongata* Voigt. Plate 4, Fig. 6. Very rare.
   Foged 1978, p. 77.
   Comparative Material. None available at the ANSP.

4. **M. corallum* Paddock and Kemp. Plate 4, Fig. 9; Plate 5, Fig. 1. Very rare.
   Paddock and Kemp 1988, 3 (1), p. 12, figs. 17–25.

Valve roundly elliptical with pointed poles, 28 µ long, 14.3 µ wide (Paddock and Kemp 1988: 24–28 µ long, 12–14 µ broad).

Costa fine, more robust near the valve margin, weakly radial, 27 in 10 µ (Paddock and Kemp 1988: 24–26 in 10 µ). Inside the valve face the areolae are arranged in groups of four between adjacent costae, Raphe leniter sinuose; central area small and round; partecta unequal in size, the middle more enlarged. 9–11 per side, inner margin convex, not reaching to the ends.

Habitat. Marine.

Distribution. Chenghang, Xisha Islands, Guangdong Province, China.
   Comparative Material. None available at the ANSP.

5. *M. cruciata* (Leud.–Fort.) Cleve. Plate 4, Figs. 4–5. Very rare.
   Comparative Material. None available at the ANSP.

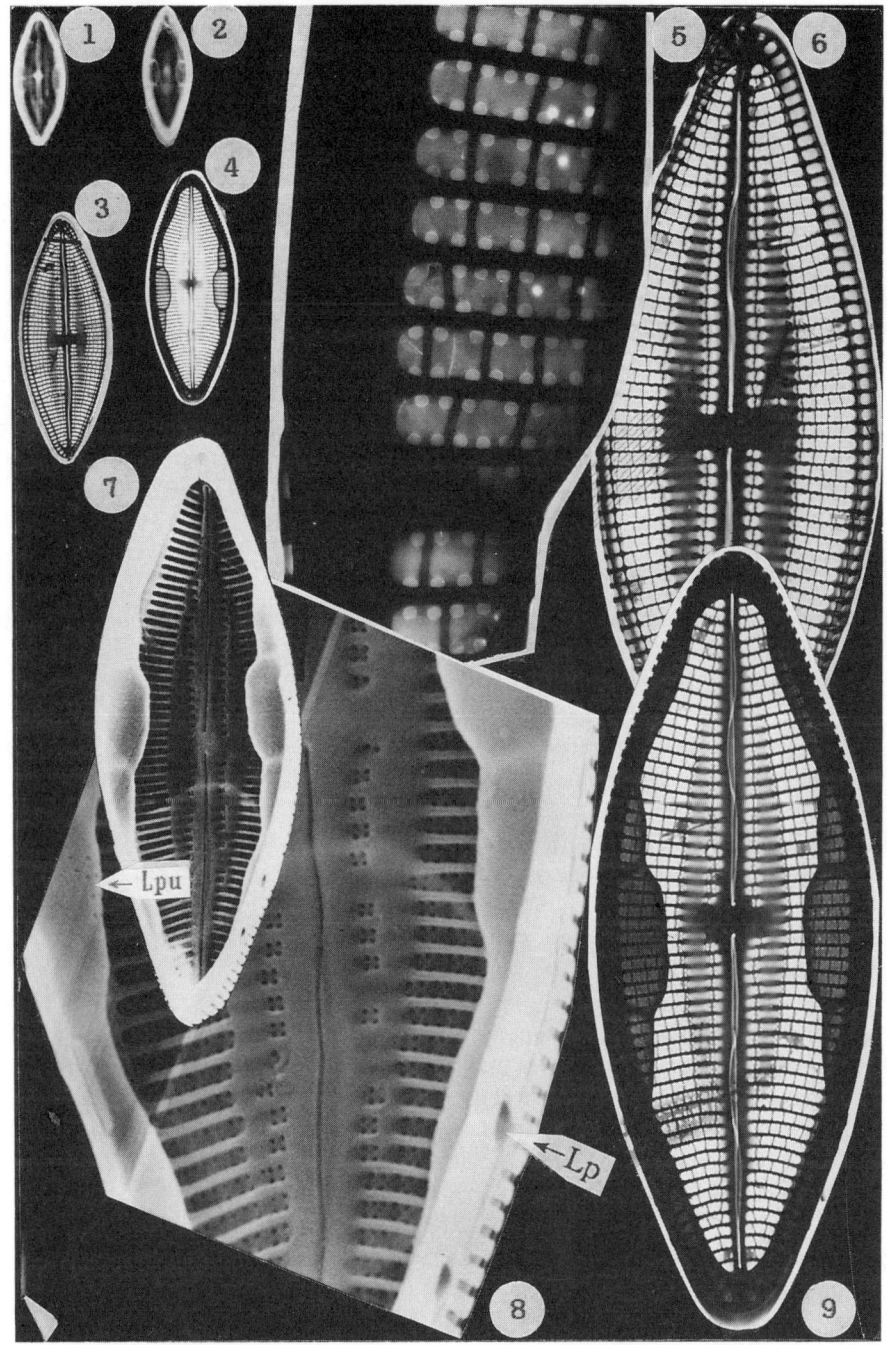

Plate 1. Figs. 1-9. *Mastogloia pseudonuiensis.* 1-2, LM x1000; 3, 6, TEM x1500, x5400 external valve; 4, 9, TEM x1500, x5400 internal valve; 5, TEM x28500 part of partectal ring; 7, 8, SEM x4000, x13500 internal valve showing partectal ring, partectal pores (Lp) and partectal puncta (Lpu).

6. *M. cruciata* var. *elliptica* Voigt. Very rare.
   Comparative Material. None available at the ANSP.

7. *M. cucurbita* Voigt. Very rare.
   Comparative Material. None available at the ANSP.

8. *M. depressa* Hustedt. Plate 5, Figs. 9–11. Very rare.
   Hustedt 1985, Plate 470 fig. 986; Van Landingham 1967–79, Plate 2145.

Valve elliptical-lanceolate, slightly protracted, 26 μ in length, 10 μ wide with a ratio of 2.6:1 (Hustedt 1985: 20–25 μ length, wide 9 μ). Raphe straight or very slightly wavy. Under the SEM, the valve face is divided into two zones: outer zone with strong costae, 24/10 μ (same Hustedt record); and an inner lanceolate zone with more or less numerous irregular longitudinal rows. Partecta ring narrow, about 1 μ wide, same size, through 7.5/10 μ. inner margin convex. The specimens from Xisha are less convex than in Hustedt (1985, fig. 986).

Habitat. marine.

Distribution. Collected in washings of *Hydroclathrus clathratus* from the lower tidal area in Chenghang, Xisha Islands, Guangdong Province, China.
   Comparative Material. None available at the ANSP.

9. *M. elegantula* Hustedt. Very rare.
   Comparative Material. None available at the ANSP.

10. *M. exilis* Hustedt. Plate 5, Figs. 6–7; Plate 8, Figs. 6–7. Rare.
    Comparative Material. None available at the ANSP.

11. *M. grunowi* A. Schmidt. Very rare.
    Foged 1975, p. 31, 16/5.

M. grunowi, *M. hustedtii* and *M. quinquecostata* are very similar. Vanlandingham (1967–79) suggests that *M. grunowi* merges into *M. quinquecostata*. I consider the two species to be different. Partecta of middle slightly larger, width about 2 μ, decreasing in size to the ends, not reaching to the ends in *M. grunowi*; partecta very narrow, equal in size, width 1–1.5 μ reaching to the ends, 4–5 in 10 μ in *M. quinquecostata.*
   Comparative Material. None available at the ANSP.

12. *M. hainanensis* Voigt. Plate 5, Fig. 8. Rare.
    Comparative Material. None available at the ANSP.

13. *M. hustedtii* Plate 5, Figs. 2–4. Rare.
    Stephens and. Gibson 1980 33:p.243, figs. 14–17 (SEM); Stephens and Gibson 1979, n.s. 14 (1):p. 25, fig. 6, p. 26, fig 13; Paddock and Kemp 1990, 5 (1) cf. 128
    Light microscopy (Plate 5, Figs. 2–4): Valve length 25–27 μ, width 10–12 with a L/W ratio of about 2.25–2.5:1. Striae 27 in 10 μ, 7 partecta at a ring.

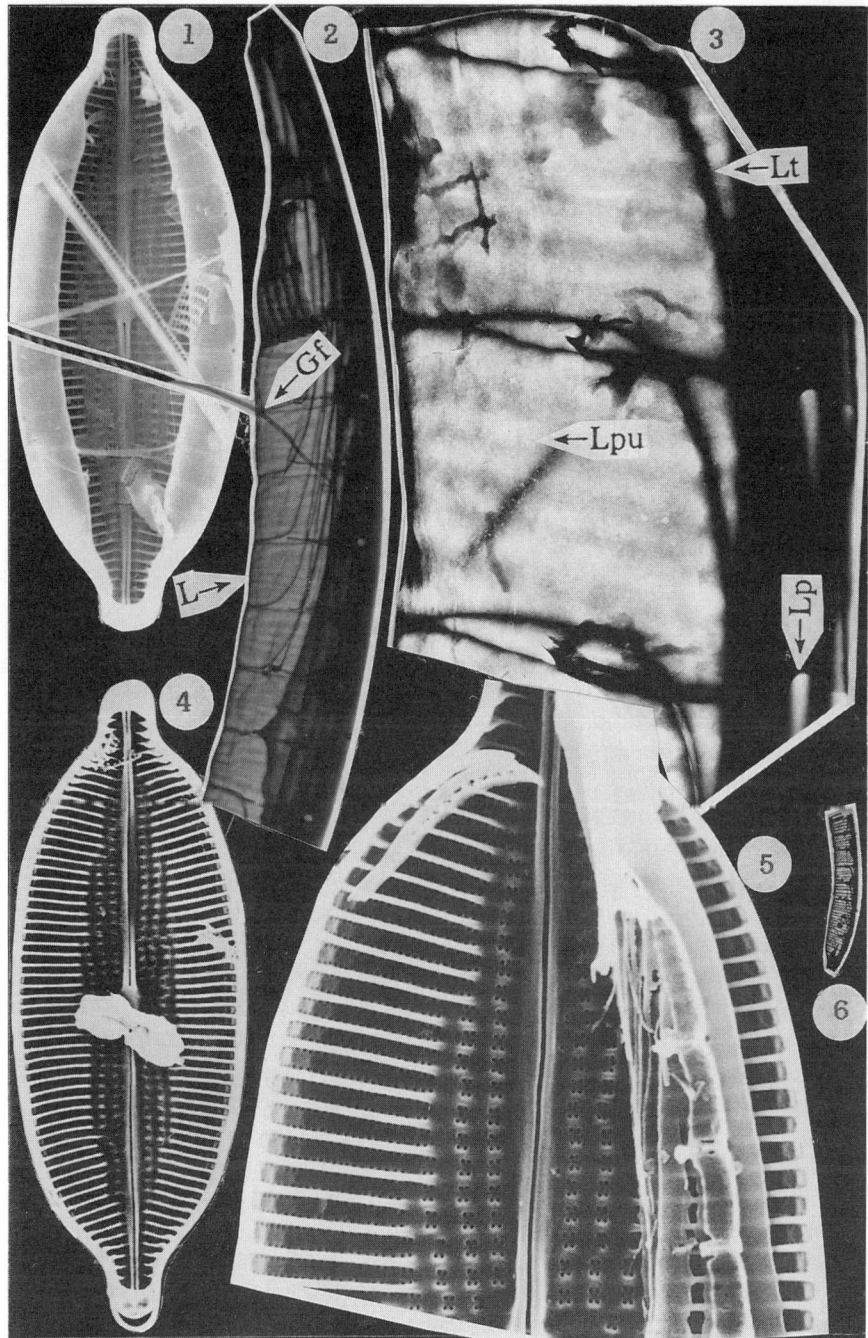

Plate 2. Figs. 1-6. *Mastogloia qionzhouensis*. 1, SEM x3500 internal valve showing partectal ring; 4, SEM x3600 external valve showing hyaline lines and costae; 2-3, 6, TEM x7200 x28500 x1500 showing partecta (L), gelatinous film (Gf), partectal pores (Lp) and partectal tubes (Lt); 5, SEM x9000 internal valve showing two zones of valve and raphe.

Comparative Material. Shulze #96a at the ANSP.

14. *M. indonesiana* Voigt. Rare.
Comparative Material. None available at the ANSP.

15. *M. intrita* Voigt. Plate 7, Figs. 1–2. Frequent.
Foged 1975, Plate 31, 16/20.
Comparative Material. None available at the ANSP.

16. *M. jaoi* Voigt. Plate 7, Fig. 3. Frequent.
This species is similar to *M. braunii*. In *M. jaoi*. the partecta are equal in size and unequal in *M. braunii*.
Comparative Material. None available at the ANSP.

17. *M. jelinecki* Grunow. Rare.
Foged 1975, p. 31 Montgomery and Miller 1978 in Vol. II Plate 129, Plate G.H., Plate 130/A,B.
Comparative Material. A–ct and Mott #320 at the ANSP.

18. *M. jelinecki* var. *extensa* Voigt. Plate 7, Fig. 4. Rare.
Comparative Material. A–Gc #35229 at the ANSP.

19. *M. lemniscata* Leud. Fortm. Frequent.
Comparative Material. None available at the ANSP.

20. *M. lentiformis* Voigt. Plate 7, Figs. 6–9. Common.
TLM: (Plate 7; Fig. 6) Valve lentiform. ends obtuse. Length 8–10 µ width 6–7u with a L/W ratio of 5.3–1.4:1. Raphe straight, lateral areas unobservable under the LM. Stria indistinct, radiate 32 in 10 µ. Largest partectum in the centre, others smaller.

External valve SEM (Plate 7, Fig. 7): Striae are slightly radiate at the centre of the valve, becoming more so toward the valve apices. Puncta are slightly elongate transapically. The lateral areas are separated from the axial areas by an apical silicious rib and a single row of puncta. Central area small and not connected to the lateral area. The raphe ends stop at the central area as tiny openings. Distal raphe ends curve slightly in the same direction at the valve apices and extend onto the valve mantle.

Internal valve face (Plate 7, Fig. 8): Double rows of puncta between the transverse costae. Raphe fissure is sinuous, flexed at about the midpoint. Partectum are attached to the intercalary band such that their attached sides appear flush with the valve margins. The largest partectum is situated in the centre of the partectal ring, becoming abruptly smaller.

Comparative Material. None available at the ANSP.

21. *M. macdonaldii* Greville. Plate 7, Fig. 5. Rare.
Comparative Material. None available at the ANSP.

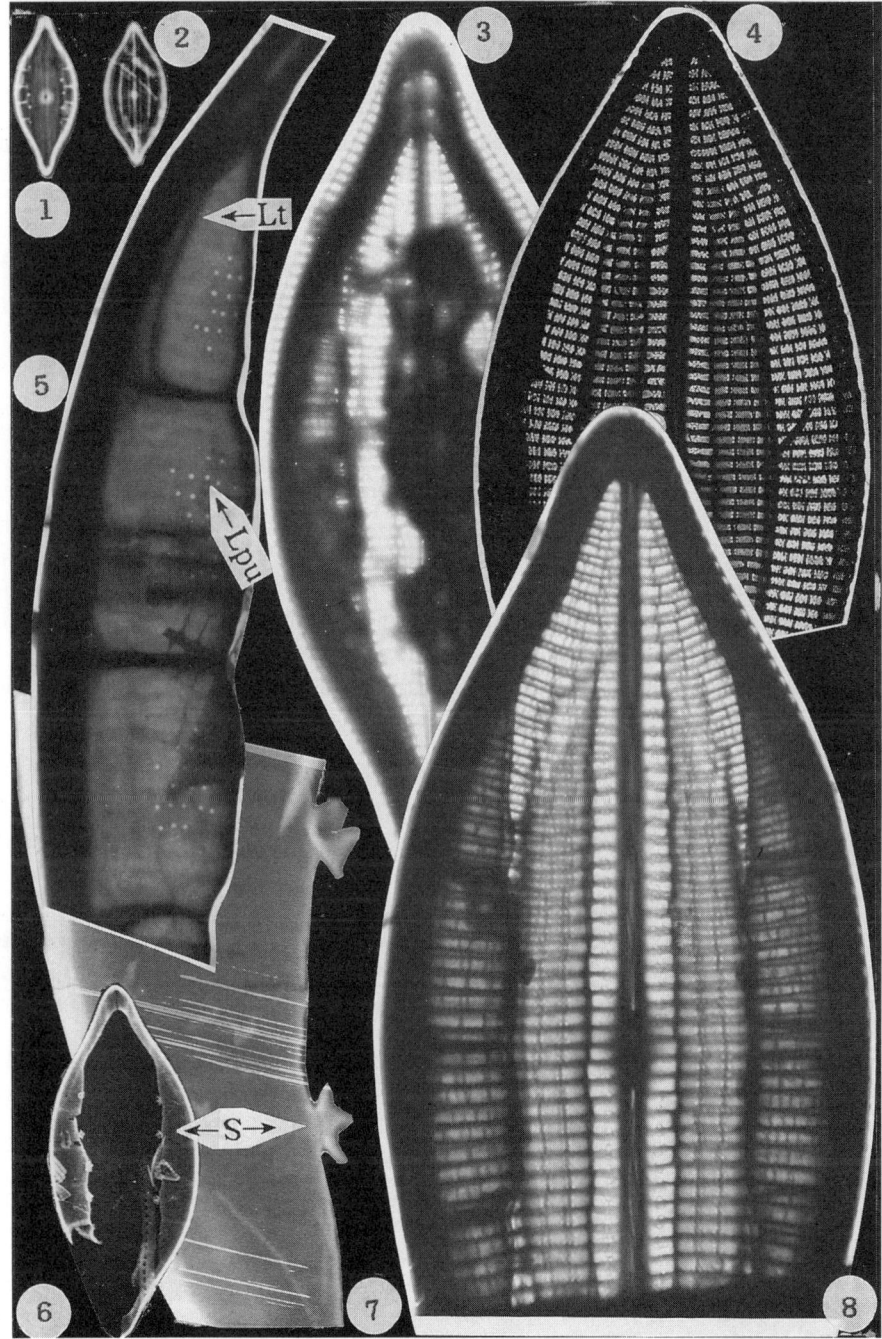

Plate 3. Figs. 1-8. *Mastogloia xishaensis*. 1-2, LM x1000; 3, 8, TEM x4350, x7200 focus on internal valve; 4, TEM x5400 external valve; 5, TEM x10800 partectal ring, showing partectal puncta (Lpu) and partectal tubes; 6, 7, SEM x2330 x19500 spinula.

22. *M. mauritiana* Brun. Plate 7, Figs. 10–12. Common.
    Comparative Material. None available at the ANSP.

23. *M. mauritiana* var. *capitata* Voigt. Plate 8, Fig. 1. Rare.
    M. mauritiana var. *capitata* Voigt can be compared with *M. mauritiana* var. *rostrata* which has a similar structure valve face structure. Thus, the separate identities of *M. mauritiana* var. *capitata* and *M. mauritiana* var. *rostrata* seem open to question.
    Comparative Material. None available at the ANSP.

24. *M. mediterranea* Hustedt. Very rare.
    Paddock and Kemp. 1990, 5 (1) 101, fig. 129a.
    Comparative Material. None available at the ANSP.

25. *M. mediterranea* var. *elliptica* Voigt. Plate 5, Fig. 5; Plate 6, Figs. 1–4. Common.
    Paddock and Kemp. 1990. 5 (1), fig. 19a, 19b, fig. 57.
    Valve rhombic-naviculoid. Ends obtuse to slightly rostrate. Length 16–25 µ, 6–8.1 µ broad with a L/W ration of about 2.3–3.3:1. Raphe straight or slightly sinuous. Axial area narrow, central area small. Transapical striae parallel near the centre of the valve, becoming slightly radiate towards the apices. Valve exterior with hyaline pseudoconopea (Plate 5, Fig. 5). Valve interior with partectal ring and a spinule (usually loose) on the inner margin of the partectum, about 1.4 µ broad, inner margin convex. (Plate 6, Fig. 3), two partectum per side.

Habitat. Marine

Distribution. Collected in washings of *Hydroclathrus clathratus* from the lower tidal area in Chenghang.
    I believe Paddock and Kemp (1990; figs. 19b and 57) to be *M. mediterranea* var. *elliptica*. This species is similar to *M. xishaensis* and *M. omissa*. Differences are listed in Table 1. The separate identities of *M. mediterranea* var. *elliptica*, *M. xishaensis* and *M. omissa* would seem open to question.
    Comparative Material. None available at the ANSP.

26. *M. minutissima* Voigt. Very rare.
    (*M. liaotungensis*). Stephens and Gibson (1980, 33:244, figs. 20–23)
    Comparative Material. None available at the ANSP.

27. *M. neorugosa* Voigt. Plate 8, Fig. 5. Rare.
    (*M. rugosa*).
    Comparative Material. None available at the ANSP.

28. *M. obesa* Cleve Rare.
    Comparative Material. None available at the ANSP.

30. *M. peragalli* Cleve. Common.

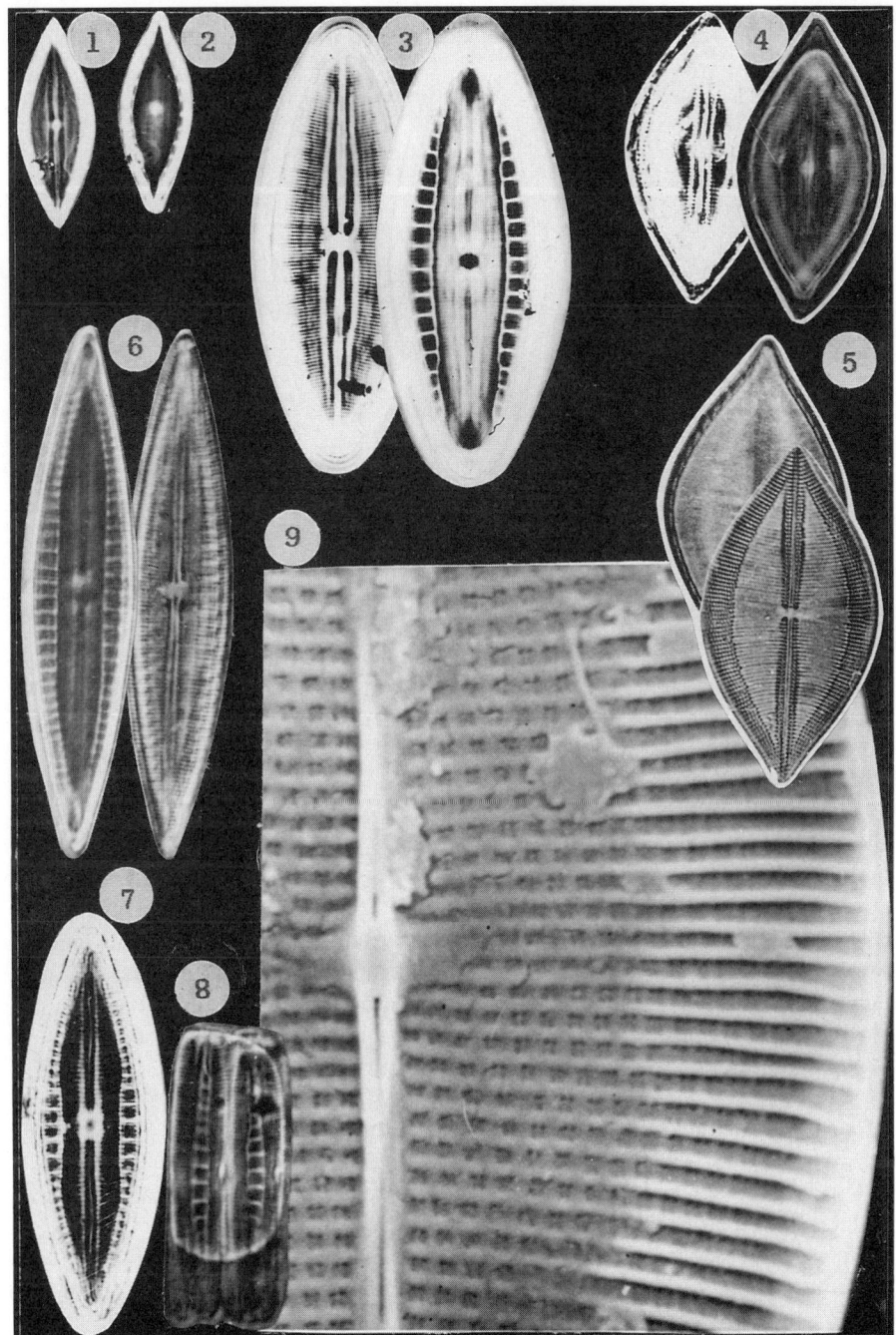

Plate 4. Figs. 1-3. *Mastogloia baldjikiana*. LM x1000. Figs. 4-5, *Mastogloia cruciata* LM x1000. (fig. 5. from Voigt 1942). Fig. 6, *Mastogloia brauni* var. *elongata* LM x1000. Figs. 7-8, *Mastogloia brauni* LM x1000. Fig. 9, *Mastogloia corallum* TEM x100000, external valve showing areolae arranged in groups of four between adjacent costae, in each group of four.

Table 1
M. mediterranea var. *elliptica* compared with similar species.

	Length x End width(μ)		Transverse striae·10μ^{-1}	Partecta· ring^{-1}
M. mediterranea v. *elliptica*	16–25x 6–8.1 2.3–3.3:1	obtuse to slightly rostrate	30–38	1–2
M. xishaensis	18–24x 8.5–9.4 2.2–2.4:1	considerably rostrate	28–32	5
M. omissa	16–30x 7.5–12 2.1–2.5:1	slightly rostrate	22–25	5

Yohn and Gibson (1982, 25 (6):p. 283, figs. 31–36.)
Comparative Material. Tempere and Peragallo 2 # 268 at the ANSP.

31. *M. pisciculus* Cleve. Plate 8, Figs. 8–11. Frequent.
Plate 8, fig. 8. of this paper is same as Foged (1975; fig. XV/11).
Comparative Material. None available at the ANSP.

32. *M. pseudexilis* Voigt. Frequent.
Comparative Material. #15411 at the ANSP.

33. *Mastogloia pseudonuiensis* Liu sp. nov. Plate 1, Figs. 1–9; Plate 6, Figs. 5–8. Rare.
Valva rhombeo-lanceolata, potis obtusa, 17–21 μ longa, 6–7.3 μ lata: 2.7–2.8-plo longiora quam latior. Raphe recta, area axillary angusta, nodulo centrali lateraliter producto, in utroque raphe latere per lineam longam hyalinam ad nodulum centralem conjunctam interruptis. Striae transversae punctatae leniter radiantes, 29–40 in 10 μ. Partecta inaequales, mediis majoribus 1.3 μ latus, a latere minores < 1 μ latus. Marginibus interioxibus convexis.

Type locality. Chenghang, Xisha Islands, Guangdong Province, China.
Coll: Cheng Zhaodi and Liu Junmin. 5 March 1982 (SX820305 - 6 (4) Holotype).
I have seen specimens in which three partecta are attached on one side and four partecta are attached on the opposite side of the same valve.
This species is similar to *M. lentiformis*, *M. mediterranea* var. *elliptica*, *M. exilis*, *M. pumila* cf. *africana*, *M. minutissima* and *M. intrita*. Differences are set out in Table 2.
TEM and SEM: External girdle (Plate 1, Fig. 8). double rows of puncta (areola) continue onto the mantle from the valve face, covering the entire mantle. Partectal pores are quite remote from parent partecta toward the valve apices. These pores (Plate 1, Fig. 8). open at an angle to the apical axis at the junction of the intercalary band and the valve matle.

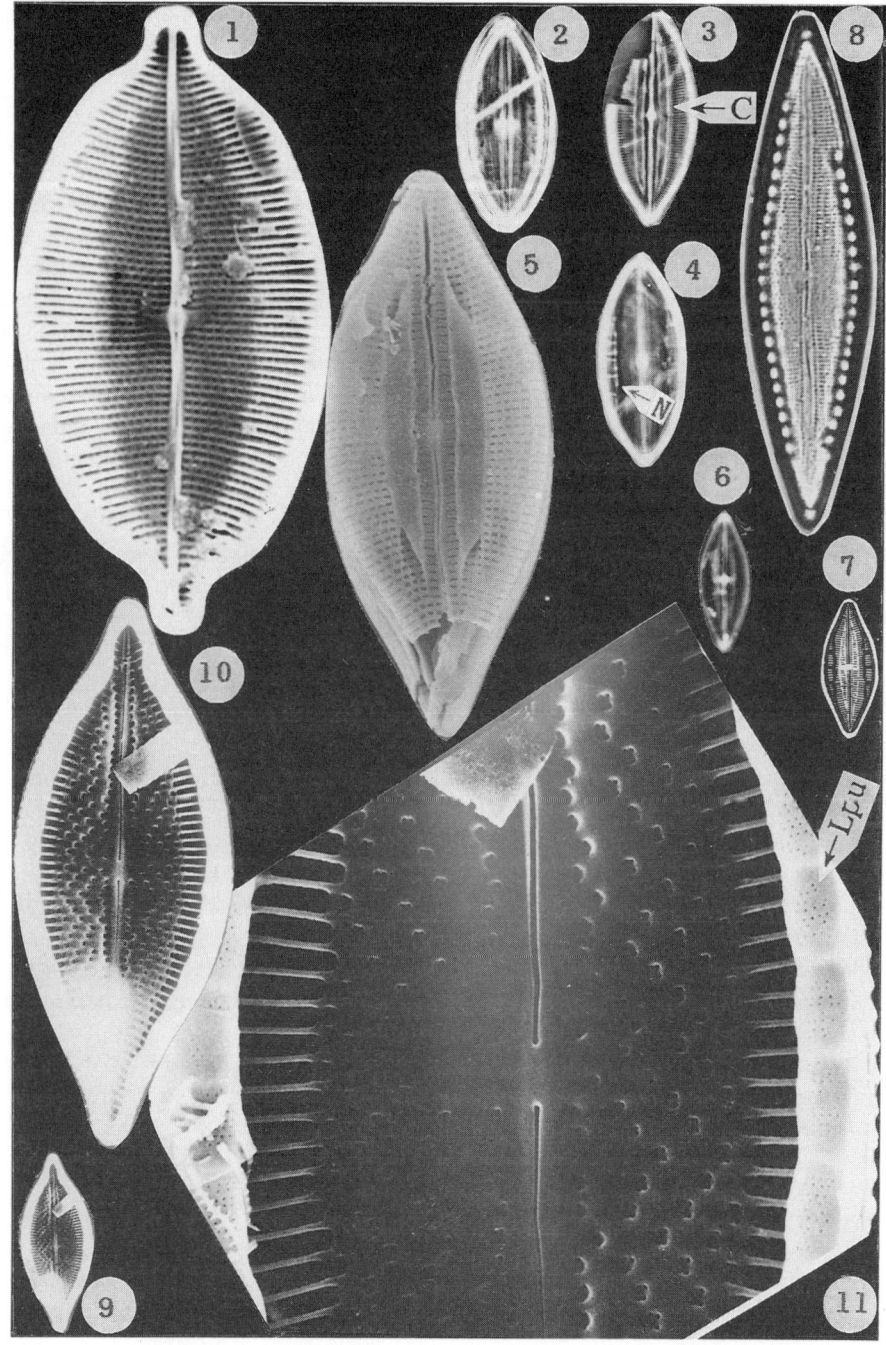

Plate 5. Fig. 1, *Mastogloia corallum* SEM x3000 external valve with costae fine, more robust near the valve margin. Figs. 2-4, *Mastogloia hustedtii*. LM x1000 showing raised plaques (arrow) on inner margin. Fig. 5, *Mastogloia mediterranea* v. *elliptica* SEM x3600 external valve showing hyaline pseudoconopea. Figs. 6-7, *Mastogloia exilis* LM x1000 (fig. 7. from Hustedt 1985). Fig. 8, *Mastogloia hainanensis* LM x1000. Figs. 9-11, *Mastogloia depressa* SEM x900, x2700, x9000 internal valve showing partectal ring and partecta punctae (Lpu).

External valve face (Plate 1, Figs. 3 and 6). Striae are slightly radiate in the centre of the valve, becoming more so toward the valve apices and are formed into double rows of small rounded puncta between the costae on another plane. Narrow lateral areas are formed by a longitudinales lineas leniter sinuosa, running parallel to margin of valve ca. 30 in 10 μ. The transapically expanded central area connects with the lateral areas. Raphe fissures are almost straight except near their midpoints. Proximate raphe ends in the central area as tiny circular expansions. Distal portion of the raphe fissures curve slightly in the same direction at the valve apices and extend onto the valve mantle.

Internal valve face (Plate 1, Figs. 4 and 7–9). Transverse silicious costae are interrupted by solid lateral areas. Double rows of puncta are situated on another transversely dilated central nodule. Raphe fissures are slightly sinuous and are bordered by thickened axial costae. Proximal raphe ends at the central nodule, appearing undifferentiated. Distal raphe fissures curve slightly in the same direction at the valve apices and extend onto the valve mantle. Partecta are attached to the intercalary band such that their attached sides appear flush with the valve margins. The largest partecta are situated in the centre of the partectal band, rather abruptly becoming smaller toward the ends of the bands. Small partectal punctate are shown in Plate 1, Fig. 8. Inner margin of partecta convex. Therefore, 81/949, 86/1030/1031 in *Marine Benthic Diatoms in China Vol. 2* must belong in this species.

34. *M. pumila* (Grun.) Cleve. Frequent.
    Comparative Material. Gen. coll. #51549a, #52304a #63000a at the ANSP.

35. *M. pumila* var. *papuarum* Chotnoky. Plate 8, Figs. 12–14. Frequent *(M. pumila)*.
    Stephens and Gibson (1980, 33:p. 242, figs. 9–11.)
    Comparative Material. None available at the ANSP.

36. **M. pumila* var. *rennellensis* Foged. Plate 8, Figs. 3–4. Rare.
    Foged (1957, p. 57, Plate 5, Fig. 2)
    Valve elongate oval, one end wider than the others. Valve length 25–28 μ width 9 μ, with a ratio of 3:1. Raphe straight. Axial area narrow. Central area expands laterally into H-shape. Transapical strial fine ca. 30 in 10 μ.
    Partectum at the centre larger, width ca 1.5 μ; other smaller, width ca. < 1 μ, inner margin convex.
    The Xisha specimens have closer striae and narrower valves than Foged (1957) figured.

Habitat. Marine, benthic.

Distribution. Collected in washings of *Hydroclathrus clathratus* from lower tidal levels in Chengha, Xisha Islands, Guangdong. Rennell Island, British Solomon Islands. (Foge, 1957).
    Comparative Material. None available at the ANSP.

37. *Mastogloia qionzhouensis* Liu sp. nov. Plate 2, Figs. 1–6. Rare.

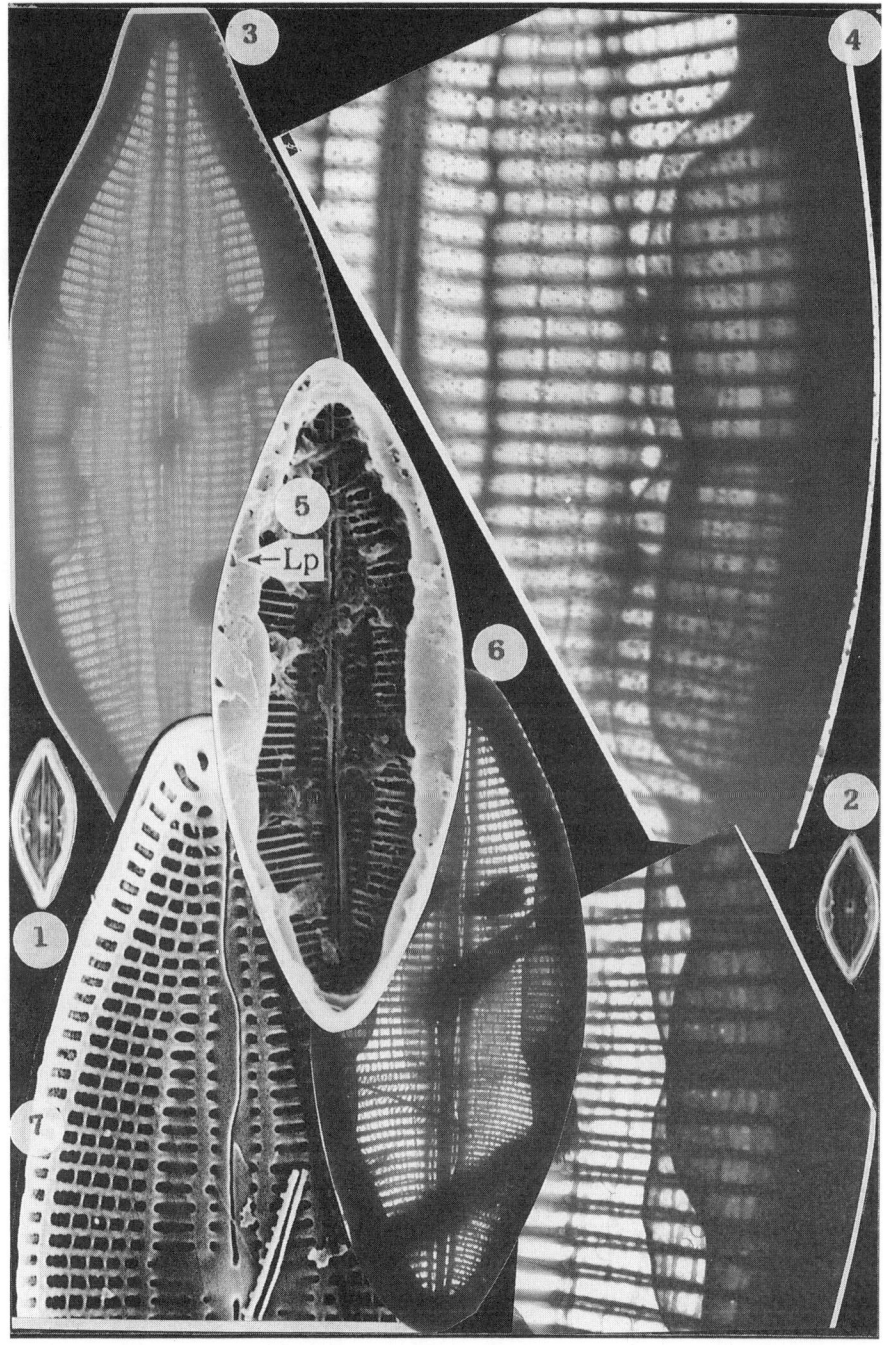

Plate 6. Fig. 1-4, *Mastogloia mediterranea* v. *elliptica*. 1-2, LM. x1000; 3, TEM x5400; internal valve showing partectal ring and spitze on inner margin; 4, TEM x15000. Figs. 5-8, *Mastogloia pseudonuiensis*. 5, SEM x5000; 6, TEM x5400; 7, SEM x9000; 8, TEM x15000.

Table 2
The characters of *M. pseudonuiensis* compared with similar species.

	Length x Width	Transverse striae·10μm^{-1} L/W	Central area expanded (or not) laterally into H-shaped area (present or absent)			Partectal number· band^{-1}	Raphe straight or leniter sinuosa (si)		
			TLM	TSM	TLM		TSM	TEM	TEM
M. pseudonuiensis	17–21 x 6–7.3 2.7–2.8:1	29–40	unable to resolve	yes	yes	3 or 4 largest 1–2 in the middle	si.	si.	si.
M. lentiformis	8–10 x 6–7 1.3–1.4:1	32	not	not	not	3 largest 1 in the middle	si.	si.	si.
M. mediterranea var. elliptica	16–25 x 6–8.1 2.3–3.3:1	30–30	not	not	not same size	1–2			
M. exilis	15–20 x 6–6 2.5:1	33	yes		4–5	si. same size			
M. pumila cf. *africana*	29–30 x 8–9 3.3–3.6:1	24	yes	yes	2–4	si. same size	si.		
M. minutissima	14–18 x 5–6	26–28 2.8–3:1	unable to resolve	yes	yes	1–2 same size	si.	si.	si.
M. intrita	32 x 8 3.2–4:1	28–29	unable to resolve	yes	yes	4–6 2–3 larger ones in the middle	si.	si.	si.

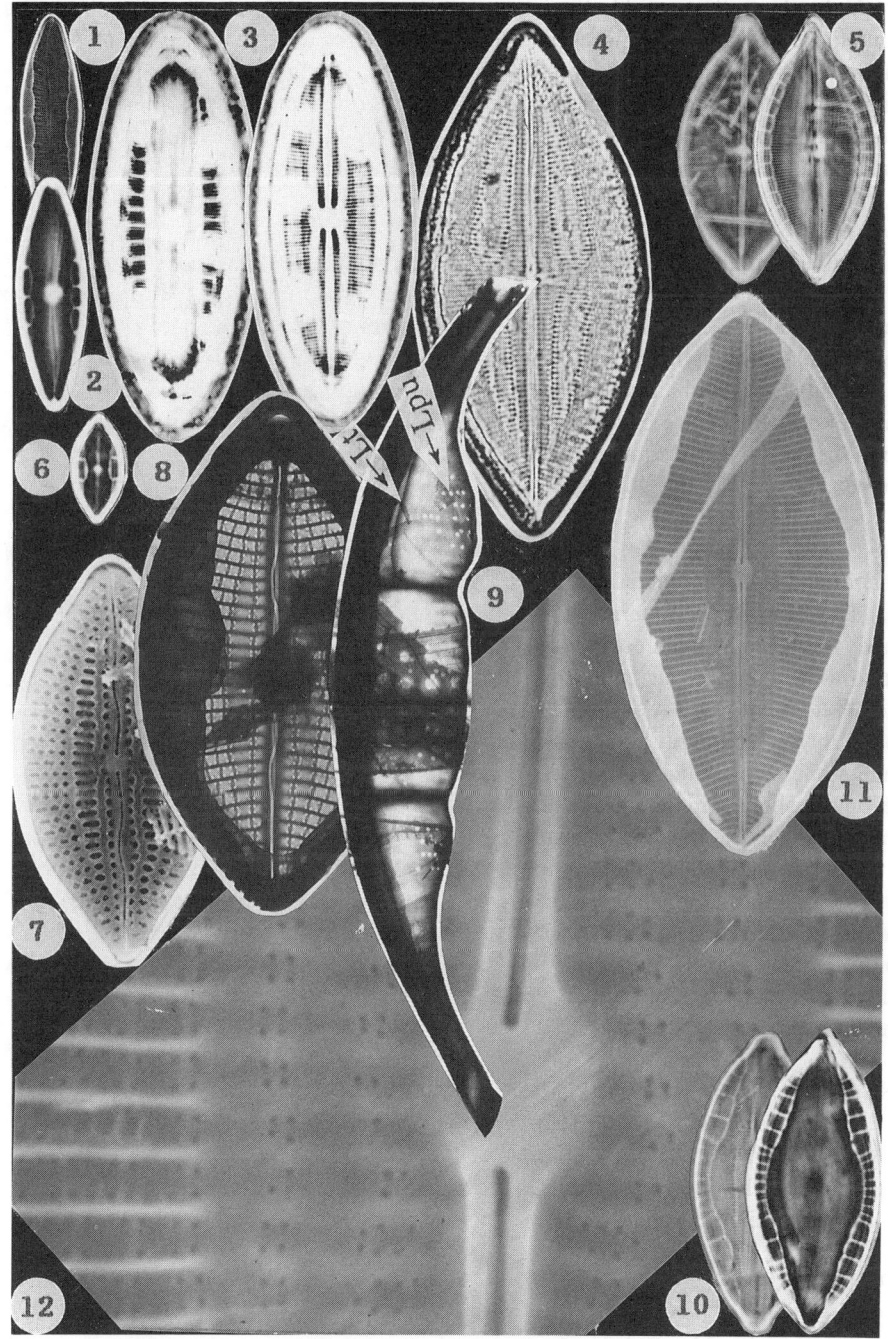

Plate 7. Figs. 1-2, *Mastogloia intrita*. 1, SEM; 2, LM x1000. Fig. 3. *Mastogloia jaoi*. LM x1000. Fig. 4, *Mastogloia jelinecki* var. *extensa*. LM x1000. Fig. 5, *Mastogloia macdonaldii*. LM x1000. Figs. 6-9, *Mastogloia lentiformis*. 6, LM x1000; 7, SEM x4400; 8, TEM x5400; 9, TEM x8700 external, internal valve and a band showing external valve, internal valve, partectal ring and partectal puncta (Lpu). Figs. 10-12. *Mastogloia mauritiana*. 10, LM x1000. 11, SEM x2250 internal valve showing partectal ring; 12, SEM x18500 internal valve showing valve face at proximal raphe end.

Valve late elliptica, 23–25 µ longa, 9–10 µ lata, ad potos producta, Propemodo capitatia; 2.5–2.8–pto longiora quam latior. Raphe recta ver leviter undulata, fronte in duobus zonis divisa, zona interiore lanceolata sine costis, aut uno aut 3–5 lineary hyatinis longitudinatibus praebenti, zona exteriore et timbo costos fortes et puncta regularia grossa praebentis, costata costis 26–28 in 10 µ. transversatibus. Locutamenta 6.5 in 10 µ, marginibus interioribus ve convexis under the LM.

Typus. SX 820305 — 6 (4). FBUA.

Valves broadly elliptical in valve view with produced almost capitate poles. 23–25 µ long, 9–10 µ broad with a L/W ratio of about 2.5–2.8:1. Raphe straight or slightly undulate. Valve face divided into two zones: an inner lanceolate zone with few costae, but bearing between three-five longitudinal hyaline lines from nearby raphe to 1/2 width of the valve face and an outer zone which has strong transverse costae, 26–28 in 10 µ, parallel near the centre becoming slightly radiate near the poles. Partecta reach almost up to the ends. Nearly equal in size, 6.5 in 10 µ. Inner margin of partecta flat or slightly convex.

Type locality. Chenghang, Xisha Islands, Guangdong Province, China. Coll.: Cheng Zhaodi and Liu Junmin. 5 March 1982 (SX820305 — 6 (4) Holotype).

TEM and SEM: External valve face (Plate 2, Fig. 4). Valve broadly elliptical in valve view. Raphe fissures are almost straight except near their midpoints (only leniter sinuosa). Proximal raphe ends stop in the central area as tiny circular expansions. Valve face divided into two zones: an inner lanceolate zone with few costae, but bearing between three-five longitudinal hyaline lines from nearby raphe to 1/2 wide of valve face and another zone which has strong transverse costae, 26–28 in 10 µ parallel near centre becoming slightly radiate near the pole. Double rows of puncta are situated on another plane between the transverse costae.

Internal valve face (Plate 2, Figs. 1 and 5). Transerve silicious ribs are interrupted by 3–5 longitudinal hyalines. Double rows of puncta are situated on another plane between the transverse ribs. Raphe fissures almost straight except near their midpoints (only leniter sinuosa). Partecta equal 11–12 ring, inner margin flat or slightly convex and shows partecta (L), partectal pores (Lp) and partectal tube (Lt) (Plate 2, Figs. 2 and 3).

38. *M. quinquecostata* Gru., Plate 8, Fig. 2. Rare.

Montgomery and Miller (1978, Vol. II Plate 138, figs. A–E; pt. 139, figs. C. D); Foged (1975, p. 33; 15/7, 8); Ricard (1975b, 11 (1): p. 58, Plate 4, figs. 32–35); Van Landingham (1967–79, p. 2165); Paddock and Kemp (1990, 5 (1)).

Comparative Material. None available at the ANSP.

39. *M. sulcata* Cleve. Very rare.

Foged (1975, p. 34, VI/6).

Comparative Material. None available at the ANSP.

40. *Mastogloia xishaensis* Liu sp. nov. Plate 3, Figs. 1–8. Rare.

Valvae late rhombeo-navicula, apicibus rostratis, rostrum 2–3 µ longa, valva 18–

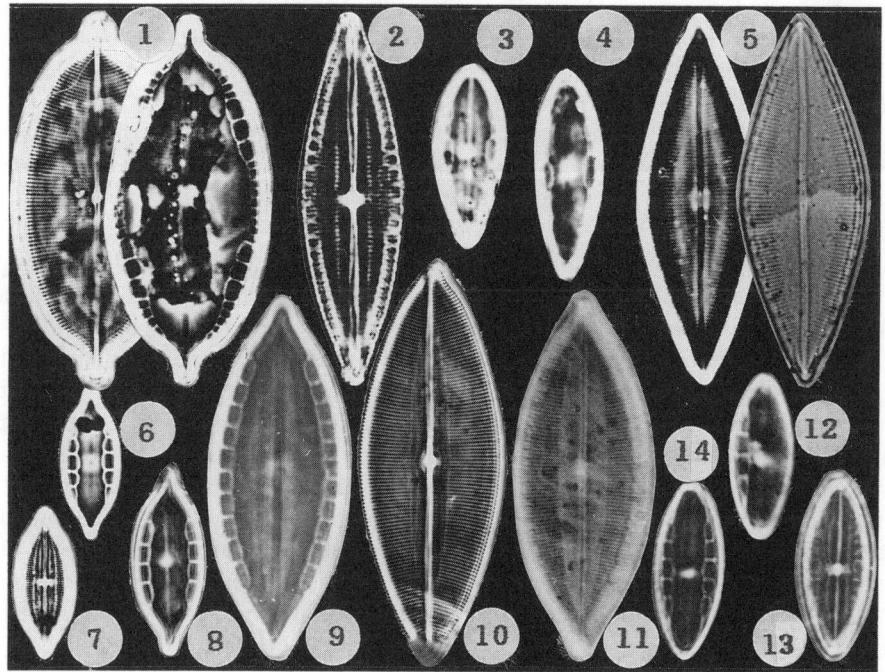

Plate 8 Fig. 1, *Mastogloia mauritiana* var. *capitata* LM x1000. Fig. 2, *Mastogloia quinquecostata* LM x1000. Figs. 3-4, *Mastogloia pumila* var. *rennellensis* LM x1000. Fig. 5, *Mastogloia neorugosa* LM x1000. Figs. 6-7, *Mastogloia exilis* LM x1000. Figs. 8-11, *Mastogloia pisciculus* LM x1000. Figs. 12-14, *Mastogloia pumila* var. *papuarum* LM x1000.

24 μ longa, 8.5–9 μ lata; 2.2–2.5-plo longiora quam latiora. Raphe recta, inter leviter costas longitudinales immergit, area centrali pusillo, punclis transversalibus prope polos leviter radiatis, 30–33 in 10 μ, punctis longitudinales 24 in 10 μ. Loculi valvae versus non extensi, in uno lutera 5, marginibus interioribus convexis, ad marginibus interioribus spinis.

Typus. SX820305 - 6 (4), FBUA

Valves rhombic-naviculoid with conspicuously rostrate ends. Length of ends about 2–3 μ. Length of valves 18–24 μ, width 8.5–9.4 μ with a L/W ratio of about 2.2–2.25:1. Raphe straight, between two narrow longitudinal ribs. Axial area narrow. Central area small. Striae fine. slightly radial, about 30–33 in 10 μ, crossed by slightly wavy longitudinal ribs, 24 in 10 μ. Partecta not leading to the ends, nearly equal in size and form except for the partectum at the end (triangular-shaped), 5 per band. Inner margin of partecta convex with tiny spitze or nipples.

Type locality. Chenghang, Xisha Islands, Guangdong Province, China. *Col.* Cheng Zhaodi and Lin Junmin. 5 March 1982 (SX820305 - 6 (4) Holotype).

This species is similar to *M. exilis*, but the former has tiny spitze or nipples; lateral area not connected by a central area; the latter has no spitze or nipples and the lateral areas connected by a central area. This species is also similar to *M. mediterranea* var. *elliptica*, but *M. xishaensis* has no hyaline pseudoconopea and *M. mediterranea* var. *elliptica* has a hyaline pseudoconopea. *Mastogloia* sp in *Marine Benthic Diatoms in China* Vol. 2. 87/1049–1051 must belong to *M. xishanensis*.

TEM and SEM: External valve face (Plate 3, Fig. 4). Striae are parallel near the centre of the valve, becoming slightly radiate towards apices. Double rows of puncta are situated between the costae on another plane. The transverse costae are interrupted by lateral narrow areas, nearly parallel to margin of valve ca. 30–33 in 10 μ, crossed by longitudinal lineas (leniter sinussa ca. 24 in 10 μ). Raphe fissures are almost straight, between two longitudinal sender costae (under LM). A longitudinal row of transapically elongate punctae separate the lateral areas from the axial areas (under the TEM).

Internal valve face (Plate 3, Figs. 3 and 8). Transverse silicious costae are interrupted by solid lateral areas. Double rows of punctae are situated on another plane between the transverse costae. The lateral areas not connected by central nodule. Raphe fissures are slightly sinuous and are bordered by a longitudinal row of transapically elongate punctae. Proximal raphe ends at the central nodule, appearing undifferentiated. Distal raphe ends are undifferentiated, stopping at the base of small terminal nodules. Partecta are attached to the intercalary band, such that their attached sides appear flush with the valve margin. Partecta same size, 4–5 per band, inner margin of partecta flat or slightly convex, with tiny spinula. Small partectal puncta are shown in Plate 3, Fig. 5.

List of *Mastogloia* species of the group *Sulcatae*.
1. *M. baldjikiana* Grunow.
2. *M. brauni* Grunow.
3. *M. brauni* cf. *elongata* Voigt
4. *M. corallum*. Paddock and Kemp
5. *M. cruciata* (Leud.-Fort.) Cl.
6. *M. cruciata* var. *elliptica* Voigt
7. *M. cucurbita* Voigt
8. *M. depressa* Hustedt
9. *M. elegantula* Hustedt
10. *M. exilis* Hustedt
11. *M. grunowi* A. Schmidt
12. *M. hainanensis* Voigt
13. *M. hustedtii* Meister
14. *M. indonesiana* Voigt
15. *M. intrita* Voigt
16. *M. jaoi* Voigt
17. *M. jelinecki* Grunow.
18. *M. jelinecki* var. *extensa* Voigt
19. *M. lemniscata* Leud. Fortm.
20. *M. lentiformis* Voigt.
21. *M. macdonaldii* Greville
22. *M. mauritiana* Brun.
23. *M. mauritiana* var. *capitala* Voigt
    (aff. *M. mauritiana* var. *rostrata*)

Fig. 1 Diagram showing a key to the species of the group Sulcatae (Mastogloia). 1, Mastogloia baldjikiana. 2, Mastogloia brauni. 3, Mastogloia brauni cf. elogata. 4, Mastogloia corallum. 5, Mastogloia cruciata. 6, Mastogloia cruciata v. elliptica. 7, Mastogloia cucurbita. 8, Mastogloia depressa. 9, Mastogloia elegantula. 10, Mastogloia exilis. 11, Mastogloia grunowi. 12, Mastogloia hainanensis. 13, Mastogloia hustedtii. 14, Mastogloia indonesiana. 15, Mastogloia intrita. 16, Mastogloia jaoi. 17, Mastogloia jelinecki. 18, Mastogloia jelinecki v. extensa. 19, Mastogloia lemniscata. 20, Mastogloia lentiformis. 21, Mastogloia macdonaldii. 22, Mastogloia mauritiana. 23, Mastogloia mauritiana v. capitata. 24, Mastogloia mediterranea. 25, Mastogloia mediterranea v. elliptica. 26, Mastogloia minutissima. 27, Mastogloia neorugosa. 28, Mastogloia obesa. 29, Mastogloia omissa. 30, Mastogloia peragalli. 31, Mastogloia pisciculus. 32, Mastogloia pseudexilis. 33, Mastogloia pseudonuiensis n. sp. 34, Mastogloia pumila. 35, Mastogloia pumila v. papuarum. 36, Mastogloia pumila v. rennellensis. 37, Mastogloia qionzhouensis n. sp.. 38, Mastogloia quinquecostata. 39, Mastogloia sulcata. 40, Mastogloia xishaensis n. sp..

24. *M. mediterranea* Hust.
25. *M. mediterranea* var. *elliptica* (Agardh) Cleve
26. *M. minutissima* Voigt
27. *M. neorugosa* Voigt
28. *M. obesa* Cleve
29. *M. omissa* Voigt
30. *M. peragalli* Cleve
31. *M. pisciculus* Cleve
32. *M. pseudexilis* Voigt
33. *M. pseudonuiensis* n. sp.
34. *M. pumila* (Grun.) Cleve
35. *M. pumila* var. *papuarum* Chotnoky
36. *M. pumila* var. *rennellensis* Foged
37. *M. qionzhouensis* n. sp.
38. *M. qunquecostata* Grunow
39. *M. sulcata* Cleve
40. *M. xishaensis* n. sp.

DISCUSSION

The group *Sulcatae* is characterized by the presence of lateral areas. Forty species of marine diatoms belonging to Hustedt's (1933) group *Sulcatae* of the genus *Mastogloia* have been recorded from the Xisha Islands, South China Sea. Ten of these have been studied by TEM and SEM.

The species studied include: *M. corallum, M. depressa, M. hustedtii, M. intrita, M. lentiformis, M. mauritiana, M. mediterranea* var. *elliptica M. pseudonuiensis, M. qionzhouensis* and *M. xishaensis*.

In the species studied, the lateral areas connect the central area into a H-shape, e.g., *M. pseudonuiensis, M. exilis* and *M. minutissima*; in other species studied, the lateral areas are not connected by a central area into a H-shape, e.g., *M. lentiformis* and *M. xishaensis*. A thin wing-like projection (canopeum) extends over a single longitudinal furrow on each side of the raphe, e.g., *M. hustedtii*. Longitudinal costae were observed in *M. lentiformis, M. pseudonuiensis,* and *M. xishaensis*. Longitudinal hyaline lines were observed in *M. mauritiana* and *M. qionzhouensis*. Partecta are isomorphic in some species of this group, e.g., *M. baldikiana, M. depressa, M. hainanensis, M. indonesiana, M. lemniscata,* and *M. macdonaldii*, but not in others, e.g., *M. brauni, M. brauni* cf. *elongata, M. corallum, M. lentiformis, M. mauritiana, M. mauritiana* var. *capitata, M. peragalli, M. pseudonuiensis, M. pumila,* and *M. pumila* var. *renellensis*. Papilla-like structures are present on the partecta of *M. mediterranea* var. *elliptica, M. hainanensis, M. hustedtii, M. minutissima, M. omissa* and *M. xishaensis*. Five terms have been used for the papillae, i.e.,'Spitze' (Hustedl 1933); 'Spines' (Voigt 1942); 'Nipples' (Voigt 1952); 'Nodules siticeux' (Ricard 1975) and 'Spitzen' (Paddock *et al.* 1990). But these papilla-like structures are not stable; I have seen individuals in which one nipple is attached to one side but not the other of the same valve and are easily lost. Partectal puncta are present in *M. depressa, M. pseudonuieusis, M. qionzhouensis* and *M. xishaensis*. The partectal tubes of *M. qionzhoueusis* more or less develop on the same plane as the partecta and are oriented towards the valve apices (Plate 2, Fig. 2), which belong to the 'locular type 2' of Stephens *et al.* (1980).

The basal structure of the valve is divided up as follows:

1. *Complete costae.* Internal valve structure appears as transverse costae with rows of areolae (puncta) between costae. The transverse costae extend all the way across the valve except where interrupted by lateral areas, e.g., *M. mediterranea* var. *elliptica*, *M. hustedtii*, *M. lentiformis*, *M. pseudonuiensis* and *M. xishaensis*.

2. *Transverse costae.* Transverse costae extend all the way across the valve from fine to robust, e.g., *M. corallum*.

3. *Marginal costae.* Transverse costae which are only marginal as opposed to complete costae, e.g., *M. depressa*, *M. mauritianna* and *M. qionzhouensis*.

Internal raphe fissures of the ten species included in this study are similar. Raphe fissures appear nearly straight and stop at undifferentialed central and terminal nodules.

External raphe fissures of these species are more varied than the internal system, e.g., *M. xishaensis*. In *M. pumila* var. *papuarum* they are almost straight on the external valve. They curve in the same direction at the valve apices where they extend onto the mantle. In contrast, the external raphe fissures of *M. lentiformis*, *M. hustedtii*, and *M. pseudonuiensis* are distinctly flexed on the external valve. They also curve in the same direction as they extend onto the mantle.

ACKNOWLEDGEMENTS

I wish to express my sincere thanks to Dr C.W. Reimer, Curator, Diatom Herbarium, Academy of Natural Sciences, Philadelphia, for inviting me to visit the collection. This visit was sponsored by Jessup-McHenry Fund Committee. My thanks are also due to Dr Reimer for help with the manuscript. Also, I wish to thank Prof. Cheng Zhaodi and Prof. Lin Junmin for the collection of material. I wish to acknowledge the technical assistance of Mrs Ni Zimian, Mr Zhuang Weijian and Mrs Wu Qian for help with use of the electron microscopes and Prof. Brian Morton for correcting the drafts of the manuscript of this paper.

REFERENCES

Anonymous. 1975. Proposals for the standardization of diatom terminology and diagnoses. *Nova Hedwigia Beiheft* 53:323–54.

Foged, N. 1975. Some littoral diatoms from the coast of Tanzania. *Bibliotheca physiologica* 16. pp, 127.

Foged, N. 1987. Diatoms in Eastern Australia. *Bibliotheca phycologica* 41:1–274.

Hustedt, F. 1988. die Kieselalgen. In *Rabenhorst's Kryptogamenftora von Deutschiand, Osterreich und der Schweiz*. Akademische Ver-lagsgesellschafl m. b. H., Leipzig.

Jin, D.X., Cheung, Z.D., Liu, J.M. and Liu, S.C. 1982. *Benthic diatoms in China* .Vol. 1. Beijing: China Ocean Press.

Jin, D.X., Cheng, Z.D., Liu, S.C. and Ma, J.X. (in press). *Marine Benthic Diatoms in China*. Vol. 2. Beijing: China Ocean Press.

Liu, S.C., Cheng, Z.D. and Jin, D.X. 1982. Diatoms from the washings of sea weeds in the Xisha Islands, China. *Acta Scientiarum Naturatium Universitatis Amoiensis* 21:92-99.

Liu, S.C., Cheng, Z.D. and Jin, D.X. 1984. A list of diatoms from intertidal zones of Yongxiang,

Shidan, Chenghang of Xisha Islands, China. *Acta Scientiarum Naturalium Universitatis Amoiensis* 23:523–31.

Paddock, T.B.B. and Kemp, K.D. 1990. An illustrated survey of the morphotogirat features of the diatom genus *Mastogloia*. *Diatom Research* 5:73–103.

Richard, M. 1975. Utrastructure de quelques *Mastogloia* (diatom'es benthiques) marines d' lagonde Tahiti. *Protistologica* 11:49–60.

Ross, R., Cox, E.J., Karayeva, N.I., Mann, D.G., Paddock, T.B., Simonsen, B.R. and Sims, P.A. 1979. An amended terminology for the siliceous components of the diatom cell. *Nova Hedwigia Beiheft* 64:513–33.

Schmidt, A. 1983. *Atlas der Diatomaceen-Kunde*. Leipzig: O. R. Reistands. Plates 367–8, 185–88, 358.

Stephens, F.C. and Gibson, R.A. 1979. Observations of loculi and associated extra cellular material in several *Mastogloia* (Bacillariophyceae) species. *Revue algologique* 14:21–32.

Stephens, F.C. and Gibson, R.A. 1980. Ultrastructural studies of some *Mastogloia* (Bacillariophyceae) species belonging to the group *Sulcatae*. *Nova Hedwigia Beiheft* 33:219–48.

Voigt, M. 1942. Contribution to the knowledge of the diatom genus *Mastogloia*. *Journal of the Royal Microscopical Society* 62:1-20.

Voigt, M. 1951. A further contribution to the knowledge of the diatom genus *Mastogloia*. *Journal of the Royal Microscopical Society* 71:440-50, Plates 1-3.

Voigt, M. 1963. Some new and interesting *Mastogloia* from the Mediterranean area and the Far East. *Journal of the Royal Microscopical Society* 82:111-21, Plates 21-25.

Yohn, T.A. and Gibson, R.A. 1982. Marine diatoms of the Bahamas. III. *Mastogloia* Thw. ex Wm. Sm. Species of the Groups Inaequales, Lanceolatae, Sulcatae and Undulatae. *Botanica Marina* 25:277-88.

The Marine Biology of the South China Sea
(ed. B. Morton). Proceedings of the First
International Conference on the Marine
Biology of Hong Kong and the South China Sea,
Hong Kong, 28 October – 3 November 1990.
Hong Kong: Hong Kong University Press, 1993.

MARINE DIATOMS OF THE XISHA ISLANDS, SOUTH CHINA SEA. II. THREE NEW SPECIES OF DIATOMS (BACILLARIOPHYCEAE)

Liu Shicheng

Department of Biology, Xiamen University, Xiamen, China

ABSTRACT

Three new diatom taxa are described from benthic seaweeds (*Hydroclathrus clathratus*) from the intertidal zone of Chenghang, Xisha Islands, China.

INTRODUCTION

In March 1982, I received from Prof. Cheng Zhaodi and Prof. Liu Junmin, samples of the intertidal seaweed *Hydroclathrus clathratus* from the Xisha Islands of the South China Sea. It is this material reported upon here and from which was obtained three new taxa of diatoms.

MATERIALS AND METHODS

All samples were cleaned using potassium dichromate-peroxide. Slides were made according to the procedure of Reimer (1962) using Hyrax as a mounting medium. Specimens were observed under Olympus phase contrast oil immersion (LM) at 1000x magnification, a JEM-100 80kv transmitted electron microscope (TEM) and a Hitachi S52 20kv scanning electron microscope (SEM).

DESCRIPTIONS OF TAXA

Plagiogramma reimeri **Liu sp. nov.. Plate 1, Figs. 1–5.**

Valvae minutissimum, medio profunde constrictis, vittis centralibus. Striis paucis, perviis, 12–16 in 10 µ. transversis parallelis in medio debiliter radialibus in terminali. a longitudinales line at each side of axial area. 9–14.29 µ longa, 2.5–3 µ late (media constrictis) 3.1–4 µ (in dilated).

Typus. XS820305-6(4). FBUA.

Valves small, abrupt constricted in the middle, then suddenly dilated and lyriform with terminal (with narrow protracted and rounded ends) and central vittae. Puncta few, large rectangular, about 12–16 in 10 μ, Transapical striae parallel in middle to slightly radiate in the protracted ends. One longitudinal line on each side of axial area. Length 9–14.29 μ, width 2.5–3 μ (constricted in middle), 3.1–4 μ (dilated).

Allied to *Plagiogramma atomus*, but original descriptions and illustration are not clear enough to confirm identity; also figured in Schmidt (1974-1979, 211/24, 25) but of a slightly different shape and details of the striae are not shown. It is also similar in shape to *P. interruptum* var. *brevis* (Zonon 1948, p. 208, cf. 11) but, again, details of the striae are not shown.

Type locality. Chenghang, Xisha Islands, Guangdong Province, China. Coll.: Cheng Zhaodi and Lin Junmin, 5 March 1982 (SX820305-6(4) Holotype)

Nitzschia amphibioides var. *chenghaensis* Liu var. nov.. Plate 1, Figs. 6–9.

Valva lanceolata late apicibus obtuse. Striis punctatis distincte, 38 in 10 μ, punctis componentibus striis 37.8 in 10 μ. Carina valida excentrica; carina punctis 13.6 in 10 μ. 8.6 μ longa 2.4 μ lata; 3.6-plo longiora quam latior.

Typus. SX830305-6(4), FBUA.

Valve broadly lanceolate with obtuse apices. Striae distinctly punctate, 38 in 10 μ. Puncta comprising striae, 37.8 in 10 μ. Keel strongly excentric; Keel puncta, 13.6 in 10 μ. Length 8.6 μ, width 2.4 μ, with a L/W ratio of about 3.6:1.

This variety differs from the nominate species by its smaller size, striae and keel puncta. The former is of length 8.6 μ, width 2.4 μ, transapical striae 36 in 10 μ, keel puncta 13.6 in 10 μ; the latter is of length 15–20 μ, width 4–6 μ, transapical striae 15–16, keel puncta 8–10 in 10 μ.

Type locality. Chenghang, Xisha Islands, Guangdong Province, China. Coll.: Cheng Zhaodi and Lin Junmin, 5 March 1982 (SX820305-6(4) Holotype).

Mastogloia pseudograciloides Liu sp. nov.. Plate 2, Figs. 1–6; Plate 3, Figs. 1–2.

Valvae lineari-ellipticae, ad polos products, 26–33 μ longa, 10–12 μ lata; 2.6–2.7-plo longiora quam latior. Raphe recta or leviter sinuosa, area centrali parva rotunda, leniter dilatata. Striae transversae punctatae leniter radiantes, 21–25 in 10 μ. Punctis in lineas longitudinales sinuosa, 12–14 in 10 μ. loculamenta 6–7 in 10 μ, marginibus interioribus flat ve convexis.

Typus. XS820305-6(4), FBUA.

Valves linear-elliptical with rostrate ends, 26–33 μ in length, 10–12 μ in width, with a L/W ratio of between 2.6–2.7. Raphe slightly undulate. Central area small. Axial area narrow. Transapical striae rather radial, about 21–25 in 10 μ, crossed by slightly undulated longitudinal costae, about 12–14 in 10 μ. Partecta nearly up to the drawn out ends, nearly equal in size, 6–7 in 10 μ, broad 2–2.5 μ. Inner margin of partectum flat or slightly convex.

Type locality. Chenghang, Xisha Islands, Guangdong Province, China. Coll.: Cheng Zhaodi and Lin Junmin, 5 March 1982 (SX820305-6(4) Holotype).

THREE NEW SPECIES OF DIATOMS

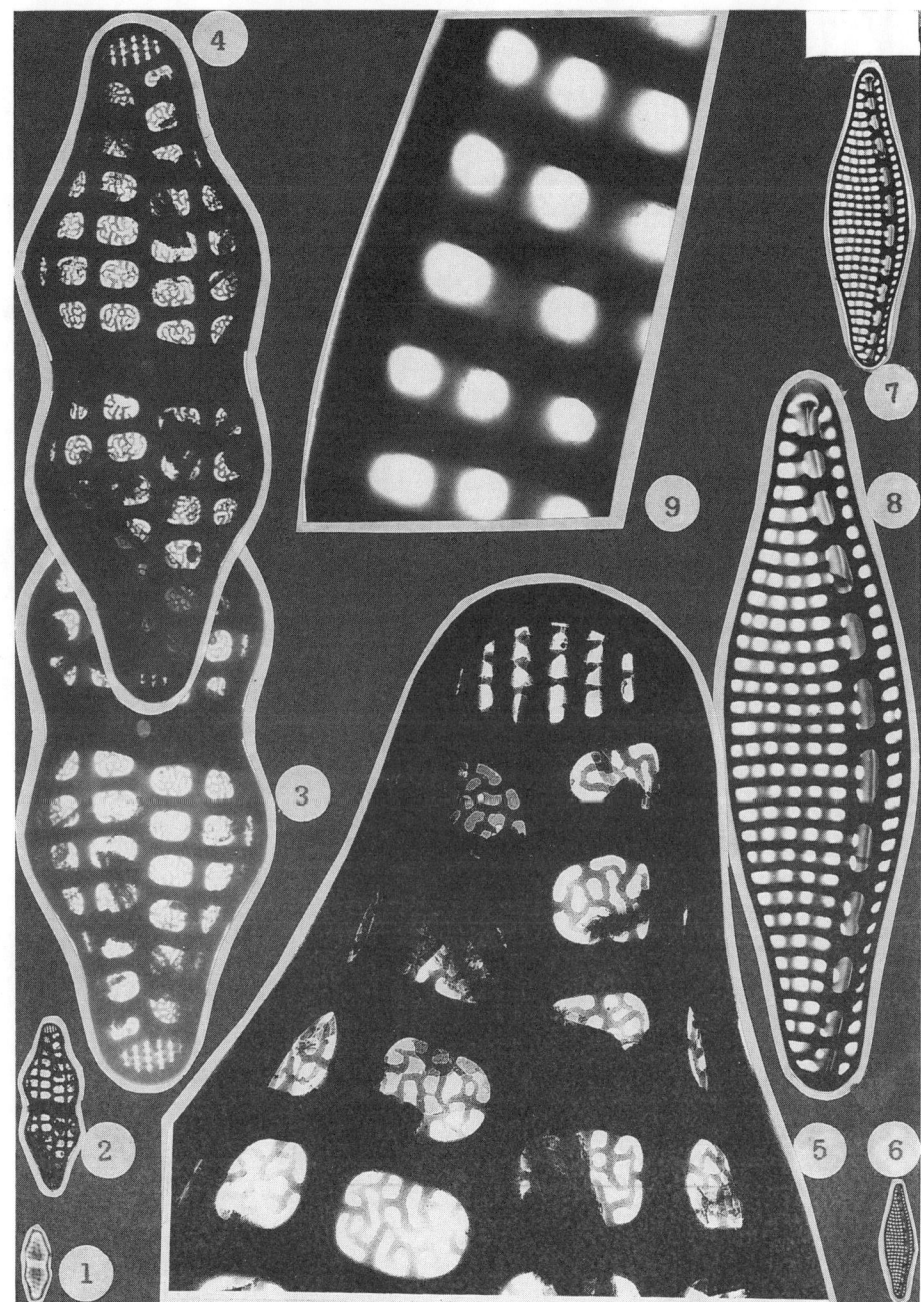

Plate 1. Figs. 1–5. *Plagiogramma reimeri*. 1, LM x1000; 2, TEM x2000; 3–4, TEM x8700; 5, TEM x28000. Figs. 6–9. *Nitzschia amphibioides* var. *chenghaensis*. 6, TEM x1500; 7, TEM x4350; 8, TEM x5400; 9, TEM x10800.

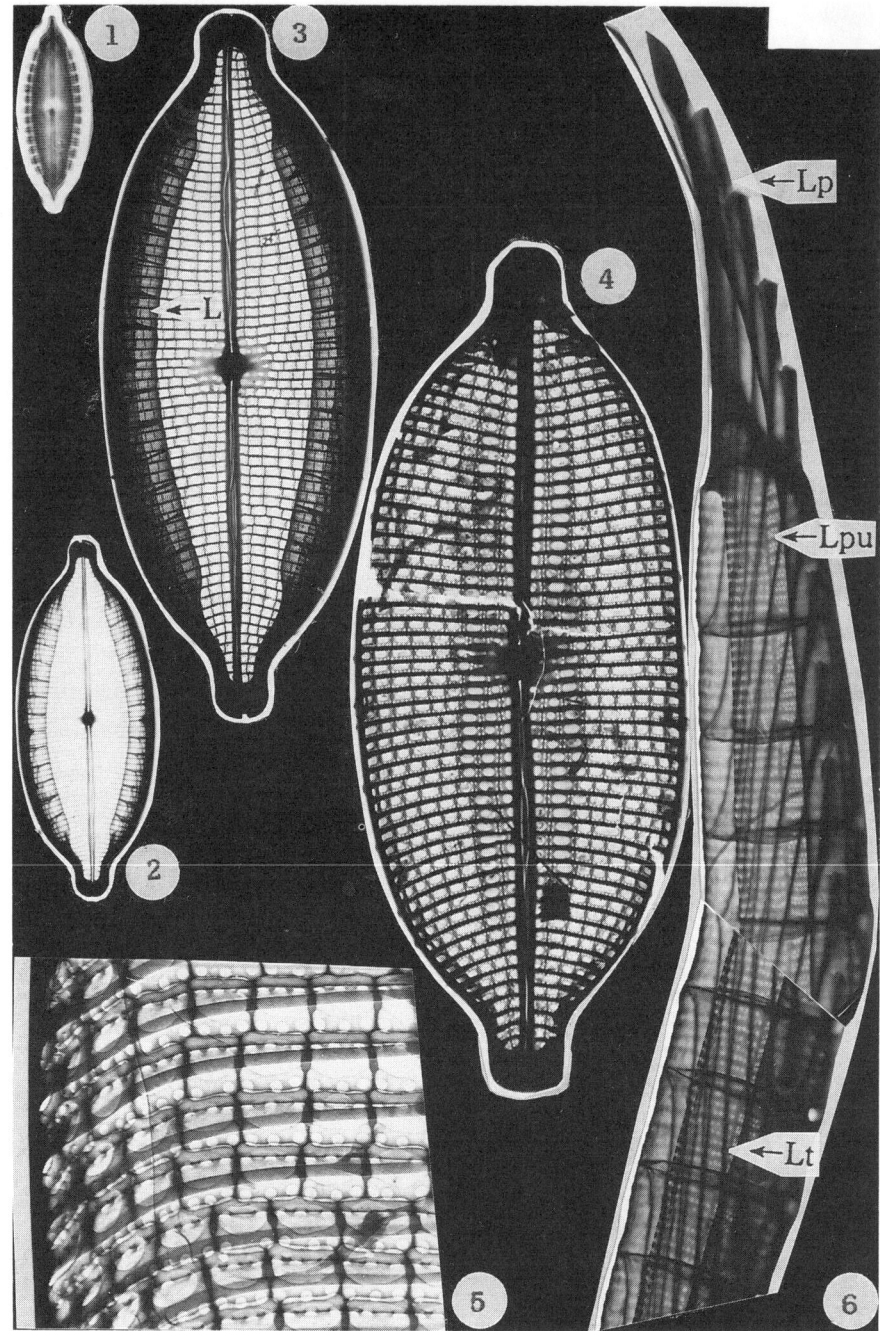

Plate 2. Figs 1–6. *Mastogloia pseudograciloides*. 1, LM ×1000; 2–3, TEM ×1500, ×2800 internal valve; 4–5, TEM ×4350, ×21000 external valve; 6, TEM ×21000 partecta showing punctae (Lpu), partecta tubes (Lt) and partecta pores (Lp).

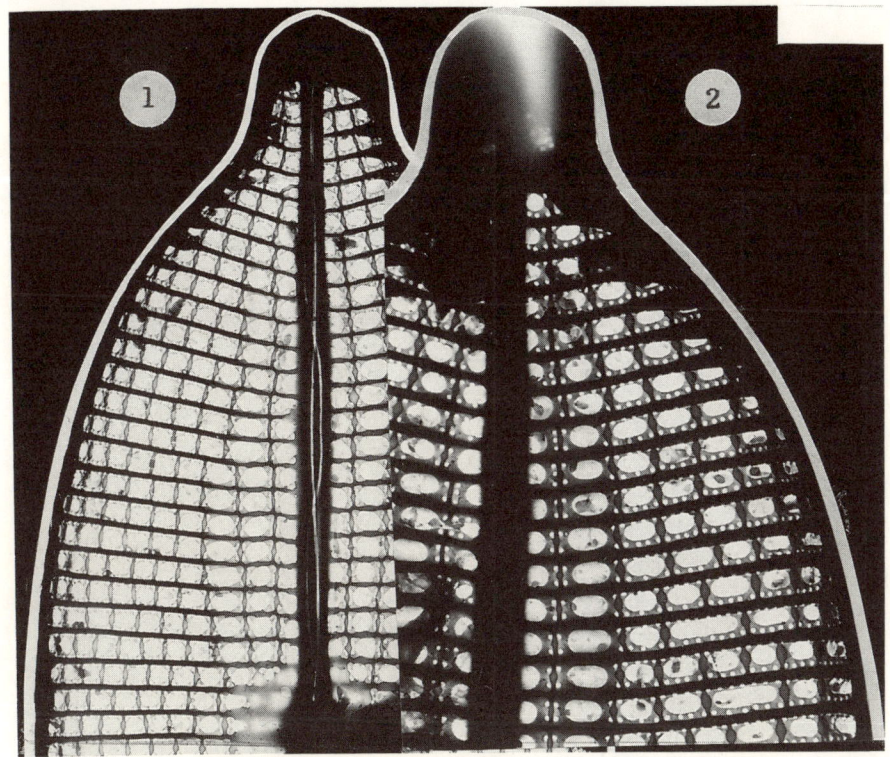

Plate 3. Figs. 1–2 *Mastogloia pseudograciloides*. 1, TEM x7200; 2, x10800 external valve.

This species is similar to *M. gracioloides* (Hustedt 1933, 1985; cf. 934), but the latter end partecta are considerably longer than the others, breadth of partecta, 1.5 µ, transapical striae about 17 in 10 µ; the former end partecta are not considerably longer than the other, breadth of partecta 2–2.4 µ, transapical striae about 25 in 10 µ.

ACKNOWLEDGEMENTS

I wish to thank Prof. Jin Dexing for helpful advice. I am indebted to Dr Schuyler and Dr C.W. Reimer for organizing an offer from the Jessup-McHenry Fund Committee, Philadelphia, to fund my research on diatoms at the Academy of Natural Science, Philadelphia. I wish to thank again Dr Reimer for help with the manuscript. Also, I wish to thank Dr Ronald K. Mahoney, Miss Ni Zimian, Mr Zhuang Weijian and Miss Wu Qiao for help with the use of the electron microscopes and Prof. Brian Morton for correcting the drafts of the manuscript of this paper.

REFERENCES

Hustedt, F. 1933. Die Kieselalgen. In *Rabenhorst's Kryptogamenflora von Deutschland, Osterreich und der Schweiz*. Leipzig: Akademische Verlagsgesellschaft m.b.H.

Hustedt, F. 1985. The pennate diatoms:a translation of Hustedt's 'Die Kieselalgen, 2 Teil' pp. 918.

Schmidt, A. 1974–1979. *Atlas der Diatomoceen-Kunde.* Leipzig: O.R. Reisland. Plates 1–420, 433–80.

Zonon, V. 1948. Le diatomee marine di Sardegna e Pugillo di Alghe Marine della Stressa. *Bollettino di Pesca, Piscicoltura e Idrobiologia.* Anno 24. t.3. n. Ser., fasc. 2:202–46.